falstaff

ULTIMATE WINE
GUIDE

AUSTRIA

2016/17

Austria's Best Wines Reviewed and Rated
by Peter Moser

Photos © ÖWM, ARGE Naturpark, Haiden Baumann, Armin Faber,
Werner Gamerith, Österreich Werbung/Himsl, iStock, Komitee Kamptal, Komitee Thermenregion,
Franz Kovacs, Joachim Lukan, Egon Mark, Peter Moser, Harry Schiffer, Claudia Schindlmaisser,
Konstantin Schindlmaisser, Anna Stöcher, Gerhard Trumler, Steiermark Tourismus,
Weingut Stadlmann, Weinkomitee Weinviertel, Weinstraße Kamptal/Robert Herbst,
Wien Tourismus/Peter Rigaud
Maps © ÖWM

Translation: Julia Sevenich
Art director/Producer: Marcus Wiesner/Lubomir Tzolov
Supported by:
Michael Breitner, Marie Theres Mikhail, Claudia Schindlmaisser,
Konstantin Schindlmaisser, Florian Schuetky, Darrel Joseph

First published in 2002
by Falstaff Publications Ltd.
Führichgasse 8/2, A - 1010 Vienna, Austria
Printed by Grasl Druck & Neue Medien GmbH
2540 Bad Vöslau, Austria
EAN: 978-3-902660-49-7

Peter Moser
Born in 1961 in Krems, descendant of the famous Austrian wine dynasty.
Since 1997 he has been Editor-in-Chief of the *Falstaff* magazine,
responsible for the wine department. He has travelled the world's wine regions
since the mid-1980s, but his expertise lies in the field of Austrian wine.
The Falstaff Weinguide is an annual compilation of Moser's
scores and wine descriptions of Austria's leading wineries.
(E-Mail: peter.moser@falstaff.at)

Falstaff Publications Ltd.
Falstaff Publications (Angelika and Wolfgang Rosam, eds.)
The publishing house, established in 1980 in Vienna by Hans Dibold
and Dr. Helmut Romé, publishes eight issues of the wine and gourmet
magazine Falstaff in German language, the *Falstaff Weinguide*,
the *Falstaff Rotweinguide* (www.falstaff.at, E-Mail: redaktion@falstaff.at),
the *Falstaff Wine Guide Germany* (www.falstaff.de, E-Mail: redaktion@falstaff.de),
the *Falstaff Restaurantguide* (www.falstaffgourmetclub.at,
E-Mail: office@falstaffgourmetclub.at) and numerous other guides.

falstaff

DEAR READERS, DEAR FRIENDS OF AUSTRIAN WINE

It is amazing how quickly time passes. It was in the year 2002 that I first wrote this English language guide to Austrian wine and producers that place value on exporting their wines outside the country. These dedicated vintners fulfil important roles as ambassadors of quality making the wines produced in our little Alpine republic known throughout the world. Grape varieties like Grüner Veltliner, Riesling, St. Laurent and Blaufränkisch have championed the hearts of wine lovers around the world. Although the volume of wine produced in Austria is barely enough to fulfil the demands of the domestic market, the share of wine exported continues to grow. A new quality pyramid for Austrian Sekt (sparkling wine with a minimum of 3 bars pressure in the bottle) has been created with three levels: Klassik, Reserve and Große Reserve. With the purchase of an Austrian Sekt with protected designation of origin, one has not only a wine of documented pedigree, but also a guarantee that the most stringent standards have been observed in its production. The term "sustainable" is not just a slogan in Austria and it is pleasing that Austrian vintners are so ambitious when it comes to environmental protection in their choice of production methods. Our vintners are justifiably viewed as environmentally conscientious and this is particularly exhibited in the way they care for their greatest capital, their vineyards. As of 2015 Austrian vintners now have the possibility of attaining official verification for their sustainable vineyard cultivation methods and

Peter Moser

labelling their wines with the seal "certified sustainable Austria". A trend in "new" vinification techniques witnesses vintners returning to old methods. Whether Sauvignon Blanc, Grüner Veltliner, Riesling, or St. Laurent one can observe experiments with vinification in clay amphora, an ancient production method stemming from Georgia where "Kvevri" have been used since the Neolithic period. There are experimental wines being produced in multiple variations with minimal intervention, even without the addition of sulphur dioxide. "Natural" and "orange" wines remain rare, but their number is growing. And that is a good thing. New taste variations are being explored and a world of wine that is off the beaten path is capturing the attention of a young, intellectual public. It is an exciting niche and simultaneously a field of interesting discussion. Due to the large spectrum of grape varieties cultivated and the highly

falstaff

diverse wine growing areas with differentiating microclimates, the wine enthusiast finds wines in nearly every style in Austria. Cool climate white wines of great finesse, fragile Pinot Noirs from cool climate regions, and full-bodied, powerful reds from the sun-pampered Burgenland that are influenced by the warm, arid Pannonian Basin – all are components of the multifaceted spectrum of wines that Austria has to offer. Between these styles one finds numerous other rarities – old grape varieties and exquisite noble sweet wine specialties. In culinary terms Austria is often called the "delicatessen of Europe", and this has also become true when it comes to the country's wines. The beauty of Austria's stunning landscapes is appreciated by anyone who has ever travelled in the country. It is not surprising that Austrian wine tourism thrives and the cutting edge winery architecture is just one of the notable details. A further pleasant attribute for the traveller is that all of the country's wine growing areas can be reached from the metropolis of Vienna within a two-hour drive. This convenient aspect also makes Austrian wine country attractive for short trips. It was a great honour, but not a surprise when Austria won the prestigious accolade "Best Wine Travel Destination Europe" at the international Travvy Awards 2016 at a gala celebration in New York. The Falstaff Ultimate Wine Guide Austria 2016 will assist you in your choice from the outstanding assortment of wines available. This annual guide is an excerpt from the Falstaff Weinguide and focuses on those wines available on the export markets. The Falstaff Weinguide appears yearly in the German language and includes descriptions of wines from more than 480 different producers. The scores for all the tasting notes in this book are awarded on the international 100-point scale and are given by the author in an open tasting. The scores are a completely subjective appraisal based on personal experience with each particular wine and vintner. Of course the very best way for you to experience current dynamic development is to come to Austria yourself and taste first-class wines directly in their stunning place of origin. Finally, I would like to thank the entire Falstaff publishing team and the Austrian Wine Marketing Board (AWMB) for their generous support, participating vintners for their cooperation, and, naturally, Julia Sevenich who has given my texts her English voice.

PETER / MOSER
Falstaff Ultimate Wine Guide Austria

WHY IS IT THAT THE SHAPE OF A BUNCH OF GRAPES **REMINDS ME OF A SMALL COUNTRY IN THE HEART OF EUROPE?**

AUSTRIAN WINE

A TASTE OF CULTURE.
Austria is located at the heart of Europe. In the exact spot where some of the world's finest wines are grown. Get to know this precious liquid culture.
In Austria, wine with "EU-protected designation of origin" is called "quality wine", and is distinguished by a red-white-red banderole – featuring the producer company number – that covers the bottle neck. **www.austrianwine.com**

CONTENTS

falstaff

Weinviertel *DAC*

The most peppery Grüner Veltliner in Austria

If you appreciate Grüner Veltliner, you'll love Weinviertel DAC. Its typical spicy-fruity taste matches this dry white wine delightfully with fine food and the modern light cuisine. Let yourself be seduced by Weinviertel DAC and have the well-known „Pfefferl" excite you: The characteristic taste of white pepper in this Austrian specialty is a special treat for wine connoisseurs.

Spice by the glass!
www.weinvierteldac.at

ÖSTERREICH WEIN

GENEROUS AND MILD

Austrian vintners breathed a happy sigh of relief at the close of this last harvest. The vintage 2015 brought not only very good quality, but also satisfying quantities. Following the challenging 2014 vintage, the year 2015 put many smiles on the faces of Austrian vintners. The beautiful spring and successful flowering was followed by a suspenseful summer. Hot days and nights were cause for concern, but mid-August provided sufficient precipitation in most regions. The final heat wave at the end of August promoted ripening, whilst the cooler nights enhanced optimal aroma development. Pleasant autumn weather permitted a relaxed harvest without time pressure from threatening weather fronts. The wines generally exhibit beautiful, fruity aroma and excellent varietal character. The vintage is further characterized by moderate acidity and powerful alcohol content that is integrated in ample body. Massive hail in the night of May 6th was a bitter pill to swallow; damage was particularly severe in Wagram, but neighbouring wine regions did not remain unscathed.

The high degree of ripeness and mild acidity are the main attributes of the 2015 vintage. Alcohol content is relatively high for both white and red wines. Expectations are exceptionally high for the red wines and it should be an outstanding vintage even for the late ripening varieties. A surprisingly good harvest of noble sweet wines was achieved in Burgenland in late autumn and was even followed with a few excellent ice wines being brought into the cellars. The Welschriesling harvest was small in Steiermark, but very promising results were achieved for Muskateller (Muscat) and the Bur-

gundian varieties. Wien (Vienna) is also justifiably very pleased with the powerful 2015 vintage.

VINEYARD WEATHER 2015

After the uneventful weather conditions in spring and advantageous weather during flowering, an unusually hot summer followed with one heat wave on the heels of the last. Vegetation came to a halt in a few places. Newly planted vineyards that could not be sufficiently irrigated suffered critical stress. Rain came just in time mid-August for most of the wine regions, bringing welcome relief for vines.

A gorgeous, stable autumn followed with numerous sunny days and relatively cool nights. The cool night temperatures significantly differentiate 2015 from other hot years like 2011 and 2006. The periodic rainfall of September was repeated again in October. Other than these brief wet periods, the beautiful autumn weather continued late into November. Grapes could generally be harvested without stress at an ideal point in time and threats from pests and fungal disease were minimal – even noble rot appeared only very localized.

FULL BODIED, RIPE WINE STYLE

Good concentration and generously proportioned body are largely the distinguishing attributes of the white wines from 2015. While the analytical values for acidity are in lower parameters, this is sensorially seldom perceptible. Characteristics like high, fiery alcohol and subdued fruit, which are usually anticipated in hot vintages, principally did not occur. To the contrary – the white wines exhibit deep, ripe fruit aroma with impressive concentration. Varietal character is also generally very well expressed. It appears to be an extraordinary vintage for red wine that combines the elegance of 2006 with the body of 2011. In nearly all regions the result is intensely coloured, fully ripe, concentrated wines with deep, dark fruit that impress with velvety tannin and tremendous elegance.

POWER AND PEDIGREE IN WHITE

A freaky night-time hailstorm in the beginning of May in Niederösterreich (Lower Austria) travelled from eastern Kremstal and Kamptal over a great part of the Wagram and caused dramatic harvest losses, particularly in Wagram. The production of the standard quality wines was only possible though purchase of fruit from neighbouring Austrian wine regions, which helped to lessen the huge

© Weinstrasse Kamptal/Robert Herbst

volume losses. Fermentation problems and the appearance of faults were very seldom this year. The adjustment of pH to raise acidity was permitted, but winemakers rarely practiced this. The predominant white wine variety Grüner Veltliner generally brought very juicy, creamy wines with mild acid structure. That both categories – the lighter, leaner wines and the powerful premium examples – are impressive is quite remarkable. Delaying the Riesling harvest was rewarded with growths that are vibrant, powerful and display wonderful balance between fruit components and acidity reserves. Just as to be anticipated in such a ripe vintage, Weissburgunder (Pinot Blanc) and Chardonnay impress with concentration and harmony. Rare autochthon varieties such as Zierfandler, Rotgipfler and Roter Veltliner also performed exceedingly well, better than in any recent vintages.

SUPERLATIVE RED WINES

The situation in Burgenland was similar to what it was in neighbouring Niederösterreich (Lower Austria). Here too, fruit-driven, full-bodied white wines with superb varietal character and discreet acidity were bottled. Particularly good results were achieved with the white Burgundian varieties, yet light wines from Welschriesling also performed well. The red wines possess the generous body already mentioned above, but they also demonstrate tremendous balance, which lends elegance and enhances ageing capacity. These are wines that are predestined for maturation in small oak barrels. All in all, it appears that this red wine vintage will achieve or even surpass the greatness of 2011. After the tiny harvest of predicated wine last year, there should be a satisfying volume of deeply fruity sweet wines this year despite the late and hesitant appearance of noble rot (botrytis).

GREAT VINTAGE IN THE SOUTH

Steiermark (Styria) suffered hail damage relatively early in the year, but this was mastered well. All of the Styrian wine regions share the virtues of highly ripe grapes of immaculate quality. A powerful, harmonious year with medium acidity is apparent; it appears similar to the great 2007 vintage. The Styrian specialties Gelber Muskateller (Muscat Blanc à petits grains) and Sauvignon Blanc excel in quality and in satisfying volumes. Ripe fruit aromas and high concentration distinguish the Sauvignon Blancs this year; green or grassy undertones are nearly non-existent. Weissburgunder (Pinot Blanc) and Morillon (Chardonnay) also benefitted from the ripe vintage. Advantageous distribution of precipitation ensured that none of the negative characteristics of a hot vintage appeared. Schilcher, the regional rosé specialty made from the Blauer Wildbacher variety achieved superb qualities in Weststeiermark, similar to the 2011 vintage so highly appreciated by loyal fans of this rarity.

METROPOLIS OF TOP WINES

Wien (Vienna) remained spared of decimating hail damage this year. Loosely set grape bunches ripened fully and were harvested at an optimal time point. For the specialty Wiener Gemischter Satz, full-bodied wines with corresponding acid structure that impress with deep fruit and concentration can be expected in both lighter and more powerful versions. This is also definitely true of Grüner Veltliner and Weissburgunder (Pinot Blanc) from the vineyard slopes of Vienna. Exceptionally successful are the Rieslings from top sites such as Nussberg, which excel with marvellous fruit intensity. The most powerful examples possess the potential for long, consistent maturation. Optimal vintage conditions also ensured that exemplary red wines with tremendous ageing capacity were produced this year in the Austrian metropolis.

myWACHAU
Wine and Vineyard Guide.

New: **Restaurants** in the Wachau and detailled information on **vineyards and geology!**

myWachau is your key
to wineries, wine taverns and vineyards in Wachau. Buying wine ex cellar, finding opened wine taverns and identifying each vineyard by its name - everything in real time. Available for iPhone, Android and as homepage on **www.mywachau.at**

WORTH THE STRUGGLE

The difficult weather conditions during the summer and autumn of 2014 were no secret. Austrian winemakers had their hands full as they worked around the clock to do everything possible to preserve the health of their grapes as they ripened in the vineyards. Ultimately, after heroic efforts and much added expense, they were rewarded with tiny quantities of lean and pleasurable wines. At an estimated two million hectolitres, the harvest was once again well below the long-term average. After a very mild winter and a dry, beautiful spring onset, an exceedingly cool and wet month of May served as a first warning. Favourable weather prevailed during the flowering period. However, after a brief heat wave, the wet conditions returned and lasted more or less throughout the entire summer. August was extremely cloudy and lacked sunshine, but the vineyards still looked satisfactory and hopes for a good vintage still remained. A very wet September was the final confirmation of a problematic vintage. Only in October did the tide turn briefly for the better. Unfriendly conditions in Austria's largest wine region, Niederösterreich (Lower Austria), even included localized hailstorms. Nevertheless, through meticulous manual selection, the resilient Grüner Veltliner delivered lean to medium bodied wines with refreshing fruit and crisp, well-integrated acidity. Higher must weights were possible only sporadically. Those who delayed the harvest of Riesling were rewarded with pleasant, ripe wines with exotic components reminiscent of pineapple and mango. Although acidity levels are signi-ficantly higher than usual, they are surprisingly well integrated in the wines. Chardonnay and Weissburgunder (Pinot Blanc) are round in structure, while the aromatic varieties like Muskateller (Muscat Blanc à petits grains) and Traminer (Gewürztraminer) reflect the merciless weather conditions they faced. In the red wine sector, lean, light, refreshingly fruity wines that offer early drinking pleasure can be expected. Circumstances in Burgenland were similar to those in the rest of Austria. Hot temperatures during flowering caused coulure and significant crop losses. Due to the lower sugar content in the grapes, the 2014 vintage will not yield as many premium or single vineyard wines as usual. For many early-ripening white varieties, as well as for the fragile Zweigelt, urgent action was necessary in order to gather a reasonable amount of healthy fruit. The robust and thick-skinned Blaufränkisch was at an advantage, according to winemakers from Mittelburgenland and Südburgenland. It even shows darker fruit notes than usual. While most French varieties struggled, Merlot survived a little better. St. Laurent and Zweigelt display supple fruit, elegant structure and moderate alcohol. In general, lean, yet appetizing red wines with red berry notes can be expected from Burgenland. It is still too early for a final sweet wine prognosis, but thus far, they reveal elegant structure, crisp acidity and a filigree expression – quite fresh and youthful with excellent ageing potential. For the dry white wines, once again, the relatively small harvest is underscored. Early ripening varieties such as Bouvier, Muskat Ottonel and Sauvignon

Blanc exhibit accentuated fruit. Later ripening varieties like Grüner Veltliner, Chardonnay and Weissburgunder (Pinot Blanc) are marked by freshness and vibrancy with nuances of exotic fruits. In Steiermark (Styria), conditions were no less challenging, particularly due to heavy rains during September. A hailstorm at the beginning of September in Südoststeiermark exacerbated the situation. Despite it all, the white wines of Steiermark are animated and vibrant, although lighter and with less alcohol content than usual. This deficiency is compensated by lovely balance and easy drinkability. Their intrinsic fruitiness accentuates the best of the varietal attributes. Welschriesling is crisp and refreshing, while Gelber Muskateller (Muscat Blanc à petits grains) is rather restrained. The region's most important grape variety, Sauvignon Blanc displays superb varietal character with expressive fruit and a herbaceous edge. Although all lighter than in the previous three strong vintages, Weissburgunder (Pinot Blanc)

and Morillon (Chardonnay) appear supple and nicely balanced. The same applies to the Schilcher (Blauer Wildbacher) of Weststeiermark. In Wien (Vienna), the complicated vintage began with a heavy hailstorm at the beginning of May that caused considerable damage and severe crop loss, especially in the prime vineyard Nussberg. Fortunately, other vineyard sites in Döbling, Mauer, and Bisamberg were spared. After this spring shock, the weather was generally similar to that of the other regions. Despite this, a higher degree of ripeness was achieved here and there. Weissburgunder (Pinot Blanc) and Chardonnay are nicely rounded, creamy and well developed. Riesling is marked by Botrytis, which is counterbalanced by racy acidity. Vienna's showcase wine, the Wiener Gemischter Satz DAC, shines bright with authentic regional character, superb balance, and complexity. In Vienna's red wine segment, the red berry expression surpasses that of the 2010 vintage.

AUSTRIA'S GRAPE VARIETIES

The small wine country of Austria has a very diversified assortment of grape varieties, with more than thirty different grape varieties currently permitted for the production of quality wines. Due to the very long and eventful history of Austrian viticulture, the present list of grapes is a colourful mixture of old indigenous varieties, fairly recent cross-breedings, and classic international varieties, which make up only a small part of the total. This latter group includes mostly whites like Chardonnay and Sauvignon Blanc, but black Bordeaux varieties like Cabernet Sauvignon, Cabernet Franc and Merlot are included and have been permitted for Austrian quality wines since 1986. In 2001, the Syrah was added to this list. Only scant basic information is provided here about these worldwide-known varieties. Our focus shall be the typical Austrian specialties that are often little known over the country's borders. Scientific ampelographic classification began in Austria around 200 years ago during the era of the Habsburg Monarchy. Vineyards were typically planted with a mixture of several different varieties during the Austro-Hungarian Empire. Hundreds of varieties thrived and were often difficult to distinguish from one another. Further complicating categorization, were multiple names for the very same variety, which differed from district to district and even from village to village. It was not until the second half of the 19th century that a vague comprehension about the enormous variety that had developed during the Habsburg Monarchy solidified. At the end of the 19th century, major vineyard epidemics spread.

Oidium and peronospora followed by phylloxera decimated vineyards in all of Europe. After the propagation of European vines on disease and phylloxera resistant American rootstocks was discovered, planting of vineyards with a single selected variety was initiated. Until World War II, vineyards were cultivated in bush or gobelet styles and it was not until the 1950s that wire-frame trellis systems caught on. The so-called Lenz Moser cultivation, conceived and propagated by a well-known Austrian winery owner and viticulture engineer revolutionized the country's viticulture and made mechanical cultivation possible for the first time. Grüner Veltliner in particular adapted well to this specific form of planting and the variety became Austria's predominant grape. Today young vines are preferably established in a cordon training system with high leaf canopies and high density of vines. It is no longer the potential quantity that is the priority, but physiologically ripe and aromatic grapes of high quality. Subsidization from the European Union has further supported the concentrated efforts on improvements in Austrian vineyards. Consumer demand is clearly moving towards red wine consumption and new plantings in suitable vineyards and microclimates reflect this. Some less fashionable or less interesting white varieties are being replaced with red wine varieties. It is easily imaginable that the number of grape varieties, which are really used for the production of high-quality wine in Austria, will decrease. Already today, wines from some of the varieties stated on the list are rarely found on the market. The Federal College and

Research Centre for Viticulture and Pomology Klosterneuburg near Vienna is the country's leader in research and cultivation innovation. This is where Professor Fritz Zweigelt worked in the early 1920s and cultivated the Blauer Zweigelt variety by crossing St. Laurent and Blaufränkisch, resulting in Austria's most successful and popular black grape. Leading scientists like Dr. Ferdinand Regner are currently researching the genetic origin of indigenous Austrian varieties and their clones by means of DNA-sequencing. Dr. Ferdinand Regner succeeded in documenting the significant role of Traminer, whose genes can be found in numerous Austrian varieties. The Austrian wine landscape offers broad varietal diversity, which is multiplied by quite differing soils and microclimates. In the end, it is the responsibility of every single vintner to select varieties most suited for each vineyard site.

WHITE WINE VARIETIES

GRÜNER VELTLINER
Synonyms: Weissgipfler, Grüner, Manhardsrebe, Grüner Muskateller
Grüner Veltliner is the main grape variety in Austria, grown predominantly in the wine-growing areas Weinviertel, Kamptal, Kremstal, Traisental, Wagram, and Wachau. Grüner Veltliner is not botanically related to other Veltliner varieties like Brauner Veltliner, Roter Veltliner or Frühroter Veltliner. Traminer has long been known as one of the parents of Grüner Veltliner, but the other parent remained unknown until recently. An old, unrecognizable variety was discovered in Burgenland and through DNA-sequencing was determined to be the second parent. This grape was named after is discovery location, St. Georgen, because its identity did not correspond to any other known variety. Nearly one third of the Austrian vineyard area is planted with Grüner Veltliner; in Niederösterreich it comprises half of the vineyards. The preference for this variety is due in part to its compatibility with the Lenz Moser vine trellising and training system. After World War II there was a search for productive varieties requiring little care. Grüner Veltliner fulfilled both these needs and moreover thrives in several different soil types. When cultivation is geared towards high yields, the resulting wine from Grüner Veltliner is light and racy, but still spicy and appetizing for everyday consumption. The typical peppery-spicy aroma and flavour of the variety is often referred to as "Pfefferl". When cultivation concentrates on quality rather than quantity, Grüner Veltliner amplifies its terroir with corresponding changes in taste and character. Meagre, poor primary rock soil, as is found in the Wachau, Krems, or Kamptal, bring wine dominated by firm mineral character and pleasant vegetal spiciness. When Grüner Veltliner is planted on fertile loess terraces in the Wagram or in the Weinviertel, the wine displays a supple, juicy fruitiness reminiscent of an exotic fruit cocktail. Yield restrictions bring intense, expressive wines of impressive depth and complexity. Another important quality of

Grüner Veltliner is its longevity. Riesling is considered internationally to be particularly capable of ageing, yet tastings of mature wines prove Grüner Veltliner to be at least as long-lived. I have tasted and drunk Grüner Veltliners on several occasions that were 50 years old or more with considerable enjoyment. In recent years experiments were performed in fermenting and maturing Grüner Veltliner in small oak barrels. These experiments have proved quite legitimate and have occasionally resulted in very interesting wines indeed. These concentrated wines are often very potent, sometimes with as much as 14.5 % alcohol.

The first maturation results show, however, that after some years in the bottle, the character of Grüner Veltliner variety is obscured by the influence of new oak and prolonged contact with the fine lees. Nevertheless, these new Veltliner types have their fans. Falstaff magazine stages an annual competition called the "Grüner Veltliner Grand Prix", which addresses the classic medium-bodied style of Grüner Veltliner. The wines involved are fermented dry with a maximum of four grams of residual sugar, have no more than 13% alcohol, and display crisp acidity. They provide refreshing drinking pleasure and are suited as ideal accompaniment to many foods. As the white wine variety that is most associated with Austria, this unique grape offers vintners a broad spectrum of styles, from light wines all the way up to noble sweet Trockenbeerenauslese. Grüner Veltliner is increasingly popular internationally and has become more easily available in recent years.

© ÖWM/Komitee Kamptal

BOUVIER

This rare variety has a striking fragrance, putting it among the aromatic varieties. It was first cultivated from a Burgundy seedling around 1900 in Radkersburg, Steiermark, by the estate owner Clotar Bouvier. The best Bouviers in Austria can be found among the sweet wine predicates Beerenauslese, Trockenbeerenauslese, and Eiswein. Though it is a white wine, it has rather low acidity. Because it has little character, its popularity in the vineyard is decreasing.

CHARDONNAY
Synonym: Morillon

When Chardonnay became fashionable in Austria 20 years ago, much was labelled Chardonnay that actually wasn't. Many a Pinot Blanc attempted to profit from word creations like Pinot Chardonnay. Styrian Morillon is identical to Chardonnay. The term Feinburgunder was once often used in the Wachau for the variety, but since 1999, this synonym is no longer permitted. Chardonnay is vinified both in steel tanks and in new oak in Austria. Terms like "classic" and "tradition" can be misleading to international consumers since they denote the fresh and fruity style without oak influence. A clue can be found in the specified alcohol content on labels since only the more potent wines, with over 13%, are matured in new oak barrels. Chardonnay occupies very small but widespread cultivation areas all over Austria, (around 3 % of Austria's vineyard area). Despite this, the variety is of increasing importance, particularly in the upper quality segment. Chardonnay is found in every Austrian wine-growing area.

FRÜHROTER VELTLINER
Synonym: Malvasier

This natural cross of Roter Veltliner x Sylvaner is not demanding in terms of its location and can even cope with meagre lime-rich soils. It is resistant against both winter and late frosts, and even against humidity. On the other hand, it ripens too early. The resulting wine has no particular bouquet, tends to be of high alcohol content, and is mild in acidity. The Frühroter Veltliner is by no means a trendy variety and makes up only 0.9 % of the Austrian vineyards.

FURMINT

This rare variety originates from the Tokaj region in north-eastern Hungary. It is the main component of the Hungarian Tokaji wine and has nothing to do with the Tokay d'Alsace. In Austria it is encountered almost exclusively in Burgenland, particularly in the region around Rust where it is experiencing a small renaissance. The Furmint is demanding of its location and requires warm, well-drained soils. It is sensitive to oidium, but has good resistance to botrytis. The wine is yellow-green when fermented dry and golden yellow in colour when sweet. It is intense in bouquet, often reminiscent of chamomile and quince, usually high in alcohol, and possesses racy acidity. Because it can achieve high degrees of extract and alcohol, it is very well suited to vinification of sweet predicated wines.

GELBER MUSKATELLER
Synonym: Muscat Blanc á petits grains

Muscat is usually fermented dry in Austria and comprises a fragrant, light aperitif wine with refreshing acidity. Muscat has been documented in the Wachau since 1400. This variety also has a long tradition in Steiermark and Burgenland, yet the vineyard area remains very small since it is extremely susceptible to rot. It is very demanding of its location, sensitive to frost and fungal attacks, matures late, but is suitable for almost any soil, except lime. In addition to racy, fragrant, light, dry wines, fascinating sweet wines are also made from this variety in Austria. The best sweet examples can age for decades.

GEWÜRZTRAMINER
Synonyms: Roter Traminer,
Gelber Traminer, Traminer

In Austria, Traminer finds its most significant dissemination in Burgenland, the Thermenregion, and Steiermark. It is very demanding of its location and soil, has a low tolerance for lime, and is sensitive to frost. The wine typically displays an intense medium yellow to golden-yellow colour, occasionally with a slightly reddish shimmer. The fragrance is intense and reminiscent of rose petals and marshmallow. Gewürztraminer achieves its best quality in the upper predicated sweet wine categories and is quite capable of extended ageing. Despite being considered a noble, aristocratic wine, it is not currently the trend among consumers. Fortunately there is a committed community of fans, and its continued existence in Austria is secured.

GRAUER BURGUNDER
Synonyms: Ruländer, Pinot Gris

This noble variety stems from Burgundy and was brought into Austria and Hungary in the 14th century by Cistercian monks. Its highest density can be found in northern Burgenland, where the Cistercians were once very diligent viticulturists. Pinot Gris requires deep soils that are rich in nutrients and a good well-drained location with regular access to a good supply of water. Fruit maturity is reached relatively soon, however the vintage is usually not until the beginning of October. A wine with an intensive golden-yellow colour that sometimes has a mild reddish shimmer and a delicious varietal bouquet with a touch of honey. It is typically full bodied and can reach high levels of alcohol. It currently makes up less than 0.5 % of Austrian vineyards.

GRÜNER SYLVANER

It is proven that this old indigenous vine variety is a cross of Traminer x Österreichisch Weiss. It is also common in Germany, where it was mentioned for the first time in 1665 in a monastery inscription. The acreage has been decreasing in Austria, and today Grüner Sylvaner is found nearly only in Niederösterreich. This variety needs fertile soils with good nutrients and water supply, as well as good hillside locations. It is sensitive to winter frost and botrytis. The wine is greenish-yellow, mild and subtly fruity. In short, it is rather neutral.

MÜLLER-THURGAU
Synonym: Rivaner

Cultivated in 1882 by Dr. Hermann Müller from Thurgau in Switzerland at the University of Geisenheim in Germany, it is a cross of Riesling x Madeleine Royal. For years it was believed to be a cross of Riesling x Sylvaner which is the base for its synonym Rivaner. This new variety was introduced in Franken in 1913, and by the 1950s it was distributed throughout the world. Fritz Salomon of the Undhof Winery in Kremstal introduced this variety in Austria in 1926. Once the second-most important grape variety in Austria, its popularity has declined rapidly over the past two decades. It is cultivated predominantly in Lower Austria and Burgenland where it occupies 4.6% of the area under vine. Although not very demanding, it does favour cooler sites and deep loam and loess soils that are rich in nutrients and have a good water supply. Müller-Thurgau is sensitive to winter frost and prone to disease. The wines are usually soft and mild, with a discreet bouquet slightly reminiscent of Muscat. Apart from the sweet predicated wines made, Müller-Thurgau is preferably drunk young.

"The greatest concentration of fascinating Blaufränkisch ... so distinctively mineral-soaked that it has earned its own special appellation."

Jancis Robinson/Austria's best red bets 12.03.2011

LEITH∧BERG DAC

TRADITION - TERROIR - DEPTH

„Schiefer und Kalk bedeuten Würze, Frische und Mineralik in den Weinen"

Peter Moser/Falstaff

www.leithaberg.at

MUSKAT OTTONEL

This aromatic variety stems from a crossing of Chasselas x Muscat d'Eisenstadt first breen in the Loire at the end of the 19th century. The main centre of Austrian plantings is in northern Burgenland, and it totals 0,8% of the Austrian area under vine. It requires deep, fertile soil with good water supply and loves a sunny site protected from the wind. The ripening is early but with unreliable yields. The wine exhibits a greenish-yellow colour and an intense spicy bouquet reminiscent of nutmeg. It is mild, usually low in alcohol and extract and most suited for the production of remarkable sweet predicated wines.

NEUBURGER

This typical Austrian variety is an old cross of Roter Veltliner x Sylvaner which apparently stems from the Spitzer Graben community in the Wachau. Today it is found in Burgenland and Lower Austria, with only a few plantings in Styria and Vienna. Neuburger is not demanding of its location. It is even thrives on heavy, lime-rich soils, but brings its best results in primary rock. It is prone to variable fruit set if the weather is poor during flowering. The Neuburger results in restrained, classy wines that are sometimes somewhat neutral in fragrance, but aristocratic in expression. Interesting Neuburger wines can be discovered in Burgenland, Thermenregion, and especially in the upper Wachau region.

RIESLING
Synonym: Weisser Riesling

The existence of this variety is documented in Rüsselsheim in Germany as early as 1435. The Wachau also lays claim to being the origin of this variety, according to a document that mentions a vineyard by the name of Ritzling. Despite the theory being based solely on hypothesis, it is nevertheless an ingenious idea. Riesling is encountered in Austria predominantly in the Wachau, Kremstal, Kamptal, Traisental and Wagram wine-growing areas where it is the source of outstanding wines. It places high demands both on location and soil. The most fragrant and raciest wines stem from schist and primary rock. Riesling is therefore also found in other areas of Austria where primary rock or schist is found, such as Röschitz in the Weinviertel, Donnerskirchen, or Jois in Burgenland. The variety matures very late with the harvest usually at the end of October or beginning of November. It tests the patience of the vintner nearly each and every year. Its aristocratic bouquet exhibits peach, apricot, and citrus. Riesling is very racy and well structured. It develops continuously, gaining in complexity making it very suitable for ageing. This holds particularly true for the late harvested Spätlese and Auslese categories, or for the Smaragd wines of the Wachau.

ROTGIPFLER

The rare Rotgipfler is a natural cross of Savagnin x Roter Veltliner, most probably from Austria's Thermenregion, and is therefore a half-sibling of Frühroter Veltliner, Neuburger and Zierfandler.. Its oldest documentation is from Styria in 1840. Together with Zierfandler, it established the reputation of the famous wines from Gumpoldskirchen. This variety exists almost exclusively in Austria, particularly in its Thermenregion origin. It favours fertile medium-weight lime soils and warm hillside locations. It is sensitive to winter frosts, prone to botrytis, and matures late. The wine is golden-yellow and possesses a pronounced bouquet. It is refreshing and spicy, and for the most part, full-bodied, and rich in extract and alcohol. It is vinified dry, off-dry and sweet and is often paired with Zierfandler in a blend.

ROTER VELTLINER

The origin of this very old variety has not yet been clearly established. It is likely from Niederösterreich (Lower Austria), where it is grown today in small quantities in the Kremstal and Wagram areas. The Roter Veltliner places moderate demands on soil, but high demands on location, requiring warm, southern hillside aspects. It is sensitive to frost and yields are unreliable. Roter Veltliner matures late. The wine is greenish-yellow, fruity and fragrant, with a subtle spicy aroma, and often exhibits racy acidity.

SAUVIGNON BLANC

In its present form, this variety probably comes from the south of France where it has been documented since the first half of the 18th century. It originates from a Traminer crossing, but seems to have developed from a preliminary stage. It is most common in Styria, but due to its general popularity is now planted in all regions. The name "Muskat-Sylvaner" was permitted until 1999. The variety places high demands on location and thrives on fertile, not overly dry soils. High humidity is important. It brings moderate, irregular yields and is sensitive to winter frost. The wine exhibits a greenish yellow colour and its grassy spiciness reminiscent of fresh bell peppers evolves into aromas of asparagus, elderflower and cassis at high stages of maturity. Sauvignon Blanc is an elegant, refreshing wine with racy structure and inimitable, stimulating character. The variety is suitable for medium-term ageing. More potent wines are sometimes vinified in new oak.

SCHEUREBE
Synonym: Sämling 88

This variety is a cross of Riesling and an unknown variety, but not Silvaner as was

once suspected. In terms of quality, this is perhaps the most successful of all the German crossings and was developed by Dr. Scheu in 1916. The variety is valued in Burgenland for noble sweet wines and in Styria for light, dry, crisp wines. Despite its quality, the variety is currently declining. It makes little demand on soil, but high demand on location. The Scheurebe matures late and provides moderate yields. Scheurebe wines are usually golden-yellow, have a subtle, aromatic bouquet, and exhibit elegant acidity and body.

WEISSBURGUNDER
Synonym: Pinot Blanc, Klevner

Burgundy is considered to be the home of this highly acclaimed variety as it was documented there in the 14th century. Pinot is quite prone to mutation and its different colour variations, –Pinot Blanc, Pinot Gris, and Pinot Noir – all have a very similar genetic fingerprint. Weissburgunder is mainly planted throughout Austria's wine regions and makes up 4.3 % of the vineyard area. This noble variety is demanding of location and soil, requiring plenty of nutrients and sufficient moisture. It is sensitive to late frost, and yields reliably and consistently. When allowed to gain full maturity, Weissburgunder develops into a white wine rich in substance with a subtle, almond flavour and racy acidity. The variety, internationally known as Pinot Blanc, usually develops very well in the bottle. Due to its discreet character, it is also suitable for blends with other varieties and for fermentation and/or maturation in new, small oak barrels.

WELSCHRIESLING

The different interpretations of its origin point towards Italy and France. Welschriesling makes up 7.8% of Austrian vineyards and is the country's second most important white grape variety behind Grüner Veltliner (29.4 %). The variety is planted predominantly in Burgenland and Niederösterreich, but it is also very popular in Steiermark. The vine requires deep, warm soils, rich in nutrients and places high demands on its location. Because it is sensitive to dryness, it favours south-facing slopes protected from the wind. It provides generous, reliable yields. When fermented dry, Welschriesling brings fresh, fruity wines with subtle spice, best enjoyed in their youth. The variety is perhaps at its best as a noble sweet predicated wine for its luscious sweetness finds perfect balance in its inherent acidity. A Welschriesling Trockenbeerenauslese can bring tremendous drinking pleasure even after two decades of bottle maturation.

ZIERFANDLER
Synonym: Spätrot

DNA parentage analysis at the Federal College and Research Centre for Viticulture and Pomology Klosterneuburg has suggested that Zierfandler could be a natural cross between Roter Veltliner and a relative of Savagnin that took place near Gumpoldskirchen in the Thermenregion of Niederösterreich (Lower Austria). Gumpoldskirchen continues to be one of the few places in the world where the variety is found. Together with another rare autochthon variety Rotgipler, Zierfandler is the foundation on which the fame of the historic wine village Gumpoldskirchen is based. It is a fickle and demanding variety that ripens late and irregularly, providing no more than moderate yields. The wine has a golden yellow colour, a distinct fruity bouquet, full body, and racy acidity. It is spicy and rich in extract and alcohol content, and is often produced with residual sweetness, blended with Rotgipfler variety and marketed as Spätrot-Rotgipfler.

RED WINE VARIETIES

BLAUFRÄNKISCH
Synonyms: Limberger, Lemberger

Although Blaufränkisch is not Austria's number one black grape in terms of planted area – with 3,225 hectares it ranks second – it is the most important variety to many Austrian red wine specialists. Its exact origin has not yet been determined, but for many centuries it has certainly been at home in Austrian vineyards. The root of the word, "fränkisch", was associated with the German Franks just as the stem "Wälsch" was connected with Italian, as is exemplified by Welschriesling. One assumes, however, that the term Blaufränkisch was meant to hint at the positive properties of the wine – "Frankish" in the sense of good, fine. By contrast, the name "Heunisch" meaning "Hunnish" was still used last century to denote a weak, less valuable wine. Both in the Viennese dialect and in English, the term "frank" also has the connotation of "honest". But enough

© Steiermark Tourismus

on etymology: Blaufränkisch thrives in deep soils and even does quite well in lime soils. It ripens relatively late and is harvested after advantageously long hang times. While not particularly susceptible to mildew diseases, it is prone to botrytis-related stem necrosis. Typically, it displays pronounced dark berry aromas reminiscent of boysenberry, sometimes intertwined with mineral notes derived from its terroir. Appetizing acidity and firm tannin structure are its trademarks. The grape calls for at least two years of ageing before it becomes approachable. Wines from good vintages exhibit surprising ageing capacity. The best Blaufränkisch wines are vinified according to international models in new French oak barrels and are often blended with small quantities of Cabernet Sauvignon or Merlot. Blaufränkisch thrives best on the west and south sides of Lake Neusiedl in Burgenland an also finds suitable locations in Carnuntum in Niederösterreich (Lower Austria). The best sites in Südburgenland are located in the Eisenberg DAC. Mittelburgenland is also referred to as "Blaufränkischland", and this is the predominant variety in prime vineyards in Neckenmarkt, Horitschon, and Deutschkreutz. Farther north on the west side of Lake Neusiedl in the Neusiedlersee-Hügelland wine-growing area and the Leithaberg DAC, Blaufränksich brings exquisite results from marine limestone and mica-schist soils slopes. It is here that the vintner Ernst Triebaumer crafted Austria's first hallmark wine in 1986 from the single vineyard Marienthal. This legendary wine, although almost completely exhausted, rings a bell for every Austrian wine buff.

ZWEIGELT
Synonyms: Blauer Zweigelt, Rotburger
The variety with the intense cherry fruit aromas and flavours is an Austrian crossing

and by far the most widely planted red vine variety in the country and the second most prolific variety after Grüner Veltliner. It grows in all Austrian wine-growing regions on 6,476 ha, covering 14.1% of the total area under vine. This successful grape goes back to Professor Fritz Zweigelt (1888–1964), who developed this cross of Blaufränkisch and St. Laurent at the ederal College and Research Centre for Viticulture and Pomology Klosterneuburg in 1922. Although the name Zweigelt may appear justified in honour of the originator, it has turned out to be a real tongue twister for non-German speaking people. The oenologist himself in a more self-effacing manner chose the designation Rotburger – to the credit of the place where it all came about. He was referring to "red from Klosterneuburg". The name "Blaue Zweigeltrebe" was officially introduced in 1975 upon intervention of another one of Austria's winegrowing pioneers – Lenz Moser, founder of the widely used high culture training system. The reasons why the Zweigelt grape is so popular among vintners are manifold: it is frost-resistant, ripens early, sets no special demands on location or soil, and has proved to be relatively disease resistant. Consumers appreciate Zweigelt for its vibrant fruitiness that bursts with fresh amarelle cherry flavour. Some of the very best Zweigelts come from the Neusiedlersee DAC on the east side of Lake Neusiedl in Burgenland and from Carnuntum to the north in Niederösterreich, but the variety finds well suited locations throughout Austria's wine regions. Weather easy-drinking approachable examples or more complex oak-matured growths, Zweigelt is the indisputable crowd-pleaser among Austria's black grape varieties. Quite frequently, the best lots of Zweigelt are added to a winemaker's master blend.

ROESLER

This new variety was developed by Dr. Gertraud Mayer at the Federal Viticulture Research Centre Klosterneuburg and the vine nursery Langenzersdorf. The crossing of Zweigelt x Sevye-Villard 18-402 x Blaufränkisch is named after the former director of Austria's oldest viticultural college and research centre, Leonard Roesler. The variety brings not only interesting aromas, deep colour, and abundant extract, it is also advantageous for vintners in cooler regions. The variety is quite frost resistant and can withstand temperatures of up to –25° C (–13° F) and is also resistant to both mildew varieties.

BLAUER BURGUNDER
Synonyms: Blauer Spätburgunder, Pinot Noir

Blauburgunder, otherwise known as Pinot Noir, stems from Burgundy and ranks among the great classic international red wine varieties. In Austria it was first mentioned in 1394, when it was planted by Cistercian monks who had brought it directly from France to Gumpoldskirchen where the Freigut Thallern monks still own the Heiligenkreuz Abbey. Blauburgunder is regarded as the prima donna among the classic grape varieties. It sets high demands on location, requiring warm and fertile soils. Bunches are rather small and compact with

berries that are round, thin-skinned, and juicy. It takes a highly skilled winemaker to bring the best out of Pinot Noir: the subtle finesse on the nose, its complex and fruity flavours, the silky texture and a longevity exceeding that of most other varieties. The increasing skill of Austrian vintners has inspired them to plant more Blauburgunder (Pinot Noir) and the variety now makes up 903 hectares of the country's vineyards. The best producers are rewarded with expressive reds; the lesser engaged vintners only too frequently obtain thin, stingy wines which lack ripeness. Top varietal representatives are found in the Thermenregion, Vienna, and on both sides of Lake Neusiedl in Burgenland.

ST. LAURENT
Synonyms: Saint Laurent, Sankt Laurent, Lorenzitraube

August 10th is the feast of Saint Laurentius and the day on which this variety usually turns colour. Its history of origin was repeatedly associated with the Bordeaux village of the same name, but it was actually discovered by a certain Mister Bronner from Wieloch in Alsace, who designated it "Schwarzer" and reported Burgundy as its original home. There are, in fact, some similarities with Pinot Noir both in the vineyard and in terms of aromas and flavours, which seem to indicate a certain relationship between the two varieties.

© ÖWM/Faber

St. Laurent grows well on light soils. Unlike Pinot Noir it is characterized by early bud-break. It is thicker skinned than Pinot Noir and produces more robust, dark, velvety reds. Yields must be limited rigorously to promote concentration and ageing capacity. Its amarelle cherry aromas and flavours, which are sometimes offset by a delicate tartness, have gained it many fans. It profits tremendously from bottle ageing. Experience has also proved St. Laurent to be a good blending partner.

BLAUBURGER
Blauburger is an Austrian crossbreed between Blauer Portugieser and Blaufränkisch and dates back to 1923. The final syllable "burger" points to the Federal College and Research Centre for Viticulture and Pomology Klosterneuburg. Its intention at that time was to surpass Zweigelt , but this eventually failed. Since the Blauburger is deeply coloured, it was soon degraded to a colouring wine in blends. In terms of aromas and flavours it resembles a milder version of Blaufränkisch. Today, some excellent oak-matured wines are made from this grape, which fell into unfortunate disrepute, but is truly worthy of note.

BLAUER WILDBACHER
Synonym: Schilcher
Schilcher is the special name of a rosé made from Blauer Wildbacher grapes. This designation is only allowed in Steiermark. Blauer Wildbacher is an old Austrian variety that is said to go back to the Celts. Manuscripts from the 16th century show the first record of the name. Genuine Schilcher comes exclusively from Weststeiermark where vines thrive up to 600 meters above sea level. Despite this, commercial success in the eighties inspired a wave of new plantings throughout Steiermark (Styria). Blauer Wildbacher is also used for the production of fragrant and refreshing bottle-fermented sparkling wine as well as deeply coloured red wine. The variety is not very demanding in terms of soil, requiring only warm and aerated sites due to its proneness to rot. The grapes ripen late and bring only moderate, often inconsistent yields. The colour spectrum of the wine ranges from onion skin shades to ruby-pink. Its red berry and herbal flavour is backed up by a tart acidity and a refreshing character.

CABERNET SAUVIGNON
The world's most famous grape variety also found its way to Austria from Bordeaux. The wine-growing pioneer Robert Schlumberger planted both Cabernet and Merlot on his estate in Bad Vöslau in the 19th century. Although Schlumberger's Privatkeller was a great "liquid" success for decades, his venture eventually fell into oblivion. The first vintner to reinstate this noble grape was Anton Kollwentz from Burgenland. In Mailberg in Niederösterreich (Lower Austria), Lenz Moser carried out tests that showed promising results on the Schlossweingut Malteser Ritterorden estate in Weinviertel, on much less suitable terroir than in Neusiedlersee-Hügelland. Progressive Austrian winegrowers really had to fight for Cabernet Sauvignon. They planted experimental vineyards and their efforts were constantly supported by Falstaff Magazine. After triumphantly showing their expected positive results, the bureaucratic hurdles were also finally cleared and Cabernet Sauvignon was officially authorized as a permitted quality grape variety on June 11, 1986. Contrary to many a false prophecy, it has not spread like a flood, drowning all indigenous grapes below it. Cabernet Sauvignon thrives almost everywhere, is disease and pest resistant and can withstand

dryness – even low temperatures do not bother it.

A miracle grape? Not at all! If you tackle this grape as a winegrower rather than a jungle-ranger, enough work still awaits. Although yields are low, additional crop restriction and rigorous green harvests are necessary to bring in ripe fruit at the end of the growing season. As the vines growing older, Cabernet Sauvignon displays its exceptional potential to an ever-increasing extent. Connoisseurs love its pronounced cassis nose, its succulence and inherent harmony. Cabernet Sauvignon turned out to be a perfect blending partner for indigenous Austrian varieties, wherein only small amounts are employed for structure and texture. Unfortunately, if weather conditions prevent the fruit from ripening fully, heavy losses will be suffered. In problematic years, many producers refrain from making varietal Cabernets altogether. In good vintages, this grape produces wines with impressive structure, pronounced aromas and flavours, and a firm tannic backbone.

MERLOT

This grape was mentioned for the first time in the Bordeaux region in the 18th century. It was permitted as a quality variety in Austria first in 1986. At present, Merlot plantings remain on a rather limited scale. The grape is mainly employed as a blending partner. Merlot is not very demanding on soil and site. It prefers dry soils and warm, medium-quality sites as well a mild climate, being sensitive to winter frost. The wine has a ruby-red colour, slightly grassy-spicy aromas and a supple mouthfeel. It is rarely bottled as a single-varietal wine in Austria.

CABERNET FRANC

This grape comes from France, having been documented there for the first time in 1635.

It was not permitted in Austria as a quality variety until 1986. Plantings in Austria are limited and very selective. Cabernet Franc is not very demanding on soil, yet it thrives best on fertile loam, while requiring sites with excellent sun exposure. It is highly frost-resistant. The wine has a garnet colour and is very dark. It tastes similar to Cabernet Sauvignon, but has less acidity and less abundant tannins.

SYRAH
Synonym: Shiraz

This top-variety from the Rhône Valley first had to go to Australia to become famous before Austrians began showing some interest in it. Until 2001, wines made from this black grape were marketed without indication of the vintage, because plantings were initially permitted for experimental purposes only. Consequently, resulting products could not be sold as vintage designated "Qualitätswein". In the meantime, Syrah was officially accepted into the catalogue of Burgenland's quality varieties. The origin of Syrah is laden with mystery and hypothesis. It was ascribed to the Persian city of Shiraz and to Egypt, Cyprus, and Greece alike. In 2001, the less prosaic truth was established. After years of DNA research work carried out by Professor Carole Meredith from the University of California at Davis and the leading French ampelographer Jean-Michel Boursiquot from L'École Nationale Supérieure Agronomique in Montpellier, the parents of Syrah could finally be determined. The prominent grape is a spontaneous cross between two lesser known French grapes. One of them is Mondeuse Blanche, which is related to the Savoie-based and better known Mondeuse Noire. The other one is called Dureza and is sporadically encountered in the northern Ardèche region between the upper courses of the Rhône and Loire Rivers.

RED CUVÉE

The category in which different vine varieties are combined in a harmonious blend enjoys great popularity among Austrian red wine vintners. While in previous years blends had the negative connotation of a mixed concoction of leftover wine batches, today's blends frequently represent the high-end wines of a winery. They are often the flagship of their respective producer, who has the chance to express his personal style preference. Like the Super Tuscan models, they often bear symbolic names that have become just as familiar to wine enthusiasts as the names of single vineyards in the case of Austria's white wines. These often-fanciful designations are borrowed from the most diverse worlds of concepts. From dogs to the universe, from mythology to song titles – anything goes; it's actually a matter of taste and marketing savvy. Austrian red-wine blends are usually aged in new French oak barrels. Many of them include a portion of Cabernet Sauvignon, Merlot, or more recently, Syrah, which marries especially well with indigenous grapes such as Blaufränkisch and Zweigelt. As a rule, such wines require sufficient maturation before its components homogenize. The category "Cuvée" to some extent also guards against annual fluctuations, offering more flexibility to the vintner than a single-varietal wine.

© ÖWM/Faber

AUSTRIAN WINE REGULATIONS

Austrian wine law is incorporated in the hierarchical structure of EU wine legislation. As with the other EU member countries, the national wine laws of Austria form a "bridge" between the general rules of the EU wine market organization and the specific circumstances within the country. Wines are put into two general categories: wines of origin (Landwein, Qualitätswein / land wine, quality wine) and wines without a specific origin (Wein aus Österreich /Wine from Austria). For Qualitätswein (quality wine), grapes must come from one of the official Austrian wine-growing area. For Landwein (land wine), the origin of the wine is a larger wine-growing region. Wine labels must contain the following information; origin, variety, vintage, quality designation, alcohol content by volume, reference to its residual sugars (i.e. dry, etc), as well as the official state control number and name of the producer or bottler. The Austrian wine law defines a maximum yield of 9,000 kg of grapes or 6,750 litres of wine per hectare for wines of origin (Landwein and Qualitätswein). If the yield is larger, then the total volume must be declassified as a wine without origin and may only be sold if there is no declaration of origin, variety or vintage on the wine label.

LANDWEIN – LAND WINE

In Austrian wine law, the traditional term "Landwein" replaces the EU wine law term "wine with protected geographical indication". Landwein comes from one of the three Austrian wine regions: Weinland (encompassing the federal states Niederösterreich/Lower Austria,

Burgenland, and Wien/Vienna), Bergland (encompassing the federal states Oberösterreich/Upper Austria, Salzburg, Kärnten/Corinthia, Tirol/Tyrol), or Steirerland (encompassing the federal state Steiermark/Styria).

QUALITÄTSWEIN – QUALITY WINE

In Austrian wine law, the traditional term "Qualitätswein" replaces the EU wine law term "wine with protected designation of origin". Quality wine must be produced from any single variety or blend of the 35 permitted grape varieties for Austrian Qualitätswein, and must come from the 25 wine-growing areas. Wine-growing areas include each of the 9 federal states and 16 specific wine-growing areas. Austrian Qualitätswein (quality wine) is given a unique state control number (for each wine submitted). This confirms that the wine submitted has undergone a chemical and sensorial analysis in a federal bureau of oenology. In Austria, bottled Qualitätswein (quality wines) can be easily recognised by the red-white-red (to symbolise the national flag) seal, imprinted with the winery registration number, on either the capsule or screwcap closure.

DAC – QUALITY WINE WITH REGIONAL CHARACTER

DAC wines are Qualitätsweine (quality wines) from demarcated wine-growing areas that display regional typicity and place of origin. The names of the DAC wine-growing areas are defined by EU legislation as Protected Designation of Origin (PDO). Since the year 1999, Austria has been working on specifications for the classification of wine according to demarcated origins with typical corresponding style along the lines of Romanic wine laws (as in France, Italy, Spain). This means that specific wine-growing areas will become better known on the market for a specific style typical for the region. This does not mean that the diversity of varieties and wine styles will be neglected; wines that are produced from other grape varieties and styles will be marketed under the name of the generic area (federal state). Thus, the consumer shall be able to associate a specific wine type/style with the name of a demarcated region. Branding wines with demarcated origins is preferable to branding with grape varieties; grape varieties can be planted anywhere, but specific places of origin are irreplaceable.

The development of DAC regulations is the responsibility of Regional Wine Committees made up of representatives from wineries, wine trade, cooperatives and sparkling wine producers according to their significance in the wine-growing area. The coordination and technical control of this wine-growing political development is regulated by the joint composition National Wine Board, in which member experts of the Ministry of Agriculture and the Austrian Wine Marketing Board have an advisory role. Typical wines of demarcated origin proposed by the National Committee are legally established by the Agriculture Minister by regulation. The wine label contains the term "Districtus Austria Controllatus" (abbreviated to DAC), and is placed next to the name of the demarcated origin. A dual strategy continues to ensure the preservation of diversity: Austria has managed to square the circle by employing the benefits of both the Romanic system of classification according to origin and the Germanic system according to Prädikat (predicate).

PRÄDIKATSWEIN – QUALITY WINES WITH PREDICATE

In Austria, Qualitätsweine of a special ripeness and harvest method can be categorized in predicates. Prädikatsweine (predicated wines) carry their wine-growing area of origin on the label. There are currently no DACs for Prädikatsweine, but it is imaginable that one could be created in the future. The system for Prädikatswein – i.e. to distinguish wines with a higher, natural residual sugar level and different harvest and maturation techniques – is a Germanic wine tradition. The declaration of a Prädikatswein based on the quality of the grapes harvested must be confirmed in the presence of a federal wine inspector. Chaptalization of the grape must is prohibited and the residual sugar may only come from the premature arrest of the fermenting must (but not by the addition of grape must to the wine).

© Steiermark Tourismus

OVERVIEW OF QUALITY LEVELS

Wine without origin: minimum of 10,7° KMW (see conversion table). No specific region of origin is permitted, only the description of "Österreich" or "Österreichischer Wein" or similar.

Landwein (land wine): minimum 14° KMW. A more specific region of origin declaration than the wine-growing region or larger sites is not permitted on the label.

Qualitätswein /quality wine/DAC: minimum 15° KMW. Grapes may only come from the list of classified Austrian varieties and only from one wine-growing area.

Kabinettwein: minimum 17° KMW. Regarded as a Qualitätswein, but must not be chaptalized. Maximum alcohol content total is 13%.

Prädikatswein: Spätlese, Auslese, Beerenauslese, Eiswein, Stohwein/Schilfwein, Ausbruch, Trockenbeerenauslese Must not be chaptalized. A Spätlese cannot be sold before March 1 following the harvest, other Prädikatswein not before May 1.

Spätlese: minimum 19° KMW. Grapes must be fully ripe.

Auslese: minimum 21° KMW. All faulty or unripe grapes must be excluded.

Beerenauslese (BA): minimum 25° KMW. Produced from overripe grapes or grapes with noble rot.

Ausbruch: minimum 27° KMW. Exclusively from overripe grapes, naturally shrivelled and affected by noble rot.

Trockenbeerenauslese (TBA): minimum 30° KMW. Produced from overripe grapes, naturally shrivelled and affected by noble rot.

Eiswein: minimum 25° KMW. Grapes must be frozen when harvested and pressed (contents are concentrated; water remains in the pressed grape skins).

Strohwein /Schilfwein: minimum 25° KMW. Produced from overripe grapes which are stored and airdried on straw or reeds for at least three months (similar to Vin Santo).

THE FALSTAFF WINE GUIDE – ITS PRACTICAL SIDE

TASTING NOTES

Extra trocken (extra dry): Up to 4 g/l residual sugar.

Trocken (dry): Up to 9 g/l residual sugar, if the total acidity is less than the residual sugar by a maximum of 2 g/l. For example, a wine with 8 g/l residual sugar must have at least 6 g/l acidity in order to be "trocken".

Halbtrocken (off-dry): Up to 12 g/l residual sugar.

Lieblich (semi-sweet): Up to 45 g/l residual sugar.

Süss (sweet): Over 45 g/l residual sugar.

CONVERSION TABLE FOR MUST WEIGHT

KMW	Öchsle	Beaumé
15.0	73	9.8
17.1	84	11.2
19.0	94	12.4
21.0	105	13.7
25.0	127	16.3

falstaff

The full page coverage of vintners provides you with a wealth of information. In order to save space, we have used abbreviations that are explained further on. The best-rated wine of every producer was described in addition to those wines that are of interest due to their style. The older ratings were taken from the relevant edition of the German-language Falstaff Wein Guide.

ABBREVIATIONS USED
White Wine Varieties

BO	Bouvier
CH	Chardonnay/Feinburgunder/Morillon
FU	Furmint
FV	Frühroter Veltliner/Malvasier
GM	Gelber Muskateller, Muscat Lunel
GO	Goldburger
GS	Grüner Sylvaner
GV	Grüner Veltliner
MO	Muskat-Ottonel
MT	Müller-Thurgau/Riesling-Sylvaner now: Rivaner
NB	Neuburger
PG	Pinot Gris/Grauburgunder/ Ruländer
RG	Rotgipfler
RR	Riesling/Rheinriesling
RV	Roter Veltliner
SÄ	Sämling 88/Scheurebe
SB	Sauvignon Blanc, Muskat-Sylvaner
SE	Semillon
TR	Gelber -/ Roter -/Gewürz- Traminer
WB	Weissburgunder/Pinot Blanc
WR	Welschriesling
ZF	Zierfandler

Red Wine Varieties

BB	Blauburger
BF	Blaufränkisch
BP	Blauer Portugieser
BW	Blauer Wildbacher/Schilcher
CF	Cabernet Franc
CS	Cabernet Sauvignon
ME	Merlot
PN	Pinot Noir/Blauer Burgunder/Spätburgunder
RO	Roesler
SG	Sangiovese
SL	St. Laurent
SY	Syrah
TN	Tannat
ZW	Blauer Zweigelt

Sweet Wine Categories

AB	Ausbruch
EW	Eiswein
BA	Beerenauslese
TBA	Trockenbeerenauslese
STW	Strohwein/Schilfwein (vin de paille)

WINERY CLASSIFICATIONS AND WINE SCORES

Each wine in this book is scored according to the international 100-point scale. Cask samples are signified by scores in parentheses and are predicted scores based on the assessed potential of the yet unfinished wine. The wines are tasted and assessed with knowledge of their origins and based on knowledge and past experience with the development of each individual winery's terroir and style. This has proved to be particularly valuable when assessing cask samples and very young wines, resulting in more accurate predictions than in blind tastings. A classification of each winery is also included in this guide and is not based solely on the assessment of the current wines. This attempt at winery classifications is quite a subjective undertaking, yet it does follow specified criteria that follow in the next paragraphs.

Since the beginning of the Austrian wine branch's era of tremendous quality improvement, which began at the end of the 1980s, Peter Moser has regularly tasted wines from leading producers, aspiring newcomers, and wineries which would like to be one of the

CLASSIFICATION

falstaff

two. Wines from 450 producers are tasted each year, which currently mean more than 50,000 individual tasting notes throughout the year. The English guide includes only a fraction of these. Continuous tastings of these wines allow a dependable overview. Apart from personal preferences, it is only natural that through regular contact friendly relationships develop, but despite this there are still objective elements that allow a fair classification. The ability of a producer to optimally express unique terroir is naturally a primary focus. Vineyards, clone selection, and just how consistently outstanding quality, even in difficult vintages, is produced are also considered. To summarize, it is talent, terroir, consistency, and sometimes originality that are desired. These are criteria not just in Austria, but in every wine-producing country. To what extent a producer has been able to achieve these goals over the past 10 years is reflected in a 5-star classification. In the past years this has been a 3-star classification, but the country's constant quality development has proved this to be too imprecise. This classification occurs in steps, or stages, beginning from a producer's acceptance into this guide, which is simultaneously a recommendation. Five stars are awarded to only an elite few and they are the country's very best producers with wines of best international standards. The five stars now allow the author the possibility to differentiate more precisely.

I would like to call your attention to the new wineries in this guide which are marked as such. These are names that we will be seeing more of in the future.

RATING

The rating of the wines follows the internationally accepted system of 100 points which allows a very differentiated and exactly accentuated rating. In addition to this, the 100-point system provides the possibility of an international comparison, since a large number of publications, especially in English-speaking countries, relies on this system.

Falstaff Rating Scale
100	not to be surpassed
95–99	absolute world class
90–94	excellent wine, among the best of its vintage
85–89	good to very good
80–84	satisfactory to good
75–79	solid wine with some limitations
(–)	barrel sample rating

THE 5-STAR CLASSIFICATIONS AND THEIR DEFINITIONS:

5 stars – A winery that always produces extraordinary quality which can be sourced only from the country's best terroir. This producer is among the best in the world and enjoys international recognition and demand.

4 stars – A producer of wines with consistent outstanding quality and class. A winery with significant international recognition.

3 stars – A producer of very high qualities that are consistently among the best of their category in Austria.

2 stars – A winery of national recognition that regularly produces wines with typical varietal and regional character of very good quality.

1 star – A winery with more than regional significance that regularly produces wines with typical varietal and regional character of good quality.

Without a star – A recommendable winery of regional significance that produces wines of dependable quality.

falstaff

IMPORTERS' COUNTRY CODES

IMPORTERS' COUNTRY CODES

The vintners were asked to name their most important supply sources outside of Austria. Therefore you can find a comprehensive index of importers and supply sources worldwide in the annex of the guide where you can find the exact address, and in most cases also the telephone number, fax number and website. The supply sources are listed alphabetically by country.

A list of the relevant country codes for the importers can be seen below.

AUS	Australia
BA	Barbados
B	Belgium
BY	Belarus
BER	Bermuda
BG	Bulgaria
BR	Brazil
CDN	Canada
CN	China
HR	Croatia
CYP	Cyprus
CZ	Czech Republic
DE	Germany
DK	Denmark
EST	Estonia
FIN	Finland
F	France
GB	Great Britain
GR	Greece
H	Hungary
IS	Iceland
RI	Indonesia
IRL	Ireland
IL	Israel
I	Italy

J	Japan
KOR	Korea
LV	Latvia
LT	Lithuania
L	Luxembourg
MAL	Malaysia
MT	Malta
MV	Maldives
NL	Netherlands
NZ	New Zealand
N	Norway
PE	Peru
RP	Philippines
PL	Poland
P	Portugal
RO	Romania
RUS	Russia
SRB	Serbia
SGP	Singapore
SK	Slovakia
SI	Slovenia
ZA	South Africa
E	Spain
CL	Sri Lanka
S	Sweden
CH	Switzerland
RC	Taiwan
TH	Thailand
TR	Turkey
UA	Ukraine
UAE	United Arab Emirates
USA	United States of America
CY	Cyprus

ORGANIZATIONS IN AUSTRIA

**Bundesministerium für Land- und Forst-
wirtschaft, Umwelt und Wasserwirtschaft**
(Federal Ministry for Agriculture,
Forestry, Environment and Water Management)
Stubenring 1, 1010 Wien/Vienna
Tel.: +43/(0)1/711 00
Fax: +43/(0)1/513 16 79-9900
www.lebensministerium.at

ÖWM Österreichische Weinmarketing GmbH
AWMB – Austrian Wine Marketing Board, Ltd.
Prinz-Eugen-Strasse 34, 1040 Wien/Vienna
Tel.: +43/(0)1/503 92 67-0
Fax: +43/(0)1/503 92 67-70
info@austrianwine.com, www.austrianwine.com

Weinakademie Österreich GmbH
(Austrian Wine Academy)
Dr. Josef Schuller, MW
Hauptstrasse 31, 7071 Rust
Tel.: +43/(0)2685/68 53
Fax: +43/(0)2685/64 51
www.weinakademie.at, info@weinakademie.at

Wirtschaftskammer Österreich
(Austrian Economic Chamber)
Wiedner Hauptstrasse 63, 1045 Wien/Vienna
Tel.: +43/(0)5 90 900
Fax: +43/(0)5 90 900-250
www.wko.at

Weinbauverband Niederösterreich
(Lower Austrian Wine Growers' Association)
Managing Director: DI Konrad Hackl
Sigleithenstrasse 50, 3500 Krems
Tel.: +43/(0)2732/770 77 36
Fax: +43/(0)2732/770 77 11
office@wbv.lk-noe.at

**Landesweinbauverband Burgenland
(Burgenland Provincial Wine Growers'
Association)**
Managing Director: Ing. Josef Finster
Esterhazystrasse 15, 7001 Eisenstadt
Tel.: +43/(0)2682/702-652
Fax: +43/(0)2682/702-691
wbv-bgld@lk-bgld.at

**Landesweinbauverband Steiermark
(Styrian Provincial Wine Growers' Association)**
Managing Director: Ing. Werner Luttenberger
Hamerlinggasse 3, 8011 Graz
Tel.: +43/(0)3168/0 50-1333
Fax: +43/(0)3168/0 50-1510
wein@lk-stmk.at

Landesweinbauverband Wien
(Vienna Provincial Wine Growers' Association)
President: Ing. Franz Windisch
Gumpendorfer Strasse 15, 1060 Wien/Vienna
Tel.: +43/(0)1/587 95 28
Fax: +43/(0)1/587 95 28-21
office@lk-wien.at

**Österreichischer Weinbauverband
(Federal Wine Growers' Association)**
Schauflergasse 6, 1014 Wien/Vienna
Tel.: +43/(0)1/534 41-8553
Fax: +43/(0)1/534 41-8549
President: Ing. Hermann Schultes
www.lk-oe.at

VINYARD CLASSIFICATION 2016
ERSTE LAGEN 1ÖTW
ALONG THE DANUBE

Kremstal   Kamptal
Wagram   Traisental

TOP-WINERIES IN THE DANUBEAREA participating in the classification process

Weingut BRÜNDLMAYER Weingut DOLLE Weingut EHN
Weingut FRITSCH Weingut GEYERHOF Weingut HIEDLER
Weingut HIRSCH Weingut HUBER Weingut JURTSCHITSCH SONNHOF
Weingut LOIMER Weingut MALAT Weingut MANTLERHOF
Weingut SEPP MOSER Weingut HERMANN MOSER Weingut NEUMAYER
Weingut NIGL Weingut OTT Weingut SALOMON UNDHOF
Weingut SCHLOSS GOBELSBURG Weingut STADT KREMS
Weingut STIFT GÖTTWEIG Weingut DR. UNGER Weingut TOPF
Weingut ALLRAM Weingut GÜNTHER BRANDL Weingut BUCHEGGER
Weingut BIRGIT EICHINGER Weingut LETH Weingut FRANZ PROIDL
Weingut JOSEF SCHMID Weingut WESZELI Weingut FRANZ TÜRK
Weingut RAINER WESS

Order your copy of the Classification book at:
www.traditionsweingüter.at

Österreichische Traditionsweingüter
1ÖTW ERSTE LAGEN®

A new wine culture – a long heuriger tradition

Winegrowing in a major capital city? While in other places this is merely a status symbol or a tourist attraction, wine cultivation has always played an important economic role in Vienna. There are 612 hectares of vineyards that contribute to the preservation of the green belt surrounding Vienna and are the basis for truly high quality wine. The excellent range of wines here include the quintessential Wiener Gemischter Satz (Viennese field blend), Grüner Veltliner, Riesling, Weissburgunder (Pinot Blanc), Chardonnay and outstanding red wines as well.

© ÖWM/Armin Faber

Up until the late Middle Ages, vines were grown within the ramparts of Vienna, lacing right to the city centre. Today's vineyards are situated mainly on the outskirts of Vienna. On Bisamberg north of the Danube River, vines from the Pinot family are cultivated by vintners from Strebersdorf, Stammersdorf and Jedlersdorf. In Heiligenstadt, Nussdorf, Grinzing, Sievering and Neustift am Walde, all districts of northwestern Vienna, the varieties Riesling, Chardonnay, and Weissburgunder (Pinot Blanc) prevail due to limestone-rich soils. In the southern parts of Vienna, namely Mauer, Rodaun and Oberlaa, cambisol soils favour powerful white wines as well as opulent red wine blends.

The classic Viennese specialty "Wiener Gemischter Satz DAC" became a designation of origin in 2013. For this traditional regional specialty, it is required that at least three different white grape varieties grow together in one vineyard and are harvested and fermented together.

In the past, this method was used to reduce the risk of variable harvesting conditions; today the method has again grown in popularity for the complexity it brings. The great cru Nussberg has been rediscovered and now seems to magically attract ambitious new vintners crossing over from other professions.

Vienna's heuriger (winery taverns) are, without a doubt, legendary. Regardless of whether they welcome all year round with their generous warm and cold buffets, or are the small, seasonal ones hidden in the cellar alleys, they are popular with people from all walks of life, both rich and poor, locals and tourists. Vintners offer top class wines that can be purchased by the glass as well as by the bottle. These wines satisfy even the most demanding connoisseurs.

Finally, another pleasant aspect of Viennese viticulture is the fact that modern cellars and technological equipment are integrated so seamlessly into the traditions of old, established family wine estates.

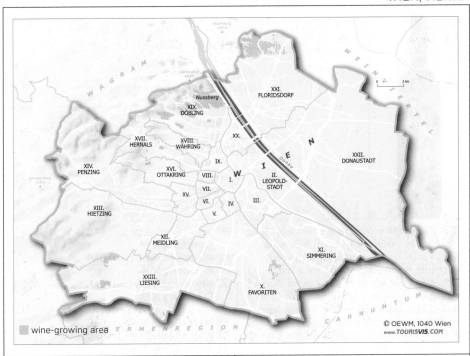

wine-growing area

© OEWM, 1040 Wien
www.TOURISVIS.COM

AUSTRIA ALTOGETHER: 45,900 ha

Wine-growing area Vienna
612 ha (1 %)

White wine altogether: 490 ha (80 %)
Grüner Veltliner:	153 ha (25 %)
Riesling:	84 ha (14 %)
Weissburgunder:	51 ha (8 %)
Gemischter Satz:	51 ha (8 %)
Chardonnay:	46 ha (7,5 %)

Red wine altogether: 122 ha (20 %)
Zweigelt:	49 ha (8 %)
Pinot Noir:	22 ha (4 %)
Blauburger:	10 ha (2 %)
Cabernet Sauvignon:	10 ha (2 %)
Sankt Laurent:	9 ha (2 %)

◆ Weingut Cobenzl, 1190 Wien/Vienna

◆ Weingut Hajszan Neumann, 1190 Wien/Vienna

◆ Landhaus Mayer, 1190 Wien/Vienna

◆ Weingut Mayer am Pfarrplatz, 1190 Wien/Vienna

◆ Weingut Rotes Haus, 1190 Wien/Vienna

◆ Wein- und Sektkellerei Schlumberger, 1190 Wien/Vienna

◆ Weingut Walter Wien, 1210 Wien/Vienna

◆ Weingut Wieninger, 1210 Wien/Vienna

◆ Weingut Zahel, 1230 Wien/Vienna

★★★

Weingut Cobenzl

1190 Wien, Am Cobenzl 96
T: +43 (1) 3205805, F: +43 (1) 3282286
office@weingutcobenzl.at, www.weingutcobenzl.at

Winemaker: Ing. Georg Königsbauer
Contact Person: Ing. Thomas Podsednik
Production: 300.000 bottles (70 % white, 30 % red)
Hectares: 60
Certified: Sustainable Austria
Fairs: ProWein, VieVinum
Distribution partners: J, DE, NL

Vineyards in Vienna are not something to be taken for granted! Vienna is the only world capital with productive vineyards within city limits. As a matter of fact, it has always been an integral part of Viennese culture ever since Emperor Probus (232–282 A.D.) permitted the Roman legions to cultivate wine in Vienna. The Cobenzl wine estate has been in ownership of the City of Vienna since 1907. Its 60 hectares of vineyards and annual production of 300,000 bottles of quality wine make it one of the most prominent wineries in the city. The vineyards are situated in the 19th and 21st districts where the wines benefit from their proximity to the Danube River and from warm Pannonian climate influences. Managing director Thomas Podsednik and oenologist Georg Königsberger have turned this traditional winery into a dynamic, modern wine producer. The Cobenzl winery offers a broad assortment of refreshing, fruity white wines like Wiener Gemischter Satz DAC, Grüner Veltliner, Riesling, and Weissburgunder (Pinot Blanc) that are made from vineyards that enjoy a stunning view over the Austrian capital and metropolitan area.

This Vienna city winery was one of the first Austrian wineries to achieve the "Sustainable Austria" accolade. Efforts for sustainability are made in the vineyard and grape production, an apiculture, and production and use of solar energy. The quality efforts of the young, ambitious team have brought numerous accolades at regional championships and the "SALON Österreich Wein", and a "highly recommended" from the Chicago Beverage Tasting Institute.

92 Wiener Gemischter Satz DAC
Reisenberg 2015
91 Wiener Gemischter Satz DAC
Reisenberg 2014
92 Wiener Gemischter Satz DAC
Reisenberg 2013

89 Wiener Gemischter Satz DAC 2015
89 Wiener Gemischter Satz DAC 2014
88 Wiener Gemischter Satz DAC 2013

92 Weißer Burgunder Senator 2014
Medium green-yellow hue. This Pinot Blanc displays inviting yellow fruit nuances reminiscent of papaya and baby banana along with ripe pear and wild meadow herbs in the background. Elegant white apple joins other fruit notes on the palate, where they are highlighted wonderfully by elegant acidity. The long finish features a pleasant lemony touch.
90 Weißburgunder Senator 2013
90 Weißburgunder Senator 2012

(91–93) Weißburgunder Seidenhaus 2015
91 Weißburgunder Seidenhaus 2013
91 Weißburgunder Seidenhaus 2012

88 Grüner Veltliner Classic 2014

91 Grüner Veltliner Senator 2015
90 Grüner Veltliner Senator 2014
89 Grüner Veltliner Senator 2013

92 Grüner Veltliner Pfeffer 2015
92 Grüner Veltliner Pfeffer 2014
Medium green-yellow. Delicate yellow apple and mango with mineral components and notes of tobacco. Juicy and complex with subtle oak spice mingling with apricot and salty elements on the long finish. Very good potential for further development.
91 Grüner Veltliner Pfeffer 2013

91 Riesling Senator 2014
92 Riesling Senator 2013
91 Riesling Senator 2012

89 Riesling Classic 2015
89 Riesling Classic 2014

88 Gelber Muskateller Senator 2015
89 Gelber Muskateller Senator 2014
88 Gelber Muskateller Senator 2013

88 Rosé vom Zweigelt 2014

90 Merlot 2011

91 Blauer Zweigelt Hofbreiten 2012

89 Pinot Noir Bellevue Reserve 2012
92 Pinot Noir Bellevue Reserve 2011

(90–92) Cabernet Sauvignon 2012
91 Cabernet Sauvignon 2011

(90–92) Jungenberg 2012 ME/CS/ZW

Weingut Hajszan Neumann

1190 Wien, Grinzinger Straße 86
T: +43 (1) 2901012
wein@hajszanneumann.com, www.hajszanneumann.com

ORGANIC

Winemaker: Luis Teixeira
Contact Person: Fritz Wieninger
Production: 50.000 bottles (70 % white, 28 % red, 2 % sweet)
Hectares: 17
Fairs: VieVinum, ProWein
Distribution partners: on request

The Hajszan Neumann winery is located in Vienna's most famous wine-growing district, Grinzing, at the foot of the Nussberg. Much passion is invested in certified biodynamic viticulture to yield elegant, pure wines with authentic expression. Fritz Wieninger, a pioneer of quality wine production in Vienna, took over management of this winery in 2014, concentrating on the production of Wiener Gemischter Satz, Riesling and Grüner Veltliner. The vineyards, most of which are owned by the star architect Heinz Neumann, are located in the best sites of Vienna with the Nussberg playing the leading role. The mineral rich limestone and weathered calcareous soils impart to the wine an expressive character. The foundation for the high quality is the biodynamic cultivation, which has been practiced here since 2006. An intact ecological system with all its facets is the central focus. The vines are tended attentively by hand and meticulous soil management ensures the vitality that promotes healthy grapes. Minimal intervention and gentle production methods are practiced in the wine cellar - and this can be tasted in the vibrant wines of Hajszan Neumann. Each wine has its own distinctive soul derived from the natural aromas and flavours of the grapes and their terroir. Particular attention should be paid to the single vineyard Wiener Gemischter Satz wines from the Nussberg and Weissleiten sites.

(92–94) Wiener Gemischter Satz DAC Weissleiten 2015
92 Wiener Gemischter Satz DAC Weissleiten 2014
92 Wiener Gemischter Satz DAC Weissleiten 2013

(91–93) Wiener Gemischter Satz DAC Weissleiten Natural 2015

91 Wiener Gemischter Satz DAC Nussberg 2015
90 Wiener Gemischter Satz DAC Nußberg 2014
89 Wiener Gemischter Satz DAC Nußberg 2013

93 Riesling Steinberg 2015
92 Riesling Steinberg 2014
89 Riesling Steinberg 2013

91 Grüner Veltliner Weissleiten 2014

91 Grüner Veltliner Nussberg 2015

(92–94) Gewürztraminer Natural 2015

91 Chardonnay Gollin 2011

(87–89) Zweigelt 2014
91 Zweigelt 2013

93 Wiener Symphonie 2012 BF/ZW/CS
Dark ruby with purple highlights and a thin transparent rim. nviting ripe cherry and a delicate touch of sandalwood with a pleasant mineral character. Juicy, elegant finesse derived from an outstanding terroir. Fresh cherries and salty minerals linger on the vibrant finish. Very appetizing drinking pleasure.

90 Quadriga 2011 ZW/BF/PN/CS

Landhaus Mayer GmbH

1190 Wien, Eroicagasse 4
T: +43 (1) 3360197, F: +43 (1) 336019799
office@landhausmayer.at, www.landhausmayer.at

Winemaker: Gerhard J. Lobner and Dr. Dragos Pavelescu
Contact Person: Gerhard J. Lobner
Production: n. a. (90 % white, 10 % red)
Distribution partners: DK, NL, GB, USA, PL

L andhaus Mayer has an excellent cooperation going with grape growers who have passionately cultivated top vineyard sites for generations. The production manager, Gerhard J. Lobner, makes viticultural decisions together with the growers. From winter pruning to canopy management to choosing the time of harvest, Lobner has the opportunity to influence all measures. "The potential that is available in this region is incredible," enthuses Lobner. Many of the best sites are at risk of being abandoned due to structural changes. However, Landhaus Mayer is striving to offer more lucrative opportunities for the region's growers by producing higher quality wines.

88 Riesling 2015
89 Riesling 2014
Pale green-yellow. Honey laced peach and a touch of pineapple with subtle mineral notes. Juicy refreshing acidity carries a white vineyard peach tone all the way through the finish. Already offering good drinking pleasure.
89 Riesling 2013

90 Riesling Maximus 2013

88 Grüner Veltliner 2015
88 Grüner Veltliner 2014
88 Grüner Veltliner 2013

89 Grüner Veltliner Maximus 2013
89 Grüner Veltliner 2012

89 Rosé 2015
87 Rosé 2014
88 Landhaus Rosé 2013

Weingut Mayer am Pfarrplatz

1190 Wien, Pfarrplatz 2
T: +43 (1) 3360197, F: +43 (1) 336019799
office@pfarrplatz.at, www.pfarrplatz.at

Winemaker: Ing. Barbara Wimmer and Dr. Dragos Pavelescu
Contact Person: Gerhard J. Lobner and Paul Kiefer
Production: n. a. (90 % white, 5 % red, 5 % sweet)
Hectares: 61
Fairs: VieVinum, ProWein
Distribution partners: RUS, J, FIN, NL, USA

This historic family winery has produced wine in the Heiligenstadt and Grinzing districts of Vienna since 1683. The house on Pfarrplatz is a synonym for wine quality and traditional Viennese heuriger (wine tavern) culture. Ludwig van Beethoven lived in an apartment in this house in 1817 while working on his greatest composition, the 9th Symphony.

The wines of this estate stem from the very best Viennese vineyards: the Nussberg and the Alsegger. Their elegant fruity aroma, balance and character are true reflections of these sites. The "Wiener Gemischter Satz DAC Nussberg" is the ultimate classic in the assortment of wines. This speciality is made from a field blend of Grüner Veltliner, Riesling, Rotgipfler and Zierpfandler, which are all harvested and fermented together. Single-vineyard Rieslings also exhibit the unique characteristics of the Nussberg and Alsegger vineyards. Varietal wines from Grüner Veltliner, Sauvignon Blanc, and Gelber Muskateller (Muscat blanc á petits grains) round out the assortment of white wines. The Mayer am Pfarrplatz winery also offers an elegant Blauburgunder (Pinot Noir) for red wine lovers.

90 Wiener Gemischter Satz DAC 2015
90 Wiener Gemischter Satz DAC 2014
92 Wiener Gemischter Satz DAC 2013

(91–93) Sauvignon Blanc Hernals 2015
93 Sauvignon Blanc Hernals 2014
Pale green-yellow with silver highlights. Green and yellow bell pepper, gooseberry, nutmeg and grapefruit zest. Full-bodied with abundant, juicy gooseberry and edgy acidity. A spicy-herbal touch reminiscent of the Loire appears on the finish.

(93–95) Riesling Nussberg Weißer Marmor 2015
93 Riesling Weißer Marmor 2013
94 Riesling Weißer Marmor 2012

(91–93) Riesling Nussberg 2015
93 Riesling Nussberg 2014
Pale green-yellow. Delicate notes of yellow peach, passion fruit and nuances of blossom honey. Juicy, elegant texture and pleasant fruit sweetness wonderfully balanced with refreshing acidity. Long finish, plenty of finesse, dependable ageing potential.
92 Riesling Nussberg 2013

90 Riesling Alsegg 2015
91 Riesling Alsegg 2014
89 Riesling Alsegg 2013

91 Grüner Veltliner Schenkenberg 2015
91 Grüner Veltliner Schenkenberg 2014
91 Grüner Veltliner Schenkenberg 2013

89 Sauvignon Blanc 2014

89 Fräulein Rosé von Döbling 2015

(88–90) Pinot Noir 2014

92 Wiener Gemischter Satz DAC Nussberg 2015
91 Wiener Gemischter Satz DAC Nussberg 2014
93 Wiener Gemischter Satz DAC Nussberg 2013

93 Riesling Trockenbeerenauslese 2013

★ ★ ★
Weingut Rotes Haus

1190 Wien, Pfarrplatz 2
T/F: +43 (1) 3360197
mayer@pfarrplatz.at, www.rotes-haus.at

Winemaker: Ing. Barbara Wimmer and Dr. Dragos Pavelescu
Contact Person: Gerhard J. Lobner and Paul Kiefer
Production: n. a. (95 % white, 5 % red)
Hectares: 9
Fairs: VieVinum, ProWein
Distribution partners: I, RUS, L, DE, GB

The Rotes Haus winery gets its name from the quaint little red house idyllically nestled in the heart of the Nussberg, the most famous vineyard slope in Vienna. his producer has been cultivating around nine vineyard hectares at this romantice site since 2001. Under the motto of "quality before quantity," the wines produced here represent the exceptional character of their origin. The unique soil and microclimate allow perfect physiological ripening of the grapes. Full bodied, well-balanced wines with crystal clear varietal expression and exquisite mineral character are produced from Grüner Veltliner, Weissburgunder (Pinot Blanc), Welschriesling, and the rare Traminer varieties. In suitable years, small quantities of noble sweet wines are also produced.

91 Wiener Gemischter Satz DAC 2015
91 Wiener Gemischter Satz DAC 2014
89 Wiener Gemischter Satz DAC 2013

93 Wiener Gemischter Satz DAC Nussberg 2014
Medium yellow hue with a slight yeasty touch. Subtle nuances of yellow pear, acacia honey, greengage plum and a bit of apricot. Complex with firm texture, elegant yellow stone fruit and nervy acidity structure. Salty mineral nuances linger on the long finish. Good aging potential.
92 Wiener Gemischter Satz DAC Nussberg 2013

(90–92) Traminer 2015
93 Traminer 2012

(91–93) Traminer Nussberg Reserve 2015

(90–92) Grüner Veltliner 2015
92 Grüner Veltliner 2014
Pale green-yellow. Pineapple, yellow apple and a hint of mango with an undertone of pepper and celery salt. Full-bodied and creamy with sweet fruitiness enveloping the firm acidity structure. Subtle notes of ripe apricot in the aftertaste. A nicely concentrated food partner.
92 Grüner Veltliner 2013

93 Chardonnay Nussberg Reserve 2011

(87–89) Merlot 2014

★★★
Wein- und Sektkellerei Schlumberger

1190 Wien, Heiligenstädter Straße 43
T: +43 (1) 3682258 0, F: +43 (1) 3682258 230
services@schlumberger.at, www.schlumberger.at

Winemaker and Contact Person: Herbert Jagersberger
Fairs: VieVinum
Distribution partners: AUS, RO, I, RUS, J, S, B, CDN, CH, HR, SK, RC, SLO, DK, L, DE, F, GR, NL, GB, N, UA, HK, H, USA, PL, P

Schlumberger is Austria's leading producer of sparkling wines and the Schlumberger Sektkellerei in Wien (Vienna) is a fascinating synthesis of history, tradition and vision for the future. Robert Schlumberger found his own personal "Champagne" in the Thermenregion south of Vienna and planted his first vineyards in Goldeck in 1842. The enterprise continues to produce sparkling wines exclusively according to the traditional method of bottle fermentation - the cellar mark on the bottom of every single bottle serves as a guarantee. The maturation cellar in the Heiligenstadt district of Vienna was designed by the famous architect Carl Ritter von Ghega in the 19th century and is quite an impressive sight. Schlumberger uses only base wines from Austria for their production – a luxury that is appreciated by wine lovers. Because tastes differ, the assortment of Schlumberger sparkling wines is broad and is constantly being expanded. New editions include the "Schlumberger Grüner Veltliner" and the "Schlumberger Chardonnay". The premium sparkling "DOM" series is a joint project between Schlumberger and the Arachon vintner trio "T.FX.T", comprised of Illa Szemes, Manfred Tement and F.X. Pichler. Both the Schlumberger DOM classic and the Schlumberger DOM Rosé are listed in top restaurants.

91 Schlumberger Dom T.F.X.T. brut 2011
Pale yellow with silver highlights and fine, persistent mousse. Delicate aromas of white blossoms, fresh apple, greengage plum and a touch of minerals. Delicate, juicy apple fruit mingles with soft smoky notes and is followed by orange and sublte grapefruit on the finish.

94 Schlumberger DOM Classic brut T.FX.T. 2009

92 Schlumberger Blanc de Noirs brut
90 Schlumberger Blanc de Noirs 2006

93 Schlumberger Chardonnay brut 2014
91 Schlumberger Chardonnay 2011

91 Schlumberger Grüner Veltliner brut 2014

90 Schlumberger Sauvignon blanc 2012

92 Schlumberger Sparkling brut 2013
90 Schlumberger Sparkling 2012
90 Schlumberger Sparkling 2011

91 Schlumberger Brut Nature 2011

90 Schlumberger Cuvée Klimt 2011

90 Schlumberger Dom T.F.X.T. brut Rosé 2013
93 Schlumberger DOM Rosé brut T.FX.T 2011

93 Schlumberger Rosé brut 2013
91 Schlumberger Rosé brut 2012

Weingut Walter Wien

1210 Wien, Untere Jungenberggasse 7
T: +43 (664) 1903469
office@weingut-walter-wien.at, www.weingut-walter-wien.at

──────── ORGANIC ────────

Winemaker: Fritz Wieninger
Contact Person: Norbert Walter
Production: 12.000 bottles (80 % white, 20 % red)
Hectares: 4
Fairs: VieVinum, ProWein
Distribution partners: on request

Norbert Walter grew up on a farm in Galtür in the Tyrolean Alps. He later worked as a mountain shepherd on Alpine pastures in Switzerland and Tyrol, where he made cheese for eight summers. He has lived and worked in Vienna since 1989 and has never lost his relationship to agriculture, even in the city; the gardens, orchards, fields and vineyards of Vienna continue to fascinate him. His dream of continuing his agricultural career was fulfilled in 2004, when he leased plots in the Nussberg, Sievering and Oberlaa vineyards of Vienna. One year later, he was thrilled to present his first wine, a Viennese Riesling. The assortment of varieties is growing and his "www" (weingut walter wien) now produces Grüner Veltliner, Gemischter Satz, Chardonnay, and Zweigelt. Norbert Walter's desire is to produce the highest quality wines possible - and therefore works sustainably, meticulously tends his vines and harvests his grapes with extreme care. Vienna's most famous vintner, Fritz Wieninger, is his good friend and helps him with the vinification of his wines. Walter purchased an idyllic little vineyard with a wine cellar on the Bisamberg in 2008. With much dedication and attention to detail, he created a quiet place of refuge for guests in the midst of the vineyard.

91 **Wiener Gemischter Satz DAC Hackenberg 2015**
91 **Wiener Gemischter Satz Hackenberg Alte Reben 2013**

89 **Wiener Gemischter Satz DAC Bisamberg 2015**
90 **Wiener Gemischter Satz DAC 2014**
89 **Wiener Gemischter Satz DAC 2013**

88 **Riesling Bisamberg 2015**
89 **Riesling Bisamberg 2012**

91 **Riesling Nussberg 2015**
92 **Riesling Nussberg 2014**
Pale yellow with silver highlights. Inviting peach, delicate blossom honey and floral nuances. White vineyard peach and litchi are elegantly highlighted by vibrant acidity and continue on the mineral finish. Will benefit from bottle maturation.

88 **Grüner Veltliner Bisamberg 2015**
89 **Grüner Veltliner Bisamberg 2014**

89 **Chardonnay Bisamberg 2015**
89 **Chardonnay Bisamberg 2014**
90 **Chardonnay Bisamberg 2013**

90 **Zweigelt 2013**
89 **Zweigelt Oberlaa 2012**
89 **Zweigelt Oberlaa 2011**

91 **Zweigelt Reserve 2013**
91 **Zweigelt Reserve 2012**
91 **Zweigelt Reserve 2011**

★ ★ ★ ★

Weingut Wieninger

1210 Wien, Stammersdorfer Straße 31
T: +43 (1) 2901012, F: +43 (1) 2901012 3
weingut@wieninger.at, www.wieninger.at

ORGANIC

Winemaker and Contact Person: Ing. Fritz Wieninger
Production: 300.000 bottles (69 % white, 30 % red, 1 % sweet)
Hectares: 45
Fairs: ProWein, VieVinum, Summa
Distribution partners: RO, I, RUS, J, S, B, CDN, BR, SGP, BG, SK, RC, DK, L, FIN,
F, NZ, CZ, TR, GB, USA, IRL, PL, P

The name "Wieninger" actually means "Man from Vienna" and anyone who carries such a name in such a grand city is obliged to give his very best. Indeed, Fritz Wieninger does this with superlative style and has long been the indisputable top producer in the city. This traditional heurigen family business has developed into an exceptional winery. Fritz Wieninger has owned vineyards on both sides of the Danube for several years now. With the purchase of plots in Vienna's best vineyard, the Nussberg, the talented vintner now has even better fruit at his disposal and he understands how to turn this into an incredibly diversified assortment of premium wines. Wieninger is most famed in Austria for the oak fermented Chardonnay and Pinot Noir in his "Grand Select" series. The Bordeaux blend, "Danubis Grand Select", exhibits extraordinary cassis fruit and spice. A further specialty of the house is the traditional Viennese "Gemischter Satz" (field blend). Various grape varieties that grow side by side in one vineyard are harvested and vinified together to yield an authentic terroir wine. As of the 2013 vintage, this wine has been certified as a wine of demarcated origin - a "Wiener Gemischter Satz DAC". To date, the export-oriented Wieninger winery is the only Viennese one to have gained acceptance in white cloth restaurants all across Austria. Moreover, it exports 40% of its production to 31 countries on three continents. The share of wine sold in Viennese restaurants has also increased in recent years. Fritz Wieninger has fulfilled a life-long dream and as of September 2012, his winery has a new vinification facility located at Stammersdorfer Strasse 31. The Viennese vintner association "WienWein" was formed together with the Christ, Edlmoser, Cobenzl, Mayer am Pfarrplatz, and Fuhrgassl-Huber wineries to promote the the the best wines of Vienna.

93 Wiener Gemischter Satz DAC Bisamberg 2015
92 Wiener Gemischter Satz DAC Bisamberg 2014
92 Wiener Gemischter Satz DAC Bisamberg 2013

93 Wiener Gemischter Satz DAC Nußberg 2014
94 Wiener Gemischter Satz DAC Nußberg 2013
94 Nußberg Alte Reben 2012 WB/NB/WR/GV/GS

(93–95) Wiener Gemischter Satz DAC
Rosengartl 2015
94 Wiener Gemischter Satz DAC
Rosengartl 2014
Pale yellow with silver highlights. A marvellously faceted bouquet exhibits ripe mango and pineapple notes, apricot and a hint of orange zest. Elegant peach and apricot are highlighted by the well-integrated acidity structure. Salty and citrus notes mark the finish.
93 Wiener Gemischter Satz DAC
Rosengartl 2013

91 Wiener Gemischter Satz DAC 2015
91 Wiener Gemischter Satz DAC 2014
91 Wiener Gemischter Satz DAC 2013

91 Grüner Veltliner Herrenholz 2015
92 Grüner Veltliner Herrenholz 2014
90 Grüner Veltliner Herrenholz 2013

(92–94) Grüner Veltliner Kaasgraben 2015
93 Grüner Veltliner Kaasgraben 2013

(93–95) Grüner Veltliner Preussen 2015
94 Grüner Veltliner Preussen 2013
92 Grüner Veltliner Preussen 2012

92 Grüner Veltliner Nußberg 2015
92 Grüner Veltliner Nußberg 2014
92 Grüner Veltliner Nußberg 2013

90 Wiener Grüner Veltliner 2015
90 Wiener Grüner Veltliner 2014
89 Grüner Veltliner Wien 2013

(93–95) Riesling Nußberg 2015
93 Riesling Nußberg 2014
93 Riesling Nußberg 2013

93 Riesling Rosengartl 2013
94 Riesling Rosengartl 2012

91 Wiener Riesling 2015
91 Wiener Riesling 2014
89 Riesling Wien 2013

95 Chardonnay Tribute 2013
96 Chardonnay Tribute 2012
Brilliant yellow with silver highlights. A multifaceted bouquet reveals subtle peach, a touch of brioche and nuances of ripe papaya and pineapple. Complex and full-bodied with nicely integrated oak spice reminiscent of coconut and nougat. The appetizing mineral finish is exceptionally long. Very dependable potential for ageing.
96 Chardonnay Tribute 2011

95 Chardonnay Grand Select 2013
94 Chardonnay Grand Select 2012
95 Chardonnay Grand Select 2011

92 Chardonnay Select 2014
92 Chardonnay Select 2013
92 Chardonnay Select 2012

90 Chardonnay Classic 2015
90 Chardonnay Classic 2014
89 Chardonnay Classic 2013

89 Gelber Muskateller Bisamberg 2015
89 Gelber Muskateller Bisamberg 2013
88 Gelber Muskateller 2012

95 Pinot Noir Tribute 2011

93 Pinot Noir Grand Select 2013
94 Pinot Noir Grand Select 2012
Deep ruby with garnet highlights and a broad transparent rim. Ripe cherry fruit and nuances of raspberry mingle with herbs, spice, mandarin zest and brioche. Highly elegant and juicy with well integrated oak spice and dark minerals continuing all the way through the long finish. This will benefit from further bottle maturation.
93 Pinot Noir Grand Select 2011

(90–92) Pinot Noir Select 2013
91 Pinot Noir Select 2012
91 Pinot Noir Select 2011

93 Merlot Grand Select 2012
94 Merlot Grand Select 2011
93 Merlot Grand Select 2009

93 St. Laurent Grand Select 2013
93 St. Laurent Grand Select 2012
93 St. Laurent Grand Select 2011

93 Danubis Grand Select 2012 CS/ZW/ME
93 Danubis Grand Select 2011 CS/ME/ZW

90 Wiener Trilogie 2013 ZW/ME/CS
91 Wiener Trilogie 2012 ZW/ME/CS
91 Wiener Trilogie 2011 ZW/CS/ME

94 Blauer Burgunder Beerenauslese 2014

94 Beerenauslese Bisamberg 2013

93 Merlot Beerenauslese 2014

92 Merlot Auslese 2014

92 Traminer Bisamberg 2012

91 Cuvée Katharina Rosé Sekt NV
91 Cuvée Katharina Rosé Sekt 2011
91 Cuvée Katharina Rosé Sekt 2010

Weingut Zahel

1230 Wien, Maurer Hauptplatz 9
T: +43 (1) 8891318, F: +43 (1) 8891318 10
winery@zahel.at, www.zahel.at

Winemaker and Contact Person: Alexander Zahel
Production: 150.000 bottles (75 % white, 25 % red)
Hectares: 25
Fairs: VieVinum, ProWein
Distribution partners: I, J, CDN, CH, B, SGP, BR, RC, DK, DE, FIN, F, NL, N, RI, USA

Richard and Alexander Zahel, the pioneers on the southern part of Vienna, are among the leading vintners in the metropolis. Their unerring quality efforts and dedication to the "Wiener Gemischter Satz" have gone hand in hand with the burgeoning of one of the city's most modern wine cellars and traditional heuriger (wine tavern). Zahel is the only winery owning vineyards in all of the Viennese wine-growing districts. The winery and the heuriger are located amongst the vines in Mauer and further vineyard plots are in the districts of Oberlaa, Neustift am Walde, Sievering, and Vienna's most famous vineyard, the Nussberg. The vineyards in Mauer are situated at the edge of the Viennese Forest and the soils are similar to those of the northern reaches of neighbouring Thermenregion. The warm Pannonian climate and cool nights benefit in particular Gemischter Satz and the Burgundian varieties, but the reds also appreciate these conditions. The diversity of sites, soils and microclimates make it fascinating to produce wines in Vienna. The opening of the new vinification facility, which includes a barrique cellar, crush house, tasting room and delicatessen, were festively celebrated with the Austrian Chancellor, Werner Faymann, and the mayor of Vienna, Dr. Michael Häupl, in 2010.

A blend of five different Gemischter Satz Vineyards called "Five Points" unites five different soils for a regional crossover expression. A series of Wiener Gemischter Satz DAC single vineyard wines from Kassgraben, Goldberg and Mauerberg will enter the market for the first time with the 2015 vintage. Richard and Alexander Zahel plan to expand the global exports of Gemischter Satz and are currently in the process of converting 100% of their vineyards to certified organic production.

(91–93) Wiener Gemischter Satz DAC Goldberg Gutsreserve 2013
94 Wiener Gemischter Satz Goldberg 2011
Medium green-yellow. A multifaceted bouquet features tropical fruit aromas reminiscent of coconut and litchi with apricot and orange zest. Juicy and complex with Burgundian silkiness. Subtle toasty aromas and hazelnut join in on the long finish. A very versatile wine at the table.

(91–93) Wiener Gemischter Satz DAC Mauerberg 2015

(92–94) Wiener Gemischter Satz DAC Kaasgraben 2015

92 Wiener Gemischter Satz DAC Reisberg Dolomitkalk 2013

(89–91) Wiener Gemischter Satz DAC Nussberg 2015
90 Wiener Gemischter Satz DAC Nussberg 2013

91 Five Points – The Star of Vienna 2013
92 Wiener Gemischter Satz Five Points – The Star of Vienna 2012
95 Five Points – The Star of Vienna 2011

92 3 Points 2013

(90–92) Grüner Veltliner Kaasgraben 2015
91 Grüner Veltliner Kaasgraben 2014
89 Grüner Veltliner Kaasgraben 2013

89 Grüner Veltliner Goldberg 2015
89 Grüner Veltliner Goldberg 2014

92 Nussberg Grande Reserve 2013
Medium green-yellow. Tropical fruit nuances reminiscent of mango and papaya mingle with blossom honey and peach. Juicy acidity nicely counters the subtle sweetness in a

creamy texture. Mineral notes appear in a long finish.
A very harmonious food accompaniment. Also has excellent
potential for further ageing.

91 Nussberg Grande Reserve 2012

88 Sauvignon Blanc Kroissberg 2015

89 Gelber Muskateller Kroissberg 2015

92 Antares Grande Reserve 2013 SL/ZW/ME/CS
94 Antares Grande Reserve 2009

92 Blaufränkisch Goldberg 2013

91 Pinot Noir Dolomitkalk 2013
92 Pinot Noir Dolomit 2011

92 Sapor 2013 ME/SL/CS

Diversity has a name

Lower Austria is the largest wine-growing area in Austria with 27,128 hectares. It is home to a rich assortment of origins and styles made not only from rare autochthon grapes, but also international varieties. Lower Austria encompasses eight smaller sub-regions. It can be divided into three climatic zones: the Weinviertel in the north, the Danube area to the west of Vienna (Wachau, Kremstal, Traisental, Kamptal, and Wagram) and the Pannonian influenced area southeast of the capital city (Thermenregion and Carnuntum).

© ÖWM/Gerhard Trumler

The large Weinviertel area made headlines in 2003 when its flagship wine, the peppery Grüner Veltliner, was introduced to the market under the Weinviertel DAC protected designation of origin. Since then, the Weinviertel DAC guarantees crisp, peppery, spicy Grüner Veltliner in the glass. The Weinviertel wine-growing area also offers wines other than Grüner Veltliner including other crisp white wines, fruity red wines and even sweet wine specialties. These wines bear the Niederösterreich protected geographical indication.

Romantic wine villages are strung like pearls along the Danube and neighbouring rivers Krems, Traisen and Kamp. From Melk to Klosterneuburg, Riesling and Grüner Veltliner are the flagships. Both of these grape varieties express the unique terroirs of the protected designations of origin Kamptal DAC, Kremstal DAC, and Traisental DAC. The steep primary rock sites of the Wachau evolve into loess terraces in the eastern part of neighboring Kremstal; this marks the character of not only the wines of the Kremstal, but also those of the Traisental and the Wagram. In the Kamptal, volcanic soils impart a distinctive character to the wines. Specialties such as Weissburgunder (Pinot Blanc) and Chardonnay, as well as elegant red wines, complete the broad spectrum of wines in this part of Niederösterreich. The Pannonian influenced part of Niederösterreich south of Vienna is home to some of Austria's most outstanding red wines. Zweigelt and Blaufränkisch feature in Carnuntum while St. Laurent and Pinot Noir set the tone in the Thermenregion. Rare autochthon specialties can be found everywhere. Zierfandler and Rotgipfler thrive around Gumpoldskirchen while Roter Veltliner enjoys a renaissance in Wagram. Niederösterreich is certainly synonymous with diversity.

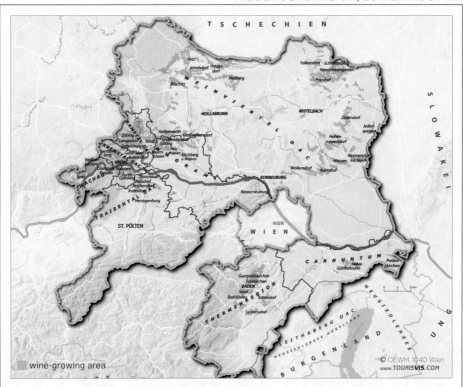

wine-growing area

© OEWM. 1040 Wien
www.TOURISVIS.COM

AUSTRIA ALTOGETHER: 45,900 ha

Wine-growing area Lower Austria   **27,128 ha (60 %)**

SPECIFIC WINE-GROWING AREA:

Carnuntum	910 ha
Kamptal	3,802 ha
Kremstal	2,243 ha
Thermenregion	2,196 ha
Traisental	790 ha
Wachau	1,350 ha
Wagram	2,451 ha
Weinviertel	13,356 ha

White wine altogether:	**20,141 ha (74 %)**	**Red wine altogether:**	**6,987 ha (26 %)**
Grüner Veltliner:	11,873 ha (44 %)	Zweigelt:	3,328 ha (12 %)
Riesling:	1,538 ha (6 %)	Blauer Portugieser:	1,593 ha (6 %)
Müller-Thurgau:	1,392 ha (5 %)	Blauburger:	701 ha (3 %)
Welschriesling:	1,346 ha (5 %)	St. Laurent:	348 ha (1 %)
Weissburgunder:	867 ha (3 %)	Pinot Noir:	271 ha (1 %)

Elegant red wines with full, deep fruit

For many years, archaeologists have been excavating the historic remains of Roman culture in Carnuntum. Just as remarkable are the treasures of the 910 hectares of vineyards here, especially the Zweigelt-based red wines that reflect their regional origins. The proud vintners create an apt expression of their unique region with their Rubin Carnuntum wines which can be recognized by the symbol of the Roman "Heidentor", or Heathen's Gate, on their label.

© ÖWM/Armin Faber

The wine-growing area of Carnuntum extends east of Vienna to the borders of Slovakia. The vineyards spread south of the Danube River over a landscape of rolling hills including the Leitha, Arbesthaler, and Hainburger Mountains. Stony, heavy soils with clay, loess, sand, and gravel offer the best conditions for red wines, especially Austria's leading varieties, Blauer Zweigelt and Blaufränkisch. These perform at their very best on the Spitzerberg where they are also accompanied by the international varieties Cabernet Sauvignon and Merlot. The hot summers and cold winters of the Pannonian climate are tempered by the nearby Danube River and Lake Neusiedl. These influences spur the red wine grapes to mature fully. Ambitious young vintners realized within a short period of time how to best utilize these advantages and attain international recognition for their region. These are sexy red wines that combine fruit and elegance in a modern style that remains true to its origins. It must not be forgotten that white wine varieties, in particular Grüner Veltliner and Burgundian varieties, as well as the traditional field blends called "Gemischter Satz" also excel here. A strategic bonus of the area is its close ties with tourism, an essential factor for wine sales. The close proximity of the beautifully renovated Marchfeld Castles, the action-packed Archaeological Park Carnuntum, Donau-Auen National Park, and Slovakia's capital, Bratislava, provide ample opportunities to introduce visitors to the local wines.

The wine villages of Göttlesbrunn, Höflein, and Prellenkirchen are well known for their buschenschank (winery taverns) and have always been attractive excursion destinations for the Viennese. A more recent fine dining culture is attracting an increasing number of discerning gourmet travellers. The wines of Carnuntum dominate the region's wine lists precisely because they accompany the evolving local cuisine so well.

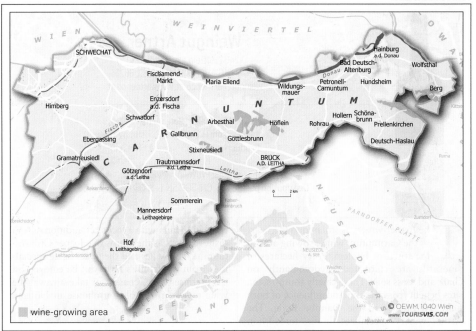

wine-growing area

© OEWM, 1040 Wien
www.TOURISVIS.COM

- ◆ Weingut Artner, Höflein
- ◆ Weingut Böheim, Arbesthal
- ◆ Weingut Walter Glatzer, Göttlesbrunn
- ◆ Weingut Gerhard Markowitsch, Göttlesbrunn
- ◆ Weingut Lukas Markowitsch, Göttlesbrunn

- ◆ Weingut Franz und Christine Netzl, Göttlesbrunn
- ◆ Weingut Robert Payr, Höflein
- ◆ Weingut Trapl, Stixneusiedl

Weingut Artner

2465 Höflein, Dorfstraße 93
T: +43 (2162) 63142, F: +43 (2162) 66255
weingut@artner.co.at, www.artner.co.at

Winemaker: Peter Artner
Contact Person: Hannes and Christoph Artner
Production: n. a. (35 % white, 65 % red)
Hectares: 40
Fairs: ProWein, VieVinum
Distribution partners: S, CH, SGP, SK, L, E, DE, CZ, NL, GB, USA, P

The Artner winery is situated in the heart of the Carnuntum wine-growing area in the town of Höflein. Forty hectares of vineyards are cultivated predominantly on chalk and loess soils. These chiefly south-facing sites benefit from the climatic influence of both Lake Neusiedl and the Danube River. The Artner winery specializes in the autochthon varieties Zweigelt and Blaufränkisch. Particularly when matured in small oak barrels, these varieties develop a unique style with an incredibly concentrated, fruity structure. This producer sets a benchmark for outstanding quality for a modest, competitive price each year with its regional blend "Rubin Carnuntum" Zweigelt Barrique. The Artner family also has years of experience with the international varieties Cabernet Sauvignon and Merlot and achieves complex harmonious varietal wines with good aging potential. Syrah is the variety that best mirrors this vintner's passion and consistently achieves international accolades. "Amarok" is a blend of Zweigelt and Syrah and has long established itself as the flagship of the house. The "massive a." has evolved into a cult wine with which Artner exhibits the potential of Syrah in Austria. This wine is produced only in exceptional vintages. The assortment of white wines includes several excellent, regional varietal wines. The producer's Grüner Veltliners excel with pronounced spicy fruit and harmonious acidity. Even varieties like Sauvignon Blanc and Gelber Muskateller (Muscat Blanc à petits grains) thrive marvellously in the Carnuntum region. It is in particular the reserve wines (Grüner Veltliner Steinacker Reserve, Sauvignon Blanc and "massive a. weiss"- from 100% Chardonnay) that exhibit the great white wine potential of the region. The family also operates two exclusive gourmet restaurants in Vienna with a focus on traditional local dishes as well as the innovative Josper Grill restaurant. The wines and the goat cheese specialities from the family's farm can be enjoyed on the premises or purchased for take-away at the wine tavern in the old farmhouse in Höflein.

(93–95) massive a. [rot] 2013 SY/ME/ZW
94 massive a. [rot] 2012 SY/ZW/ME
Deep ruby with an opaque core, purple highlights and a discreet transparent rim. Intense dark berry jam, black cherry, spice, nougat and fresh herbs. The full body is flavoured with blackberry and structured with abundant firm tannins and appetizing acidity. Chocolate and minerals linger on the finish. This powerful wine will benefit from further bottle maturation.
94 massive a. [rot] 2011 SY/ZW/ME/BF

(92–94) Amarok 2014 ZW/SY/ME/BF
92 Amarok 2013 ZW/SY/ME/CS/BF
91 Amarok 2012 ZW/SY/ME/BF/CS

(90–92) Blaufränkisch Kirchweingarten
Reserve 2014
91 Blaufränkisch Kirchweingarten Reserve 2013
92 Blaufränkisch Kirchweingarten Reserve 2012

(91–93) Syrah and ever 2014
92 Syrah and ever 2013
92 Syrah and ever 2012

92 Zweigelt Steinäcker Reserve 2014
90 Zweigelt Steinäcker Reserve 2013
91 Zweigelt Steinäcker Reserve 2012

89 Zweigelt Rubin Carnuntum 2015
89 Zweigelt Rubin Carnuntum 2014
89 Zweigelt Rubin Carnuntum 2013

93 Chardonnay massive a. [weiß] 2014
93 Chardonnay massive a. [weiß] 2013
Medium green-yellow with silver highlights. Ripe yellow apple and pineapple with a touch of vanilla and rhubarb compote. Juicy and elegant with racy acidity that lends this powerful wine a sleek structure. Finesse continues on the long finish. Good ageing potential.
93 Chardonnay massive a. [weiß] 2012

90 Grüner Veltliner Kirchberg 2015

90 Grüner Veltliner Steinäcker Reserve 2014
91 Grüner Veltliner Steinäcker Reserve 2013
91 Grüner Veltliner Steinäcker Reserve 2012

88 Gelber Muskateller 2015

89 Sauvignon Blanc Bühlweingarten 2012

Weingut Böheim

2464 Arbesthal, Hauptstraße 38–40
T: +43 (2162) 8859, F: +43 (2162) 8859 59
wein@gut-boeheim.at, www.gut-boeheim.at

Winemaker and Contact Person: Johann Böheim
Production: n. a. (49 % white, 50 % red, 1 % sweet)
Hectares: 18
Fairs: Vinova, VieVinum, ProWein
Distribution partners: CH, LV, LT, L, DK, DE, NL

The Böheim Winery is nestled in the Arbesthaler hills of Austria's wine region Carnuntum. The production assortment includes both red and white still wines. The appetizing blend called "Stuhlwerker Privat" excels each year, but usually requires a bit of time before the oak fully integrates; the appetizing "Stuhlwerker" blend offers more immediate drinking pleasure. Blaufränkisch is increasing in focus with this producer and his examples show that there is true potential for the variety in Carnuntum. These deep-coloured wines are truly impressive. Among the white wines, Grüner Veltliner is the flagship variety. Consistent success and top placings at the Falstaff Grüner Veltliner Grand Prix confirm this producer's quality efforts. The Böheim wines offer superb price-quality value.

93 Stuhlwerker Privat 2012 SY/CS
93 Stuhlwerker Privat 2011 SY/BF

92 Stuhlwerker 2013 ZW/ME/SY
Dark ruby with purple highlights and a thin transparent rim. Fine tobacco notes under aromas and flavours of cherry fruit, a touch of cassis and subtle mandarin zest. Juicy and elegant with a fine acidity structure. Red berries remain long on the aftertaste. Ready to enjoy.
91 Stuhlwerker 2012 ZW/ME/SY
92 Stuhlwerker 2011 ZW/ME/SY

91 Merlot Reserve 2013
90 Merlot Reserve 2012
92 Merlot Reserve 2011

(91–93) Blaufränkisch Reserve 2015
91 Blaufränkisch Reserve 2011

(90–92) Zweigelt Reserve 2015
90 Zweigelt Reserve 2013

(88–90) Zweigelt Rubin Carnuntum 2015
89 Zweigelt Rubin Carnuntum 2014
89 Zweigelt Rubin Carnuntum 2013

(89–91) Grüner Veltliner Privat 2015
90 Grüner Veltliner Privat 2013
90 Grüner Veltliner Privat 2012

(89–91) Grüner Veltliner Reserve 2015
90 Grüner Veltliner Reserve 2014
89 Grüner Veltliner Reserve 2013

90 Chardonnay 2012

89 Veltliner & Friends 2014 GV/RR/SB

Weingut Walter Glatzer

2464 Göttlesbrunn, Rosenbergstraße 5
T: +43 (2162) 8486, F: +43 (2162) 8486 4
info@weingutglatzer.at, www.weingutglatzer.at

Winemaker and Contact Person: Walter Glatzer
Production: 250.000 bottles (30 % white, 70 % red)
Hectares: 30 + 30
Fairs: VieVinum, ProWein
Distribution partners: on request

Walter Glatzer is one of the great catalysts of quality in the Carnuntum winegrowing region. His red wines, in particular his Blauer Zweigelt "Dornenvogel", are among the wines with the very best price/quality ratios in all of Austria. The leading variety at the Glatzer winery, Zweigelt, is also the base for the easy-drinking "Riedencuvée" and "Rubin Carnuntum", which are best enjoyed in their fruity, fragrant youth. Blaufränkisch also enjoys a strong tradition in Carnuntum and from this grape there is a simple varietal bottling as well as a "Reserve", which has been matured for about a year in used small oak barrels. Quite a classy wine is the elegant St. Laurent from the Altenberg vineyard, which was produced for the first time in the year 2002. The dynamic vintner also demonstrates his oenological talent with the traditional white wine variety of Göttlesbrun – Weissburgunder (Pinot Blanc) – as well as Sauvignon Blanc. The flagship blend, which is naturally matured in new small oak barrels, carries the old historic name of the village "Gotinsprun". A single vineyard Blaufränkisch "Bernreiser" rounds out the assortment since 2009. It is marked by intense spice and mineral character and is produced only in exceptional vintages. As of the year 2015, there is a new, striking label that shall distinguish the Glatzer labels and their increasingly more individual wines.

94 Merlot Haidacker 2012
Dark ruby with violet highlights and a thin transparent rim. The attractive bouquet displays blackberry, wild cherry notes, nougat and a touch of orange zest. This complexity continues on the palate, where the aromas and flavours meet abundant tannins that are round, silky and sweetly textured. The finish is long and chocolaty. Although already offering drinking pleasure, there is very good potential for further ageing.

92 Merlot Haidacker 2011

91 Zweigelt Dornenvogel 2012
91 Zweigelt Dornenvogel 2011

91 Blauer Zweigelt Rubin Carnuntum 2013

92 St. Laurent Altenberg 2013
92 St. Laurent Altenberg 2012
92 St. Laurent Altenberg 2011

94 Blaufränkisch Bernreiser 2012
Dark ruby with garnet highlights and a transparent rim. Intense fragrance of dark forest berry mingles with fine spicy notes, roasted coffee beans and a touch of orange zest. This aroma complexity continues on the palate and is elegantly framed with fine grained tannins and refreshing acidity. Sweet wild cherry and plenty of minerals on the long finish. Tremendous potential for further development and ageing.

94 Blaufränkisch Bernreiser 2011

90 Pinot Noir 2013

(92–94) Gotinsprun 2013 BF/SY/ME
92 Gotinsprun 2012 ME/BF/SY/ZW
93 Gotinsprun 2011 BF/SY/ME/ZW

92 Chardonnay Kräften 2015
91 Chardonnay Kräften 2014
89 Chardonnay Kräften 2013

92 Sauvignon Blanc Schüttenberg 2015
90 Sauvignon Blanc Schüttenberg 2013
89 Sauvignon Blanc Schüttenberg 2012

91 Weißburgunder 2015

★★★★
Weingut Gerhard Markowitsch
2464 Göttlesbrunn, Pfarrgasse 6
T: +43 (2162) 8222, F: +43 (2162) 8222 11, M: +43 (676) 3063075
weingut@markowitsch.at, www.markowitsch.at

Winemaker: Gerhard Markowitsch
Contact Person: Christine and Gerhard Markowitsch
Production: 500.000 bottles (25 % white, 75 % red)
Hectares: 39
Fairs: ProWein, VieVinum
Distribution partners: B, DK, NL, USA

The Markowitsch winery secured its place among the Austrian wine elite with dizzying speed. This achievement was made possible by striving for quality without compromise – efforts that were acknowledged with the "Falstaff Vintner of the Year 1999" award. Approximately 39 hectares of vineyards are planted with 75% red wine varieties and 25% white. Zweigelt, Pinot Noir, Merlot, and Cabernet Sauvignon dominate the red wines and Grüner Veltliner, Chardonnay, and Sauvignon Blanc the whites. To fulfil the international demand for top quality wines, fruit from another 40 vineyard hectares cultivated according to the strictest quality standards is purchased from contracted growers. In 2001, the Markowitsch family built a 27,000-square-foot winery facility that meets the growing needs and challenges facing modern quality vinification. This has made it possible to vinify unique, inimitable wines that reflect the Carnuntum terroir. Markowitsch focuses on autochthon grape varieties like Zweigelt, but also includes international varieties like Pinot Noir in his repertoire - reflecting his global outlook. Gerhard Markowitsch won the prestigious Erste Bank Trophy 2007 with his "M1" from the 2004 vintage. The "Rosenberg" 2010 won overall second place in the prestigious Falstaff Red Wine Premier in 2012. And this past autumn, the winemaker won the Erste Bank Reserve Trophy with his "M1" from the 2012 vintage.

95 M1 2012 ME/ZW/BF
Medium ruby with purple highlights and a broad transparent rim. Plum and blackberry with herbs, spice, tobacco and a touch of candied orange peel. Juicy acidity and abundant fine grained tannins comprise an elegant structure. Ripe wild cherry and salty minerals on the finish. Excellent potential for further development and ageing.
95 M1 2011 ME/ZW

(92–94) Rosenberg 2014 ZW/ME/LE
93 Rosenberg 2013 ZW/ME/BF
Dark ruby with purple highlights and a broad transparent rim. Dark berries with delicate nougat, cassis and tobacco nuances. Juicy and elegant with subtle cherry and spice on a palate laced with plush tannins. Plenty of finesse and ageing potential.
92 Rosenberg 2012 ZW/ME/CS

(90–92) Redmont 2014 ZW/BF/CS/SY
91 Redmont 2013 ZW/BF/CS/SY
91 Redmont 2012 ZW/BF/CS/SY

(91–93) Pinot Noir Reserve 2014
92 Pinot Noir Reserve 2013
92 Pinot Noir Reserve 2012

91 St. Laurent Rothenberg 2012
90 St. Laurent Rothenberg 2011

(89–91) Zweigelt Rubin Carnuntum 2015
90 Zweigelt Rubin Carnuntum 2014
90 Zweigelt Rubin Carnuntum 2013

93 Chardonnay Schüttenberg 2014
93 Chardonnay Schüttenberg 2013
93 Chardonnay Schüttenberg 2011

(91–93) Grüner Veltliner Alte Reben 2015
91 Grüner Veltliner Alte Reben 2014
92 Grüner Veltliner Alte Reben 2013

91 Sauvignon Blanc 2015
89 Sauvignon Blanc 2014
91 Sauvignon Blanc 2013

Weingut Lukas Markowitsch

2464 Göttlesbrunn, Kiragstettn 1
T: +43 (2162) 8226, F: +43 (2162) 8226 99
weingut@lukas-markowitsch.com, www.lukas-markowitsch.com

Winemaker and Contact Person: Lukas Markowitsch
Production: 180.000 bottles (30 % white, 70 % red)
Hectares: 14
Fairs: VieVinum ProWein Vinobile Montfort
Distribution partners: J, CH, DE, CZ

The brothers Lukas and Johann Markowitsch form an ideal team. Despite his relative youth, Lukas is already quite a knowledgeable oenologist. Johann, graduate of the University of Natural Resources and Life Sciences in Vienna, is an expert when it comes to soil and plants. The results of their teamwork are unique wines with terroir character. The Schüttenberg, Rosenberg and Haidacker vineyards are all first class south-facing sites and are the wine estate's prime capital. Merlot, Blaufränkisch, Cabernet Sauvignon and Chardonnay thrive in the gravelly portions of the vineyards. Zweigelt, St. Laurent, Sauvignon Blanc and Grüner Veltliner are cultivated in loamy soils. A core principal of their philosophy is to have each variety planted in an optimal place. Whether vinified as varietal wines or complex blends, all wines demonstrate an inimitable signature.

92 Merlot Schüttenberg 2013
Dark ruby with purple highlights and a thin transparent rim. An inviting bouquet of wild cherry with nuances of sandalwood and spice. Juicy, elegant and harmonious with firm, well integrated tannins. Red berries and juniper linger on the finish.
92 Merlot Schüttenberg 2012
93 Merlot Schüttenberg 2011

92 Cuvée Lukas 2013 ZW/ME
92 Cuvée Lukas 2012 ZW/ME
92 Cuvée Lukas 2011 ZW/ME

90 Cuvée Eisenbach 2013 ZW/ME
91 Cuvée Eisenbach 2012 ZW/ME
91 Eisenbach 2011 ZW/ME

92 Blaufränkisch Spitzerberg 2013

91 Zweigelt Haidacker 2013
92 Zweigelt Haidacker 2012
91 Zweigelt Haidacker 2011

88 Zweigelt Rubin Carnuntum 2014
89 Zweigelt Rubin Carnuntum 2013
91 Zweigelt Rubin Carnuntum 2012

90 Chardonnay Russischer Botschaftswein 2013

91 Chardonnay Rosenberg Reserve 2013

90 Chardonnay Rosenberg 2013
90 Chardonnay Rosenberg 2012

89 Grüner Veltliner Perfektion 2015

88 Sauvignon Blanc 2015
89 Sauvignon Blanc 2013

Weingut Franz und Christine Netzl

2464 Göttlesbrunn, Rosenbergstraße 17
T: +43 (2162) 8236, F: +43 (2162) 8236 14
weingut@netzl.com, www.netzl.com

Winemaker: Franz and Christina Netzl
Contact Person: Franz, Christine and Christina Netzl
Production: 180.000 bottles (30 % white, 70 % red)
Hectares: 26
Fairs: ProWein, VieVinum
Distribution partners: RUS, S, CH, B, SK, RC, L, DK, DE, FIN, CZ, NL, GB, USA, PL

S ome things must change to keep things as they are." (Luchino Visconti) True to this motto, Franz Netzl has developed his wine estate in the heart of the Carnuntum region into one of the leading red wine producers in Austria. In the meantime, he works together with his daughter, Christine, to produce wines with character, finesse and depth. It is their goal to express varietal character and the terroir of each individual vineyard in their wines. Their success confirms their efforts. Despite this, they continue to work very hard and spend many hours in the vineyard and cellar perfecting their craft. While Franz contributes experience, knowledge and tradition to their efforts, Christina brings fresh new ideas and innovations. A perfect combination that forms a solid foundation for inimitable Netzl wines. Zweigelt continues to be the king of their assortment, which is only logical for the variety absolutely thrives in the climatic and soil conditions of Carnuntum. As the base for nearly all of their wines, the Zweigelt fascinates with is incredibly broad array of styles, which range from easy-drinking fruity renditions to spicy, complex versions. Netzl demonstrates how this variety is not to be underestimated. The single vineyard "Zweigelt Haidacker" and the Zweigelt based blend "Anna-Christina" are the pinnacle of their range of wines. The success of Anna-Christina was confirmed at the most recent Falstaff Red Wine Premier, where the 2013 version was awarded as champion. This direction will certainly continue as the Zweigelt vineyards are old and yield increasingly interesting wines each year. Autochthon, authentic and outstanding quality – a very promising future indeed!

95 Privat 2012
Deep dark ruby, nearly black core and purple highlights. Ripe blackberry, cassis and chocolate over a background of spice and sandalwood. The full body and juicy fruit is nicely framed with abundant fine grained tannin. The finish features blackberry and nougat. Superb ageing potential.
95 Privat 2011

(92–94) Anna-Christina 2014 ZW/CS/ME
93 Anna-Christina 2013 ZW/CS/ME
Dark ruby with violet highlights and a transparent rim. The multifaceted bouquet features blackberry jam, ripe wild cherry and sandalwood. Juicy red berries and pleasant sweet extract with firm tannins that continue through the long fruity finish. Will benefit from bottle maturation.
92 Anna-Christina 2012 ZW/ME/CS

(90–92) Edles Tal 2014 ZW/ME/SY
89 Edles Tal 2013 ZW/ME/SY
90 Edles Tal 2012 ZW/ME/SY

(92–94) Cabernet Sauvignon Aubühel 2014
93 Cabernet Sauvignon Aubühel 2013
92 Cabernet Sauvignon Aubühel 2012

89 St. Laurent Selection 2014
90 St. Laurent Selection 2013
91 Sankt Laurent Selection 2012

92 Syrah Schüttenberg 2013
92 Syrah Schüttenberg 2012
93 Syrah Schüttenberg 2011

(89–91) Zweigelt Rubin Carnuntum 2015
90 Zweigelt Rubin Carnuntum 2014
89 Zweigelt Rubin Carnuntum 2013

(90–92) Weißburgunder Bärnreiser 2015
92 Weißburgunder Bärnreiser 2014
90 Weißburgunder Bärnreiser 2013

(91–93) Grüner Veltliner Bärnreiser 2015
91 Grüner Veltliner Bärnreiser 2014
89 Grüner Veltliner Bärnreiser 2013

(89–91) Sauvignon Blanc Schüttenberg 2015
89 Sauvignon Blanc Schüttenberg 2014
91 Sauvignon Blanc Schüttenberg 2013

★ ★ ★

Weingut Payr

2465 Höflein, Dorfstraße 18
T: +43 (2162) 62356, F: +43 (2162) 62356, M: +43 (664) 2307535
robert@weingut-payr.at, www.weingut-payr.at

Winemaker and Contact Person: Robert Payr
Production: n. a. (25 % white, 74 % red, 1 % sweet)
Hectares: 12
Fairs: VieVinum, ProWein
Distribution partners: RO, S, SK, RC, L, DE, N, PL, P

Robert Payr Jr., fourth generation winemaker in this family winery, currently manages the enterprise with his father, Robert Sr. Together they have built up the wine estate in recent years to become on of Carnuntum's top wineries - well recognized both domestically and abroad. What's more, for the last year or so, Robert Payr has been a driving force in the region as president of the Rubin Carnuntum vintners association. A third of Robert Payr's vineyards are planted with the white varieties Grüner Veltliner and Chardonnay; two-thirds with the red grapes Zweigelt, Blaufränkisch, Merlot and Cabernet Sauvignon. Payr also leases another Blaufränkisch vineyard in Prellenkirchen, on the south-facing slope of the Spitzerberg. The single-vineyard wines are called Rothenberg (Grüner Veltliner from a south-facing slope with red loam and pebble soil); Bühl (Zweigelt, Blaufränkisch and Merlot from south-facing slopes with limestone and loess soils); and Spitzerberg (Blaufränkisch from very meagre limestone soils, facing directly south). The Payr wines are now known for their chiselled and fine-grained structure. This inherent style will continue despite changing trends. Grapes are harvested and selected exclusively by hand to ensure that only fully ripe grapes are fermented. The white wines and the Zweigelt Classic are vinified in stainless steel to preserve the clear expression of fruit. The powerful wines destined for ageing are vinified as single vineyard wines and matured traditionally in small oak barrels.

92 Bühl Reserve Carnuntum 2013 ZW/ME/BF
Dark ruby with violet highlights and a thin transparent rim. Blackberry, herbs and peppery spice over a background of bitter chocolate and tobacco nuances. Juicy acidity and elegant fine-grained tannins frame fine cherry fruit. Long finish and good ageing potential.
92 Bühl Reserve Carnuntum 2012 BF/ZW/ME

(92–94) Granat Reserve Carnuntum 2014 ZW/CS
90 Granat Reserve Carnuntum 2013 ZW/CS
90 Granat Reserve Carnuntum 2012 ZW/CS

(91–93) Blaufränkisch Spitzerberg Reserve Carnuntum 2014
90 Blaufränkisch Spitzerberg Reserve Carnuntum 2013
90 Blaufränkisch Spitzerberg Reserve Carnuntum 2012

(91–93) Zweigelt Steinäcker Reserve Carnuntum 2014
91 Zweigelt Steinacker Reserve Carnuntum 2013
91 Zweigelt Steinacker Reserve Carnuntum 2012

(89–91) Zweigelt Rubin Carnuntum Selection 2015
89 Zweigelt Rubin Carnuntum Selection 2014
90 Rubin Carnuntum Zweigelt Selection 2013

(91–93) Grüner Veltliner Rothenberg Reserve Carnuntum 2015
92 Grüner Veltliner Rothenberg Reserve Carnuntum 2014
Medium green-yellow with silver highlights. The attractive nose exhibits subtle notes of peach and mango with a touch of hazelnut and wild herbs in the background. Juicy and elegant with a refreshing acidity structure. Plenty of finesse and a long lemony mineral finale.
91 Grüner Veltliner Rothenberg Reserve Carnuntum 2013

★★★
Weingut Johannes Trapl

2463 Stixneusiedl, Hauptstraße 16
T: +43 (2169) 2404, F: +43 (2169) 2404
wein@trapl.com, www.trapl.com

── ORGANIC ──

Winemaker and Contact Person: Johannes Trapl
Production: n. a. (30 % white, 70 % red)
Hectares: 18
Fairs: VieVinum, ProWein, Vinexpo HongKong
Distribution partners: I, B, CH, SK, RC, DK, L, DE, FIN, F, NL, N, HK, H

Johannes Trapl directs this family winery. He is a purist seeking to express the authentic character of Carnuntum in his wines. Most of the vines in his vineyards were planted by his grandfather and are older than Johannes himself! These vines are deeply rooted and yield grapes with intense and complex aromas. Trapl truly appreciates the character and depth derived from his unique vineyard soils. As the grapes arrive in the cellar, Johannes Trapl assumes his role with a gentle hand, guiding his wines in their natural development. The intrinsic aromas, such as pepper, cherry and lilac, should remain unadulterated. Zweigelt and St. Laurent find ideal preconditions on the gravel and loam dominated Arbestaller hills. The Spitzerberg, which belongs to the Hainburger range, offers the possibility to produce Blaufränkisch with the unique character that can only be derived from a slate-dominated site. Of particular finesse is the Blaufränkisch Stix, which for this reason, tops this year's list of wines. Says Johannes Trapl: "I want to feel the diversity, finesse and power of the vines and express this in my wines without sacrificing drinkability."

(93–95) Blaufränkisch Spitzerberg 2014
94 Blaufränkisch Spitzerberg 2013
Medium ruby with garnet highlights and a broad transparent rim. Raspberry jam and elegant cherry notes mingle with subtle tobacco and a touch of orange zest. Juicy, elegant acidity is cloaked in delicious blackberry fruit and wild heather. Very long finish and superb ageing potential.
93 Blaufränkisch Spitzerberg 2012

(92–94) Blaufränkisch Stix 2014
93 Blaufränkisch Stix 2013
Dark ruby with garnet highlights and a broad transparent rim. Blackberry and tobacco with notes of cassis and candied orange peel. Firm tannins and juicy acidity lend structure and finesse. Fruit and minerals linger on the long appetizing finish. Demonstrates poised elegance and good ageing potential.
94 Blaufränkisch Stix 2012

(91–93) Blaufränkisch Reserve 2014
92 Blaufränkisch Reserve 2013
91 Blaufränkisch Reserve 2012

(91–93) St. Laurent Reserve 2014
91 Sankt Laurent Reserve 2013
91 Sankt Laurent Reserve 2012

(92–94) Syrah Kirchberg 2014
92 Syrah Kirchberg 2013
93 Syrah Kirchberg 2012

(91–93) Tilhofen 2014 ME/CS/ZW
92 Tilhofen 2013 CS/ME/ZW
92 Tilhofen 2012 ME/CS/ZW

(90–92) Blauer Zweigelt Rubin Carnuntum 2015

(91–93) Grüner Veltliner Karpatenschiefer 2015
92 Grüner Veltliner Karpatenschiefer 2014
92 Grüner Veltliner Karpatenschiefer 2013

KAMPTAL DAC
Cool valleys and ancient soils, fragrant Grüner Veltliner and Riesling of great finesse

The Kamp River lends its name to the 3,802-hectare Kamptal DAC protected designation of origin for unique varietal wines vinified from Grüner Veltliner or Riesling. The lovely regional capital, Langenlois, is the country's largest wine village and popular destination for wine tourists.

© Weinstraße Kamptal/Robert Herbst

The Kamptal's two main grape varieties, Grüner Veltliner and Riesling, have defined the Kamptal DAC protected designation of origin since its establishment in 2008. The Kamptal DAC wines must be made exclusively from one of these two varieties. The deeper, weightier, dry late harvest examples are labelled "Kamptal DAC Reserve".

The Heiligenstein is one of the Kamptal's most famous vineyards. Its unique soil is comprised of desert sandstone with volcanic components dating back to the Palaeozoic Era 270 million years ago. Vigorous, old Riesling vines thrive on the steep terraces of its southern slope.

The soils of Kamptal change with their proximity to the Danube River. Loess and loam terraces provide optimal conditions for a wide range of grape varieties. Along with the Kamptal DAC Grüner Veltliner and Kamptal DAC Riesling, wines are made from other varieties that appear under the Niederösterreich protected geographical indication. The Burgundian family of grapes, for example, as well

as Zweigelt also find ideal conditions. The dynamic exchange between the hot, Pannonian Basin and the cool Forest Quarter (Waldviertel) climate brings impressive results.

Wine culture and tourism, strengthened by heurige and wine shops, are of great economic importance to the region. A highly recommendable tourist attraction is the Loisium, a futuristic wine theme park with mystical underground wine adventures and a chic regional wine shop, restaurant and hotel. It represents the symbiosis of tradition and innovation, which are an inherent part of Kamptal life. Langenlois and the communities of Gobelsburg, Haindorf, and Zöbing are exemplary villages for Austrian wine culture.

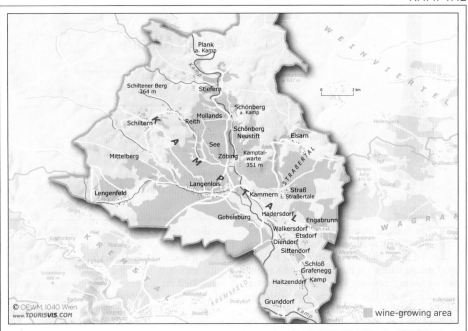

wine-growing area

© OEWM, 1040 Wien
www.**TOURISVIS**.COM

- ◆ Weingut Allram, Strass
- ◆ Weingut Martin & Anna Arndorfer, Strass
- ◆ Weingut Bründlmayer, Langenlois
- ◆ Weingut Schloss Gobelsburg, Gobelsburg
- ◆ Weingut Matthias Hager, Mollands
- ◆ Weingut Hiedler, Langenlois
- ◆ Weingut Hirsch, Kammern
- ◆ Weingut Jurtschitsch, Langenlois

- ◆ Laurenz V., Zöbing/Wien
- ◆ Weingut Fred Loimer, Langenlois
- ◆ Weingut Rudolf Rabl, Langenlois
- ◆ Weingut Peter Schweiger, Zöbing
- ◆ Weingut Steininger, Langenlois
- ◆ Weingut Weixelbaum, Strass
- ◆ Weingut Weszeli, Langenlois

Weingut Allram

3491 Straß im Straßertale, Herrengasse 3
T: +43 (2735) 2232, F: +43 (2735) 2232 3, M: +43 (664) 1215983
weingut@allram.at, www.allram.at

Winemaker: Erich and Lorenz Haas
Contact Person: Michaela Haas-Allram
Production: n. a. (80 % white, 18 % red, 2 % sweet)
Hectares: 26 + 5
Fairs: ProWein, VieVinum
Distribution partners: J, S, CDN, CH, B, SK, DK, DE, EST, CZ, NL, N, GB, USA, PL

The historic Allram wine estate belongs to the Haas-Allram family and is located in the picturesque village of Strass in the Strasser Valley - in the heart of the Kamptal wine-growing region. The family aspires to producing wines that are an honest expression of the vintage and the unique terroir and climate of the Kamptal region. The finest nuances and multiple complexities of each individual site should be tangible in the wines. It is precision of expression and enormous length that distinguish the wines of this producer.

Besides the plots in the prime vineyards Gaisberg, Renner and Hasel, the family is particularly proud of the 1.5-hectare parcel in the famous Heiligenstein. After 30 years of lying fallow, this parcel was re-cultivated and is now the source of an absolutely stunning Riesling. Erich Haas and his son, Lorenz, take responsibility for optimal conditions in the vineyards, as it has always been the tenet of the Allram estate that wine quality truly originates there. Each vine is tended with great individual care. After the wine is bottled, the winery manager, Michaela Haas-Allram, begins marketing and distribution efforts. The family prizes wines that pair power with elegance and that possess ageing potential and the highest finesse in regional expression. Next to complex Grüner Veltliner and Riesling wines, there is also an impressive series of wines from Burgundian varieties, in particular from Grauburgunder (Pinot Gris). The export share of 80% as well as numerous national and international accolades confirm the quality of their work.

The most recent challenge at Allram is the 3.5 hectares of vineyards in Wagram, from which a powerful Grüner Veltliner is produced. An absolute must is to see not only the tasteful façade of the winery, but also the 3-storey vinification facility. The old wooden cask cellar and the tradition crush house now serve as a sales and tasting room that wonderfully integrates historic elements with the modern. The estate's renovated art nouveau style villa in the middle of the village is within walking distance of the winery and offers comfortable accommodations for customers and wine enthusiasts.

(91–93) Grüner Veltliner Kamptal DAC Reserve Renner 1 ÖTW 2015
93 Grüner Veltliner Kamptal DAC Reserve Renner 1 ÖTW 2014
Pale green-yellow with silver highlights. Mandarin and mango with notes of tobacco comprise an elegant bouquet. Juicy and tightly woven with mineral-laced golden apple wrapped around a taut backbone of acidity. Delicate pepper notes linger on the finish. Plenty of finesse and ageing potential.
93 Grüner Veltliner Kamptal DAC Reserve Renner 1 ÖTW 2013

(92–94) Grüner Veltliner Kamptal DAC Reserve Gaisberg 1 ÖTW 2015
92 Grüner Veltliner Kamptal DAC Reserve Gaisberg 1 ÖTW 2014
92 Grüner Veltliner Kamptal DAC Reserve Gaisberg 1 ÖTW 2013

91 Grüner Veltliner Kamptal DAC Reserve Alte Reben 2015
91 Grüner Veltliner Kamptal DAC Reserve Hasel Alte Reben 2014
92 Grüner Veltliner Kamptal DAC Reserve Hasel Alte Reben 2013

91 Grüner Veltliner Kamptal DAC Hasel 2015

92 Grüner Veltliner Kamptal DAC
Rosengartl 2015

(93–95) Riesling Kamptal DAC Reserve
Heiligenstein 1 ÖTW 2015
95 Riesling Kamptal DAC Reserve
Heiligenstein 1 ÖTW 2014
Brilliant yellow-green hue with silver highlights. Delicate exotic fruit reminiscent of mango and litchi mingle with blossom honey and wild herbs. Tropical fruit nuances continue in the mouth with sweet extract that is lifted with juicy acidity. Complex aromas and flavours continue with abundant, fine minerals and ripe stone fruit on the finish. An optimal wine to accompany food. Good ageing potential.
94 Riesling Kamptal DAC Reserve
Heiligenstein 1 ÖTW 2013

(92–94) Riesling Kamptal DAC Reserve
Gaisberg 1 ÖTW 2015
93 Riesling Kamptal DAC Reserve
Gaisberg 1 ÖTW 2014
93 Riesling Kamptal DAC Reserve
Gaisberg 1 ÖTW 2013

89 Riesling Kamptal DAC Strassertaler 2015

91 Weißburgunder Papageno 2015

92 Chardonnay Wechselberg 2015

91 Sankt Laurent Gaisberg Reserve 2013

94 Grüner Veltliner Eiswein 2015

Martin & Anna Arndorfer

3491 Straß im Straßertale, Weinbergweg 16
T: +43 (2735) 2254, F: +43 (2735) 2254 4
info@ma-arndorfer.at, www.ma-arndorfer.at

Winemaker: Martin Arndorfer
Contact Person: Martin and Anna Arndorfer
Production: n. a. (80 % white, 20 % red)
Hectares: 16
Fairs: VieVinum, real wine fair London
Distribution partners: AUS, I, S, B, CH, DK, DE, FIN, F, NZ, CZ, GB, USA, IRL

From our viewpoint, wine is a craft that allows freedom for creativity, emotion and personality,"says Martin Arndorfer. "In some instances, this craft can even become an art. We have made it our mission to produce wines that unite handcraftsmanship, place of origin and passion - wines that stir interest and curiosity within the wide world of wine." The vineyards with which Martin and Anna Arndorfer strive to realize their vision are set around the village of Strass in Strassertal. Included are parcels in top vineyards such as Gaisberg, Offenberg, Wechselberg, Wechselberg-Spiegel, Hasel, Stangl, Hölle and Brunngasse. Three lines of wines are produced: "Gemischter Satz", "Strasser Weinberge" and "die Leidenschaft". The Gemischter Satz series is comprised of wines from the most important varieties of the region, Grüner Veltliner and Riesling for the whites, and Zweigelt and Pinot Noir for the reds. These wines transport pronounced regional character more than varietal typicity. One Riesling and one Grüner Veltliner comprise the "Strasser Weinberge" wine series. For these wines, grapes are selected from various sites and vinified together to relate a good general impression of the village character of Strass. The very best grapes are selected for the die Leidenschaft series, and fermented either in small oak barrels or stainless steel. These wines are distinguished by superb balance, harmony and complexity and are particularly good accompaniments to food. Beyond this are a few selected specialties, for example, a field blend from the Wechselberg site called "von den Terrassen 1958"; a Roter Veltliner from the mineral-rich parcel in the Gaisberg named "von den Terrassen 1979", and an exceptional Grüner Veltliner called "grenzenlos", which is matured for five years on the lees before bottling.

92 Grüner Veltliner die Leidenschaft 2014
92 Grüner Veltliner »die Leidenschaft« 2013
Medium green-yellow. Yellow apple and papaya with subtle nutty aromas, blossom honey notes and wild meadow herbs. Abundant juicy fruit elegantly supported by a well-integrated acidity backbone. Apple and mango linger on the finish of this appetizing and very versatile food wine.
92 Grüner Veltliner »die Leidenschaft« 2012

92 Grüner Veltliner Per se 2014

(90–92) Grüner Veltliner Strasser Weinberge 2015
91 Grüner Veltliner Strasser Weinberge 2014
91 Grüner Veltliner Kamptal DAC Reserve Strasser Weinberge 2013

93 Riesling die Leidenschaft 2014
91 Riesling »die Leidenschaft« 2013
92 Riesling »die Leidenschaft« 2012

91 ChNb die Leidenschaft 2014
93 ChNb »die Leidenschaft« 2013
Medium yellow with silver highlights. Yellow apple fruit, subtle hazelnut and delicate citrus notes over a background of wild herbs. Complexly structured with sweetly extracted mango fruit elegantly highlighted by juicy acidity. Good length and ageing potential
93 ChNb »die Leidenschaft« 2012

91 Müller-Thurgau Per se 2014

(91–93) Riesling Strasser Weinberge 2015
90 Riesling Strasser Weinberge 2014
91 Riesling Kamptal DAC Reserve Strasser Weinberge 2013

92 Rosa Marie 2015
90 Rosa Marie 2013
89 Rosa Marie 2012 (ZW)

★★★★★
Weingut Bründlmayer

3550 Langenlois, Zwettler Straße 23
T: +43 (2734) 21720, F: +43 (2734) 3748
weingut@bruendlmayer.at, www.bruendlmayer.at

Winemaker: Christopher Forst
Contact Person: Willi Bründlmayer, Thomas Klinger
Production: 350.000 bottles (70 % white, 29 % red, 1 % sweet); **Hectares:** 80
Certified: Sustainable Austria
Fairs: VieVinum, ProWein
Distribution partners: AUS, BDS, I, RUS, J, S, B, CDN, CH, BR, HR, SGP, BG, LV, SK, RC, DK, L, E, DE, MV, FIN, T, F, CZ, GR, NL, GB, N, UA, HK, H, USA, IRL, PL, UAE, IS, CY

Many things are impressive at the Bründlmayer estate: the people; the quality of the wines; 80 hectares of vineyards, and of course the friendly, humble man who has been responsible for one of Austria's model wineries since 1980. Nearly every single wine, from the lightest Grüner Veltliner to the remarkable red and sparkling wines, has the potential to be the best-in-vintage in its category. The vineyards are predominantly terraced slopes. Around one third of the vines are trained in the "lyra" split canopy system. The vineyards are cultivated sustainably and no herbicides are used. The geologically oldest and certainly most interesting site is the Zöbinger Heiligenstein. This soil stems from the Permian period 270 million years ago. Desert sand with volcanic components are the origin of the rock here. Exceptional Riesling, Merlot and Cabernet grow high on the mountain, which is part of a wildlife preservation area. The most important variety is Grüner Veltliner and it yields a broad assortment of wines ranging from the light, dry quality and kabinett wines all the way through complex, concentrated single-vineyard spätlese. Rieslings grow on the meagre rock of the Steinmassl and Heiligenstein vineyards and are famous for their potential to reach a near-Biblical age. Specialties of the house are Chardonnay and the other Burgundian varieties, Blauburgunder (Pinot Noir), Weissburgunder (Pinot Blanc), and Grauburgunder (Pinot Gris), which were planted by Wilhelm Bründlmayer Sr. in the 1950s and '60s. The red wines make up an impressive one third of the production. Willi's father planted red varieties because his wife enjoyed drinking a glass of red wine in the evening. The red wines excel with finesse rather than power. It is a challenge to ripen red wine varieties in the marginal Kamptal climate, but tasty wines with unique personality are achieved. Classy sparkling wines, Bründlmayer Brut and Bründlmayer Brut Rosé, are bottle-fermented and spend three years on the yeast during which they are riddled by hand and then disgorged on the premises. The cellar archive includes wines from the best vintages since 1947. Much experience and knowledge about the various vineyards and vintage character and winemaking is gained through private tastings of these old wines. The family is quite successful internationally and exports 30% of the production. Wine & Spirits Magazine (USA) awarded Bründlmayer the "Winery of the Year" title for five consecutive years, and the Financial Times in Great Britain described the estate as a "beacon of Austrian viticulture". All wines from the current range can be enjoyed by the glass at Heurigenhof Bründlmayer in a beautifully restored renaissance building.

(96–98) Grüner Veltliner Kamptal DAC Reserve Lamm 1ÖTW 2015
94 Grüner Veltliner Kamptal DAC Reserve Lamm 1 ÖTW 2014
Deep yellow with green highlights. A multifaceted bouquet displays apricot and mango over a discreet background of oak spice. Juicy acidity nicely counters extract sweetness and highlights the fruit in this round, harmonious wine. Mandarin and peach remain long on the finish. Plenty of ageing potential.
94 Grüner Veltliner Kamptal DAC Reserve Lamm 1 ÖTW 2013

(94–96) Grüner Veltliner Kamptal DAC Reserve
Käferberg 1ÖTW 2015
93 Grüner Veltliner Kamptal DAC Reserve
Käferberg 1 ÖTW 2014
92 Grüner Veltliner Kamptal DAC Reserve
Käferberg 1 ÖTW 2013

(92–94) Grüner Veltliner Kamptal DAC Reserve
Alte Reben 2015
92 Grüner Veltliner Kamptal DAC Reserve
Alte Reben 2014
93 Grüner Veltliner Kamptal DAC Reserve
Alte Reben 2013

(93–95) Grüner Veltliner Kamptal DAC Reserve
Spiegel Vincent 1ÖTW 2015
93 Grüner Veltliner Kamptal DAC Reserve
Vincents Spiegel 1 ÖTW 2014
92 Grüner Veltliner Kamptal DAC Reserve
Vincents Spiegel 1 ÖTW 2012

91 Grüner Veltliner Kamptal DAC Berg
Vogelsang 2015
90 Grüner Veltliner Kamptal DAC Berg
Vogelsang 2014

90 Grüner Veltliner Kamptal DAC Terrassen 2015
89 Grüner Veltliner Kamptal DAC Terrassen 2014
89 Grüner Veltliner Kamptal DAC Terrassen 2013

(95–97) Riesling Kamptal DAC Reserve Zöbinger
Heiligenstein Alte Reben 1ÖTW 2015
94 Riesling Kamptal DAC Reserve Zöbinger
Heiligenstein Alte Reben 1 ÖTW 2014
Medium green-yellow with silver highlights. Peach and greengage plum with nuances of orange zest and flinty minerals. Sweet stone fruit is laced with salty minerals on the juicy palate. Well structured and focused. Passion fruit and lemon salt remain appetizingly long on the finish. Dependable ageing potential.
94 Riesling Kamptal DAC Reserve Zöbinger
Heiligenstein Alte Reben 1 ÖTW 2013

(94–96) Riesling Kamptal DAC Reserve Zöbinger
Heiligenstein Lyra 1ÖTW 2015
94 Riesling Kamptal DAC Reserve Zöbinger
Heiligenstein Lyra 1 ÖTW 2014
94 Riesling Kamptal DAC Reserve Zöbinger
Heiligenstein Lyra 1 ÖTW 2013

(92–94) Riesling Kamptal DAC Zöbinger
Heiligenstein 1ÖTW 2015
92 Riesling Kamptal DAC Zöbinger
Heiligenstein 1 ÖTW 2014
92 Riesling Kamptal DAC Zöbinger
Heiligenstein 1 ÖTW 2013

(91–93) Riesling Kamptal DAC
Steinmassel 1 ÖTW 2015
91 Riesling Kamptal DAC
Steinmassel 1 ÖTW 2014
90 Riesling Kamptal DAC
Steinmassel 1 ÖTW 2013

91 Riesling Kamptal DAC Terrassen 2015
89 Riesling Kamptal DAC Terrassen 2014
90 Riesling Kamptal DAC Terrassen 2013

(92–94) Langenloiser Spiegel 2015 PG/WB
90 Langenloiser Spiegel 2013 PG/WB
90 Langenloiser Spiegel 2012 WB/PG

(91–93) Gelber Muskateller 2015

(93–95) Chardonnay 2015
92 Chardonnay 2013

92 Bründlmayer Brut 2010
92 Bründlmayer Brut traditionelle
Flaschengärung, handgerüttelt 2008
PN/CH/WB/PG

93 Bründlmayer Brut

93 Bründlmayer Brut Rosé

92 Pinot Noir Reserve 2011

90 St. Laurent Ried Ladner 2012
90 St. Laurent Ried Ladner 2011

91 Willi & Vincent 2012 ME/CF

93 Riesling Auslese Steinmassel 2013

94 Riesling Beerenauslese Heiligenstein 2013

93 Chardonnay Beerenauslese 2013

95 Chardonnay Trockenbeerenauslese 2013
Medium green-yellow with silver highlights. Pronounced aromas of tropical fruit reminiscent of passion fruit and papaya with peach and citrus zest. Plenty of finesse is demonstrated by luscious honey-laced fruit that is wonderfully balanced with juicy acidity. The complex aromas and flavours linger deliciously long on the finish.

94 Gelber Muskateller Auslese 2012

91 Grüner Veltliner Beerenauslese Spiegel 2013

Weingut Schloss Gobelsburg

3550 Gobelsburg, Schlossstraße 16
T: +43 (2734) 2422, F: +43 (2734) 2422 20
schloss@gobelsburg.at, www.gobelsburg.at

Winemaker and Contact Person: Michael Moosbrugger
Production: 300.000 bottles (75 % white, 25 % red)
Hectares: 70
Certified: Sustainable Austria
Fairs: VieVinum, ProWein
Distribution partners: AUS, IL, I, J, S, B, CDN, SGP, RC, DK, MV, FIN, F, NZ, NL, GB, N, USA, IRL, PL, P

The Cistercian Abbey Zwettl in the Austrian Waldviertel purchased this palace winery from an aristocratic family and has owned extensive acreage including some of the best vineyard sites in Kammern and Gobelsburg since 1171. The late Abbot of Zwettl, Father Bertrand Baumann, acted as able manager of the estate from 1958. The matured wines from his time continue to reflect impressively his capable hand. Michael Moosbrugger from the renowned Hotel Gasthof Post in Arlberg, Austria, was appointed manager in 1996. And the winery once again quickly found its place among the country's elite wine producers. The best vineyards are cultivated according to organically integrated principals. Riesling grows on the famous Zöbinger Heiligenstein and on Kammerner Gaisberg, while the best vineyards for Grüner Veltliner are Ried Lamm, Ried Grub, and Kammerner Renner. Other white wine varieties are not cultivated. Red wine varieties take up 25% of the vineyard acreage, while Pinot Noir plays homage to the Cistercian roots in Burgundy. Michael Moosbrugger strives to produce authentic wines that, depending on juice potential, are either fermented in stainless steel or oak. The newest innovation in Schloss Gobelsburg winemaking is called the "Dynamic Cellar Concept." Rather than pumping wines from one place to another, casks and barrels are transported on wheels within the winery. All barrels and casks are manufactured from local Manhartsberg oak. Moosbrugger's idea for a "Tradition" series of wines, where wines are vinified in traditional manner and allowed more time to evolve before being released, has enjoyed all around success in recent years. Falstaff Magazine voted Michael Moosbrugger "Vintner of the Year 2006," honouring his impressive achievements.

(93–95) Grüner Veltliner Kamptal DAC Reserve Ried Renner 1 ÖTW 2015
94 Grüner Veltliner Kamptal DAC Reserve Renner 1 ÖTW 2014
Medium greenish-yellow hue. Notes of crisp golden apple, a touch of honey-laced apricot and peppery spice. Juicy acidity elegantly lifts papaya and apple fruit. The finish is long and harmonious. Plenty of finesse and potential for further development.

94 Grüner Veltliner Kamptal DAC Reserve Renner 1 ÖTW 2013

(93–95) Grüner Veltliner Kamptal DAC Reserve Ried Grub 1 ÖTW 2015
93 Grüner Veltliner Kamptal DAC Reserve Grub 1 ÖTW 2014
94 Grüner Veltliner Kamptal DAC Reserve Grub 1 ÖTW 2013

(94–96) Grüner Veltliner Kamptal DAC Reserve Ried Lamm 1 ÖTW 2015
93 Grüner Veltliner Kamptal DAC Reserve Lamm 1 ÖTW 2014
93 Grüner Veltliner Kamptal DAC Reserve Lamm 1 ÖTW 2013

(91–93) Grüner Veltliner Kamptal DAC Ried Steinsetz 2015
90 Grüner Veltliner Kamptal DAC Reserve Steinsetz 2014
90 Grüner Veltliner Kamptal DAC Reserve Steinsetz 2013

(91–93) Grüner Veltliner Kamptal DAC Ried Spiegel 2015
92 Grüner Veltliner Kamptal DAC Reserve Spiegel 2014
92 Grüner Veltliner Kamptal DAC Reserve Spiegel 2013

(92–94) Grüner Veltliner Tradition 2014
94 Grüner Veltliner Tradition 2013
93 Grüner Veltliner Kamptal DAC Reserve
Tradition 2012

(90–92) Grüner Veltliner Kamptal DAC
Langenlois 2015
89 Gobelsburger Grüner Veltliner Kamptal DAC 2014
89 Gobelsburger Grüner Veltliner
Kamptal DAC 2013

89 Domaene Gobelsburg Grüner Veltliner
Kamptal 2015
88 Domaene Gobelsburg Grüner Veltliner
Kamptal DAC 2014
88 Domaene Gobelsburg Grüner Veltliner
Kamptal DAC 2013

88 Gobelsburger Grüner Veltliner Messwein 2014
89 Gobelsburger Messwein Grüner Veltliner
Kamptal DAC 2013

(93–95) Riesling Kamptal DAC Reserve Ried
Heiligenstein 1 ÖTW 2015
94 Riesling Kamptal DAC Reserve
Heiligenstein 1 ÖTW 2014
Pale green-yellow with silver highlights. White vineyard
peach, lime, and wet stone on the nose. Complex and
tightly woven on the palate. Refreshing acidity elegantly
lifts the honey-laced mandarin fruit. Firm, but still
embryonic – will benefit greatly from further bottle
maturation.
94 Riesling Kamptal DAC Reserve
Heiligenstein 1 ÖTW 2013

(91–93) Riesling Kamptal DAC Reserve Ried
Gaisberg 1 ÖTW 2015
93 Riesling Kamptal DAC Reserve
Gaisberg 1 ÖTW 2014
92 Riesling Kamptal DAC Reserve
Gaisberg 1 ÖTW 2013

(94–96) Riesling Tradition 2014
94 Riesling Kamptal DAC Reserve Tradition 2013
91 Riesling Kamptal DAC Reserve Tradition 2012

(91–93) Riesling Kamptal DAC Zöbing 2015
88 Gobelsburger Riesling Urgestein 2014
89 Gobelsburger Riesling Urgestein 2013

89 Domaene Gobelsburg Riesling
Kamptal 2015
87 Domaene Gobelsburg Riesling
Kamptal DAC 2014
87 Domaene Gobelsburg Riesling
Kamptal DAC 2013

92 Brut Reserve Niederösterreich Sekt g.U.

94 Vintage Extra Brut Langenlois Sekt g.U. 2004

90 Gobelsburger Rosé Cistercien Zweigelt 2012

91 Zweigelt Schloss Gobelsburg Haide 2011

92 Merlot Schloss Gobelsburg Privatkeller 2011

92 Pinot Noir Schloss Gobelsburg
Alte Haide 2011

92 Sankt Laurent Schloss Gobelsburg
Haidegrund 2011

89 Schloss Gobelsburg Cuvée Bertrand
2011 SL/PN/ME

89 Gobelsburger Zweigelt 2011

97 Riesling Trockenbeerenauslese 2013
Medium yellow with silver highlights. The expressive nose
displays pronounced peach and tropical fruit with blossom
honey and minerals. Lusciously sweet apricot, peach and
passion fruit are nicely balanced and integrated with a
firm acidity backbone. Very lengthy finish. This wine is still
quite youthful and will gain in character with extended
bottle maturation.
93 Riesling Trockenbeerenauslese 2012
98 Riesling Trockenbeerenauslese Schloss
Gobelsburg 2011

96 Riesling Beerenauslese 2014

91 Riesling Auslese 2012

96 Grüner Veltliner Eiswein 2014
93 Grüner Veltliner Eiswein 2013

Weingut Matthias Hager

3562 Mollands, Weinstraße 45
T: +43 (2733) 8283, F: +43 (2733) 76494
wein@hagermatthias.at, www.hagermatthias.at

— ORGANIC —

Winemaker: Matthias Hager
Contact Person: Doris and Matthias Hager
Production: n. a. (70 % white, 29 % red, 1 % sweet)
Hectares: 12
Fairs: VieVinum, ProWein
Distribution partners: LT, DE, CZ, NL, GB, USA, PL

Family Hager has grown grapes in the Kamptal for several generations. The estate is a member of the Austrian Demeter Association and adheres to their very strict regulations for biodynamic wine production in the vineyard and the cellar. The results are unique wines of character that reflect the diversity of soils found in the Kamptal. Loam, loess and primary rock including gneiss, granite and weathered schist all lend their special character. The wine village of Mollands is situated on a plateau at 350 metres above sea level in the most northern part of the Kamptal. Brisk winds from the Forest Quarter and high diurnal temperature fluctuations in summer enhance vibrant fruit aroma in the wines. The best vineyards sites of the estate are Hiesberg, Soos, and Seeberg. To ease the communication of a versatile wine assortment to the consumer, Matthias Hager has divided his wines into two distinct ranges. The "blue line" is light and refreshing while the "brown line" is earthier, more concentrated and has the capacity to age longer in the bottle. One could describe both the brown line of wines and the vintner as deep, consistent and having a close relationship with the land. New in the wine assortment is a "red line" series. Red is the colour of kings and is a rare signal colour in nature. This colour represents something rare and extreme in the wines: no addition of sulphur dioxide; fermentation on the skins, and no filtration. The preservation of biological and ecological balance is highly valued. As just one example, the vintner cultivates his own chamomile to use as a substance for plant protection in the vineyard. Minimal intervention is practiced in the cellar. Wines are fermented spontaneously with their own native yeast and the reduction of the use of sulphur dioxide is a key goal. Wines are given the time they need to mature.

(91–93) Grüner Veltliner Urgestein 2015
92 Grüner Veltliner Urgestein blaue Linie 2014

91 Grüner Veltliner Mollandser Berg 2015
90 Grüner Veltliner Kamptal DAC Mollandser Berg blaue Linie 2014

92 Grüner Veltliner Alte Reben 2014

92 Grüner Veltliner Seeberg braune Linie 2013
92 Grüner Veltliner Seeberg 2012

92 Riesling Kamptal DAC Reserve Seeberg braune Linie 2013
Medium yellow with silver highlights. Attractive tropical fruit nuances reminiscent of pineapple, passion fruit and fresh lime zest. The juicy, sweet fruit is lifted by a fine accent of acidity. Yellow fruit laced with salty minerals remain on the finish.

90 Riesling Kamptal DAC Terrassen 2013
88 Riesling Kamptal DAC Terrassen 2012

89 Sauvignon Blanc blaue Linie 2014

(89–91) Gemischter Satz 2015
90 Gemischter Satz 2013

91 Hager Rot 2013 PN/BB/ZW/SL
92 Hager Rot 2011 ZW/SL/PN

90 Blauer Zweigelt Pur rote Linie 2012
90 Blauburger Pur 2012

89 Brut Zweigelt Rosé 2012

93 Riesling Auslese 2014

Weingut Hiedler

3550 Langenlois, Am Rosenhügel 13
T: +43 (2734) 2468, F: +43 (2734) 2468 5
office@hiedler.at, www.hiedler.at

Winemaker: Ludwig Hiedler
Contact Person: María Ángeles and Ludwig Hiedler
Production: 225.000 bottles (95 % white, 5 % red)
Hectares: 30
Fairs: VieVinum, ProWein
Distribution partners: AUS, RUS, J, S, CDN, CH, B, BR, RC, L, DK, DE, NZ, CZ, NL, N, H, USA, PL, P

The Hiedler wine estate was founded in 1856 and now counts among the oldest, most historic wineries in Langenlois. An owl is the inimitable mascot of the winery and symbolises a philosophy that balances nature and science and unites wine and culture. As a founding member of the prestigious vintners' association "Österreichischen Traditionsweingüter", the winery possesses a pronounced conscientiousness for terroir and origin. The uniqueness of the Hiedler Grüner Veltliner and Riesling wines is derived from the clayey calcareous loess and loam soils as well as the meagre, crystalline metamorphic rock of the Kamptal region. For sustainable production of great growths, the energetic vintner tends the vines by hand and abstains from the use of herbicides. Minimal intervention is practiced in the cellar to ensure the maximum possibility for the development of his wines. Hiedler's style is achieved through slow fermentation with wild yeasts, prolonged contact with the fine lees, and delayed bottling. The resulting wines are delicately fruity and mineral, yet also deep, powerful, and worthy of ageing. Wines are vinified predominantly in stainless steel and large acacia wood barrels and a very small portion in small oak barrels. The primary varieties at the Hiedler estate are Grüner Veltliner and Riesling, but the Burgundian varieties Chardonnay and Weissburgunder (Pinot Blanc), with which Ludwig Hiedler achieved early recognition, remain cult. A very small share of the vineyard area is dedicated to the production of red wines, foremost finely structured Pinot Noir. A unique specialty for the Danube region is Sangiovese. Ludwig's wife, María Ángeles, originates from Spain and is responsible for the public face of the winery while handling marketing and export activities. Together, they have led their winery to an internationally-respected reputation without ever losing touch with its Kamptal roots.

(92–94) Grüner Veltliner Kamptal DAC Reserve Maximum 2014
93 Grüner Veltliner Kamptal DAC Reserve Maximum 2013
Brilliant, shiny yellow. Delicate blossom honey notes interchange with apricot, wild herbs and a touch of mandarin zest. Complex and well-structured with a backbone of minerals and acidity Sweetly extracted fruit remains long on the elegant aftertaste. A versatile wine with food that demonstrates plenty of finesse and tremendous ageing potential.

93 Grüner Veltliner Kamptal DAC Reserve Maximum 2012

94 Grüner Veltliner Familienreserve 2007

(92–94) Grüner Veltliner Kamptal DAC Reserve Schenkenbichl 1 ÖTW 2015
92 Grüner Veltliner Kamptal DAC Reserve Schenkenbichl 1 ÖTW 2014

(92–94) Grüner Veltliner Kamptal DAC Reserve Kittmannsberg 1 ÖTW 2015
92 Grüner Veltliner Kamptal DAC Reserve Kittmannsberg 1 ÖTW 2014
92 Grüner Veltliner Kamptal DAC Reserve Kittmannsberg 1 ÖTW 2013

(90–92) Grüner Veltliner Kamptal DAC Reserve Thal 1 ÖTW 2015
90 Grüner Veltliner Kamptal DAC Reserve Thal 1 ÖTW 2014
90 Grüner Veltliner Kamptal DAC Reserve Thal 1 ÖTW 2013

92 Grüner Veltliner Kamptal DAC Spiegel 2015
89 Grüner Veltliner Kamptal DAC Spiegel 2014
89 Grüner Veltliner Spiegel 2013

89 Grüner Veltliner Löss 2015

(92–94) Riesling Kamptal DAC Reserve
    Heiligenstein 1 ÖTW 2015
94 Riesling Kamptal DAC Reserve
    Heiligenstein 1 ÖTW 2014
Pale yellow with silver highlights. Initially restrained, but with just a little aeration, a complex bouquet of peach, pineapple, papaya, blossom honey and wild meadow herbs is revealed. Juicy and elegant with a taut acidity backbone. Peach and salty minerals linger on the finish. Plenty of finesse and potential for further development.
94 Riesling Kamptal DAC Reserve
    Heiligenstein 1 ÖTW 2013

(92–94) Riesling Kamptal DAC Reserve
    Gaisberg 1 ÖTW 2015
92 Riesling Kamptal DAC Reserve
    Gaisberg 1 ÖTW 2014
92 Riesling Kamptal DAC Reserve
    Gaisberg 1 ÖTW 2013

(92–94) Riesling Kamptal DAC Reserve
    Kogelberg 1 ÖTW 2015
92 Riesling Kamptal DAC Reserve
    Kogelberg 1 ÖTW 2014

(91–93) Riesling Kamptal DAC Reserve
    Steinhaus 1 ÖTW 2015
91 Riesling Kamptal DAC Reserve
    Steinhaus 1 ÖTW 2014
92 Riesling Kamptal DAC Reserve
    Steinhaus 1 ÖTW 2013

93 Riesling Kamptal DAC Reserve Maximum 2013
93 Riesling Maximum 2012
94 Riesling Maximum 2011

92 Riesling Kamptal DAC Urgestein 2015
90 Riesling Kamptal DAC Urgestein 2014
90 Riesling Urgestein 2013

(93–95) Weißer Burgunder Maximum 2014
93 Weißburgunder Maximum 2013
93 Weißburgunder Maximum 2011

92 Pinot Blanc 2015
89 Pinot Blanc 2014
92 Pinot Blanc Spiegel 2013

92 Sauvignon Blanc Reserve 2012
93 Sauvignon Blanc Reserve 2011

93 Chardonnay Toasted & Unfiltered 2013
92 Chardonnay toasted & unfiltered 2012
93 Chardonnay toasted & unfiltered 2011

92 Pinot Noir Reserve 2011

91 Pinot Noir 2012

92 Riesling Auslese 2011

93 Weißburgunder Beerenauslese 2013

94 Weißburgunder Eiswein 2011
95 Weißburgunder Eiswein 2008

Weingut Hirsch

3493 Kammern, Hauptstraße 76
T: +43 (2735) 2460, F: +43 (2735) 2460 60
info@weingut-hirsch.at, www.weingut-hirsch.at

ORGANIC

Winemaker and Contact Person: Johannes Hirsch
Production: n. a. (100 % white)
Hectares: 30
Fairs: VieVinum, ProWein
Distribution partners: AUS, J, S, CDN, CH, DE, CZ, NL, N, GB, USA, PL, CY, IL

Vintner Johannes Hirsch is an unerring quality fanatic. A 500-year-old tithing farm in Kammern, in the Kamptal, is where the Hirsch family dedicates their passion to production of Grüner Veltliner and Riesling. They cultivate their estate vineyards biodynamically to produce unique wines that unite lightness, intensity and vitality, wines that reflect the best attributes of the region. Juicy, spicy and fresh are good descriptors for the new 2015 wines from Johannes Hirsch. Hirsch wines now appear with fresh new packaging and a new label design. Even the "Hirschvergnügen", which was always the light-bodied exception to the rule, now appears with the same label design as the rest of the assortment. Not just the labels are new, though. The Kammerner Heiligenstein Grüner Veltliner is now simply called "Kammern Grüner Veltliner". The new name follows the Burgundian village classification: wines from large "Grosslagen" shall not carry a single-vineyard name, but be named for their village, or commune of origin - thus Kammern Grüner Veltliner. The 2014 single vineyard wines have been available since last September, complete with new labels. The new presentation embodies the philosophy of the renowned vintner from Kammern in Kamptal. At the core of his thinking is that the soil determines the wine, that the vineyard of origin is more decisive for wine character than grape variety. The Hirsch wines are terroir wines that express specific origins. The famous Riesling vineyards Zöbinger Heiligenstein and Zöbinger Gaisberg and the prime Grüner Veltliner vineyards Kammerner Lamm, Kammerner Grub, and Kammerner Renner bring expressive single vineyard wines with firm mineral character and mouth-filling texture.

(93–95) Grüner Veltliner Kamptal DAC Reserve Kammerner Lamm 1 ÖTW 2015

94 Grüner Veltliner Kamptal DAC Reserve Kammerner Lamm 1 ÖTW 2014
Medium green-yellow. The inviting nose displays pineapple, papaya, yellow apple, fresh meadow herbs and mineral nuances. Complex and juicy with plenty of yellow fruit and discreet extract sweetness refreshingly balanced with juicy acidity. Delicate blossom honey notes come in on the finish. Dependable ageing potential.

94 Grüner Veltliner Kamptal DAC Reserve Kammerner Lamm 1 ÖTW 2013

(93–95) Grüner Veltliner Kamptal DAC Reserve Kammerner Grub 1 ÖTW 2015

93 Grüner Veltliner Kamptal DAC Reserve Kammerner Grub 1 ÖTW 2014

93 Grüner Veltliner Kamptal DAC Reserve Kammerner Grub 1 ÖTW 2013

(92–94) Grüner Veltliner Kamptal DAC Kammerner Renner 1 ÖTW 2015

92 Grüner Veltliner Kamptal DAC Kammerner Renner 1 ÖTW 2014

92 Grüner Veltliner Kamptal DAC Kammerner Renner 1 ÖTW 2013

(91–93) Grüner Veltliner Kamptal DAC Kammerner Gaisberg 1 ÖTW 2015

91 Grüner Veltliner Kamptal DAC Kammerner Heiligenstein 2014

91 Grüner Veltliner Kamptal DAC Kammerner Heiligenstein 2013

93 Grüner Veltliner Kamptal DAC Kammerner Heiligenstein 2012

91 Grüner Veltliner Hirschvergnügen 2015

90 Grüner Veltliner Hirschvergnügen 2014

90 Grüner Veltliner Hirschvergnügen 2013

92 Grüner Veltliner Kamptal DAC Kammern 2015

(93–95) Riesling Kamptal DAC Reserve Zöbinger
      Heiligenstein 1 ÖTW 2015
94 Riesling Kamptal DAC Zöbinger
      Heiligenstein 1 ÖTW 2014

Medium green-yellow with silver highlights. Initially re-strained, but with aeration, inviting blossom honey, deli-cate peach and greengage plum are revealed. Well concen-trated fruit and a sharply delineated acidity structure. Litchi, lemon, lime and salty minerals linger long on the finish. Although already offering plenty of drinking pleas-ure, this wine will definitely benefit from another couple years of bottle maturation.

95 Riesling Kamptal DAC Reserve Zöbinger
      Heiligenstein 1 ÖTW 2013

(92–94) Riesling Kamptal DAC Reserve
      Zöbinger Gaisberg 1 ÖTW 2015
93 Riesling Kamptal DAC
      Zöbinger Gaisberg 1 ÖTW 2014
93 Riesling Kamptal DAC Reserve
      Zöbinger Gaisberg 1 ÖTW 2013

91 Riesling Kamptal DAC Zöbing 2015
92 Riesling Kamptal DAC Zöbing 2014
91 Riesling Kamptal DAC Zöbing 2013

Weingut Jurtschitsch

3550 Langenlois, Rudolfstraße 39
T: +43 (2734) 2116, F: +43 (2734) 2116 11
weingut@jurtschitsch.com, www.jurtschitsch.com

ORGANIC

Winemaker: Stefanie and Alwin Jurtschitsch
Contact Person: Alwin Jurtschitsch
Production: n. a. (74 % white, 25 % red, 1 % sweet)
Hectares: 62
Fairs: VieVinum, ProWein
Distribution partners: J, S, CH, B, LV, SK, LT, L, DK, DE, FIN, CZ, N, GB, USA

With its harvest house that stems from the 16th century and the cool cellar that was carved out of the loess 700 years ago, the Jurtschitsch estate is without question one of the most beautiful and most traditional in Austria. Alwin and Stefanie Jurtschitsch are passionately dedicated to their vineyards and their wines. It was their parents that first applied organic viticulture techniques. Their commitment to nature motivated them to finally initiate official conversion to organic certification in 2006. This change in the vineyard was the catalyst for a new way of thinking about vinification. The single-vineyard wines are now fermented with indigenous yeast in large wooden casks. The old cellar vaults provide the ideal conditions for maturation. The Jurtschitsch wines are sourced from the best sites in the famous vineyards of Kamptal: Zöbinger Heiligenstein, Loiserberg, Dechant, Schenkenbichl, Käferberg, Lamm, and Tanzer. There is hardly another winery in Austria that is able to produce with such exceptional quality and dependability through their entire range of wines. The estate has set standards for the region not only for white wines, but for red and sweet wines as well. Their efforts towards uncompromising quality have been acknowledged by numerous, repeated national and international accolades. The GrüVe® has been a consistent bestseller in restaurants and specialty shops for over two decades. This light, youthful Grüner Veltliner features a new label from the artist Christian Ludwig Attersee each year and has become a classic that has outlived changing wine fashions and passing trends; it celebrates its 30th anniversary this year.

(94–96) Grüner Veltliner Kamptal DAC Reserve Käferberg 1 ÖTW 2015
94 Grüner Veltliner Kamptal DAC Käferberg 1 ÖTW 2014
Medium greenish-yellow hue. Delicate nuances of tropical fruit reminiscent of mango mingle with apple and orange zest. Good complexity and structure is demonstrated with a firm acidity backbone wrapped in a veil of spice and yellow fruit. Salty mineral notes come in on the long finish. Very dependable potential for ageing.
93 Grüner Veltliner Kamptal DAC Reserve Käferberg 1 ÖTW 2012

(93–95) Grüner Veltliner Kamptal DAC Reserve Lamm 1 ÖTW 2015
93 Grüner Veltliner Kamptal DAC Lamm 1 ÖTW 2014
95 Grüner Veltliner Kamptal DAC Reserve Lamm 1 ÖTW 2013

(93–95) Grüner Veltliner Kamptal DAC Reserve Schenkenbichl 1 ÖTW 2015
93 Grüner Veltliner Kamptal DAC Schenkenbichl 1 ÖTW 2014
93 Grüner Veltliner Kamptal DAC Reserve Schenkenbichl 1 ÖTW 2013

(91–93) Grüner Veltliner Kamptal DAC Reserve Loiserberg 1 ÖTW 2015
92 Grüner Veltliner Kamptal DAC Loiserberg 1 ÖTW 2014
92 Grüner Veltliner Kamptal DAC Reserve Loiserberg 1 ÖTW 2013

(92–94) Grüner Veltliner Kamptal DAC Reserve Dechant Alte Reben 1 ÖTW 2015
92 Grüner Veltliner Kamptal DAC Dechant Alte Reben 1 ÖTW 2014
94 Grüner Veltliner Kamptal DAC Reserve Dechant Alte Reben 1 ÖTW 2013

91 Grüner Veltliner Kamptal DAC Stein 2015
90 Grüner Veltliner Kamptal DAC Stein 2014
90 Grüner Veltliner Kamptal DAC Stein 2013

89 Grüner Veltliner Kamptal DAC Löss 2014
90 Grüner Veltliner Kamptal DAC Löss 2013

(93–95) Riesling Kamptal DAC Reserve Zöbinger
      Heiligenstein 1 ÖTW 2015
94 Riesling Kamptal DAC Zöbinger
      Heiligenstein 1 ÖTW 2014
Medium green-yellow with silver highlights. Attractive nuances of tropical fruit, such as pineapple and passion fruit, are underscored by minerals and blossom honey. Racy acidity lends to a firm, balanced structure. Juicy, sweet litchi comes in on the finish. This wine will benefit from further bottle maturation.
93 Riesling Kamptal DAC Reserve Zöbinger
      Heiligenstein 1 ÖTW 2013

(95–97) Riesling Kamptal DAC Reserve Zöbinger
      Heiligenstein Alte Reben 1 ÖTW 2015
97 Riesling Kamptal DAC Reserve Zöbinger
      Heiligenstein Alte Reben 1 ÖTW 2013
94 Riesling Kamptal DAC Reserve Zöbinger
      Heiligenstein Alte Reben 1 ÖTW Lage 2012

(92–94) Riesling Kamptal DAC Reserve
      Loiserberg 1 ÖTW 2015
92 Riesling Kamptal DAC Loiserberg 1 ÖTW 2014
92 Riesling Kamptal DAC Reserve
      Loiserberg 1 ÖTW 2013

93 Jurtschitsch Grüner Veltliner Sekt Brut
      Nature 2010
91 Méthode Jurtschitsch Grüner Veltliner Brut
      Nature 2008
91 Méthode Jurtschitsch Grüner Veltliner Brut
      Nature 2007

91 Jurtschitsch Rosé Sekt Brut

92 Pinot Noir Reserve 2011
91 Pinot Noir Reserve 2010
92 Pinot Noir Reserve 2009

91 Zweigelt Tanzer Reserve 2012

94 Riesling Spätlese Zöbinger Heiligenstein 2014
91 Riesling Spätlese Zöbinger Heiligenstein 2013

93 Riesling Auslese Loiserberg 2014
94 Riesling Auslese Loiserberg 2013

LAURENZ V.

Production: Zöbing; Office: 1070 Wien, Mariahilfer Straße 32
T: +43 (1) 5224791, F: +43 (1) 5224791 55
info@laurenzfive.com, www.laurenzfive.com

Winemaker: Peter Schweiger jr.
Contact Person: Dieter Hübler
Production: n. a. (100 % white)
Fairs: ProWein, The London International Wine & Spirits Fair, Vinexpo
Distribution partners: AUS, J, S, B, CDN, HR, LV, SK, RC, DK, L, EST, FIN, M, T, NZ, NL, TR, GB, N, UA, HK, USA, IRL, PL, UAE, P, CY

Laurenz Moser V, Franz Schweiger and Dieter Hübler established LAURENZ V. in 2004. The mission of the winery was to firmly establish Austria's leading variety, Grüner Veltliner, as one of the very best white wine grapes in the world. The grape variety was at the time still little known outside of the German-speaking world and LAURENZ V. intended to contribute to the deserved international fame of Grüner Veltliner. Six different Grüner Veltliner are produced under the LAURENZ V. label. The grapes are sourced from the Kamptal region, but also from other neighbouring Austrian regions as well. The stylish wines are given well-suited, trendy names such as "Charming", "Friendly", "Singing", "Sunny" and "Forbidden Grüner". "FOUR" by LAURENZ V. is dedicated to the viticultural pioneer Laurenz Moser IV. This oak-fermented wine is a single vineyard Grüner Veltliner from the Zöbinger Gaisberg and produced only in outstanding vintages. Fifteen generations of Austria's Moser wine dynasty stand behind the name LAURENZ V. The last five generations of Laurenz (Lenz) Moser have left a significant mark on Austrian viticulture. The Professor/Doctor h.c. Lenz Moser is considered to be the "godfather" of modern Grüner Veltliner. It was he who developed the Lenz Moser high-culture vine training for which Grüner Veltliner was an ideal candidate. LAURENZ V. markets around 100 hectares of Grüner Veltliner and exports to more than 40 countries on all five continents. The name stands for elegant, well-balanced and complex wines that are a worthy legacy of the many generations of the Moser family: "strictly Grüner and sheer drinking pleasure!"

92 Grüner Veltliner Kamptal DAC Reserve Silver Bullet Grüner 2014
Brilliant yellow hue with silver highlights. A touch of mango mingling with subtle apricot, peppery spice and a touch of anise. Full-bodied and concentrated with elegant acidity lending to a satiny texture. Lengthy, minerally and well-balanced. A very versatile wine at the table.

91 Silver Bullet Grüner Kamptal DAC Reserve 2013 GV (0,5 l)

92 Silver Bullet Grüner Kamptal DAC Reserve 2012 GV

92 Grüner Veltliner Four by LAURENZ V. 2012

92 Grüner Veltliner Four 2011

91 Forbidden Grüner by LAURENZ V. 2015

90 Grüner Veltliner Forbidden Grüner 2013

(90–92) Grüner Veltliner Kamptal DAC Reserve Charming by LAURENZ V. 2015

91 Grüner Veltliner Kamptal DAC Reserve Charming 2014

90 Charming Grüner Veltliner Kamptal DAC Reserve 2013

(89–91) Grüner Veltliner Kamptal DAC Friendly by LAURENZ V. 2015

90 Grüner Veltliner Kamptal DAC Friendly 2014

89 Grüner Veltliner Singing by LAURENZ V. und Sophie 2015

89 Grüner Veltliner Singing by LAURENZ V. und Sophie 2014

(88–90) Grüner Veltliner Sunny by LAURENZ V. und Anna 2015

88 Grüner Veltliner Sunny by LAURENZ V. und Anna 2014

88 Grüner Veltliner Sunny by LAURENZ V. und Anna 2013

Weingut Fred Loimer

3550 Langenlois, Haindorfer Vögerlweg 23
T: +43 (2734) 2239, F: +43 (2734) 2239 4
weingut@loimer.at, www.loimer-shop.at

ORGANIC

Winemaker and Contact Person: Fred Loimer
Production: 350.000 bottles (80 % white, 19 % red, 1 % sweet)
Hectares: 60 + 30
Fairs: ProWein, VieVinum
Distribution partners: AUS, J, S, CDN, CH, B, ROK, HR, SGP, BR, LV, SK, LT, SLO, RC, L, E, DK, CL,
DE, MV, EST, T, FIN, NZ, CZ, F, NL, N, GB, RP, USA, IRL, UAE, P, CY

I love being surprised," says Fred Loimer, who has been responsible for a surprise or two himself. In 2000, he raised a few local eyebrows when he built a minimalistic black cube over a historic vaulted brick cellar in a quaint little cellar alley ensemble. And in 2006, he began to cultivate his vineyards according to biodynamic principles, and then a year later founded the vintner association "respekt" to further develop biodynamic methods in the vineyard. The Loimer winery currently cultivates nearly 60 hectares in famous vineyards like Käferberg, Spiegel, Steinmassl, Seeberg, Heiligenstein, Loiserberg, Eichelberg and Dechant. Grüner Veltliner and Riesling play the leading role and Muscat, Pinot Gris, Chardonnay, Zweigelt and Pinot Noir also receive the attention they deserve. Fred Loimer's wines do not boast superficial fruit, heady alcohol, or sweetness. These are seemingly effortless wines that are marked by their origin and biodynamic viticulture. At the Loimer winery, they are convinced that regional character and typicity can only be achieved through organic cultivation. In the end it is not only a question of protecting the earth and its resources, but also a question of wine quality.

(92–94) Grüner Veltliner Kamptal DAC
    Langenlois Käferberg 1 ÖTW 2015
94 Grüner Veltliner Kamptal DAC Reserve
    Langenlois Käferberg 1 ÖTW 2013
91 Grüner Veltliner Kamptal DAC Reserve
    Langenlois Käferberg 1 ÖTW 2012

(92–94) Grüner Veltliner Kamptal DAC
    Langenlois Spiegel 1 ÖTW 2015
92 Grüner Veltliner Kamptal DAC Reserve
    Langenlois Spiegel 1 ÖTW 2013
93 Grüner Veltliner Kamptal DAC Reserve
    Langenlois Spiegel 1 ÖTW 2012

(91–93) Grüner Veltliner Kamptal DAC
    Langenlois Loiserberg 2015

90 Grüner Veltliner Kamptal DAC
    Langenlois 2015
90 Grüner Veltliner Kamptal DAC
    Langenlois 2014
90 Grüner Veltliner Kamptal DAC
    Langenlois 2013

(92–94) Riesling Kamptal DAC Langenlois
    Seeberg Erste Lage 1 ÖTW 2015
94 Riesling Kamptal DAC Reserve Langenlois
    Seeberg 1 ÖTW 2013
95 Riesling Kamptal DAC Reserve Langenlois
    Seeberg 1 ÖTW 2012

(93–95) Riesling Kamptal DAC Langenlois
    Steinmassl 1 ÖTW 2015
92 Riesling Kamptal DAC Reserve Langenlois
    Steinmassl 1 ÖTW 2013
93 Riesling Kamptal DAC Reserve Langenlois
    Steinmassl 1 ÖTW 2012

(94–96) Riesling Kamptal DAC Zöbing
    Heiligenstein 1 ÖTW 2015
93 Riesling Kamptal DAC Reserve Zöbing
    Heiligenstein 1 ÖTW 2013
93 Riesling Kamptal DAC Reserve Zöbing
    Heiligenstein 1 ÖTW 2012

(91–93) Riesling Kamptal DAC Langenlois
    Loiserberg 2015

90 Riesling Kamptal DAC Langenlois 2015
90 Riesling Kamptal DAC Langenlois 2014
90 Riesling Kamptal DAC Langenlois 2013

(90–92) Am Manhartsberg 2015 CH/PG/WB
92 Am Manhartsberg 2013 CH/WB/PG

(92–94) Chardonnay Gumpold 2014
93 Chardonnay Gumpold Gumpoldskirchen 2012
Medium yellow with green highlights. Toasted hazelnut, oak
spice, ripe yellow apple, peach and wild herbs on the nose.
Medium complexity. Pronounced dark minerals, white apple
and salty nuances linger on the firm finish. A multifaceted
accompaniment to food with good ageing potential.
93 Chardonnay Gumpold Reserve 2010

93 Achtung! Traminer Alte Reben 2014
93 Achtung! Traminer Alte Reben 2013
Pale amber with orange highlights. Smoky nuances accompany candied mandarin zest and nuances of mallow, rose oil
and peach. Dry, tautly structured with plenty of minerals,
dark spice and a salty texture. Rose petals linger on the finish of this versatile food wine. An alternatively styled example of the variety.

(91–93) Achtung! Gelber Muskateller 2015

92 In Gumpoldskirchen 2013 ZF/RG
91 In Gumpoldskirchen 2011 RG/ZF

(90–92) Pinot Noir Gumpoldskirchen 2014
92 Pinot Noir Anning Gumpoldskirchen 2013
91 Pinot Noir Gumpoldskirchen 2012

★ ★ ★
Weingut Rudolf Rabl

3550 Langenlois, Weraingraben 10
T: +43 (2734) 2303, F: +43 (2734) 2303 10
office@weingut-rabl.at, www.weingut-rabl.at

Winemaker and Contact Person: Rudolf Rabl
Production: n. a. (68 % white, 30 % red, 2 % sweet)
Hectares: 80
Fairs: ProWein, VieVinum
Distribution partners: AUS, I, RUS, S, BY, CDN, CH, B, SGP, LV, SK, BG, LT, RC, L, DK, DE, EST, T, FIN, CZ, F, NL, N, GB, RP, USA, IRL, PL

Anyone seeking wines that express the typical regional character of Kamptal and their grape variety will certainly strike it lucky at Weingut Rabl. Rudolf Rabl is very proud of his historic wine estate, which was documented as long ago as 1750. With the same matter of course that father and son share the name Rudolf, they also share all the winery work. Rudolf Rabl Sr. is a lover of nature and master of around 80 hectares of vines (nearly 200 acres). He has a deep understanding and rapport with his vines and his work in the vineyards is the foundation of the high quality of the family's wines. Rudolf Rabl Jr. takes care of the vinification amongst other things, and is proud of having been one of the first in Austria to return to spontaneous fermentation and abstain from the addition of cultured yeasts. He believes it is essential to use the natural yeasts that come in with the grapes from the vineyard if he is to make wines that are a true reflection of the terroir. Restrictive pruning, meticulous canopy management, and green harvesting provide healthy, intensely flavoured grapes. The grapes are handpicked and, depending on variety, either destalked or gently pressed as whole bunches. Maturation and storage is in stainless steel tanks or wooden vats in a cellar dug seven meters (23 feet) into the earth. At the appropriate point in the maturation process, the wine is bottled, and then stored in the cellar at constant temperature. Weingut Rabl exports e.g. to Germany, the Netherlands, Belgium, Norway, Sweden, Denmark, England, Canada, Latvia, Russia, USA, Switzerland and the Philippines.

(91–93) Grüner Veltliner Kamptal DAC Reserve Käferberg Alte Reben 2015
93 Grüner Veltliner Kamptal DAC Reserve Käferberg Alte Reben 2014
Brilliant green-yellow with silver highlights. The elegant bouquet displays subtle yellow apple and pineapple with delicate wild meadow herbs. Sweet extract and mango are elegantly lifted with juicy acidity. Exotic fruit and salty minerals on the aftertaste. Good potential for development.
92 Grüner Veltliner Kamptal DAC Reserve Käferberg 2013

(92–94) Grüner Veltliner Kamptal DAC Reserve Dechant Alte Reben 2015
93 Grüner Veltliner Kamptal DAC Reserve Dechant Alte Reben 2014
Brilliant yellow with silver highlights. An intense fragrance of Golden Delicious apple, passion fruit, wild herbs and orange zest. Sweet fruit extract is elegantly balanced with juicy acidity. Yellow tropical notes on the finish. Superb finesse and potential for further development.
93 Grüner Veltliner Kamptal DAC Reserve Dechant 2013

(92–94) Grüner Veltliner Kamptal DAC Reserve Loiserberg Alte Reben 2015
92 Grüner Veltliner Kamptal DAC Reserve Loiserberg Alte Reben 2014
91 Grüner Veltliner Kamptal DAC Reserve Loiserberg 2013

(91–93) Grüner Veltliner Kamptal DAC Reserve Schenkenbichl Alte Reben 2015

91 Grüner Veltliner Kamptal DAC Reserve Vinum Optimum 2015
91 Grüner Veltliner Kamptal DAC Reserve Vinum Optimum 2014
91 Grüner Veltliner Kamptal DAC Reserve Vinum Optimum 2013

89 Grüner Veltliner Kamptal DAC Terrassen 2015
89 Grüner Veltliner Kamptal DAC Terrassen 2014
88 Grüner Veltliner Kamptal DAC
   Kittmansberg 2013

89 Grüner Veltliner Kamptal DAC
   Langenlois 2015
90 Grüner Veltliner Kamptal DAC
   Langenlois 2014

91 Riesling Kamptal DAC Langenlois 2015
90 Riesling Kamptal DAC Langenlois 2014

(92–94) Riesling Kamptal DAC Reserve
         Steinhaus Rote Erde 2015
92 Riesling Kamptal DAC Reserve Steinhaus
   Rote Erde 2014
92 Riesling Kamptal DAC Reserve Steinhaus
   Rote Erde 2013

(91–93) Riesling Kamptal DAC Reserve
         Schenkelbichl Alte Reben 2015
91 Riesling Kamptal DAC Reserve
   Schenkenbichl Alte Reben 2014
91 Riesling Kamptal DAC Reserve
   Schenkenbichl 2013

92 Riesling Kamptal DAC Reserve Vinum
   Optimum 2015
91 Riesling Kamptal DAC Reserve Vinum
   Optimum 2014
91 Riesling Kamptal DAC Reserve Vinum
   Optimum 2013

89 Riesling Kamptal DAC Terrassen 2015
89 Riesling Kamptal DAC Terrassen 2014
89 Riesling Kamptal DAC Terrassen 2013

Weingut Peter Schweiger

3561 Zöbing, Hauptstraße 29
T: +43 (2734) 4512, M: +43 (664) 4510162
office@schweiger-wein.at, www.schweiger-wein.at

Winemaker and Contact Person: Peter Schweiger
Production: n. a. (95 % white, 5 % red)
Hectares: 18
Distribution partners: on request

The Schweiger winery is located in the wine village Zöbing in the heart of the Kamptal wine region. Peter Schweiger and his son, Peter Jr. place great value on environmentally friendly and sustainable viticulture. Both generations respect the soil and nature tremendously. In producing great wines, two things are decisive for them: environmental conscientiousness and meticulous care of the vines. This dedicated philosophy marks all of their work as vintners and can be tasted in the outstanding quality of their wines.

The wine labels transport the Schweiger philosophy visibly. The compass represents their dedication to the region. The clock embodies the intention to give wines the time they need to evolve. According to this thinking, the wines from the previous year first enter the market in April. Grüner Veltliner and Riesling, and even the black autochthon variety Zweigelt, ripen in their best plots on Heiligenstein.

(90–92) Grüner Veltliner Kamptal DAC Reserve
Zöbinger Heiligenstein 2015
91 Grüner Veltliner Kamptal DAC Reserve
Zöbinger Heiligenstein 2014
90 Grüner Veltliner Kamptal DAC Reserve
Zöbinger Heiligenstein 2013

93 Grüner Veltliner Kamptal DAC Reserve
Zöbinger Heiligenstein »96« 2013

(89–91) Grüner Veltliner Kamptal DAC Reserve
Zöbinger Terrassen 2015
91 Grüner Veltliner Kamptal DAC Reserve
Zöbinger Terrassen 2014
89 Grüner Veltliner Kamptal DAC Reserve
Zöbinger Terrassen 2013

(89–91) Grüner Veltliner Kamptal DAC
Zöbinger Kogelberg 2015
90 Grüner Veltliner Kamptal DAC
Zöbinger Kogelberg 2014
89 Grüner Veltliner Kamptal DAC
Zöbinger Kogelberg 2013

89 Grüner Veltliner Zöbinger Grüner 2015
89 Grüner Veltliner Kamptal DAC 2012

(90–92) Riesling Kamptal DAC Reserve
Zöbinger Heiligenstein 2015
93 Riesling Kamptal DAC Reserve
Zöbinger Heiligenstein 2014
Medium green-yellow with silver highlights. Attractive yellow tropical fruit reminiscent of passion fruit and litchi with a mineral touch. Nuances of pineapple and yellow peach are highlighted by refreshing acidity and carry through the long mineral finish. Good potential for further development.
91 Riesling Kamptal DAC Reserve
Zöbinger Heiligenstein 2013

(88–90) Riesling Kamptal DAC Reserve
Zöbinger Terrassen 2015
91 Riesling Kamptal DAC Reserve
Zöbinger Terrassen 2014
90 Riesling Kamptal DAC Reserve
Zöbinger Terrassen 2013

★ ★ ★

Weingut Steininger

3550 Langenlois, Walterstraße 2
T: +43 (2734) 2372, F: +43 (2734) 2372 11
office@weingut-steininger.at, www.weingut-steininger.at

Winemaker: Karl and Peter Steininger
Contact Person: Eva Steininger
Production: n. a. (80 % white, 19 % red, 1 % sweet)
Hectares: 55
Fairs: VieVinum, ProWein
Distribution partners: J, S, DK, FIN, NL, GB, N, USA, PL

With its production of single-varietal vintage sparkling wines with Kamptal regional character, the Steininger family has established a unique Austrian sparkling wine philosophy. The key factor to their success is the use of the finest base wines that display clearly defined, fragrant fruit and fine mousse derived from a gentle second fermentation in the bottle. These two factors come together to enhance the varietal character and flavour profile of each base wine. The single vineyard sparkling wines "Riesling Heiligenstein" and "Grüner Veltliner Steinhaus" are prime examples of variety and terroir standing in the foreground. The same quality consciousness is displayed in the production of still wines. The focus is dedicated to Grüner Veltliner and Riesling. The signature style is, just as with the sparkling wines, clear, proud, and expressive. The most important vineyards of the winery are the Loisiumweingarten and Kittmannsberg for Grüner Veltliner and Steinhaus and Seeberg for Riesling. The vinification facility of the Steininger winery is integrated in the Loisium wine experience centre. Visitors follow the path of grapes through their evolvement to wine and can look over the shoulder of the winemaker as he works. The Loisium Wine and Spa Hotel is a luxurious accommodation that more than adequately fills the desires of wine-loving travellers.

(91–93) Grüner Veltliner Kamptal DAC Reserve Kittmannsberg 2015
92 Grüner Veltliner Kamptal DAC Reserve Kittmannsberg 2014
Medium green-yellow. Initially rather restrained, but then delicate pear fruit, a touch of orange zest, peppery spice and tobacco notes appear. Complexity intensifies on the palate with white tropical fruit highlighted by refreshing acidity. Displays apple and mango on the finish. A nice, spicy food partner.
91 Grüner Veltliner Kamptal DAC Reserve Kittmannsberg 2013

(91–93) Grüner Veltliner Kamptal DAC Reserve Grand Grü 2015
92 Grüner Veltliner Kamptal DAC Reserve Grand Grü 2014
92 Grüner Veltliner Kamptal DAC Reserve Grand Grü 2013

(92–94) Grüner Veltliner Kamptal DAC Reserve Lamm 2015

(88–90) Grüner Veltliner Kamptal DAC Reserve Loisiumweingarten 2015
90 Grüner Veltliner Kamptal DAC Reserve Loisiumweingarten 2014
90 Grüner Veltliner Kamptal DAC Reserve Loisiumweingarten 2013

89 Grüner Veltliner Kamptal DAC 2015
89 Grüner Veltliner Kamptal DAC 2014

(92–94) Riesling Kamptal DAC Reserve Steinhaus 2015
91 Riesling Kamptal DAC Reserve Steinhaus 2014
90 Riesling Kamptal DAC Reserve Steinhaus 2013

(91–93) Riesling Kamptal DAC Reserve
          Seeberg 2015
92 Riesling Kamptal DAC Reserve Seeberg 2014
92 Riesling Kamptal DAC Reserve Seeberg 2013

(90–92) Riesling Kamptal DAC Reserve
          Koglberg 2015

SPARKLING WINES

92 Grüner Veltliner Sekt 2014
93 Grüner Veltliner Sekt 2013
Pale green-yellow and a fine mousse. Delicate blossom
honey notes mingle with apple, mandarin zest and lime.
Taut, complex and layered with balanced acidity. Refreshing pear lingers on the finish of this versatile accompaniment to food.
91 Grüner Veltliner Sekt 2012

93 Riesling Sekt 2014
93 Riesling Sekt 2013
92 Riesling Sekt 2012

92 Sauvignon Blanc Sekt 2014
91 Sauvignon Blanc Sekt 2013
92 Sauvignon Blanc Sekt 2012

93 Traminer Sekt 2012
91 Traminer Sekt 2011

93 Grüner Veltliner vom Steinhaus Sekt 2012

93 Weißburgunder vom Panzaun Sekt 2012

92 Burgunder Sekt 2013
92 Burgunder Sekt 2012
91 Burgunder Sekt 2010 WB/CH/PN

92 Cabernet Sauvignon Rosé Sekt 2013

Weingut Weixelbaum

3491 Straß im Straßertale, Weinbergweg 196
T: +43 (2735) 2269, F: +43 (2735) 2269 16, M: +43 (676) 3258483
weixelbaum@vinoweix.at, www.vinoweix.at

Winemaker: Heinz Weixelbaum
Contact Person: Heinz and Gabi Weixelbaum
Production: n. a. (88 % white, 8 % red, 1 % sweet, 3 % rose)
Hectares: 22
Fairs: ProWein
Distribution partners: S, CH, DK, DE, CZ, F, NL, GB, USA, IRL

The motto of the Weixelbaum vintner family is: "We adore wine and treasure authentic values". Those authentic values are what accompany the family in the vineyard, the cellar – and their everyday lives. The success of this award-winning winery is based on the ideal combination of modern technology and oenological fundamentals with traditional values. The professionalism and passion with which work is done is reflected again in Heinz Weixelbaum's stated aspiration: to produce wines that he himself likes to drink and to watch others as they have the same enjoyment. Authentic values do not mean stagnation, but attentive further development. A new plot was purchased in the east section of the Gaisberg vineyard on Ofenberg in 2015. In a "family council" together with the children, it was decided that Grüner Veltliner would be planted in this marvellous loess site. The vines planted today will be the heritage of the next generation who will harvest their fruit and produce inimitable wines to be enjoyed for many years. Because a well-assorted wine shop should exhibit the history of a good vintner, the wine library was enlarged and includes wines from the 1969 vintage onwards. This makes the creation of exciting vertical wine tastings a realistic opportunity.

94 Grüner Veltliner Kamptal DAC Reserve Anno Dazumal 2012
Medium yellow-green. Stone fruit nuances reminiscent of apricot over a background of blossom honey and wild herbs. A juicy texture is flavoured with sweetly extracted stone fruit that is wrapped around a well-integrated spine of acid. A touch of honey comes in on the finish. Although already offering drinking pleasure, will continue to age gracefully.
95 Grüner Veltliner Anno Dazumal 2011

(92–94) Grüner Veltliner Kamptal DAC Reserve Ried Gaisberg Wahre Werte 2015
92 Grüner Veltliner Kamptal DAC Reserve Ried Gaisberg Wahre Werte 2014
92 Grüner Veltliner Kamptal DAC Reserve Ried Gaisberg Wahre Werte 2013

(91–93) Grüner Veltliner Kamptal DAC Reserve Ried Rosengarten 2015
90 Grüner Veltliner Kamptal DAC Reserve Rosengarten 2014

92 Grüner Veltliner Kamptal DAC Ried Wechselberg 2015

(91–93) Riesling Kamptal DAC Reserve Ried Gaisberg Wahre Werte 2015
93 Riesling Kamptal DAC Reserve Ried Gaisberg Wahre Werte 2014
91 Riesling Kamptal DAC Reserve Ried Gaisberg Wahre Werte 2013

(90–92) Riesling Kamptal DAC Ried Renner 2015

92 Sauvignon Blanc Ried Wechselberg-Himmel Wahre Werte 2015
91 Sauvignon Blanc Wahre Werte 2014
90 Sauvignon Blanc Wahre Werte 2013

91 Weißburgunder Ried Gaisberg Wahre Werte 2015
90 Weißburgunder Ried Gaisberg Wahre Werte 2013
90 Weißburgunder Gaisberg Wahre Werte 2012

89 Rosé Gemischter Satz 2015

94 Sauvignon Blanc Auslese Wahre Werte 2013
Yellow-green with silver highlights. Intense yellow bell pepper, black currant, tarragon and a touch of pineapple. Juicy, sweet fruit is nicely integrated due to the elegantly poised acidity. A touch of honey on the long finish. Great ageing potential.

Weingut Weszeli

3550 Langenlois, Großer Buriweg 16
T: +43 (2734) 3678
weingut@weszeli.at, www.weszeli.at

NEW

Winemaker: Rupert Summerer
Contact Person: Davis Weszeli
Production: n. a. (100 % white)
Distribution partners: I, J, B, CDN, CH, SK, DE, FIN, F, CZ, NL, GB, N, USA, UAE

The vineyards of the Weszeli estate are located near the wine town of Langenlois in Kamptal. Around 30 hectares planted with Grüner Veltliner and Riesling vines are attentively cultivated. Historically, the winery's tradition reaches all the way back to 1679. Davis Weszeli combines the collected wisdom of generations with his own philosophy, which he calls "Prinicipal Terrafactum". The vineyard is the central focus of his work, for he deeply believes that is where the character of his wine is formed. He invests his efforts in supporting biodiversity, and minimal intervention vinification is given the same respect. Weszeli wines are pure, honest an unadulterated.

93 Riesling Kamptal DAC Reserve Seeberg
1 ÖTW 2013
Brilliant yellow with shiny gold highlights. Subtle ethereal nuances reminiscent of mint comprise the background for peach, lime zest, and minerals. Juicy acid refreshes litchi fruit and lends an elegant, silky texture. Salty mineral components join in on the long appetizing finish. Good potential for further ageing.

92 Riesling Kamptal DAC Reserve
Steinmassl 1 ÖTW 2013

93 Grüner Veltliner Kamptal DAC Reserve
Schenkenbichl 1 ÖTW 2013

92 Grüner Veltliner Kamptal DAC Reserve
Käferberg 1 ÖTW 2012

KREMSTAL DAC
Modern interpretations of ancient wine culture, Grüner Veltliner and Riesling rooted in rock and loess

If vineyards could speak, there would be endless hours of exciting discussion in the Kremstal DAC controlled designation of origin. 2,243 hectares of vineyards are distributed in three distinct zones: the city of Krems, the eastern lying areas, and the small wine villages south of the Danube River. Despite this division, there are uniting elements, not only in the regional art and culture, but also in the key vinophile representatives, Grüner Veltliner and Riesling.

© ÖWM/Egon Mark

In the old town of Krems, the intimate link to wine is more than evident. This is a place that has superbly fulfilled its role as an ambassador of Austrian wine culture throughout the ages. Many of the estates in Krems have existed for centuries. This tradition continues to thrive due to the many young and successful vintners, an innovative wine co-operative, and an outstanding wine school.

Like its adjoining neighbour, Wachau, Kremstal vineyards are based predominantly on primary rock. Well-known vineyards such as Pfaffenberg and Steiner Hund produce elegant, mineral wines. Small microclimates such as Senftenberg and its surrounding wine villages along the river Krems are home to truly unique wines. The vineyards to the east contrast starkly and yield much richer, rounder, full-bodied wines. The massive loess terraces in the wine villages of Rohrendorf and Gedersdorf add a very special appeal to the landscape.

The magnificent Benedictine Göttweig Monastery (founded in 1083) is perched on a mountain top on the south side of the Danube River and appears to stand guard over the wine villages of Furth-Palt, Krustetten, Hollenburg, Oberfucha and Tiefenfucha at its feet. Many small heuriger in the area help preserve the quaint and rustic charm of the villages.

As with the neighbouring Wachau and Kamptal wine-growing areas, the Kremstal also lies in the centre of climatic tension. Cool humidity from the adjacent Forest Quarter (Waldviertel) meets the dry warmth stretching in from the Pannonian Basin to the east.

The Danube Valley benefits from the temperatureregulating effect of the river's large flowing surface. Kremstal's two main grape varieties, Grüner Veltliner and Riesling, have defined the juicy, elegant wines of the Kremstal DAC protected designation of origin since its establishment in 2007. The Kremstal DAC wines must be made exclusively from one of these two varieties. The deeper, weightier, dry late harvest examples are labelled "Kremstal DAC Reserve". Other white and black grape varieties find suitable terroir here and are bottled under the Niederösterreich protected geographical indication.

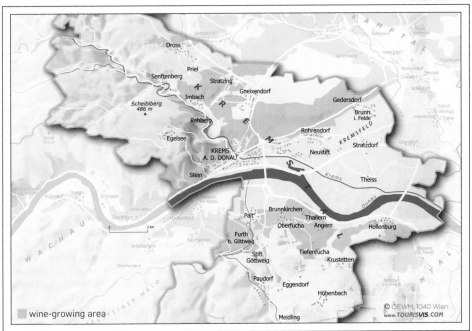

- ◆ Weingut Aigner, Krems
- ◆ Weingut Josef & Philipp Bründlmayer, Grunddorf
- ◆ Winzerhof Familie Dockner, Höbenbach
- ◆ Weingut Manfred Felsner, Grunddorf
- ◆ Weingut Meinhard Forstreiter, Krems-Hollenburg
- ◆ Weingut Malat, Palt/Krems
- ◆ Weingut Mantlerhof, Gedersdorf/Brunn im Felde
- ◆ Weingut Hermann Moser, Rohrendorf
- ◆ Weinkellerei Lenz Moser, Rohrendorf

- ◆ Weingut Müller, Krustetten
- ◆ Weingut Müller-Großmann, Furth/Palt
- ◆ Weingut Nigl, Senftenberg
- ◆ Weingut Familie Proidl, Senftenberg
- ◆ Weingut Salomon Undhof, Stein an der Donau
- ◆ Weingut Josef Schmid, Stratzing
- ◆ Weingut Stadt Krems, Krems
- ◆ Weingut Stift Göttweig, Furth bei Göttweig
- ◆ Weingut Türk, Stratzing
- ◆ Weingut Petra Unger, Furth/ Göttweig
- ◆ Weingut Wess, Krems
- ◆ Winzer Krems – Sandgrube 13, Krems
- ◆ Weingut Alois Zimmermann, Theiss

Weingut Aigner

3500 Krems, Wiener Straße 133
T: +43 (2732) 84558, F: +43 (2732) 84558 14
info@aigner-wein.at, www.aigner-wein.at

Winemaker and Contact Person: Wolfgang Aigner
Production: 80.000 bottles (80 % white, 19 % red, 1 % sweet)
Hectares: 15
Fairs: VieVinum
Distribution partners: CZ, NL, GB

Winemaking is in Wolfgang Aigner's genes. As the son of a vintner, he took over the family winery in Krems at the age of 21. From the very beginning, he worked diligently at getting the very most out of the exceptional sites he had at hand. The extraordinary terroir of the Sandgrube and Weinzierlberg is the pulsing heart of the 15-hectare estate, which produces some of the most interesting white wines in the Kremstal wine region. Nearly all of the estate's vines were planted by the vintner's grandfather more than 40 years ago. The predominant varieties are Grüner Veltliner and Riesling. The Aigner wines exhibit a unique profile: they are powerful, but never clumsy and they make a refreshing impression with marked spice and pleasing aroma intensity. Aigner produces wines that are quite worthy of bottle maturation. The reserve wines continue to offer plenty of refreshing drinking pleasure even after 20 years. The clearly defined fruit and complex tertiary aromas are what make these wines so impressive.

94 Grüner Veltliner Kremstal DAC Reserve Sandgrube Elitär 2013
Brilliant green-yellow with silver highlights. Ripe litchi, carambola, and pear with rhubarb compote and mandarin zest in the background. Complex with sweet extract nicely lifted with an elegant balance of acidity. Pleasant salty minerals linger on the finish. Despite all its power, well-balanced and elegantly poised.

90 Grüner Veltliner Kremstal DAC Reserve Sandgrube Elitär 2012

93 Grüner Veltliner Kremstal DAC Reserve Sandgrube Elitär 2011

(91–93) Grüner Veltliner Kremstal DAC Reserve Sandgrube Privat 2015

92 Grüner Veltliner Kremstal DAC Reserve Sandgrube Privat 2014
Medium green-yellow. Ripe yellow apple and pineapple over a background of fresh wild herbs and orange zest. Pineapple and carambola flavour the creamy texture and are lifted by a vibrant, juicy acidity backbone. An elegant accompaniment to food with good ageing potential.

92 Grüner Veltliner Kremstal DAC Reserve Sandgrube Privat 2013

91 Grüner Veltliner Kremstal DAC Sandgrube 2015
91 Grüner Veltliner Kremstal DAC Sandgrube 2014
89 Grüner Veltliner Sandgrube 2013

89 Grüner Veltliner Kabinett Weinzurl 2015
89 Grüner Veltliner Kremstal DAC Weinzurl 2014
88 Grüner Veltliner Kremstal DAC Weinzurl 2013

88 Grüner Veltliner Kabinett Grünello 2015

91 Riesling Kremstal DAC Weinzierlberg 2015
90 Riesling Kremstal DAC Weinzierlberg 2014
89 Riesling Kremstal DAC Weinzierlberg 2013

90 Gelber Muskateller Kabinett Sandgrube 2015

Weingut Josef & Philipp Bründlmayer

3485 Grunddorf, Ortsring 44
T/F: +43 (2735) 5112, M: +43 (676) 5706940
office@josef-bruendlmayer.at, www.josef-bruendlmayer.at

NEW

Winemaker and Contact Person: Philipp Bründlmayer
Production: n. a. (85 % white, 10 % red, 5 % rose)
Hectares: 18
Fairs: VieVinum, Prowein
Distribution partners: CH, DK, DE, CZ, NL, GB

You could write a book about the unavoidable conflicts between vintner fathers and sons, but you wouldn't fine Josef and Philipp Bründlmayer in it. There would simply be nothing dramatic to write. Things may appear to be different since Phillip has taken the lead in management, but his father still plays a decisive role. This is no wonder, because he knows each and every vine in all 52 vineyard parcels of the family estate. He planted many of them himself, rescued others and he tends all of them meticulously to suit the shared intention of father and son to produce origin-specific wines. As a student of oenology, Philipp continues with the same impetus for innovation and ideas with which his father began in 1980. The initial starting point is naturally much better now than it was then. While his father began producing wines without pumps or even a cellar, Philipp today produces from 18 vineyard hectares. The vineyards count among the best in Kremstal and are planted predominantly with Grüner Veltliner. Moosburgerin, Gebling, Tiefenthal, Vordernberg and Steingraben are sites that are synonymous for concentrated, powerful wines that nevertheless don't lack in vibrancy and structure. To bring these inherent attributes from the vine into the bottle, Philipp follows a handful of principles. He abstains completely from insecticides and herbicides, and the grapes are picked exclusively by hand. Minimal intervention and long maturation on the lees belong on his list of "benevolent neglect". Understanding the essence of the estate has two aspects: the first is capturing the natural conditions in the bottle, and the second is to this with autochton varieties. Next to Grüner Veltliner and Riesling, Neuburger is playing an increasingly significant role.

(89–91) Riesling Kremstal DAC Reserve Steingraben 2015
Medium green-yellow. White vineyard peach and a touch of blossom honey with a hint of citrus zest. The medium body displays an elegant play between sweet fruit and vibrant acidity. Juicy fruit and salty notes linger on the finish of this wonderfully balanced wine. Superb ageing potential.

92 Riesling Kremstal DAC Reserve Steingraben 2014

91 Riesling Kremstal DAC Reserve Steingraben 2013

(89–91) Riesling Kremstal DAC Reserve Moosburgerin 2015

90 Riesling Kremstal DAC Reserve Moosburgerin 2014

90 Riesling Kremstal DAC Reserve Moosburgerin 2013

(90–92) Grüner Veltliner Kremstal DAC Reserve Moosburgerin 2015

(89–91) Grüner Veltliner Kremstal DAC Reserve Vordernberg 2015

89 Grüner Veltliner Kremstal DAC Kaiserstiege 2015

91 Neuburger Vordernberg 2015

 ★ ★ ★
Winzerhof Familie Dockner
3508 Höbenbach, Ortsstraße 30
T: +43 (2736) 7262, F: +43 (2736) 7262 4
winzerhof@dockner.at, www.dockner.at

Winemaker: Josef Dockner jun.
Contact Person: Josef Dockner sen.
Production: 600.000 bottles (70 % white, 29 % red, 1 % sweet)
Hectares: 65 + 40
Fairs: ProWein, VieVinum
Distribution partners: I, CH, B, SK, DK, DE, FIN, CZ, NL

The Dockner family from Höbenbach in the southern Kremstal is elated with the 2015 vintage. They have had many successes in recent years and now market wines from their own 75 estate hectares and another 55 hectares of contracted vineyards. Grüner Veltliner is the leading variety of the estate and Josef Dockner produces not only first class representatives in the lighter categories such as Kremstal DAC from the Frauengrund vineyard, but also reserve wines sourced from his very best grapes. The young winemaker also aptly demonstrates his skill with Riesling. Father Sepp takes responsibility for vineyard management and marketing. That father and son also succeed in producing excellent red wines in a place that is considered a white wine region, is nothing new. It is in particular the blend called "Sacra" with which the father-son team have repeatedly proven that top red wines can indeed be produced in Kremstal.

The newest project of the dedicated vintner family is the production of their own sparkling wines, which are produced according to the traditional method of bottle fermentation and even riddled by hand. To realize this ambitious undertaking, several historic cellars in the old cellar-alley slope of the Kremser Frauengrund have been restored and remodelled and opened in 2014. A sparkling rosé from Pinot Noir that was matured for 18 months on the lees and a white sparkling from Chardonnay, Pinot Blanc and Pinot Gris that spent 20 months on the lees now complete the range of Winzerhof Josef Dockner wines.

(92–94) Grüner Veltliner Kremstal DAC Reserve
Leithen Privatfüllung Gudrun 2015
93 Grüner Veltliner Kremstal DAC Reserve
Leithen Privatfüllung Gudrun 2014
Medium green-yellow with silver highlights. Fine notes of fresh apricot, dark minerals and .tobacco nuances with an undertone of ripe yellow apple. Complex, sweetly extracted, subtle nuances of banana and pear are supported by a well-integrated backbone of acidity. Long finish and good ageing potential.
91 Grüner Veltliner Kremstal DAC Reserve
Leithen Privatfüllung Gudrun 2013
92 Grüner Veltliner Kremstal DAC Reserve
Leithen Privatfüllung Gudrun 2012

(92–94) Grüner Veltliner Kremstal DAC Reserve
Hollenburger Lusthausberg 2015
92 Grüner Veltliner Kremstal DAC Reserve
Hollenburger Lusthausberg 2014
92 Grüner Veltliner Kremstal DAC Reserve
Hollenburger Lusthausberg 2013

90 Grüner Veltliner Kremstal DAC
Further Oberfeld 2015
90 Grüner Veltliner Kremstal DAC
Further Oberfeld 2014
89 Grüner Veltliner Kremstal DAC
Further Oberfeld 2013

90 Grüner Veltliner Kremstal DAC
Kremser Frauengrund 2015
89 Grüner Veltliner Kremstal DAC
Kremser Frauengrund 2014
89 Grüner Veltliner Kremstal DAC
Kremser Frauengrund 2013

92 Grüner Veltliner Wachau
Alte Reben Reserve 2015
89 Grüner Veltliner Wachau
Alte Reben Reserve 2013

(92–94) Riesling Kremstal DAC Reserve Leithen
    Privatfüllung Sepp 2015
93 Riesling Kremstal DAC Reserve Leithen
    Privatfüllung Sepp 2014
92 Riesling Kremstal DAC Reserve Leithen
    Privatfüllung Sepp 2013

(92–94) Riesling Kremstal DAC Reserve
    Rosengarten 2015
92 Riesling Kremstal DAC Reserve
    Rosengarten 2014
92 Riesling Kremstal DAC Reserve
    Rosengarten 2013

91 Riesling Kremstal DAC
    Further Gottschelle 2015
91 Riesling Kremstal DAC
    Further Gottschelle 2014
91 Riesling Kremstal DAC
    Further Gottschelle 2013

91 Riesling Kremstal DAC Antonius 2015
90 Riesling Kremstal DAC Antonius 2014
89 Riesling Kremstal DAC Antonius 2013

94 Sacra Grande Reserve 2011 CS/ME

91 Sacra 2013 CS/ZW/ME
91 Sacra 2012 CS/ZW/ME
92 Sacra 2011 ME/CS/ZW

93 Merlot Iosephos 2011

90 Burgunder-Cuvée 2014 PN/SL

92 Cabernet Sauvignon Neubergen Reserve 2013

90 Pinot Noir Wachau Reserve 2012
93 Pinot Noir Reserve Wachau 2009

90 Josef Dockner Brut Rosé 2013

94 Riesling Eiswein Rosengarten 2013
Pale golden yellow with silver highlights. Intense sweet tropical fruit aromas and flavours reminiscent of passion fruit,
litchi, mandarin and honey. The luscious sweetness is nicely
buffered by juicy, racy acidity, which also lends a vibrant,
lively character. A subtle dried fruit touch comes in on the
long finish. Already offering tremendous drinking enjoyment.

92 Grüner Veltliner Eiswein Frauengrund 2012

88 Muskat d'Oro Likörwein 2012 GM

Weingut Felsner

3485 Grunddorf, Ortsring 61
T: +43 (2735) 5122, F: +43 (2735) 5526
office@weingut-felsner.at, www.weingut-felsner.at

Winemaker and Contact Person: Manfred Felsner
Production: n. a. (68 % white, 30 % red, 2 % sweet)
Hectares: 16
Fairs: VieVinum
Distribution partners: on request

Manfred Felsner and his family cultivate 16 hectares of some of the best vineyards around Gedersdorf and Rohrendorf. His goals can be summarized by three essential elements: regional authenticity, varietal character and terroir. Since taking over the family winery in 1990, Manfred concentrates on the expression of the typical fruitiness of the Kremstal wine region as well as pronounced varietal character. New vines stem from shoots of the best old vines, building a selective foundation for quality. Manfred Felsner is an uncompromising advocate of the philosophy of terroir and sustainable viticulture. The primary goal of this Grüner Veltliner specialist is to highlight the diversity of this autochthon variety. The Felsner Grüner Veltliner thrives on well-exposed terraced vineyards with either ancient loess or calcareous conglomerate soils. The mild Pannonian influence from the east and the cool winds from the Waldviertel lend the wines spice and finesse. Each Grüner Veltliner, from the fragrant "Moosburgerin" to the full bodied "Vordernberg" to the mineral "Kremser Gebling" and the complex "Alte Reben", has its very own personality.

91 **Grüner Veltliner Kremstal DAC Reserve Alte Reben 2014**
91 **Grüner Veltliner Kremstal DAC Reserve Alte Reben 2014**
Medium green-yellow. Mango and apricot mingle with anise and subtle notes of orange zest. Juicy and elegant acidity structure nicely balances the extract sweetness. Mango and apricot remain on the finish. Ready to drink.
92 **Grüner Veltliner Kremstal DAC Reserve Alte Reben Rohrendorfer Leiten 2013**

(89–91) **Grüner Veltliner Kremstal DAC Reserve Vordernberg 2015**
89 **Grüner Veltliner Kremstal DAC Reserve Vordernberg 2014**
90 **Grüner Veltliner Kremstal DAC Reserve Vordernberg 2013**

89 **Grüner Veltliner Kremstal DAC Moosburgerin 2015**
89 **Grüner Veltliner Kremstal DAC Moosburgerin 2014**
89 **Grüner Veltliner Kremstal DAC Moosburgerin 2013**

(89–91) **Riesling Kremstal DAC Gebling 2015**
90 **Riesling Kremstal DAC Gebling 2014**
90 **Riesling Kremstal DAC Gebling 2013**

90 **Neuburger Reisenthal 2014**

88 **Hesperia 2014**

90 **St. Laurent Thalland 2013**

Weingut Meinhard Forstreiter

3506 Krems-Hollenburg, Hollenburger Kirchengasse 7
T: +43 (2739) 2296, F: +43 (2739) 22 96 4
weingut@forstreiter.at, www.forstreiter.at

Winemaker and Contact Person: Meinhard Forstreiter
Production: n. a. (80 % white, 19 % red, 1 % sweet)
Hectares: 28
Fairs: ProWein, Vinexpo, VieVinum
Distribution partners: S, CDN, NL, USA

Passion for wine has been in the Forstreiter family's DNA for centuries, with this wine estate alone in existence since 1868. The estate is situated in Hollenburg, which belongs to the city of Krems on the Danube River. Saint Severin was documented with producing wine in this area in 400 A.D. Wine quality stems from the vineyard and so it is with optimal soil and canopy management that the family based their production. Protective handling and minimal intervention are practiced to preserve the quality provided by nature. "I make wines that I like, wines that I like to drink," states winemaker Meinhard Forstreiter. "Those are the only wines I can sell." The majority of the estate's vines grow on south- to southeast-facing vineyard terraces on Hollenburg conglomerate soils with varying depths of loess topsoil. Combined with a special microclimate, this terroir yields fruity mountain wines with peppery spice.

Vinification takes place with the most modern cellar technology. Whole bunch pressing ensures the fermentation of clear juice to yield dry, fruity, elegant wines with pronounced varietal character. In suitable years, noble sweet wines are also produced. The Forstreiter wines are highly appreciated both by the on and off trade. The Forstreiter family places great value on personal contact with their customers.

94 Grüner Veltliner Kremstal DAC Reserve Tabor 2013
Medium green-yellow. Delicate nuances of honeydew melon mingle with notes of blossom honey, yellow apple and delicate mineral accents. Full-bodied and complex with sweet extract and a silky texture structured with a taut backbone of acidity. Plenty of finesse continues on the spicy mineral finish. Dependable ageing potential.

92 Grüner Veltliner Kremstal DAC Reserve Tabor 2012

(91–93) Grüner Veltliner Kremstal DAC Reserve Schiefer 2015
92 Grüner Veltliner Kremstal DAC Reserve Schiefer 2014
91 Grüner Veltliner Kremstal DAC Reserve Schiefer 2013

93 Grüner Veltliner Kremstal DAC Reserve Das weiße Mammut 2013
92 Grüner Veltliner Kremstal DAC Reserve Das Weiße Mammut 2012
92 Grüner Veltliner Kremstal DAC Reserve Das Weiße Mammut 2011

90 Grüner Veltliner Kremstal DAC Kremser Kogl 2015
90 Grüner Veltliner Kremstal DAC Kremser Kogl 2014
88 Grüner Veltliner Kremstal DAC Kremser Kogl 2013

(90–92) Grüner Veltliner Kremstal DAC Alte Reben 2015
91 Grüner Veltliner Alte Reben 2014
90 Grüner Veltliner Alte Reben 2013

(91–93) Riesling Kremstal DAC Reserve Schiefer 2015
92 Riesling Kremstal DAC Reserve Schiefer 2014
Pale green-yellow with silver highlights. Inviting notes of yellow peach and delicate blossom honey. Complex with juicy white vineyard peach and a refreshing mineral and acidity backbone. The mineral finish is long and very good potential for further development is displayed.
91 Riesling Kremstal DAC Reserve Schiefer 2013

90 Pinot Noir 2013

★★★★
Weingut Malat
3511 Palt, Hafnerstraße 12
T: +43 (2732) 82934, F: +43 (2732) 82934 13
weingut@malat.at, www.malat.at

Winemaker and Contact Person: Michael Malat
Production: 250.000 bottles (68 % white, 25 % red, 2 % sweet, 5 % rose)
Hectares: 50
Fairs: VieVinum, ProWein
Distribution partners: RUS, J, S, B, CDN, SGP, DK, L, CL, MV, CZ, NL, N, USA

The Malat winery is among the few that are able to excel in all categories (white, red, sparkling and sweet) with estate fruit only. Since 2008, Michael Malat has directed the family winery in Furth-Palt, which was established in 1722. "I strive to make wines that people like to drink, not just taste," says Michael Malat. "Each wine should carry my personal signature: elegance, finesse and drinkability!" This is a continuation of the style that his father, Gerald, also followed. Gerald - the oenological pioneer of the Kremstal - had such visionary creativity, that it placed this winery firmly among the top producers of the country.

"The diversity of our assortment of wines reflects on one side, our own long traditions, and on the other side the potential of our wine region," says Michael Malat enthusiastic about the tremendous opportunities that are open to him as a vintner in Kremstal. This vintner abstains from the common regional practice of irrigating vineyards. "This would alter the character of the vineyard sites," Malat states. "Only when vines are forced to drive their roots deep in search of water and nourishment, can the true site specific character be authentically expressed in the wine." Spontaneous fermentation and rejection of all botrytis-infected grapes are a dependable guarantee for the precision and inimitable character of all the Malat single vineyard wines. These wines exhibit vibrancy and transparent clarity of varietal character. The Malat family has a deep understanding of how to eloquently play the entire repertoire from light white wines to complex red wines. Austria's first growth sparkling was produced here in 1976. Malat Brut and Malat Brut Rosé are produced according to the traditional method of bottle fermentation. Noble sweet wines with excellent varietal character, which are also among the best in Austria, complete the impressive assortment of products. One can dependably look forward to extraordinary wines from this producer each year. Perfection has been the Malat motto for several generations.

94 Grüner Veltliner Kremstal DAC Reserve »Das Beste vom Veltliner« 2014
93 Grüner Veltliner Kremstal DAC Reserve »Das Beste vom Veltliner« 2013
Brilliant golden yellow. Apricot jam, baked apple, candied orange zest, blossom honey and subtle botrytis spice. Complex and powerful with an elegant expression of acidity lending lift to tropical fruit. Nutty flavours linger on the finish of this well-concentrated accompaniment to food.
94 Grüner Veltliner Kremstal DAC Reserve Das Beste vom Veltliner 2012

92 Grüner Veltliner Kremstal DAC Reserve Höhlgraben Alte Reben 2014
92 Grüner Veltliner Kremstal DAC Reserve Höhlgraben Alte Reben 2013
92 Grüner Veltliner Kremstal DAC Reserve Höhlgraben Alte Reben 2012

91 Grüner Veltliner Kremstal DAC Reserve Gottschelle 1 ÖTW 2014
92 Grüner Veltliner Kremstal DAC Reserve Gottschelle 1 ÖTW 2013
93 Grüner Veltliner Kremstal DAC Reserve Gottschelle 1 ÖTW 2012

90 Grüner Veltliner Kremstal DAC
   Höhlgraben 2015
90 Grüner Veltliner Kremstal DAC
   Höhlgraben 2014
90 Grüner Veltliner Kremstal DAC
   Höhlgraben 2013

88 Grüner Veltliner Kremstal DAC
   Furth - Palt 2015
88 Grüner Veltliner Kremstal DAC 2014
88 Grüner Veltliner Kremstal DAC
   Göttweiger Berg 2013

93 Riesling Kremstal DAC Reserve
   »Das Beste vom Riesling« 2014
93 Riesling Kremstal DAC Reserve
   »Das Beste vom Riesling« 2013
94 Riesling Kremstal DAC Reserve
   Das Beste vom Riesling 2012

92 Riesling Kremstal DAC Reserve
   Silberbichl 1 ÖTW 2014
92 Riesling Kremstal DAC Reserve
   Silberbichl 1 ÖTW 2013
93 Riesling Kremstal DAC Reserve
   Silberbichl 1 ÖTW 2012

92 Riesling Kremstal DAC Steinbühel 1 ÖTW 2014
90 Riesling Kremstal DAC Steinbühel 1 ÖTW 2013
93 Riesling Kremstal DAC Steinbühel 1 ÖTW 2012

90 Riesling Kremstal DAC Furth - Palt 2015
89 Riesling Kremstal DAC 2014
88 Riesling Kremstal DAC Göttweiger Berg 2013

88 Sauvignon Blanc Brunnkreuz 2014
88 Sauvignon Blanc Brunnkreuz 2013

89 Gelber Muskateller Landwid 2015
89 Gelber Muskateller Landwid 2014
89 Gelber Muskateller Landwid 2013

92 Gewürztraminer Katzengraben Reserve 2014
89 Gewürztraminer Katzengraben Reserve 2013
89 Gewürztraminer Katzengraben Reserve 2012

92 Chardonnay Hochrain Reserve 2014
92 Chardonnay Hochrain Reserve 2013
92 Chardonnay Hochrain Reserve 2012

89 Chardonnay Steinpoint 2015
88 Chardonnay Steinpoint 2014
89 Chardonnay Steinpoint 2013

93 Pinot Gris Zistel Reserve 2013
92 Pinot Gris Zistel Reserve 2012

89 Pinot Blanc Am Zaum Hefeabzug 2015
89 Pinot Blanc Am Zaum 2014
88 Pinot Blanc Am Zaum Hefeabzug 2013

90 Rosé vom Cabernet 2015
88 Rosé vom Cabernet 2013
88 Rosé 2012 CS

(92–94) Pinot Noir Reserve 2014
93 Pinot Noir Reserve 2012
92 Pinot Noir Reserve 2011

(88–90) Pinot Noir 2015

(89–91) Sankt Laurent Reserve 2014
90 St. Laurent Reserve 2012
90 Sankt Laurent Reserve 2011

(87–89) Zweigelt 2015
87 Zweigelt 2013
89 Zweigelt 2012

93 Merlot Reserve 2011

92 Cabernet Sauvignon Reserve 2011

(91–93) Cabernet-Merlot Reserve 2013 CS/ME
91 Cabernet - Merlot Reserve 2012 CS/ME

(93–95) Grüner Veltliner Beerenauslese 2014

93 Riesling Beerenauslese 2012

95 Chardonnay Trockenbeerenauslese 2013
Brilliant golden yellow. A highly attractive bouquet displays
sweet apricot jam, a touch of baked apple and an intense
note of honey. Luscious sweetness is marvellously balanced
by refreshing, juicy acidity. Ripe apricot, peach and hazelnut
linger long on the finish. Well equipped for a long and successful life.

92 Malat Brut 2012
91 Brut Reserve 2011
92 Malat Brut Reserve 2010

92 Malat Brut Rosé 2012
92 Brut Rosé Reserve 2011
93 Malat Brut Rosé Reserve 2010

Weingut Mantlerhof

3494 Gedersdorf/Brunn im Felde, Hauptstraße 50
T: +43 (2735) 8248, F: +43 (2735) 8248 33
mantlerhof@aon.at, www.mantlerhof.com

— ORGANIC —

Winemaker: Sepp Mantler
Contact Person: Sepp Mantler, Margit Mantler
Production: n. a. (98 % white, 2 % sweet)
Hectares: 14
Fairs: ProWein, VieVinum, Millésime Bio
Distribution partners: I, RUS, J, CH, B, DE, CZ, NL, N, GB, USA, UAE

A s one approaches the winery in the centre of Brunn, a picturesque view of a biotope appears. On the west side of the pond is an imposing manor with a classic façade. The Mantlerhof was originally owned by the Admont Abbey, but was sold in the 16th century. It has been in the capable hands of the Mantler family now for 200 years. One wins the immediate impression of solidity and dependability which is repeated on the label of the wines made here. Despite the impression of a highly conservative estate, one realizes upon meeting the owners, Margit and Sepp Mantler, that innovative spirit is at work here. The Mantlers cultivate not only wines, but also other crops – all of which are certified organic. The classic white wines of the region, Grüner Veltliner and Riesling under the Kremstal DAC and Kremstal DAC Reserve appellation designations are produced. The vineyards can be seen from the estate on impressive south-facing loess terraces which glow yellow in the sunlight. Another specialty that thrives under the aegis of the Mantlers is the rare indigenous variety Roter Veltliner. Smaller shares of Chardonnay, Gelber Muskateller (Muscat blanc à petits grains) and Neuburger are cultivated with no less care to detail. Margit, who stems originally from the Wachau, has a special connection to Neuburger since one of her ancestors was one of the first to be documented with the variety in their vineyard. The prime vineyards of the estate are Spiegel (Grüner Veltliner), Wieland (Riesling), Steingraben (Riesling), and Mossburgerin (Grüner Veltliner). All are classified as "Erste Lagen" (premier cru) by the vintners association Österreichischen Traditionsweingüter as of the 2010 vintage. The loess soil stems from windblown material from the ice age and its porous attributes and high lime content mark the essential character of the wines – even the light wines are juicy and exhibit good depth and persistence. The wines of Mantlerhof all exhibit extraordinary varietal character and enjoy a reputation for graceful longevity. Although the majority of the wines are vinified dry, there is a small assortment of noble sweet wines from suitable vintages. The archive of wines stored at the estate reach back to the 1947 vintage. The Mantlerhof wines are marketed predominantly to restaurants and specialty shops, with 45% of the production exported abroad.

**(91–93) Grüner Veltliner Kremstal DAC Reserve
Mosburgerin 1 ÖTW 2015**

**93 Grüner Veltliner Kremstal DAC Reserve
Mosburgerin Veltlinerin 1 ÖTW 2013**

Brilliant yellow with shiny gold highlights. Apple and subtle pineapple notes are enhanced by touches of herbs, peppery spice and a dash of lemon. Sweet extract of tropical yellow fruit is balanced by a taut, juicy acidity backbone. This finesse continues through the very long mineral finish. Very good ageing potential.

**92 Grüner Veltliner Kremstal DAC Reserve
Mosburgerin 1 ÖTW 2012**

**(92–94) Grüner Veltliner Kremstal DAC Reserve
Spiegel 1 ÖTW 2015**

**92 Grüner Veltliner Kremstal DAC Reserve
Spiegel 1 ÖTW 2013**

**93 Grüner Veltliner Kremstal DAC Reserve
Spiegel 1 ÖTW 2012**

(90–92) Neuburger Hommage 2015

91 Neuburger Hommage 2013

(90–92) Grüner Veltliner Kremstal DAC
    Lössterrasen 2015
91 Grüner Veltliner Kremstal DAC
    Lössterrassen Gedersdorf 2014

(93–95) Riesling Kremstal DAC Reserve
    Wieland 1 ÖTW 2015
95 Riesling Kremstal DAC Reserve
    Wieland 1 ÖTW 2014

Pale greenish-yellow with silver highlights. Initially rather restrained, but given aeration apricot and greengage plum, wild herbs, Turkish honey, and a touch of lemon appear. Plenty of finesse is displyed with tautly woven fruit elegantly supported with a vibrant, juicy acid structure. Subtle tropical fruit notes and mineral components join in on the long finish. Very classy.

94 Riesling Kremstal DAC Reserve
    Wieland 1 ÖTW 2013

(92–94) Riesling Kremstal DAC Reserve
    Steingraben 1 ÖTW 2015
93 Riesling Kremstal DAC Reserve
    Steingraben 1 ÖTW 2013

(91–93) Riesling Kremstal DAC
    Zehetnerin 1 ÖTW 2015
90 Riesling Kremstal DAC Zehetnerin 2014
90 Riesling Kremstal DAC Zehetnerin 2012

(91–93) Roter Veltliner Reisenthal 2015
92 Roter Veltliner Reisenthal 2014
92 Roter Veltliner Reisenthal 2013

94 Roter Veltliner Reisenthal Selection 2013
93 Roter Veltliner Reisenthal Selection 2012

94 Roter Veltliner Reisenthal Reserve
    (Magnum) 2011

★ ★ ★

Weingut Hermann Moser

3495 Rohrendorf, Bahnstraße 36
T: +43 (2732) 83841, M: +43 (676) 4232024
office@moser-hermann.at, www.moser-hermann.at

Winemaker: Martin Moser
Contact Person: Martin and Carmen Moser
Production: n. a. (90 % white, 9 % red, 1 % sweet)
Hectares: 22
Fairs: ProWein, VieVinum, Meran Wine Festival, DAC-Präsentationen
Distribution partners: USA

With over twenty hectares (50 acres) in the best sites of Rohrendorf, Martin and Carmen Moser possess an optimal foundation for their broad assortment of first-class wines. Martin Moser has proved his remarkable consistency and skill over the years, setting standards of quality among the prestigious vintners association "Österreichische Traditionsweingüter" (ÖTW). Year for year, he delivers an impressive series of expressive wines that range from light white wines to compact red wines. Special attention is given Grüner Veltliner, which thrives in the typical loess soil of the region.

A large tasting room with an expansive glass front offers a generous view of the loess terraces of the Rohrendorf vineyards. This attractive venue can be hired for wine tastings and culinary events. Martin Moser exports his wines predominantly to the USA, but also enjoys a successful presence in Holland, Denmark, Germany, England and Hong Kong.

92 Grüner Veltliner Kremstal DAC Reserve
   Rohrendorfer Gebling Der Löss 1 ÖTW 2015
92 Grüner Veltliner Kremstal DAC Reserve
   Gebling »der Löss« 1 ÖTW 2014
92 Grüner Veltliner Kremstal DAC Reserve
   Gebling »der Löss« 1 ÖTW 2013

92 Grüner Veltliner Kremstal DAC Reserve
   Fortissimo 2015
92 Grüner Veltliner Kremstal DAC Reserve
   Gebling Fortissimo 1 ÖTW 2013
92 Grüner Veltliner Kremstal DAC Reserve
   Gebling Fortissimo 2012

91 Grüner Veltliner Kremstal DAC
   Karmeliterberg 2015
90 Grüner Veltliner Kremstal DAC
   Karmeliterberg 2014
90 Grüner Veltliner Kremstal DAC
   Karmeliterberg 2013

90 Grüner Veltliner Kremstal DAC per due 2015
89 Grüner Veltliner Kremstal DAC per due 2014
89 Grüner Veltliner Kremstal DAC PerDue 2013

91 Grüner Veltliner Kremstal DAC Gebling 2013
90 Grüner Veltliner Kremstal DAC Gebling 2012

89 Grüner Veltliner Kaiserstiege 2015

91 Riesling Kremstal DAC Kaiserstiege 2015

93 Riesling Kremstal DAC Reserve Rohrendorfer
   Gebling Kellerterrasse 1 ÖTW 2015
92 Riesling Kremstal DAC Reserve Gebling
   Kellerterrassen 1 ÖTW 2014
Medium yellow-green with silver highlights. White vineyard peach, a touch of blossom honey, herbal spice and a bit of lime zest. Juicy, vibrant acidity counters the sweet extract on the palate. Papaya and salty minerals remain long on the

93 Grüner Veltliner Kremstal DAC Reserve
   Rohrendorfer Gebling HannaH 1 ÖTW 2015
93 Grüner Veltliner Kremstal DAC Reserve
   Gebling »HannaH« 1 ÖTW 2013
Brilliant yellow with silver highlights. Delicate hazelnut aroma, subtle orange marmalade and ripe yellow apple comprise a multifaceted bouquet. Full bodied and powerful. Subtle honey and pleasant pepper spice linger on the dark mineral finish. Dependable ageing potential.
93 Grüner Veltliner Kremstal DAC Reserve
   Gebling »HannaH« 1 ÖTW 2012

finish. Good aging potential.
**92 Riesling Kremstal DAC Reserve Gebling
Kellerterrassen 1 ÖTW 2013**

**90 Riesling Kremstal DAC Gebling
Lössterrassen 2014**
89 Riesling Kremstal DAC Gebling 2013
90 Riesling Kremstal DAC Gebling 2012

88 Sauvignon Blanc 2015
88 Sauvignon Blanc 2014

(88–90) Gelber Muskateller 2015
89 Gelber Muskateller 2014
88 Gelber Muskateller 2013

89 Rosi Mosi 2014
88 Rosi Mosi 2013

93 Pinot Blanc Beerenauslese 2011

Weinkellerei Lenz Moser

3495 Rohrendorf, Lenz-Moser-Straße 1
T: +43 (2732) 85541, F: +43 (2732) 85900
marketing@lenzmoser.at, www.lenzmoser.at

Winemaker: Ing. Ernest Großauer
Contact Person: Friedrich Wimmer
Production: 10.000.000 bottles (50 % white, 49 % red, 1 % sweet)
Fairs: ProWein, VieVinum, Vinexpo, Alles für den Gast (Salzburg, Wien), Anuga
Distribution partners: RUS, J, S, CDN, SK, DK, DE, EST, FIN, CZ, NL, N, GB, PL

The wines of Lenz Moser are a visiting card for Austrian wines in export markets. This winery based in Rohrendorf near Krems is not only market leader for Austrian quality wines, but has historically been and, indeed still is, an innovative company. They introduced screw caps as early as 1984 and from 2008 you'll find a screw cap on nearly every bottle of Lenz Moser wine. "Small is beautiful" – this slogan is surprisingly appropriate for the Lenz Moser estate. The grapes are supplied to the winery in small plastic boxes by a large number of small growers, who together own around 2,700 hectares of vineyards (6,670 acres). A team of experts led by chief oenologist Ernest Grossauer stays in close contact with the growers, giving detailed consultation throughout the year to ensure the delivery of healthy and perfectly ripe grapes. Customers appreciate the excellent quality of conscientiously produced wines as well as the modest prices. Lenz Moser wines receive deserving recognition from expert juries both on a national and international level.

89 Pinot Gris Lenz Moser Prestige 2014
88 Pinot Gris Lenz Moser Prestige 2013
88 Pinot Gris Prestige 2012

86 Riesling Lenz Moser Prestige 2013
88 Riesling Prestige 2012

89 Blaufränkisch Barrique Lenz Moser Prestige 2012
90 Blaufränkisch Lenz Moser Prestige Barrique 2011
90 Blaufränkisch Prestige Barrique 2009

87 Blauer Zweigelt Lenz Moser Selection 2015
88 Blauer Zweigelt Lenz Moser Selection 2014

89 Blauer Zweigelt Lenz Moser Prestige Reserve 2012
89 Zweigelt Lenz Moser Prestige Reserve 2011

88 Zweigelt Rosé Lenz Moser Selection 2015
88 Zweigelt Rosé Lenz Moser Selection 2014

93 Trockenbeerenauslese Lenz Moser Prestige 2014 WR/BO/WB/CH
92 Lenz Moser Prestige Trockenbeerenauslese 2012 SÄ/CH/WR/MO/BO
Brilliant golden yellow. Inviting fragrance of apricot jam, subtle dried fruit nuances, peach compote and delicate spicy botrytis notes on the nose. Complex and round with pleasant sweetness harmoniously countered by refreshing acidity. Spiced fig compote and honey remain on the finish.

90 Grüner Veltliner Lenz Moser Prestige 2015
89 Grüner Veltliner Lenz Moser Prestige 2013
89 Grüner Veltliner Prestige 2012

89 Grüner Veltliner Lenz Moser Selection 2015
89 Grüner Veltliner Lenz Moser Selection 2014
87 Grüner Veltliner Selection 2012

91 Beerenauslese Lenz Moser Prestige 2012 SÄ/CH/WB/NB
90 Beerenauslese Prestige 2009 SÄ/WR

SCHLOSSWEINGUT MALTESER RITTERORDEN

91 Grüner Veltliner Lenz Moser Carpe Diem
   Reserve 2013
91 Grüner Veltliner Lenz Moser Carpe Diem
   Reserve 2012

90 Grüner Veltliner Hundschupfen 2015
90 Grüner Veltliner Hundschupfen 2014
89 Grüner Veltliner Hundschupfen 2013

89 Weinviertel DAC 2015
89 Weinviertel DAC 2014
88 Weinviertel DAC 2013

90 Chardonnay 2015
88 Chardonnay 2013
88 Chardonnay 2012

90 Malteser Brut Sekt 2012

92 Kommende Mailberg 2013 CS/ME
91 Kommende Mailberg 2012 CS/ME
91 Kommende Mailberg 2011 CS/ME

90 Merlot Malteser Ritterorden 2013
90 Merlot 2012
92 Merlot 2011

88 Zweigelt 2013

KLOSTERKELLER SIEGENDORF

92 O'Dora 2013 CS/CF
92 O'Dora 2012 CS/CF
92 O'Dora 2011 CS/CF

91 Cabernet Sauvignon 2013

89 Lenz Moser Carpe Diem Prestige Cuvée
   Siegendorf 2013 CS/ME/CF
90 Lenz Moser Carpe Diem Prestige Cuvée 2012
   CS/ME/CF

90 Siegendorf Rot 2011 ME/CS

90 Merlot 2013

(88–90) Weißburgunder 2015
88 Weißburgunder 2014
89 Weißburgunder 11 1/2 2012

★ ★ ★
Weingut Müller

3508 Krustetten, Hollenburger Straße 12
T: +43 (2739) 2691, F: +43 (2739) 2691 14, M: +43 (676) 4234170
info@weingutmueller.at, www.weingutmueller.at

Winemaker: Leopold Müller
Contact Person: Leopold and Stefan Müller
Production: n. a. (82 % white, 17 % red, 1 % sweet) **Hectares:** 90
Certified: Sustainable Austria
Fairs: ProWein, VieVinum, Alles für den Gast
Distribution partners: RUS, S, CDN, CH, B, DK, DE, F, NL, GB, IRL, PL

One can see the Müller winery in the centre of the little wine village Krustetten in the southern Kremstal from a considerable distance. The recently constructed, modern vinification facility and the cosy, panoramic tasting room rises well above the roofs of the village. From here, one has a marvellous view of the Benedictine monastery Stift Göttweig, the best vineyards of the Kremstal wine region, and the wine city of Krems on the Danube River.

It is with much passion and dedication that Leopold Müller vinifies his fruit-driven white wines with pronounced varietal character. Grüner Veltliner and Riesling from the best vineyards in southern Kremstal are his special focus. Despite this, the winemaker is very enthusiastic about his velvety, spicy red wines, an enthusiasm that is shared by his customers. The Müllers' consistent efforts to strive for the highest possible quality have been confirmed by numerous successes over the years. Eighteen of their wines have appeared in the Austrian SALON showcase, twice as national champion for Grüner Veltliner and Riesling.

Leopold's younger brother, Stefan, takes care of the well-planned vineyards in outstanding sites on and around Göttweig Mountain. He tends the 90 hectares of vineyards with great passion and competence. Advantageous influences of the Danube river, deep loam, loess and even gravelly soils, support him in his efforts by providing ideal preconditions for high-quality grapes. In addition to this, Stefan is a born restaurateur and pampers guests in the on-premise heuriger (wine tavern) with regional specialties and of course, the Müller wines.

(91–93) Grüner Veltliner Kremstal DAC Reserve Eichbühel 2015
92 Grüner Veltliner Kremstal DAC Reserve Eichbühel 2014
Brilliant green-yellow with silver highlights. Papaya, subtle hazelnut, fine minerals and a touch of candied orange peel. Juicy and elegant with sweet ripe apricot balanced with a fine acidity backbone. Subtle, sweet fruit remains in the aftertaste.
92 Grüner Veltliner Kremstal DAC Reserve Eichbühel 2013

(90–92) Grüner Veltliner Kremstal DAC Reserve Gottschelle 2015
90 Grüner Veltliner Kremstal DAC Reserve Gottschelle 2014
91 Grüner Veltliner Kremstal DAC Reserve Gottschelle 2013

90 Grüner Veltliner Kremstal DAC Kremser Kogl 2015
89 Grüner Veltliner Kremstal DAC Kremser Kogl 2014
89 Grüner Veltliner Kremstal DAC Kremser Kogl 2013

89 Grüner Veltliner Kremstal DAC Frauengrund 2015
88 Grüner Veltliner Kremstal DAC Kremser Frauengrund 2014

90 Grüner Veltliner Bergkristall 2015
89 Grüner Veltliner Bergkristall 2014
90 Grüner Veltliner Bergkristall 2013

(91–93) Riesling Kremstal DAC Reserve Leiten 2015
92 Riesling Kremstal DAC Reserve Leiten 2014
Medium yellow with silver highlights. Inviting yellow peach, greengage plum and blossom honey. Medium complexity,

white currant and refreshing acidity. Sweetly extracted fruit remains on the mineral aftertaste.

91 Riesling Kremstal DAC Reserve Leiten 2013

(92–94) Riesling Kremstal DAC Reserve
Goldberg 2015
92 Riesling Kremstal DAC Reserve Goldberg 2014
92 Riesling Kremstal DAC Reserve Goldberg 2013

91 Riesling Kremstal DAC Neubergen 2015
90 Riesling Kremstal DAC Neubergen 2014
90 Riesling Kremstal DAC Neubergen 2013

(88–90) Chardonnay Mugeln Reserve 2015
90 Chardonnay Mugeln Reserve 2013

89 Sauvignon Blanc Eichbühel 2013

90 Zweigelt Reserve 2014
88 Zweigelt Reserve 2013

89 Pinot Noir Süßenberg Reserve 2011

92 Diana Große Reserve 2011 ZW/SL/ME
92 Diana Große Reserve 2011 ZW/SL/ME

89 Diana 2013 ZW/ME/CS
90 Diana 2012 ZW/ME/CS
90 Diana 2011 ZW/ME/CS

94 Neuburger Trockenbeerenauslese
Therese 2013

Weingut Müller-Großmann

3511 Furth-Palt, Lindengasse 25
T: +43 (2732) 83146, F: +43 (2732) 83146 4, M: +43 (664) 2165443
office@mueller-grossmann.at, www.mueller-grossmann.at

Contact Person: Marlies Müller
Production: n. a. (100 % white)
Hectares: 10
Fairs: VieVinum, ProWein
Distribution partners: J, S, CDN, CH, B, RC, DE, FIN, CZ, NL, N, USA

Helma and Marlies Müller-Grossmann cultivate ten hectares of vines at the foot of the Göttweig mountain in the historic wine region of Kremstal. Their primary goal is to provide high-quality, sustainable enjoyment. The foundation for their work lies in vines that are cared for according to the demands of the climate, the soil and attributes of each vineyard. The final polish is given in the cellar where wines further evolve their own unique characteristics and benefit from the inimitable signature of Helma and Marlies Müller-Grossmann. The complexity of their wines is derived from the diversity of soils and the high temperature differences between day and night. The majority of the estate's plots are found either on loess or on light, fertile, rocky soils. Pronounced fruitiness and crystal clear varietal character are the distinguishing attributes of the Müller-Grossmann wines. Next to the regional classics, Grüner Veltliner and Riesling, their efforts are also dedicated to Burgundian varieties, a rosé from Zweigelt, Muskateller (Muscat), and a sparkling "MG Brut".

(91–93) Grüner Veltliner Kremstal DAC Reserve
 Alte Reben 2015
92 Grüner Veltliner Kremstal DAC Reserve
 Alte Reben 2014
Pale green yellow with silver highlights. Yellow apple, papaya, peach and delicate floral nuances comprise a fascinating bouquet. Plenty of finesse is demonstrated with a juicy backbone of acidity balanced with sweet tropical fruit notes. Papaya and orange zest on the finish. Good potential for further development.
91 Grüner Veltliner Kremstal DAC Reserve
 Alte Reben 2013

(91–93) Grüner Veltliner Kremstal DAC Reserve
 Silberbichl 2015

89 Grüner Veltliner Kremstal DAC Hochrain 2015
90 Grüner Veltliner Kremstal DAC Hochrain 2014
88 Grüner Veltliner Kremstal DAC Hochrain 2013

(92–94) Riesling Kremstal DAC Reserve
 Steinbühel 2015
91 Riesling Kremstal DAC Reserve
 Steinbiegl 2014
92 Riesling Kremstal DAC Reserve
 Steinbiegl 2013

90 Riesling Kremstal DAC Steiner Point 2015
89 Riesling Kremstal DAC Steiner Point 2014
90 Riesling Kremstal DAC Steiner Point 2013

88 Weißburgunder 2014

91 MG Brut 2013
88 MG Brut 2012
89 MG BRUT

★★★★
Wein-Gut Nigl

3541 Senftenberg, Kirchenberg 1
T: +43 (2719) 2609, F: +43 (2719) 2609 4
info@weingutnigl.at, www.weingutnigl.at

Winemaker and Contact Person: Martin Nigl
Production: n. a. (90 % white, 9 % red, 1 % sweet)
Hectares: 25
Fairs: ProWein, VieVinum
Distribution partners: on request

The Nigl Winery is situated at the entrance to the hamlet of Senftenberg in the Kirchengasse alley at the foot of the Burgberg. The winery possesses over 25 vineyard hectares in premium Kremstal sites. The vineyards are distributed between Senftenberg, Rehberg, and Krems. The most important sites are Pellingen, planted with Riesling and Grüner Veltliner, and Hochäcker, planted with Riesling. The vineyards are located in Senftenberg, Rehberg, and in Krems. The flagship series at Nigl carries the label "Privat". The fruit for both "Privat" bottlings is sourced from old vines in the Senftenberger Pellingen vineyard. Growing in meagre primary rock soils are 40-year-old vines that bring very small grape yields of exceptional quality. Vintage for vintage, two great wines of striking concentration and mineral character that are worthy of extended bottle ageing are vinified.

**(93–95) Grüner Veltliner Kremstal DAC Reserve
Senftenberger Pellingen Privat 1 ÖTW 2015**
**94 Grüner Veltliner Kremstal DAC Reserve
Senftenberger Pellingen Privat 1 ÖTW 2014**
Medium green-yellow. Highly attractive aromas and flavours of apricot, mango, pleasant blossom honey and herbal spice. Complex and juicy. Apple, salty minerals and a touch of lemon remain long on the finish. Plenty of finesse and ageing potential.
**93 Grüner Veltliner Kremstal DAC Reserve
Senftenberger Pellingen Privat 1 ÖTW 2013**
**(92–94) Grüner Veltliner Kremstal DAC Reserve
Rehberger Zwetl 2015**

**(92–94) Grüner Veltliner Kremstal DAC Reserve
Herzstück vom Kirchenberg 2015**
**93 Grüner Veltliner Kremstal DAC Reserve
Herzstück vom Kirchenberg 2013**
**94 Grüner Veltliner Kremstal DAC Reserve
Herzstück vom Kirchenberg 2012**

**93 Grüner Veltliner Kremstal DAC
Alte Reben 2015**
**93 Grüner Veltliner Kamptal DAC Reserve
Alte Rebe 2014**
**93 Grüner Veltliner Kremstal DAC Reserve
Alte Reben 2012**

**92 Grüner Veltliner Kremstal DAC
Senftenberger Piri 2015**
91 Grüner Veltliner Senftenberger Piri 2014

**(94–96) Riesling Kremstal DAC Reserve
Senftenberger Pellingen
Privat 1 ÖTW 2015**
**94 Riesling Kremstal DAC Pellingen
Privat 1 ÖTW 2014**
Medium green-yellow with silver highlights. Ripe peach, subtle pineapple and passion fruit over elegant honey nuances and abundant minerals. An elegant, sweet, juicy texture

and fine acidity structure. Nuances of apricot on the finish. Will benefit from further bottle maturation.

94 Riesling Kremstal DAC Reserve
Senftenberger Pellingen Privat 1 ÖTW 2013

(95–97) Riesling Kremstal DAC Reserve
Rehberger Goldberg 2015
94 Riesling Kremstal DAC Reserve
Rehberger Goldberg 2014
92 Riesling Kremstal DAC Reserve
Rehberger Goldberg 2013

(92–94) Riesling Kremstal DAC Reserve
Hochäcker 1 ÖTW 2015
93 Riesling Kremstal DAC Reserve
Hochäcker 1 ÖTW 2013

92 Riesling Kremstal DAC
Senftenberger Piri 2015
92 Riesling Kremstal DAC
Senftenberger Piri 2014
92 Riesling Kremstal DAC
Senftenberger Piri 2012

91 Riesling Dornleiten 2014
91 Riesling Kremstal DAC Dornleiten 2012

90 Gelber Muskateller 2015
90 Gelber Muskateller 2014

90 Sauvignon Blanc 2015
89 Sauvignon Blanc 2014
91 Sauvignon Blanc 2013

Weingut Familie Proidl

3541 Senftenberg, Oberer Markt 5
T: +43 (2719) 2458, F: +43 (2719) 2458 4
weingut@proidl.com, www.proidl.com

Winemaker and Contact Person: Franz Proidl
Production: 75.000 bottles (90 % white, 5 % red, 5 % sweet)
Hectares: 20
Fairs: VieVinum
Distribution partners: CH, SGP, DE, CZ, NL, GB, N, USA

Coming from the north, Senftenberg is the first wine village in the Kremstal wine region. Just as in the Wachau, the forests and deep, rocky river gorges of the Waldviertel have a strong influence on the climate. The clash of cold air from the Bohemian Massif and the warm air masses from the Danube area combine with the weathered granite soils to create ideal preconditions for wines of distinctive character. The greatest capital of this winery is the extremely steep vineyards overlooking the Krems River. A prime example is the Ehrenfels vineyard, which after years of hard toil to restore it from overgrowth and the encroaching forest, now yields exquisite Riesling and Grüner Veltliner. The mica-schist slopes of the Pfeningberg vineyard and the Gfoehler gneiss slopes of the Hockäcker vineyard have similar histories and are the origins of highly mineral wines from Grüner Veltliner, Riesling, Traminer and Gelber Muskateller (Muscat Blanc à petits grains). The winery typically harvests late and the quality is enhanced by manual selection. Abstinence from cultured yeasts is practiced as far as possible and slow fermentation of up to six months is the rule. The wines from Franz Proidl never appear at young wine premiers, for vinification is aimed at the long term and the wines benefit tremendously from unhurried vinification and later release. Highest accolades and scores testify to the stunning quality and reliability of these concentrated, mineral wines from the steepest slopes of the Kremstal. Franz's son, Patrick - of the 10th Proidl generation - enjoys the best perspectives for the future and is now embarking on his own exploration of the magic of the Senftenberg sites. The first results are a Riesling and Grüner Veltliner fermented in 500-litre barrels called "Generation X". The stunning assortment of mountain wines is completed with red wines from the varieties Zweigelt, Merlot and Cabernet Sauvignon.

94 Riesling Kremstal DAC Reserve
Ehrenfels 1 ÖTW 2014
Medium green yellow. Smoky minerals and orange zest mingle with subtle vineyard peach and discreet tropical fruit nuances. Complexly structured with juicy acidity, elegantly lifting fruit and abundant minerals. Delicate apple and fresh mandarin linger on the aftertaste. Good potential for further development

93 Riesling Kremstal DAC Reserve
Ehrenfels 1 ÖTW 2013
94 Riesling Kremstal DAC Reserve
Senftenberger Ehrenfels 1 ÖTW 2012

92 Riesling Generation X 2014
93 Riesling Senftenberg Generation X 2013
Medium green-yellow. Ripe peach and a touch of yellow apple and blood orange mingle with spicy herbs and delicate yellow sponge cake notes. Juicy, refreshing acidity elegantly highlights the fruitiness on the palate. Peach, apricot and citrus notes linger long on the finish of this complex food wine.

91 Riesling Senftenberger Rameln
»Generation X« 2012

(92–94) Riesling Kremstal DAC Reserve
Hochäcker 1 ÖTW 2015
92 Riesling Kremstal DAC Reserve
Hochäcker 1 ÖTW 2014
92 Riesling Kremstal DAC Reserve
Hochäcker 1 ÖTW 2013

92 Riesling Kremstal DAC Reserve
Pfeningberg 1 ÖTW 2013
93 Riesling Kremstal DAC Reserve
Senftenberger Pfeningberg 1 ÖTW 2012

91 Riesling Kremstal DAC
   Senftenberger Rameln 2015
89 Riesling Kremstal DAC Rameln 2013
91 Riesling Kremstal DAC
   Senftenberger Rameln 2012

94 Grüner Veltliner Kremstal DAC Reserve
   Ehrenfels 1 ÖTW 2014
93 Grüner Veltliner Kremstal DAC Reserve
   Ehrenfels 1 ÖTW 2013
95 Grüner Veltliner Kremstal DAC Reserve
   Senftenberger Ehrenfels 1 ÖTW 2012

95 Grüner Veltliner Generation X 2014
92 Grüner Veltliner Senftenberg
   Generation X 2013

92 Grüner Veltliner Kremstal DAC Reserve
   Pellingen 1 ÖTW 2013
93 Grüner Veltliner Kremstal DAC Reserve
   Senftenberger Pellingen Alte Reben 1 ÖTW 2012

90 Grüner Veltliner Kremstal DAC Burg 2015
90 Grüner Veltliner Kremstal DAC Burg 2014
89 Grüner Veltliner Senftenberger »Burg« 2012

89 Grüner Veltliner Kremstal DAC Rameln 2013

90 Grüner Veltliner Gärtling 2012

90 Gelber Muskateller 2015
89 Gelber Muskateller 2014

92 Gelber Traminer 2012

95 Riesling Auslese Rameln 2014

98 Riesling Trockenbeerenauslese 2012

94 Traminer Auslese 2014

92 Riesling »Proidl spricht Deutsch« 2013

★★★★
Weingut Salomon Undhof

3500 Stein/Donau, Undstraße 10
T: +43 (2732) 83226, F: +43 (2732) 83226 78
office@salomonwines.com, www.salomonwines.com

Winemaker: Dr. Bertold Salomon
Contact Person: Dr. Bertold and Gertrud Salomon
Production: 140.000 bottles (100 % white)
Hectares: 30
Fairs: ProWein
Distribution partners: AUS, IL, I, S, CDN, SGP, BG, LV, RC, LT, DK, L, EST, T, NZ, CZ, NL, GB, USA, PL

It was exactly 225 years ago that the Salomon family became owners of the former monastery vineyards. The monks had chosen prime parcels in the very best vineyards, which have now been in the Salomon family hands for seven generations. These "grand cru" vineyards overlooking the Danube River are the origin of famous wines such as the "Undhof Kögl", "Wachtberg", and "Lindberg". The soils are comprised predominantly of primary rock types such as gneiss, granite, and schist. In some vineyard terraces, also loess deposits are found. In 1930, Fritz Salomon, Bert's father, was the first winemaker to bottle his own wines in the greater Wachau and Krems region. Today, Bert Salomon's Riesling and Grüner Veltliner wines excel with brilliant, crystal clear mineral expression. Extraordinary character, balance and harmony distinguish the style of the Salomon Undhof wines. The wines conceived for early enjoyment are light and fragrant, while the great growths evolve increasing complexity and nuance with bottle maturation.

The bridge between nature and human intervention is achieved with manual vineyard cultivation and the employment of the simple principle of gravity in the wine cellar. Vineyards are cultivated sustainably according to the regulations of Controlled Integrated Production. The resulting Kremstal DAC wines reflect the unmistakable terroir with their inimitable elegance, mineral character, and clear expression fruit. Salomon-Undhof is famed for elegant wines with incredible ageing potential. More than half of the 30 vineyard hectares are planted with Riesling, the remainder with Grüner Veltliner and a small portion of Gelber Traminer (a rare regional mutation of Gewürztraminer). Bert and Gertrud Salomon complete their assortment of white wines from Stein an der Donau with classy Australian red wines from their Salomon Estate in Finnis River, and most recently, from a joint venture called Salomon & Andrew in New Zealand. In its October 2013 issue, the highly respected Wine & Spirits Magazine in the USA rated Salomon-Undhof among the 100 best wineries in the world.

(93–95) Grüner Veltliner Kremstal DAC Reserve Lindberg 1 ÖTW 2015
93 Grüner Veltliner Kremstal DAC Reserve Lindberg 2014
Pale green-yellow with silver highlights. Fresh yellow pear and Golden Delicious apple over a background of fresh meadow herbs. Complex structure with pleasant extract sweetness lifted by fine, balanced acidity. Lemon, minerals and subtle blossom honey on the aftertaste.
94 Grüner Veltliner Kremstal DAC Reserve Lindberg 1 ÖTW 2012

(92–94) Grüner Veltliner Kremstal DAC Reserve Von Stein 2015
92 Grüner Veltliner Kremstal DAC Reserve Von Stein 2014
93 Grüner Veltliner Kremstal DAC Reserve Von Stein 2013

(91–93) Grüner Veltliner Kremstal DAC Reserve Kremser Tor Alte Reben 2015
91 Grüner Veltliner Kremstal DAC Reserve Kremser Tor Alte Reben 2014
92 Grüner Veltliner Kremstal DAC Reserve Kremser Tor Alte Reben 2013

(91–93) Grüner Veltliner Kremstal DAC
           Wachtberg 1 ÖTW 2015
90 Grüner Veltliner Kremstal DAC
     Wachtberg 1 ÖTW 2014
92 Grüner Veltliner Kremstal DAC Reserve
     Wachtberg 1 ÖTW 2013

91 Grüner Veltliner Kremstal DAC
     Wieden & Berg 2015
91 Grüner Veltliner Kremstal DAC
     Wieden & Berg 2014
92 Grüner Veltliner Kremstal DAC
     Wieden & Berg 2013

89 Grüner Veltliner Kremstal DAC Messwein 2015
89 Grüner Veltliner Kremstal DAC
     Franziskus Messwein 2014
90 Grüner Veltliner Kremstal DAC
     Franziskus Messwein 2013

88 Grüner Veltliner Hochterrassen 2014
88 Grüner Veltliner Hochterrassen 2013

(94–96) Riesling Kremstal DAC Reserve
           Pfaffenberg 1 ÖTW 2015
93 Riesling Kremstal DAC Reserve
     Pfaffenberg 1 ÖTW 2014
Pale green-yellow with silver highlights. Peach and blossom
honey with lime zest in the background. Complex, with
sweet juicy orange fruit nicely countered with racy acidity.
White vineyard peach on the aftertaste. Good potential for
further development.
94 Riesling Kremstal DAC Reserve Pfaffenberg
     »Metternich & Salomon« 1 ÖTW 2013

(94–96) Riesling Kremstal DAC Reserve
           Steiner Kögl 1 ÖTW 2015

(91–93) Riesling Kremstal DAC
           Undhof Kögl 1 ÖTW 2015
91 Riesling Kremstal DAC
     Undhof Kögl 1 ÖTW 2014
91 Riesling Kremstal DAC
     Undhof Kögl 1 ÖTW 2013

(91–93) Riesling Kremstal DAC Reserve
           Steiner Tor Alte Reben 2015
92 Riesling Kremstal DAC Reserve
     Steiner Tor Urgestein Alte Reben 2014
91 Riesling Kremstal DAC Reserve
     Steiner Tor Alte Reben 2013

90 Riesling Kremstal DAC Steinterrassen 2015
90 Riesling Kremstal DAC Steinterrassen 2014
90 Riesling Kremstal DAC Stein.Terrassen 2013

90 Riesling Alma 2013
92 Riesling Alma 2012

90 Gelber Muskateller 2014
89 Gelber Muskateller 2012

92 Gelber Traminer Wildrosen 2012

94 Gelber Traminer Noble Reserve 2011

91 Sekt Rosé Brut Nature 2013
90 Brut Nature Rosé 2012

92 Riesling Beerenauslese 2009

Weingut Josef Schmid

3552 Stratzing, Obere Hauptstraße 38
T: +43 (2719) 8288, F: +43 (2719) 8288 18
weingut@j-schmid.at, www.j-schmid.at

Winemaker: Josef Schmid
Contact Person: Irene Schmid
Production: 100.000 bottles (90 % white, 10 % red)
Hectares: 18
Fairs: VieVinum
Distribution partners: CH, B, D

The attractive Schmid family winery is situated in the little village of Stratzing on a high plateau between Krems and Langenlois. The vineyards are distributed around Stratzing, on mountain slope terraces near Senftenberg, and the city of Krems. Family Schmid has both loess soils and mineral-rich primary rock at their disposal, which make it possible to produce a broad assortment of white varietal wines grown in ideally suited plots. Eighteen hectares of vines are cultivated according to Controlled Integrated Production regulations. The goal is to produce elegant, fruit-driven wines in the dry late-harvest category. The surprisingly inexpensive wines of Josef Schmid have won numerous competitions and are a favourite on the wine lists of many top restaurants in Austria.

(91–93) Grüner Veltliner Kremstal DAC Reserve Kremser Gebling 1 ÖTW 2015
92 Grüner Veltliner Kremstal DAC Reserve Kremser Gebling 1 ÖTW 2014
Pale green-yellow with silver highlights. Subtle tropical fruit aromas and flavours reminiscent of pineapple and mango mingle with a touch of blossom honey an subtle orange zest nuances. Juicy, elegant and well structured. Yellow apple and light salty components on the finish. The versatile accompaniment to food also has good ageing potential.
92 Grüner Veltliner Kremstal DAC Reserve Kremser Gebling 1 ÖTW 2013

92 Grüner Veltliner Kremstal DAC Reserve Alte Reben 2015
91 Grüner Veltliner Kremstal DAC Reserve Alte Reben 2014
91 Grüner Veltliner Kremstal DAC Reserve Kremser Alte Reben 2013

(93–95) Grüner Veltliner Kremstal DAC Reserve Kremser Frechau 1 ÖTW 2015

93 Grüner Veltliner Kremstal DAC Reserve Perval 2013
93 Grüner Veltliner Kremstal DAC Reserve Perval 2012

91 Grüner Veltliner Kremstal DAC Kremser Weingärten 2015
89 Grüner Veltliner Kremstal DAC Kremser Weingärten 2013
91 Grüner Veltliner Kremstal DAC Kremser Weingärten 2012

91 Grüner Veltliner Kremstal DAC Pfarrweingarten 2014

(91–93) Riesling Kremstal DAC Reserve Stratzinger Sunogeln 1 ÖTW 2015
93 Riesling Kremstal DAC Reserve Stratzinger Sunogeln 1 ÖTW 2014
Pale green-yellow. Ripe vineyard peach and apricot with blossom honey, herbs, spice and a touch of grapefruit. JJuicy and elegant acidity refreshes complex sweet fruit. Light extract sweetness and plenty of fruit on the long finish. Very good potential for further development.
93 Riesling Kremstal DAC Reserve Sunogeln 1 ÖTW 2013

93 Riesling Kremstal DAC Reserve Steiner Pfaffenberg 2015
92 Riesling Kremstal DAC Reserve Steiner Pfaffenberg 2013
93 Riesling Kremstal DAC Reserve Steiner Pfaffenberg 2012

90 Riesling Kremstal DAC vom Urgestein 2014

89 Chardonnay Kremser Kerschbaum 2014

★ ★ ★
Weingut Stadt Krems
3500 Krems, Stadtgraben 11
T: +43 (2732) 801441, F: +43 (2732) 801442
office@weingutstadtkrems.at, www.weingutstadtkrems.at

Winemaker: Fritz Miesbauer and Peter Rethaller
Contact Person: Fritz Miesbauer
Production: 200.000 bottles (100 % white); **Hectares:** 31
Certified: Sustainable Austria
Fairs: VieVinum, ProWein, Vinexpo
Distribution partners: AUS, J, S, B, CDN, CH, BG, LV, DK, L, DE, EST, FIN, NL, GB, N, USA, PL

With a history of over 550 years, the municipal Weingut Stadt Krems is among the oldest wine producers in Austria and also in Europe. Fritz Miesbauer took the helm of the winery in 2003 and together with a young and ambitious team has turned a basically satisfactory but stagnant winery into a model enterprise. Through an ambitious revitalization program in the vineyard and in the winemaking facility, it has been possible to attain a clear profile and produce regionally authentic, high-quality wines in a surprisingly short period of time. Production concentrates fully on Grüner Veltliner and Riesling (99%) planted in 31 hectares in the best sites within the city limits of Krems. The best sites have been ordained "1. Lage" (grand cru) by the vintners association "Traditionsweingütern Österreich": Kögl, Grillenparz and Wachtberg. The dry, authentic Kremstal DAC and Kremstal Reserve DAC wines are sold exclusively in specialty shops and restaurants. The export share is an impressive 60%. The winery can be particularly proud of the recognition they have received for their wines from Wine Spectator who have listed their wines in their Top 100 list twice. Falstaff Magazine awarded the 2014 Riesling Grillenparz 95 points in the Falstaff Weinguide 2015/16. The rise to become one of the leading wine producers in Kremstal has been achieved in a very short time indeed.

(93–95) Riesling Kremstal DAC Reserve Steiner Ried Grillenparz 1 ÖTW 2015
95 Riesling Kremstal DAC Reserve Steiner Ried Grillenparz 1 ÖTW 2014
Medium green-yellow with silver highlights. Attractive stone fruit reminiscent of white vineyard peach mingles with blossom honey, orange zest and mineral notes. Full-bodied and juicy with sweet extract and elegant spice. Well balanced with lovely acidity, plenty of finesse and superb length - everything that a truly great, dry Riesling should have.

92 Riesling Kremstal DAC Reserve Grillenparz 1 ÖTW 2013

94 Riesling Exceptional Grillenparz 2014
Pale green-yellow. Initially somewhat restrained, but soon releases elegant peach notes, a touch of mandarin zest and honey nuances. Complex and juicy with delicate sweetness buffered by vibrant acidity. Delicate pineapple and apricot linger on the long finish. Already incredibly seductive in its youth.

(91–93) Riesling Kremstal DAC Reserve Schieferterrassen 2015
93 Riesling Kremstal DAC Reserve Schieferterrassen 2014

92 Riesling Kremstal DAC Steinterrassen 2015
90 Riesling Kremstal DAC Steinterrassen 2014

(92–94) Grüner Veltliner Kremstal DAC Reserve Kremser Ried Wachtberg 1 ÖTW 2015
93 Grüner Veltliner Kremstal DAC Reserve Kremser Ried Wachtberg 1 ÖTW 2014
92 Grüner Veltliner Kremstal DAC Reserve Wachtberg 1 ÖTW 2013

(91–93) Grüner Veltliner Kremstal DAC Reserve Stein 2015
92 Grüner Veltliner Kremstal DAC Reserve Stein 2014
90 Grüner Veltliner Kremstal DAC Reserve Stein 2013

91 Grüner Veltliner Kremstal DAC Kremser Ried Weinzierlberg 2015
90 Grüner Veltliner Kremstal DAC Weinzierlberg 2014
89 Grüner Veltliner Kremstal DAC Weinzierlberg 2013

89 Grüner Veltliner Kremstal DAC 2015
89 Grüner Veltliner Kremstal DAC 2014

★ ★ ★
Weingut Stift Göttweig

3511 Furth bei Göttweig, Göttweig 1
T: +43 (2732) 801440, F: +43 (2732) 801442
office@weingutstiftgoettweig.at, www.weingutstiftgoettweig.at

Winemaker: Fritz Miesbauer and Peter Rethaller
Contact Person: Fritz Miesbauer and Franz-Josef Gansberger
Production: 120.000 bottles (90 % white, 10 % red); **Hectares:** 26
Certified: Sustainable Austria
Fairs: VieVinum, ProWein, Vinexpo
Distribution partners: AUS, J, S, CDN, CH, B, SGP, DE, FIN, NL, N, GB, USA, PL

O n the southern bank of the Danube River, directly opposite the wine city of Krems and right on top of Mount Göttweig, lies the Benedictine Abbey of Göttweig. The monastery complex, which was built according to plans of the well-known architect Johann Lucas von Hildebrandt, is famous well beyond the borders of Austria. The impressive baroque imperial staircase with its magnificent ceiling fresco, created by Paul Troger, makes a visit well worthwhile. The capsules of all bottles from the resurrected wine estate are adorned with a miniature image of this work of art. Benedictine monks settled at this location as early as 1083. The wines of the abbey were already famed for their quality by the 16th century and very popular with Austrian nobility as well as the troops of the imperial army. In more recent times general manager Fritz Miesbauer has injected a breath of fresh air into all operations of the venerable wine estate. Already having made a name for himself at home and abroad more than a decade ago for his work at the Freie Weingärtner Wachau cooperative, he was presented with Sweden's Winemaker of the Year award in 1996, when only 27 years old. At Göttweig he has been in charge of vineyard management, winemaking and marketing since 2006 and is supported by an able team. A particular mention must go to sales director Franz Josef Gansberger, who is responsible for the restaurant and wine trade. The most recent vintage once again serves to demonstrate the great potential of the wines of Stift Göttweig.

(92–94) Riesling Kremstal DAC Reserve Steiner Ried Pfaffenberg 1 ÖTW 2015

(91–93) Riesling Kremstal DAC Reserve Further Ried Silberbichl 1 ÖTW 2015
93 Riesling Kremstal DAC Reserve Further Ried Silberbichl 1 ÖTW 2014
Medium green-yellow. Attractive nuances of ripe vineyard peach and passion fruit over a subtle background of blossom honey. Complex peach and apricot combine with extract sweetness and are elegantly carried by lovely acidity. Plenty of finesse, a long finish Plenty of finesse, a long finish, and dependable ageing potential.
92 Riesling Kremstal DAC Reserve Silberbichl 1 ÖTW 2013

90 Riesling Kremstal DAC Göttweiger Berg 2015
89 Riesling Kremstal DAC Göttweiger Berg 2014
89 Riesling Kremstal DAC Göttweiger Berg 2013

(92–94) Grüner Veltliner Kremstal DAC Reserve Further Ried Gottschelle 1 ÖTW 2015
92 Grüner Veltliner Kremstal DAC Reserve Further Ried Gottschelle 1 ÖTW 2014
Medium green-yellow- Yellow apple, honeydew melon, and subtle wild herbs. Elegantly textured with sweet nuances of papaya fruit and a well integrated curve of acidity. A versatile accompaniment to food.
92 Grüner Veltliner Kremstal DAC Reserve Gottschelle 1 ÖTW 2013

90 Grüner Veltliner Kremstal DAC Göttweiger Berg 2015
90 Grüner Veltliner Kremstal DAC Göttweiger Berg 2014
90 Grüner Veltliner Kremstal DAC Göttweiger Berg 2013

89 Grüner Veltliner Messwein 2015
89 Grüner Veltliner Messwein 2014
88 Grüner Veltliner Messwein 2013

92 Brut 2011

Weingut Türk

3552 Stratzing, Kirchengasse 16
T: +43 (2719) 28460, F: +43 (2719) 28460 4
info@weinguttuerk.at, www.weinguttuerk.at

Winemaker and Contact Person: Franz Türk
Production: n. a. (85 % white, 10 % red, 5 % sweet)
Hectares: 16
Fairs: ProWein, VieVinum
Distribution partners: CH, B, RC, DK, DE, EST, CZ, NL, GB, USA, IRL, PL

The Türk winery lies to the west of Vienna, in the idyllic wine village of Stratzing, some six kilometres north of Krems. The roots of this highly respected family winery go back to the 18th century. The current estate was acquired in 1836 and was gradually expanded by each following generation. The estate's main focus is indigenous varieties with Grüner Veltliner accounting for 75% of the area under vine. Türk conscientiously applies gentle vinification and maturation techniques to achieve his goal of producing concentrated and vibrant wines with typical regional character. The character of the wines indeed represents a true reflection of the soil and microclimate of the Kremstal wine region. An insider's tip is certainly the award-winning sweet wine specialties of the estate. As to be expected, the current ice wines from Grüner Veltliner and Zweigelt are particularly impressive.

94 »Veltiner 333« 2013
Brilliant golden yellow. A very inviting bouquet displays elegant nuances of ripe quince and orange zest, accompanied by pleasant blossom honey and a touch of rhubarb. Complex, juicy pineapple notes and litchi compote are enhanced by a fine acidity structure. Yellow apple lingers on the long finish of this multifaceted accompaniment to food.

92 Grüner Veltliner Kremstal DAC Reserve
    Kremser Sandgrube 2015
93 Grüner Veltliner Kremstal DAC Reserve
    Kremser Sandgrube 2014
Medium yellow with silver highlights. Aromas and flavours

of delicate, sweet stone fruits reminiscent of apricot and white vineyard peach with a trace of blossom honey. Refreshing acidity structure and good complexity provide plenty of finesse. Lemon salt lingers on the long finish. Dependable ageing potential.

92 Grüner Veltliner Kremstal DAC Reserve
    Kremser Sandgrube 2013

(92–94) Grüner Veltliner Kremstal DAC Reserve
    Thurnerberg 1 ÖTW 2015
92 Grüner Veltliner Kremstal DAC Reserve
    Kremser Thurnerberg 1 ÖTW 2014
92 Grüner Veltliner Kremstal DAC Reserve
    Kremser Thurnerberg 1 ÖTW 2013

(92–94) Grüner Veltliner Kremstal DAC Reserve
    Frechau 1 ÖTW 2015
94 Grüner Veltliner Kremstal DAC Reserve
    Kremser Frechau 1 ÖTW 2013
93 Grüner Veltliner Kremstal DAC Reserve
    Kremser Frechau 2012

91 Grüner Veltliner Kremstal DAC
    Kremser Weinberge 2015
89 Grüner Veltliner Kremstal DAC
    Kremser Weinberge 2014
90 Grüner Veltliner Kremstal DAC
    Kremser Weinberge 2013

91 Grüner Veltliner Kremstal DAC
    Vom Urgestein 2015
90 Grüner Veltliner Kremstal DAC
    Vom Urgestein 2014
90 Grüner Veltliner Kremstal DAC
    Vom Urgestein 2013

89 Grüner Veltliner »Der Leichte« 2015

(91–93) Grüner Veltliner Edition Witzigmann
    »Mein Grüner Veltliner« 2015

(91–93) Riesling Kremstal DAC Reserve
      Kremser Wachtberg 1 ÖTW 2015
92 Riesling Kremstal DAC Reserve
      Kremser Wachtberg 1 ÖTW 2014
92 Riesling Kremstal DAC Reserve
      Kremser Wachtberg 1 ÖTW 2013

92 Riesling Kremstal DAC Kremser
      Weinzierlberg 2015
91 Riesling Kremstal DAC Kremser
      Weinzierlberg 2014
92 Riesling Kremstal DAC Kremser
      Weinzierlberg 2012

89 Gelber Muskateller 2015

89 Chardonnay 2015

91 Cabernet Sauvignon Rosé Brut Nature 2013

(92–94) Blauer Zweigelt Eiswein 2015
93 Blauer Zweigelt Eiswein 2014

(93–95) Grüner Veltliner Eiswein 2015
92 Grüner Veltliner Eiswein 2012

93 Gelber Muskateller Eiswein 2012

(93–95) Gelber Muskateller Beerenauslese 2015
92 Gelber Muskateller Beerenauslese 2012

Weingut Petra Unger

3511 Furth/Göttweig, Zellergraben 245
T: +43 (676) 848622822, F: +43 (2732) 76801
office@ungerwein.at, www.ungerwein.at

Winemaker and Contact Person: Petra Unger
Production: n. a. (75 % white, 20 % red, 5 % sweet)
Hectares: 11
Fairs: ProWein, VieVinum
Distribution partners: S, CDN, CH, B, SK, DK, DE, FIN, CZ, NL, N, GB, USA, PL

Petra Unger's wines tell a story of great passion and dedicated handcraftsmanship. Her 11 vineyard hectares are distributed on both sides of the Danube River right at the gates to the Wachau. The dry stacked stone walls that brace the steep primary rock terraces of the Gaisberg and Hinters Kirchl vineyards are a typical feature of the regional landscape and they also help store the warmth of the day that is so advantageous for Unger's elegant, mineral Rieslings. The view from here sweeps over the Danube River and the sun-drenched slopes of her Gottschelle and Oberfeld vineyards at the foot of the Benedictine monastery Stift Göttweig. Nimble "Ziesel" ground squirrels play among the vines – testimony to the respectful ecological philosophy practiced here. Petra Unger strives to bring the unadulterated character of the region into the wine glass to provide consumers the purest enjoyment possible. The temperature-regulating Danube River, cool evening fall winds, and warm Pannonian influences provide ideal preconditions for her expressive, fresh white wines from her predominant variety Grüner Veltliner, Riesling and Sauvignon Blanc as well as for elegant, cool, fruity red wines like Pinot Noir and Zweigelt. As a founding member of the prestigious vintners association Traditionsweingüter Österreich, Petra Unger is proud that her award-winning wines carry the "1er ÖTW" vineyard classification. She also takes a look over the rim of her own plate through the group "11 Women & Their Wines". Unger and vintner colleague Josef Edlinger began working together in cooperation in 2010, but each still remains responsible for their own wines and their own inimitable signature. That the Unger wines are distributed in numerous countries around the world is a fulfilling confirmation for the passionate vintner.

(92–94) Grüner Veltliner Kremstal DAC Reserve
Oberfeld Alte Reben 1 ÖTW 2015
93 Grüner Veltliner Kremstal DAC Reserve
Oberfeld Alte Reben 1 ÖTW 2014
Pale green-yellow with silver highlights. Aromas and flavours of yellow apple, honeydew melon and peach over a background of peppery spice and orange zest. Juicy, elegant, tightly woven, elegantly integrated acidity. Yellow apple, sweet extract and minerals on the long finish. Plenty of finesse and superb ageing potential.
93 Grüner Veltliner Kremstal DAC Reserve
Oberfeld Alte Reben 1 ÖTW 2013

(91–93) Grüner Veltliner Kremstal DAC Reserve
Gottschelle 1 ÖTW 2015
92 Grüner Veltliner Kremstal DAC Reserve
Gottschelle 2014
91 Grüner Veltliner Kremstal DAC Reserve
Gottschelle 1 ÖTW 2013

(89–91) Grüner Veltliner Kremstal DAC
Zieselrain 2015
90 Grüner Veltliner Kremstal DAC Zieselrain 2014
89 Grüner Veltliner Kremstal DAC Zieselrain 2013

(92–94) Riesling Kremstal DAC Reserve
Gaisberg 1 ÖTW 2015
91 Riesling Kremstal DAC Reserve
Gaisberg 1 ÖTW 2014
92 Riesling Kremstal DAC Reserve
Gaisberg 1 ÖTW 2013

(90–92) Riesling Hinters Kirchl 2015
89 Riesling Hinters Kirchl 2014
89 Riesling Kremstal DAC Reserve
Hinters Kirchl 2013

(88–90) Gelber Muskateller Innausen 2015

88 Sauvignon Blanc Obere Point 2014

★ ★ ★
Weingut Rainer Wess

3500 Krems, Sandgrube 24
T: +43 (2732) 72389, F: +43 (2732) 72389 99
info@weingut-wess.at, www.weingut-wess.at

Winemaker and Contact Person: Rainer Wess
Production: 90.000 bottles (100 % white)
Hectares: 7 + 8
Fairs: ProWein, VieVinum, Vinexpo
Distribution partners: I, RUS, J, CDN, CH, B, SRB, LV, SK, BG, DK, DE,
CZ, F, NL, GB, PE, USA, PL

Primary rock meets schist, Loibenberg meats Kögl, and Kremstal meets Wachau. Rainer Wess produces wines from both regions. The winery itself is located in the Sandgrube vineyard on the periphery of Krems. The majority of the 15 vineyard hectares are located in the Wachau in the Loibenberg vineyard slope or at the foot of the Loibenberg. Together with fruit from vineyards in Stein, Kögl and Pfaffenberg, and plots in the Krems vineyards, Weinzierlberg, this well-travelled winemaker produces a unique spectrum of wines that reflect the geological, climatic and geographic diversity of two prime wine regions. The enterprise began in the year 2003 when Wess leased his first vineyard plots on the Loibenberg slope. He quickly established a reputation for his own particular style: highly elegant wines with crystal clear precision in their expression of origin. To achieve this, he employs two varieties, Riesling and Grüner Veltliner, and strives to bring out their fullest potential. Light, fruit-driven wines find a place in his assortment just as do powerful, intense interpretations and an occasional sweet wine. In just over ten years, Rainer Wess has evolved from a garagist to a full-fledged member of the prestigious vintner association Österreichischen Traditionsweingüter and a respected protagonist of the Wachau. His faithful customers come from 20 countries and the number is growing.

**(92–94) Grüner Veltliner Kremstal DAC Reserve
Steiner Kögl 1 ÖTW 2015**
**92 Grüner Veltliner Kremstal DAC Reserve
Steiner Kögl 1 ÖTW 2014**
Medium green-yellow. Yellow apple, fresh meadow herbs and tropical fruit notes reminiscent of papaya and mango with a touch of orange zest. Full bodied yet elegant with a racy acidity and mineral structure. Stone fruit and salty minerals on the finish. Good potential for further development.
**92 Grüner Veltliner Kremstal DAC Reserve
Steiner Kögl 1 ÖTW 2012**

**(92–94) Grüner Veltliner Kremstal DAC Reserve
Kremser Weinzierlberg 2015**
**92 Grüner Veltliner Kremstal DAC Reserve
Weinzierlberg wurzelecht 1 ÖTW 2014**
Medium green yellow. Yellow apple and notes of apricot are backed with subtle blossom honey, anise and wild meadow herb nuances. Juicy refreshing acidity and abundant minerals lace tropical fruit notes and continue all the way through the spicy finish. Good ageing potential.

**(92–94) Grüner Veltliner Kremstal DAC Reserve
Steiner Pfaffenberg 1 ÖTW 2015**
**91 Grüner Veltliner Kremstal DAC Reserve
Steiner Pfaffenberg 1 ÖTW 2014**
**90 Grüner Veltliner Kremstal DAC Reserve
Pfaffenberg 1 ÖTW 2013**

(91–93) Grüner Veltliner Loibenberg 2015
91 Grüner Veltliner Loibenberg 2014
92 Grüner Veltliner Loibenberg 2013

**(90–92) Grüner Veltliner Kremstal DAC
Krems 2015**
91 Grüner Veltliner Stein-und-Krems 2013

89 Grüner Veltliner Kremstal DAC 2015

90 Grüner Veltliner Wachau 2015

(91–93) Riesling Kremstal DAC Reserve Steiner
    Pfaffenberg 1 ÖTW 2015
91 Riesling Kremstal DAC Reserve Steiner
    Pfaffenberg 1 ÖTW 2014
92 Riesling Kremstal DAC Reserve
    Pfaffenberg 1 ÖTW 2013

(92–94) Riesling Loibenberg 2015
90 Riesling Loibenberg 2014

89 Riesling Wachau 2015

(89–91) Riesling Kremstal DAC Krems 2015
90 Riesling Kremstal DAC Reserve
    Stein-und-Krems 2013

(91–93) Neuburger Selection 2015

Winzer Krems – Sandgrube 13

3500 Krems, Sandgrube 13
T: +43 (2732) 85511, F: +43 (2732) 85511 6
office@winzerkrems.at, www.winzerkrems.at, www.sandgrube13.at

Winemaker: Ing. Franz Arndorfer
Contact Person: Dir. Franz Ehrenleitner
Production: n. a. (70 % white, 30 % red)/ **Hectares:** 990
Fairs: ProWein, Alles für den Gast Salzburg and Wien, GAST Klagenfurt, fafga Innsbruck, AB
HOF – Wieselburg, Vinexpo, Anuga
Distribution partners: RUS, J, S, CDN, CH, B, SGP, LV, SK, BG, LT, DK, EST, T,
FIN, CZ, F, NL, N, GB, USA, IRL

SANDGRUBE 13 is without question one of the first addresses for Kremstal wine. Visitors are always very impressed by WINZER KREMS. This highly modern winery is set in the famous Kremser Sandgrube vineyard and the philosophy is directed towards the very highest quality. Grapes are harvested manually from selected top sites in the Kremstal region and are vinified in a spanking clean facility equipped with the most modern technology. The cooperative member vintners set the foundation for high quality in the vineyard. They are accompanied by a highly engaged team of quality consultants and customized programs for canopy management, soil management and plant protection. The visitor can experience this attention to detail first-hand during the wine experience tour "SANDGRUBE 13 wein.sinn". Eight stations on the tour offer an insider's view of winemaking at Winzer Krems. A special highlight is the "4D" film in the cellar cinema, which along with the latest 3D-technology also offers aromas and wind. The "Vinothekkeller Bründlgraben" was opened in 2014. This ensemble of seven formerly abandoned historic vineyard cellars in the immediate vicinity of the winery were carefully restored while respecting historic detail and thus rescued from complete deterioration. The romantic "Vinothekkeller Bründlgraben" can now be rented as a venue for special events. Since 2016, it is even an official venue for legal marriages. The vaulted rooms also offer the opportunity for clients to store wines in ideal conditions in individually locked spaces.

**(90–92) Riesling Kremstal DAC Reserve
Kremser Pfaffenberg 2015**
**92 Riesling Kremstal DAC Reserve
Kremser Pfaffenberg 2013**
Medium green-yellow. Nuances of peach and ripe pineapple with a touch of orange zest in the background. Juicy pineapple, peach and litchi are highlighted by a refreshing acidity structure. Sweetly extracted tropical fruit and orange on the long mineral finish. A complex accompaniment to food with good ageing potential.
**91 Riesling Kremstal DAC Reserve
Kremser Pfaffenberg 2012**

**(89–91) Grüner Veltliner Kremstal DAC Reserve
Kremser Wachtberg 2015**
**91 Grüner Veltliner Kremstal DAC Reserve
Kremser Wachtberg 2013**

**89 Grüner Veltliner Kremstal DAC Kremser
Goldberg Kellermeister Privat 2015**
**89 Grüner Veltliner Kremstal DAC Kremser
Goldberg Kellermeister Privat 2014**
**89 Grüner Veltliner Kremstal DAC Kremser
Goldberg Kellermeister Privat 2013**

(88–90) Grüner Veltliner Edition Chremisa 2015
91 Grüner Veltliner Edition Chremisa 2014
90 Grüner Veltliner Edition Chremisa 2013

89 Chardonnay Weinmanufaktur Krems 2015

89 Gelber Muskateller Weinmanufaktur Krems 2013

88 Chardonnay Kellermeister Privat 2013

89 Zweigelt Kellermeister Reserve 2013
89 Zweigelt Kellermeister Reserve 2012
90 Blauer Zweigelt Kellermeister Reserve 2011

91 Zweigelt »Glatt & Verkehrt« 2011

★ ★ ★

Weingut Alois Zimmermann

3494 Theiß, Obere Hauptstraße 20
T: +43 (2735) 8209, F: +43 (2735) 8209 4
office@weingut-zimmermann.at, www.weingut-zimmermann.at

Winemaker and Contact Person: Alois Zimmermann jun.
Production: n. a. (100 % white)
Hectares: 11
Fairs: ProWein, VieVinum, Vinobile Montfort
Distribution partners: DE, NL

The Alois Zimmermann Winery is situated in the charming wine village of Theiss, north of the Danube river and not far from the city of Krems. Zimmermann took over responsibility for management of the winery from his parents Alois senior and Edeltraud Zimmermann in 2007. The winery has grown to its present size under the visionary eyes of a father and son team. t was always clear to Alois Jr. that he would become a vintner. The creation of wine throughout the year, from the work in the vineyard to the guidance in the cellar, was always a process that fascinated him. He sees the care of the vines as of central importance and for that reason you will find him more often in the vineyard than in the office. Before Zimmermann took over complete responsibility for the family winery he sought international experience to broaden his perspective. The essence of his experience has helped him to concentrate on the inherent strengths of his own winery.

(89–91) Grüner Veltliner Kremstal DAC Reserve Kremser Gebling 2015
91 Grüner Veltliner Kremstal DAC Reserve Kremser Gebling 2014
90 Grüner Veltliner Kremstal DAC Reserve Kremser Gebling 2013

90 Grüner Veltliner Kremstal DAC Sandgrube 2015
90 Grüner Veltliner Kremstal DAC Sandgrube 2014
89 Grüner Veltliner Kremstal DAC Sandgrube 2013

90 Grüner Veltliner Kremstal DAC Gernlüssen 2015

(92–94) Riesling Kremstal DAC Reserve Kremser Krax'n 2015
92 Riesling Kremstal DAC Reserve Kremser Krax'n 2014
Pale green-yellow with silver highlights. Greengage plum and apricot mingle with nuances of mandarin peel and blossom honey. White vineyard peach is complicated with dark minerals and lime and highlighted by refreshing acidity. This complexity continues on the nearly salty mineral finish.
92 Riesling Kremstal DAC Reserve Kremser Krax'n 2013

91 Riesling Kremstal DAC Kapuzinerberg 2015
91 Riesling Kremstal DAC Kapuzinerberg 2014
88 Riesling Kremstal DAC Kapuzinerberg 2013

90 Riesling Kremstal DAC Rosshimmel 2015
90 Riesling Kremstal DAC Rosshimmel 2014
90 Riesling Kremstal DAC Rosshimmel 2013

(91–93) Grüner Veltliner Kremstal DAC Reserve Rosshimmel 2015
93 Grüner Veltliner Kremstal DAC Reserve Rosshimmel 2014
Medium green-yellow. Anise, tobacco, honeydew melon, subtle mandarin zest and a touch of minerals. Juicy nuances of apricot and yellow apple are balanced by fine acidity and joined by an orange tone on the finish. Good ageing potential.
92 Grüner Veltliner Kremstal DAC Reserve Rosshimmel 2013

Autochthon grapes and heuriger, a cradle of authenticity

South of Vienna, there is a wonderful recreational area that features not only cosy heuriger (winery taverns), but also rich, historical terroir where rare autochthon varieties thrive. 2,196 hectares of vineyards lie at the edge of the Vienna Woods and extend to the south of Baden. White wine dominates in the north with the indigenous grapes Zierfandler and Rotgipfler. The south yields velvety red wines with St. Laurent and Pinot Noir leading the way.

© ÖWM/Weingut Stadlmann

The Thermenregion takes its name from the hot, sulphuric thermal springs just south of Vienna where Romans cultivated wine 2,000 year ago. Not only do the Thermenregion vines benefit from the balmy summers and dry autumns of the Pannonian-influenced Vienna Basin, but also from an average of 1,800 hours of sunshine every year.

The region is also geologically quite diverse. Heavy soils comprised of loam and cambisols interchange with marine limestone and then weathered pebbles and stones or well-drained, deep alluvial soils. Gumpoldskirchen, Traiskirchen, and Baden are home to the rare indigenous white grape varieties Neuburger, Zierfandler, and Rotgipfler. These are produced as superb varietal wines or the legendary regional blend of Zierfandler and Rotgipfler called "Spätrot-Rotgipfler".

Red wines are found mainly in the vicinity of Bad Vöslau, Sooss, Tattendorf and Teesdorf where Sankt Laurent and Pinot Noir produce exquisite results. Other traditional varieties of the region are Chardonnay, Weissburgunder (Pinot Blanc), Blauer Portugieser, and Zweigelt. The combination of culture, thermal baths, and hilly, forested areas provides for varied leisure-time activities. Interesting highlights include visiting the health spa and cultural resort town of Baden, or wine route excursions and hikes in the vineyards located alongside Vienna's famous aqueduct.

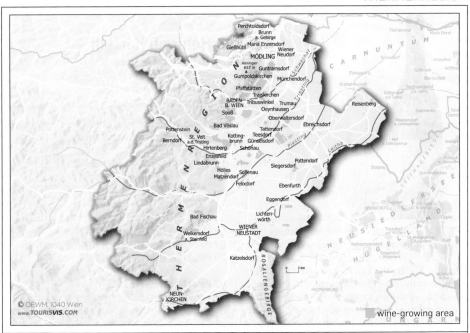

© OEWM, 1040 Wien
www.**TOURISVIS**.COM

wine-growing area

◆ Weingut Heinrich Hartl III,
  Oberwaltersdorf

◆ Weingut Johanneshof Reinisch,
  Tattendorf

◆ Weingut Krug, Gumpoldskirchen

◆ Weingut Stadlmann, Traiskirchen

Weingut Heinrich Hartl III

2522 Oberwaltersdorf, Trumauer Straße 24
T: +43 (2253) 6289, F: +43 (2253) 6289, M: +43 (664) 2124589
office@weingut-hartl.at, www.weingut-hartl.at

Winemaker and Contact Person: Heinrich Hartl III
Production: n. a. (30 % white, 67 % red, 1 % sweet, 2 % rose)
Hectares: 13 + 2
Distribution partners: AUS, CH, SK, DK, DE, FIN, GB, PL

Wine cultivation now defines the lifestyle and livelihood of the seventh generation of the Hartl family. Today, the Hartls dedicate much time and attentiveness to their vineyards, which are located predominantly in the Steinfeld vineyard near the village of Oberwaltersdorf. Heinrich Hartl III has become an enthusiastic fan of Thermenregion's autochthon variety, Rotgipfler, and to this end has acquired plots in famous sites in Gumpoldskirchen and Pfaffstätten. While gaining experience in Austria and abroad, Heinrich developed a passion for the red Burgundian varieties Pinot Noir and St. Laurent. Rotgipfler the two red varieties exhibit particularly good potential in the complex terroir of the region. This winery combines an uncompromising quality philosophy and extensive know-how with sensitivity and intuition, something that can already be noticed in the wines from the mid-price segment. The producer is also a founding member of "Die Burgundermacher" vintners' association. The dedicated Hartl has demonstrated impressively in recent years just what potential lies in the Thermenregion. Hartl's wines recently won medals for nearly every single wine that he entered in the Decanter World Wine Awards and the International Wine Challenge. He is also continuously present in the Austrian Wine Salon, most recently with three champions (St. Laurent and two Pinot Noirs). With such inspiration, Heinrich Hartl III strives for even more and continues to demonstrate the potential of his region, even gaining for the Thermenregion increased international recognition.

92 Pinot Noir Graf Weingartl 2012
92 Pinot Noir Graf Weingartl 2011
93 Pinot Noir Graf Weingartl 2010

92 Pinot Noir Reserve 2013
Crimson with garnet highlights and a broad ochre rim. This highly attractive bouquet displays wild forest berry jam, raspberry and hibiscus. Medium complexity on the palate. Sweet strawberry and cherry are laced with spicy, fine-grained tannins. Good length and very promising potential.
91 Pinot Noir Reserve 2012
91 Pinot Noir Reserve 2011

92 Sankt Laurent Reserve 2012
90 Sankt Laurent Reserve 2011
91 Sankt Laurent Reserve 2010

90 Rotgipfler 2014

91 Traminer 2015

Weingut Johanneshof Reinisch

★★★★

2523 Tattendorf, Im Weingarten 1
T: +43 (2253) 81423, F: +43 (2253) 81423 4
office@j-r.at, www.j-r.at

—— ORGANIC ——

Winemaker and Contact Person: Johannes Reinisch
Production: 220.000 bottles (37 % white, 60 % red, 3 % sweet)
Hectares: 40
Fairs: ProWein, VieVinum
Distribution partners: I, RUS, J, S, CDN, CH, B, ROK, SGP, BR, RC, L, DK, DE, FIN, F, NL, N, GB, H, USA, IRL, PL, P, RO

A fourth Reinisch generation continues to cultivate wine in some of the very best sites around the historic wine villages of Tattendorf and Gumpoldskirchen. The intrinsic quality of the alluvial cambisol soil is its superb drainage and capacity to warm quickly, which is highly advantageous for the grape ripening process. High limestone content lends the wines their pronounced mineral character and renders the Johanneshof Reinisch sites particularly well-suited for the cultivation of Burgundian varieties. Pinot Noir, St. Laurent and Chardonnay are the prime focus of the Johanneshof Reinisch estate. A unique terroir in Gumpoldskirchen is planted with the rare white indigenous varieties Rotgipfler and Zierfandler. Vinification for all of the wines is focused on preserving pronounced varietal character. In accordance with the climatic preconditions, 60% of the wines are red and 40% are white and sweet wines. Dedicated personal engagement to their vines and wines is a matter of lifestyle for the three brothers Johannes, Christian and Michael. Organic viticulture with the employment of beneficial insects and diverse green cover between the vine rows is a simple matter of principle and integrity.

93 St. Laurent Holzspur 2013
Dark ruby with an opaque core, purple highlights and a thin, transparent rim. Attractive nose with wild blackberry, ripe plum and touches of herbal spice, nougat and orange zest. Juicy and elegant with silky tannins and ripe red berry fruit. Well structured, plenty of finesse, good length and excellent ageing potential.
93 St. Laurent Holzspur 2012
94 Sankt Laurent Holzspur 2011

93 St. Laurent Frauenfeld 2014
92 St. Laurent Frauenfeld 2013
92 St. Laurent Frauenfeld 2012

91 St. Laurent Sommelier Edition 2014

90 St. Laurent 2014
90 St. Laurent 2013
88 St. Laurent 2012

94 Pinot Noir Kästenbaum 2013

93 Pinot Noir Holzspur 2013
93 Pinot Noir Holzspur 2012
94 Pinot Noir Holzspur 2011

92 Pinot Noir Grillenhügel 2014
92 Pinot Noir Grillenhügel 2013
91 Pinot Noir Grillenhügel 2012

90 Pinot Noir 2014
89 Pinot Noir 2013
89 Pinot Noir 2012

94 Steingarten 2013 SL/PN

92 Cabernet Sauvignon – Merlot Reserve 2012 ME/CS
92 Cabernet Sauvignon – Merlot 2011 ME/CS

88 Alter Rebstock 2013 SL/BF/ZW
88 Alter Rebstock 2012 SL/BF/ZW
89 Alter Rebstock 2011 SL/BF/ZW

91 Zweigelt Frauenfeld 2014
91 Zweigelt Frauenfeld 2013
90 Zweigelt Frauenfeld 2012

89 Zweigelt 2014
89 Zweigelt 2013

93 Rotgipfler Satzing 2014
92 Rotgipfler Satzing 2013
90 Rotgipfler Satzing 2012

90 Rotgipfler 2015
89 Rotgipfler 2014
89 Rotgipfler 2013

91 Zierfandler Spiegel 2014
91 Zierfandler Spiegel 2013
90 Zierfandler Spiegel 2012

91 Gumpoldskirchner Tradition 2015 ZF/RG
90 Gumpoldskirchner Tradition 2014 ZF/RG
89 Gumpoldskirchner Tradition 2013 ZF/RG

93 Spiegel-Satzing S 2009 ZF/RG

88 Dialog 2015 SB/CH
88 Dialog 2014 SB/CH
88 Dialog 2013 SB/CH

93 Chardonnay Lores 2014
92 Chardonnay Lores 2013
92 Chardonnay Lores 2012

91 Pinot Noir Brut 2010

94 Rotgipfler Auslese 2014
Pale yellow with silver highlights. A touch of grapefruit zest,
fresh pineapple and blossom honey. Elegant notes of carambola and white currant are highlighted by a racy acidity
structure. Lingering lime note on the long sweet finish.
Wonderful potential for long bottle ageing.

92 Zierfandler Eiswein 2013
92 Zierfandler Eiswein 2012

89 Merlot Eiswein 2013
93 Merlot Eiswein 2012

Weingut Krug

2352 Gumpoldskirchen, Kirchenplatz 1
T: +43 (2252) 22 47, F: +43 (2252) 22 47 4
office@krug.at, www.krug.at

Winemaker and Contact Person: Gustav Krug
Production: 250.000 bottles (50 % white, 45 % red, 5 % sweet)
Hectares: 34
Fairs: ProWein, VieVinum
Distribution partners: B, BG, RC, DE, NL

The Krug wine estate was established in Gumpoldskirchen in 1746. Today it is comprised of 34 hectares of vineyards on loam and calcareous soils in the best sites of Gumpoldskirchen. The mild climate of the Thermenregion and its superb soils provide advantageous conditions for Krug to produce wonderfully powerful, multilayered white and red wines that offer both early drinking pleasure and good ageing potential. White wine makes up 60% of production. The goal of the winery is to produce high quality wines with outstanding regional character. To achieve this, the vineyards are meticulously cared for. Only ripe and healthy grapes arrive in the crush house. The most comfortable way to discover to discover and taste the wines of Gustav Krug is to visit the family heuriger (wine tavern) called Alten Zechhaus, which is located directly on the Kirchenplatz.

92 Rotgipfler Privat 2013
Medium green-yellow. Bartlett pear and blossom honey with nuances of papaya and orange zest. Juicy acidity elegantly balances the full body. Tightly woven flavours of yellow apple and papaya are accompanied by tobacco notes that continue to linger on the long finish. Superb ageing potential.

88 Rotgipfler Rasslerin 2015
88 Rotgipfler Rasslerin 2014

92 Rotgipfler Vollendung 2015
92 Rotgipfler Vollendung 2011

89 Zierfandler Sonnberg 2012

91 Kreuzweingarten 2015
90 Kreuzweingarten 2014
91 Kreuzweingarten 2012 ZF/RG

91 Pinot Gris Die Versuchung 2014

88 Chardonnay Selektion 2014

92 Cabernet Sauvignon Privat 2012
92 Cabernet Sauvignon Privat 2011

91 Merlot Reserve 2013
91 Merlot 2011

91 Die Versuchung 2012 CS/ZW/ME

90 Zweigelt Eichkogel 2011

Weingut Stadlmann

2514 Traiskirchen, Wiener Straße 41
T: +43 (2252) 52343, F: +43 (2252) 56332
kontakt@stadlmann-wein.at, www.stadlmann-wein.at

— ORGANIC —

Winemaker and Contact Person: Johann and Mag. Bernhard Stadlmann
Production: n. a. (80 % white, 15 % red, 5 % sweet)
Hectares: 20
Fairs: VieVinum, ProWein
Distribution partners: RUS, J, B, CDN, FIN, NL, GB, N, USA

Wine cultivation at the Stadlmann estate can be traced back to 1780. Knowledge has grown and been passed on continuously for seven generations. There is no one who has occupied themselves more intensely with the unique autochthon varieties of the Thermenregion than Johann Stadlmann. His profound knowledge has been deepened through extensive experience abroad. He engages this knowledge and experience with a sure and sensitive hand in the most highly valued vineyard sites of the region. He tends predominantly old vines that are deeply rooted in marine limestone on the slopes of the Anninger mountain. He conscientiously practices restraint in the wine cellar and allows wines time to mature. His continuity, precision and craftsmanship lead to authentic wines that express all the facets of their origin. The complexity, depth and extraordinary ageing potential of Stadlmann's Zierfandler and Rotgipfler are incomparable. The Stadlmann Winery is deeply dedicated to the typical regional varieties in all their diversity, yet also vinifies superb Weissburgunder (Pinot Blanc), Grüner Veltliner, St. Laurent, and Pinot Noir in large wooden casks. Johann Stadlmann is the chairman of the regional wine committee and was honoured as "Falstaff Vintner of the Year" in 1994.

93 Zierfandler Mandel-Höh 2014
93 Zierfandler Mandel-Höh 2013
Brilliant golden-yellow hue. A touch of blossom honey with nuances of orange zest and delicate pear. Full-bodied with a firm structure and well-integrated acidity. Subtle herbs, spice, salty minerals and a touch of orange on the lingering finish.
92 Zierfandler Mandel-Höh 2012

91 Zierfandler Igeln 2014
89 Zierfandler Igeln 2013
91 Zierfandler Igeln 2012

90 Zierfandler Anninger 2015
90 Zierfandler Anninger 2014

93 Zierfandler Große Reserve 2012
94 Zierfandler Große Reserve 2011

93 Rotgipfler Tagelsteiner 2014
92 Rotgipfler Tagelsteiner 2013
Medium yellow with gold highlights. Subtle nuances of quince jelly and fresh honey with candied orange peel in the background. Complex, full bodied, and powerful. Ripe pineapple with a touch of peach and nougat on the long finish. A spicy accompaniment to food.
92 Rotgipfler Tagelsteiner 2012

89 Rotgipfler Anniger 2015
88 Rotgipfler Anninger 2014
90 Rotgipfler Anninger 2013

89 Weißer Burgunder Höfen 2012

89 St. Laurent 2011

94 Zierfandler Beerenauslese 2010

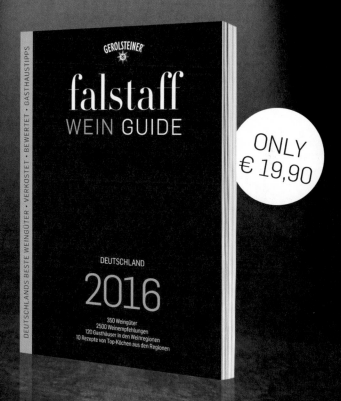

TRAISENTAL DAC
Grüner Veltliner and Riesling with charm and depth

In no other Austrian wine region does Grüner Veltliner play such a dominant role: 60% of the region's 790 hectares. Just outside the Lower Austrian capital city St. Pölten, boutique wineries await discovery from wine lovers, hikers, bicyclists, and cultural explorers in a tranquil countryside destination.

© ÖWM / Himml

© ÖWM/Himml

Despite, or perhaps because of its tiny size, Traisental is a relaxing, idyllic region that is truly worthy of exploration. Delicately spicy Grüner Veltliners dominate here, but juicy Rieslings with firm mineral backbone are also a coveted specialty.

Since 2006, these two varieties appear under the "Traisental DAC" protected designation of origin. Fuller bodied, dry late harvest editions are labelled "Traisental DAC Reserve".

The landscape rises gently from the fertile banks of the crystal clear Traisen River to vines planted in free-draining gravel, marl and sand to tiny terraced vineyards carved out of meagre, highly calcareous Hollenburger conglomerate and sediment. Warm, arid Pannonian climate influences collide with Alpine air masses and cool Dunkelsteiner Wald breezes resulting in extreme diurnal temperature fluctuations that are mildly moderated by the Traisen and Danube Rivers. These attributes yield aromatic, mineral wines with a taut spine of acid.

Not only Traisental DAC Grüner Veltliner and Riesling, but also wines from other varieties find well-suited plots and appear under the Niederösterreich protected geographical indication. While most of the quaint wine villages here feature traditional, rustic heurige (winery taverns), not only St. Pölten, but the larger towns like Traismauer and Herzogenburg, offer more delicate Asian-influenced cuisine or Mediterranean fish dishes that allow the Traisental wines to show that they have potential far beyond their regional borders.

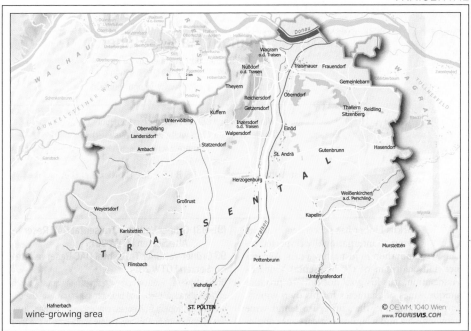

wine-growing area

© OEWM, 1040 Wien
www.TOURISVIS.COM

◆ Weingut Markus Huber, Reichersdorf

◆ Weingut Ludwig Neumayer,
   Inzersdorf ob der Traisen

◆ Weinkultur Preiß, Theyern

★★★★

Weingut Markus Huber

3134 Reichersdorf, Weinriedenweg 13
T: +43 (2783) 82999, F: +43 (2783) 82999 4
office@weingut-huber.at, www.weingut-huber.at

Winemaker and Contact Person: Markus Huber
Production: n. a. (97 % white, 2 % red, 1 % sweet)
Hectares: 40
Fairs: VieVinum, ProWein
Distribution partners: AUS, J, S, B, CDN, SGP, DK, NL, GB, N, USA

Markus Huber has succeeded in achieving an internationally respected reputation in just a few years. As vintner and chairman of the Traisental Vintner's Association, it is his goal not only to produce unique wines of character for his own winery, but to help make the entire Traisental wine growing area and its unique calcareous conglomerate soils better known. Crystal clear varietal expression and the pronounced mineral character that can only be derived in an outstanding terroir are the attributes that distinguish his wines. The main variety is clearly Grüner Veltliner that represents two thirds of production. Four different styles of Grüner Veltliner are produced, each defined by its respective soil and fruit potential. On this basis, either stainless steel or wooden casks are chosen for vinification. The second most important variety is Riesling, followed by Weissburgunder (Pinot Blanc), Sauvignon Blanc and Gelber Muskateller. When the vintage is suitable, sweet wines are also produced. Huber can boast many accolades including SALON Selection 2003, regional champion; four-time champion of the Falstaff Grüner Veltliner Grand Prix; "Best White Wine Producer" and gold medal winner at the London International Wine and Spirit Competition; "Newcomer of the Year" title from Falstaff, and named "Wunderkind" by Decanter magazine in Great Britain. Indeed, Markus Huber is well on his way. To assure quality, Markus Huber's winery has been IFS and BRC certified since 2007. Markus makes no compromises when it comes to quality and says: "I strive to improve a little more each year." The winery is a member of the prestigious Traditionsweingüter Österreich vintner association. Markus Huber was named Vintner of the Year 2015 by Falstaff magazine.

(91–93) Grüner Veltliner Traisental DAC Reserve Alte Setzen 1 ÖTW 2015
93 Grüner Veltliner Traisental DAC Reserve Alte Setzen 1 ÖTW 2014
Brilliant greenish-yellow hue with silver highlights. A touch of fresh meadow herbs and blossom honey provide the undertone for tropical fruit notes reminiscent of mango. Juicy and elegant with fine acidity. Yellow apple note in the long finish of this multifaceted food partner.
92 Grüner Veltliner Traisental DAC Reserve Alte Setzen 1 ÖTW 2013

(93–95) Grüner Veltliner Traisental DAC Reserve Berg 1 ÖTW 2015
93 Grüner Veltliner Traisental DAC Reserve Berg 1 ÖTW 2014
93 Grüner Veltliner Traisental DAC Reserve Berg 1 ÖTW 2013

(92–94) Grüner Veltliner Traisental DAC Reserve Zwirch 1 ÖTW 2015
92 Grüner Veltliner Traisental DAC Reserve Zwirch 1 ÖTW 2014

91 Grüner Veltliner Traisental DAC Obere Steigen 2015
91 Grüner Veltliner Traisental DAC Obere Steigen 2014
91 Grüner Veltliner Traisental DAC Obere Steigen 2013

90 Grüner Veltliner Traisental DAC Terrassen 2015
90 Grüner Veltliner Traisental DAC Terrassen 2014
90 Grüner Veltliner Traisental DAC Terrassen 2012

89 Nussdorfer Grüner Veltliner Traisental DAC 2015

**(93-95) Riesling Traisental DAC Reserve
        Berg 1 ÖTW 2015**
**93 Riesling Traisental DAC Reserve
        Berg 1 ÖTW 2014**
Pale green-yellow with silver highlights. White vineyard pe-ach and greengage plum laced with blossom honey on the nose. Juicy, well-integrated acidity structure lends mouth-watering juiciness. A discreet touch of honey comes in on the finish. Good potential for further development.
**93 Riesling Traisental DAC Reserve
        Berg 1 ÖTW 2013**
95 Riesling Traisental DAC Reserve Berg 2012

91 Riesling Traisental DAC Engelsberg 2015
91 Riesling Traisental DAC Engelsberg 2014
89 Riesling Traisental DAC Engelsberg 2013

91 Riesling Traisental DAC Terrassen 2015
92 Riesling Traisental DAC Terrassen 2014
91 Riesling Traisental DAC Terrassen 2012

89 Nussdorfer Riesling Traisental DAC 2015

(90–92) Weißer Burgunder Hochschopf 2015
91 Weißburgunder Hochschopf 2014
90 Weißburgunder Hochschopf 2013

92 Sauvignon Blanc 2015
88 Sauvignon Blanc 2014
90 Sauvignon Blanc 2012

90 Gelber Muskateller 2015

88 Chardonnay 2015

(92–94) Riesling Auslese 2015
92 Riesling Auslese 2013

92 Riesling Eiswein 2013
96 Riesling Eiswein 2012

★★★★
Weingut Ludwig Neumayer

3131 Inzersdorf ob der Traisen, Dorfstraße 37
T: +43 (2782) 81110, F: +43 (2782) 82985
neumayer@weinvomstein.at, www.weinvomstein.at

Winemaker and Contact Person: Ludwig Neumayer
Production: n. a. (98 % white, 2 % sweet)
Hectares: 12
Fairs: VieVinum, ProWein
Distribution partners: B, CH, DE, F, CZ, NL, GB, USA

This leading winery of the Traisental wine region is completely dedicated to white wine production. The meagre, rocky soils of the Neumayer estate vineyards yield wines of extraordinary finesse. Grüner Veltliner and Riesling are the most important varieties, which appear as reserve wines that are labelled "Der Wein von Stein" and as single vineyard wines "Grüner Veltliner Zwirch", "Grüner Veltliner Rafasetzen", and "Riesling Rothenbart". In addition to these are a nicely concentrated Weissburgunder (Pinot Blanc) and a Sauvignon Blanc labelled "Ikon". It is Ludwig Neumayer's goal to produce wines with inimitable style, wines that possess both intensity and freshness. The pale colour that is so typical of the Neumayer wines is not due to lack of fruit ripeness, but to the highly calcareous soils. A further virtue of the wines is the pronounced acidity structure; residual sweetness is tolerated only when it truly contributes something positive. Neumayer also abstains completely from animal derived proteins during wine production.

Top restaurants in Austria and abroad have long discovered the exceptional wines of this producer. Ludwig Neumayer can be pleased over being listed at such admirable gourmet establishments as the 3-Michelin-star "Astrance" and Alain Ducasse's "Plaza Athénée" in Paris.

**94 Grüner Veltliner Traisental DAC Reserve
Ikon 2015**
**95 Grüner Veltliner Traisental DAC Reserve
IKON-Stein 2014**
Pale green-yellow with silver highlights. Initially restrained, but then fine yellow fruit notes reminiscent of Golden Delicious apple appear with a touch of blossom honey. The pala-

te is complex and silky. Sweet fruit is elegantly balanced with refreshing acidity. Equipped with a very long finish and tremendous ageing potential.
**94 Grüner Veltliner Traisental DAC Reserve
Ikon Stein 2013**

**93 Grüner Veltliner Traisental DAC Reserve
Der Wein vom Stein 2015**
**93 Grüner Veltliner Traisental DAC Reserve
Der Wein vom Stein 2014**
**93 Grüner Veltliner Traisental DAC Reserve
Der Wein vom Stein 2013**

**92 Grüner Veltliner Traisental DAC Reserve
Zwirch 1 ÖTW 2015**
**92 Grüner Veltliner Traisental DAC Reserve
Zwirch 1 ÖTW 2014**
**92 Grüner Veltliner Traisental DAC Reserve
Zwirch 1 ÖTW 2013**

91 Grüner Veltliner Traisental DAC Zwiri 2015
**92 Grüner Veltliner Traisental DAC
Traisenstein 2014**

**89 Grüner Veltliner Traisental DAC
Rafasetzen 2015**

**88 Grüner Veltliner Traisental DAC
Traisenberg 2015**

**93 Riesling Traisental DAC Reserve
Der Wein vom Stein 2015**
93 Riesling Der Wein vom Stein 2014
Pale green-yellow. White vineyard peach and blossom honey over a background of orange zest and spice. Complex with discreet residual sweetness and fruit nicely countered with well integrated, appetizing acidity. Long, sweet finish and good ageing potential.
**92 Riesling Traisental DAC Reserve
Der Wein vom Stein 2013**

92 Riesling Traisental DAC Reserve
   Rothenbart 1 ÖTW 2015
92 Riesling Rothenbart 1 ÖTW 2014
92 Riesling Traisental DAC Reserve
   Rothenbart 1 ÖTW 2013

92 Riesling Traisental DAC Grillenbart 2015

93 Weißburgunder Der Wein vom Stein 2015

93 Sauvignon Blanc Der Wein vom Stein 2015
93 Sauvignon Blanc Der Wein vom Stein 2013
93 Sauvignon Blanc Der Wein vom Stein 2012

90 Sauvignon Blanc Giess 2015

★ ★

Weinkultur Preiß

3134 Theyern, Ringgasse 4
T: +43 (2783) 6731, F: +43 (2783) 6731, M: +43 (676) 9418580
wine@kulturpreiss.at, www.weinkulturpreiss.at

Winemaker and Contact Person: Friedrich Preiß
Production: n. a. (90 % white, 10 % red)
Hectares: 12
Fairs: VieVinum, ProWein
Distribution partners: CZ, NL

The Weinkultur Preiß winery has a history of more than 100 years. The family stems originally from the Wachau and purchased this farm in Theyern in 1913. Back then it was a mixed agriculture enterprise that included not only grape vines and orchards, but also field crops, pastures and livestock. Today they are specialized in viticulture and fruit orchards. The Preiß family has an uncompromising will and the experience to produce outstanding grapes and great wines. They cultivate 12 hectares of vineyards and nine hectares of fruit orchards. The vineyards comprise predominantly terraces based on ancient calcareous conglomerate, partially covered with deep deposits of loess. The limestone content lends spice, firm structure and mineral character to the wines. A medium-high vine trunk, high leaf canopy, high planting density and rigorous yield reduction are further pillars of quality cultivation. The assortment of grapes is led by a 60% share of Grüner Veltliner; Riesling and Zweigelt each represent a 10% share. The goal in vinification is the preservation of pronounced fruit and flavour intensity as well as the expression of terroir and the passion of the vintner. The classic wines are designated with the word "Kammerlingen" on the labels. "Kammerlingen" are foraminifera, amoeboid protists – and drawings of these shells by the famous biologist and artist Ernst Haeckl (1834-1919) adorn the bottle labels. One might ask what "Kammerlinge" have to do with wine, but one finds their numerous fossils in the local conglomerate and they also find a habitat on the vines in the vineyard. "Kammerlingen" contribute to the high calcareous content of the soil, which lends wines their fruit, spice, mineral character and ageing capacity.

(91–93) Grüner Veltliner Traisental DAC Reserve Ried Brunndoppel 2015
91 Grüner Veltliner Traisental DAC Reserve Brunndoppel 2014
Pale golden yellow. Ripe pear, honeydew melon, a touch of anise and subtle blossom honey. Concentrated and complex with delicate white pear and mild acidity. Delicate nutty nuances on the finish. Fully developed.
91 Grüner Veltliner Traisental DAC Reserve Brunndoppel 2012

90 Grüner Veltliner Traisental DAC Ried Hochschopf 2015
91 Grüner Veltliner Traisental DAC Hochschopf 2014
90 Grüner Veltliner Traisental DAC Reserve Hochschopf 2013

91 Grüner Veltliner Traisental DAC Kammerling 2015
90 Grüner Veltliner Traisental DAC Kammerling 2014
90 Grüner Veltliner Traisental DAC 2013

(90–92) Riesling Traisental DAC Reserve Ried Pletzengraben 2015
89 Riesling Traisental DAC Pletzengraben 2014

90 Riesling Traisental DAC Kammerling 2015
91 Riesling Traisental DAC 2013

88 Gelber Muskateller Kammerling 2015
88 Gelber Muskateller 2013

88 Sauvignon Blanc Kammerling 2014

90 Chardonnay Brunndoppel 2014

91 Blauer Zweigelt vom kleinen Holz 2011

Monumental wines from steep terraces, a breath-taking UNESCO World Heritage Site

The narrow Danube River Valley between Melk and Krems is a landscape that induces both awe and a sense of well-being. 1,350 hectares of vineyards overlooking the Danube River are held into place by hand-stacked, dry stone walls on precariously steep primary rock slopes. This is the home to Austria's most famous Grüner Veltliner and Riesling.

© ÖWM/Werner Gamerith

In the mid 1980's the Vinea Wachau vintners' association created a codex of purity in which they commit to the production of unadulterated wine from a specific geographic origin. They established three trademarks to represent three categories of Vinea Wachau members' dry white wines. Steinfeder® are aromatic, light-bodied wines with up to 11.5% ABV. The most prolific category is the elegant, medium-bodied Federspiel® with 11.5% to 12.5% ABV. The rich and powerful late-harvest wines carry the name Smaragd®.

The Wachau is a fascinating wine region. Over millions of years, the Danube River gorged its winding waterway through consolidated gneiss and amphibolite. Outstanding Rieslings now thrust their roots in these steep crystalline rock slopes. Prevailing winds during the Ice Age deposited glacial dust and silt in the lee of the east-facing mountainsides, resulting in layers of loess. This is where great, opulent and expressive Grüner Veltliner is now cultivated. Bavarian monasteries constructed terraces held in place by dry stone walls during the Middle Ages to prevent erosion and facilitate wine cultivation. A unique geology and human intervention has resulted in a spectacular and unique cultural landscape.

The climate also plays a dramatic role. Two major climatic influences collide and complement one another here; the cold and damp continental air from the west meets warm and arid Pannonian air from the east. A myriad of microclimates are also at work with varying slope aspects and inclinations, proximity to cool north to south side valleys, or the presence of heat-storing stone walls or cliff faces. Hot, dry summers and cold winters are counterbalanced by the large water surface of the Danube River. Cold lee winds from the northern Forest Quarter in the evening enhance high diurnal temperature fluctuations. All of these factors contribute to depth and complexity of aromas in the grapes.

Numerous culinary highlights are nestled in the historic Wachau wine villages. High

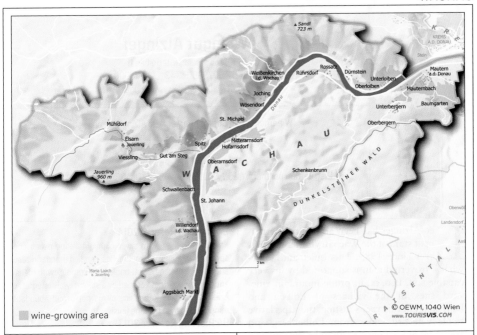

wine-growing area

© OEWM, 1040 Wien
www.TOURISVIS.COM

profile winemakers and top chefs abound in every part of the Wachau – from Spitz to Weissenkirchen, Joching, Dürnstein and Loiben, and even across the river, on the Danube's lesser-known right bank. In addition to the Wachau's two leading varieties Grüner Veltliner and Riesling, Neuburger, Weissburgunder (Pinot Blanc), Gelber Muskateller (Muscat Blanc à petits grains) and a little Sauvignon Blanc and Zweigelt are produced. Extraordinary tasting experiences are guaranteed.

◆ Weingut Alzinger, Dürnstein-Unterloiben

◆ Weingut Atzberg, Spitz/Donau

◆ Domäne Wachau, Dürnstein

◆ Weingut Johann Donabaum, Spitz/Donau

◆ Weingut Franz Hirtzberger, Spitz/Donau

◆ Weingut Josef M. Högl, Spitz/Donau

◆ Weingut Karl Holzapfel, Joching

◆ Weingut Hutter Silberbichlerhof, Mautern an der Donau

◆ Weingut Josef Jamek, Joching

◆ Weingut Knoll, Dürnstein-Unterloiben

◆ Weingut F.X. Pichler, Dürnstein-Oberloiben

◆ Weingut Rudi Pichler, Wösendorf

◆ Weingut Prager, Weissenkirchen

◆ Weingut Schmelz, Joching

◆ Tegernseerhof – Mittelbach, Dürnstein-Unterloiben

★ ★ ★ ★

Weingut Alzinger

3601 Dürnstein, Unterloiben 11
T: +43 (2732) 77900, F: +43 (2732) 77900 50
weingut@alzinger.at, www.alzinger.at

Winemaker and Contact Person: Leo Alzinger sr. and jr.
Production: n. a. (100 % white)
Hectares: 10
Fairs: VieVinum, ProWein
Distribution partners: AUS, I, S, CDN, CH, B, SK, E, DK, DE, NZ, CZ, F, NL, GB, H

L eo Alzinger has been among the permanent stars of the Wachau vintner heavens ever since 1983. This quiet and somewhat introverted man is supported by his very capable son, Leo, jr., in prime mountain vineyard sites in the villages of Loiben and Dürnstein. In this year's tasting, the superlative single vineyard wines from Loibenberg and Steinertal proved once again to be the pinnacle of Alzinger's assortment, excelling with precision and depth. The patience of Wachau vintners was tested particularly with the Smaragd wines, but Alzinger was rewarded with exceptional finesses in his single vineyard wines. These very ageworthy examples deserve the undivided attention of wine lovers for they represent the very best of what this region has to offer. It does not matter if one prefers Riesling or Grüner Veltliner, one has an extraordinary selection of more than recommendable wines from Alzinger, of which only a few can be listed here. It is first with the opportunity to taste mature wines that the marvellous potential of the Loiben wines can be fully appreciated. It is Alzinger's wines in particular that are shy in their youth, and after several years of adolescence, their true character and expressiveness become apparent. If one wants to truly learn to understand and appreciate the essence of a super-premium Grüner Veltliner, one should decant a mature bottle of Alzinger and marvel in leisure.

94 Riesling Reserve 2014
Pale green-yellow with silver highlights. Ripe peach and apricot with honeydew melon, figs, candied mandarin zest, and a touch of honey. Full-bodied and complex with pleasant extract sweetness carried by a vibrant, well-integrated acidity backbone. Refreshing citrus notes and abundant minerals linger on the long finish.
94 Riesling Reserve 2013

(94–96) Riesling Smaragd Loibenberg 2015
95 Riesling Smaragd Loibenberg 2013
95 Riesling Smaragd Loibenberg 2012

(95–97) Riesling Smaragd Steinertal 2015
96 Riesling Smaragd Steinertal 2013
95 Riesling Smaragd Steinertal 2012

93 Riesling Smaragd Liebenberg 2015
93 Riesling Smaragd Liebenberg 2013
92 Riesling Smaragd Liebenberg 2012

93 Riesling Smaragd Hollerin 2015
93 Riesling Smaragd Hollerin 2013
94 Riesling Smaragd Hollerin 2012

94 Riesling Smaragd Höhereck 2015
94 Riesling Smaragd Höhereck 2013
93 Riesling Smaragd Höhereck 2012

92 Riesling Federspiel Loibenberg 2014

90 Dürnsteiner Riesling Federspiel 2014
91 Dürnsteiner Riesling Federspiel 2013
91 Dürnsteiner Riesling Federspiel 2012

**(93–95) Grüner Veltliner Smaragd
Loibenberg 2015**
93 Grüner Veltliner Smaragd Loibenberg 2014
Medium green-yellow with silver highlights. An inviting fragrance of Golden Delicious apple, delicate tobacco, and

dark smoky minerals. The taut structure and tightly woven texture comprise a refreshing frame for white apple fruit. The long finish features salty mineral notes. Will benefit from further bottle maturation.

94 Grüner Veltliner Smaragd Loibenberg 2013

93 Grüner Veltliner Smaragd Liebenberg 2015
93 Grüner Veltliner Smaragd Liebenberg 2013
93 Grüner Veltliner Smaragd Liebenberg 2012

(93–95) Grüner Veltliner Smaragd Steinertal 2015
95 Grüner Veltliner Smaragd Steinertal 2013
95 Grüner Veltliner Smaragd Steinertal 2012

93 Grüner Veltliner Smaragd Mühlpoint 2015
93 Grüner Veltliner Smaragd Mühlpoint 2013
93 Grüner Veltliner Smaragd Mühlpoint 2012

(92–94) Grüner Veltliner Reserve 2015
94 Grüner Veltliner Reserve 2013
94 Grüner Veltliner Reserve 2012

92 Grüner Veltliner Federspiel Mühlpoint 2015
91 Grüner Veltliner Federspiel Mühlpoint 2014
91 Grüner Veltliner Federspiel Mühlpoint 2013

92 Grüner Veltliner Federspiel Hochstrasser 2015
90 Grüner Veltliner Federspiel Hochstrasser 2014
91 Grüner Veltliner Federspiel Hochstrasser 2013

91 Grüner Veltliner Federspiel Frauenweingarten 2015
90 Grüner Veltliner Frauenweingarten 2014
90 Grüner Veltliner Federspiel Frauenweingarten 2013

92 Grüner Veltliner Federspiel Steinertal 2014

Weingut Atzberg

3620 Spitz/Donau, Kirchenplatz 13
T: +43 (2713) 2450
office@atzberg.at, www.atzberg.at

NEW

Winemaker and Contact Person: Franz-Josef Gritsch
Hectares: 2
Distribution partners: CH, B, SK, DK, DE, CZ, NL, N, GB

The Atzberg is an extremely steep site in Spitz. Franz-Josef Gritsch revitalized this historic vineyard site, which now brings forth wines that impress with their deep Wachau soul. These wines combine spectacular Veltliner spice with the darkest mineral-schist notes of the Wachau terroir. After many decades of laying fallow, two hectares of vineyards have been re-cultivated and planted with Grüner Veltliner. The results prove that the laborious efforts required to bring this exceptional site back to life were certainly worthwhile.

(92–94) Grüner Veltliner Atzberg Obere Steilterrassen 2015

Brilliant green-yellow. Inviting fragrance of ripe tropical fruit reminiscent of mango and honeydew melon with notes of herbs and peppery spice. Complex structure with elegant acidity and minerals. Stone fruit and spicy tobacco linger on the finish. Good potential for further development.

(91–93) Grüner Veltliner Atzberg Steilterrassen 2015

Domäne Wachau

3601 Dürnstein, 107
T: +43 (2711) 371, F: +43 (2711) 371 13
office@domaene-wachau.at, www.domaene-wachau.at

Winemaker: Heinz Frischengruber
Contact Person: Roman Horvath MW
Production: 2.000.000 bottles (95 % white, 4 % red, 1 % sweet)
Hectares: 440
Fairs: VieVinum, ProWein
Distribution partners: AUS, I, S, B, CDN, SGP, LV, RC, LT, DK, L, EST, FIN, M, CZ, NL, GB, N, UA, USA, PL, UAE

The Domäne Wachau has been more dynamic than ever with the duo Horvath and Frischengruber, who took the fate of the winery into their hands. Within just a short period of time the Domäne has risen to be among the very top wine producers on the Danube River. Essential to this success have been sustainable viticultural improvements and attentive quality management. The elevation and the steepness of individual vineyards is paid tribute and all plots are vinified separately. Manual harvest and meticulous sorting are essential for perfect fruit. The result is an unsurpassably diverse spectrum of Grüner Veltliner and Riesling that express the uniqueness and versatility of Wachau vineyard sites – top wines that are astounding the wine world. Despite the fact that the Domäne Wachau possesses the most modern vinification facility in the region, the time-proven philosophy of minimal intervention is still respected as the ideal. Convincing results can be seen and tasted. One has the opportunity to taste the complete product assortment daily in the on-premise wine shop: from the light, fragrant Muskateller to the complex Smaragd Grüner Veltliner; from the youthful sparkling Riesling to the aged Grüner Veltliner brandies. The wine shop offers a modern contrast to the Domäne's Baroque Cellar Palace just opposite. The legendary palace at the foot of the famous Kellerberg vineyard is the well-suited venue for numerous events and eclectic wine tastings.

(93–95) Riesling Smaragd Kellerberg 2015
93 Riesling Smaragd Kellerberg 2014
Pale green-yellow with silver highlights. Lemon-laced vine-

yard peach and greengage plum mingle with herbal spice and delicate notes of tobacco. Juicy, elegant and plenty of finesse. Delicious ripe apple fruit and abundant minerals cling to a taut acidity backbone and linger on the lengthy finish. Very good potential for further development.
93 Riesling Smaragd Kellerberg 2013

(91–93) Riesling Smaragd Weissenkirchen 2015
90 Riesling Smaragd Weissenkirchen 2014
91 Riesling Smaragd Weissenkirchen 2013

(91–93) Riesling Smaragd Terrassen 2015
91 Riesling Smaragd Terrassen 2014
91 Riesling Smaragd Terrassen 2013

(92–94) Riesling Smaragd Singerriedel 2015
92 Riesling Smaragd Singerriedel 2014
93 Riesling Smaragd Singerriedel 2013

(91–93) Riesling Smaragd Loibenberg 2015
92 Riesling Smaragd Loibenberg 2014
92 Riesling Smaragd Loibenberg 2013

(93–95) Riesling Smaragd Achleiten 2015
92 Riesling Smaragd Achleiten 2014
93 Riesling Smaragd Achleiten 2013

(89–91) Riesling Smaragd Classic 2015

89 Riesling Federspiel Weissenkirchen 2015
88 Riesling Federspiel Weissenkirchen 2014
89 Riesling Federspiel Weissenkirchen 2013

90 Riesling Federspiel Loibenberg 2015
90 Riesling Federspiel Loibenberg 2014
91 Riesling Federspiel Loibenberg 2013

89 Riesling Federspiel Dürnstein 2015
89 Riesling Federspiel Dürnstein 2014
88 Riesling Federspiel Dürnstein 2013

91 Riesling Federspiel Bruck 2015
90 Riesling Federspiel Bruck 2014
89 Riesling Federspiel Bruck 2013

90 Riesling Federspiel 1000-Eimer-Berg 2015
89 Riesling Federspiel 1000-Eimer-Berg 2014
89 Riesling Federspiel 1000-Eimer-Berg 2013

91 Riesling Federspiel Steinriegl 2015

(92–94) Grüner Veltliner Smaragd
Achleiten 2015
93 Grüner Veltliner Smaragd Achleiten 2014
Pale yellow with silver highlights. Apple, subtle notes of pineapple and and delicate greengage plum with an undertone of fresh tobacco. Full-bodied and juicy with a wonderfully poised and balanced acidity structure. Yellow apple and abundant minerals remain on the finish. Very good ageing potential.
93 Grüner Veltliner Smaragd Achleiten 2013

(91–93) Grüner Veltliner Smaragd Axpoint 2015
93 Grüner Veltliner Smaragd Axpoint 2013
92 Grüner Veltliner Smaragd Axpoint 2012

(92–94) Grüner Veltliner Smaragd
Kellerberg 2015
92 Grüner Veltliner Smaragd Kellerberg 2014
92 Grüner Veltliner Smaragd Kellerberg 2013

(90–92) Grüner Veltliner Smaragd
Weissenkirchen 2015
89 Grüner Veltliner Smaragd
Weissenkirchen 2014
90 Grüner Veltliner Smaragd
Weissenkirchen 2013
91 Grüner Veltliner Smaragd
Weissenkirchen 2012

(90–92) Grüner Veltliner Smaragd
Terrassen 2015
91 Grüner Veltliner Smaragd Terrassen 2013
90 Grüner Veltliner Smaragd Terrassen 2012

(90–92) Grüner Veltliner Smaragd
Himmelstiege 2015

(89–91) Grüner Veltliner Smaragd
Dürnstein 2015
91 Grüner Veltliner Smaragd Dürnstein 2014
92 Grüner Veltliner Smaragd Dürnstein 2013

92 Grüner Veltliner Smaragd Pichlpoint 2013
92 Grüner Veltliner Smaragd Pichlpoint 2012

(91–93) Grüner Veltliner Smaragd Kirnberg 2015

(89–91) Grüner Veltliner Smaragd Classic 2015

92 Grüner Veltliner Federspiel Loibenberg 2015
92 Grüner Veltliner Federspiel Loibenberg 2013
92 Grüner Veltliner Federspiel Loibenberg 2012

91 Grüner Veltliner Federspiel Liebenberg 2015

90 Grüner Veltliner Federspiel Kreuzberg 2015

91 Grüner Veltliner Federspiel Kollmitz 2015
89 Grüner Veltliner Federspiel Kollmitz 2014
90 Grüner Veltliner Federspiel Kollmitz 2013

91 Grüner Veltliner Federspiel Kaiserberg 2015
90 Grüner Veltliner Federspiel Kaiserberg 2014

90 Grüner Veltliner Federspiel Dürnstein 2015
88 Grüner Veltliner Federspiel Dürnstein 2014

89 Grüner Veltliner Federspiel
Weissenkirchen 2015
87 Grüner Veltliner Federspiel
Weissenkirchen 2014
90 Grüner Veltliner Federspiel
Weissenkirchen 2013

(91–93) Gemischter Satz Ried Seiber
Smaragd 2015

(92–94) Roter Traminer Setzberg Reserve 2015
91 Roter Traminer Setzberg Reserve 2014

(89–91) Neuburger Terrassen Spitz
Sommelier-Edition 2015

(90–92) Rosé 1805 Reserve 2015

90 Rosé Federspiel Terrassen 2015
89 Rosé Reserve Terrassen 2014

93 Beerenauslese Terrassen 2014 RR/CH/WB/GM
93 Beerenauslese Terrassen 2013
Pale golden yellow with brilliant highlights. Inviting tropical fruit aromas reminiscent of passion fruit with ripe, juicy peach and subtle notes of blossom honey. Medium complexity, ripe pineapple and refreshing acidity that nicely balances the luscious sweetness. Spicy piquancy lingers on the finish.

92 Grüner Veltliner Vintage 2014

94 Riesling Beerenauslese Kellerberg 2014

93 Riesling Trockenbeerenauslese
Kellerberg 2012

★ ★ ★
Weingut Johann Donabaum

3620 Spitz/Donau, Laaben 15
T: +43 (2713) 2488, F: +43 (2713) 2488, M: +43 (676) 9313150
info@weingut-donabaum.at, www.weingut-donabaum.at

Winemaker and Contact Person: Johann Donabaum jr.
Production: 70.000 bottles (100 % white)
Hectares: 8
Fairs: VieVinum, ProWein
Distribution partners: on request

The Johann Donabaum winery is currently among the most aspirational producers in the Wachau. The son of the house is supported by the experienced and continued work of his parents on the steep and demanding terraced vineyard slopes. The single vineyard wines of the house – Offernberg Riesling, Setzberg Riesling and Spitzer Point Grüner Veltliner – are found on wine lists of the best restaurants in Austria. The grape variety Neuburger is given merited attention as a Smaragd from the Spitzer Biern vineyard and is one of the very best examples from this rare variety. The old historic winery building stems from the 16th century and is reached via a small bridge in the Spitz gorge. The unerring diligence of the entire Donabaum family lays the foundation for quality by ensuring optimal fruit that is capable of expressing the soil, climate and signature of the vintner. The greatest success of this producer to date took place at the Decanter World Wine Awards in 2009 in London. There, the Riesling Smaragd Setzberg 2007 won the Interntional Riesling trophy, making it the best Riesling with a retail price of more than 10 British pounds.

(92–94) Riesling Smaragd Setzberg 2015
93 Riesling Smaragd Setzberg 2014
Pale green-yellow with silver highlights. Apricot and papaya notes with subtle honey and wild meadow herbs. A refreshing backbone of acidity elegantly accents the peach and apricot flavours. Stone fruit continues with subtle mineral nuances on the long finish. A superb accompaniment to food.
93 Riesling Smaragd Setzberg 2013

94 Riesling Smaragd Offenberg 2015
93 Riesling Smaragd Offenberg 2014
92 Riesling Smaragd Offenberg 2013

(93–95) Riesling Smaragd
    Limitierte Edition 2015
95 Riesling Smaragd Limitierte Edition 2013

(90–92) Riesling Federspiel Bergterrassen 2015
90 Riesling Federspiel Bergterrassen 2014

(93–95) Grüner Veltliner Smaragd
    Limitierte Edition 2015
94 Grüner Veltliner Limitierte Edition 2013
Medium golden yellow. Aromas and flavours of yellow apple and a touch of white vineyard peach are accompanied by delicate peppery spice, brioche, and a touch of orange zest. The juicy acidity elegantly balances and integrates the fruity sweetness. Passion fruit and light salty notes come in on the aftertaste. Good ageing potential.

(92–94) Grüner Veltliner Smaragd Wösendorfer
    Kirchweg 2015
92 Grüner Veltliner Smaragd Wösendorfer
    Kirchweg 2014
93 Grüner Veltliner Smaragd Kirchweg 2013

(92–94) Grüner Veltliner Smaragd
    Spitzer Point 2015
93 Grüner Veltliner Smaragd Spitzer Point 2014
94 Grüner Veltliner Smaragd Spitzer Point 2013

(91–93) Grüner Veltliner Smaragd Zornberg 2015
92 Grüner Veltliner Smaragd Zornberg 2013

(90–92) Grüner Veltliner Federspiel Point 2015
91 Grüner Veltliner Federspiel Point 2014

89 Grüner Veltliner Federspiel Johann 2014

(92–94) Neuburger Smaragd 2015
92 Neuburger Smaragd 2012

Weingut Franz Hirtzberger

3620 Spitz/Donau, Kremser Straße 8
T: +43 (2713) 2209, F: +43 (2713) 2209 20
weingut@hirtzberger.com, www.hirtzberger.com

Winemaker: Franz Hirtzberger
Contact Person: Irmgard Hirtzberger
Production: 200.000 bottles (99 % white, 1 % sweet)
Hectares: 25
Fairs: VieVinum, ProWein
Distribution partners: AUS, I, J, S, B, DK, L, FIN, F, CZ, NL, GB, N, USA

The Hirtzberger family cultivates some of the very best sites in the Wachau near the wine village of Spitz. The terraced site, Singerriedel, located directly behind an old picturesque vintner house, has brought the estate near-legendary fame for its magnificent Riesling. The Ried Hochrain is yet another famous Riesling site which can certainly be considered a "grand cru" of Austria. The Honivogel vineyard is to Grüner Veltliner what Singerriedel is for Riesling. New in the assortment is the Grüner Veltliner from the Kirchweg vineyard in Wösendorf. Franz Hirtzberger Sr. and his son, Franz Jr., complement one another perfectly in the vineyards and cellar, which is reflected in the entire assortment of wines. ranz Jr. has now taken responsibility for vinification without erring from the father's style and quality demands.

(95–97) Riesling Smaragd Singerriedel 2015
95 Riesling Smaragd Singerriedel 2014
Pale green-yellow with silver highlights. Nuances of mandarin zest, greengage plum, and fine smoky mineral components. Complex structure with racy acidity, nuances of pineapple and apricot, and sweet extract on the finish. Citrus and mineral notes remain in the long aftertaste.
97 Riesling Smaragd Singerriedel 2013

(95–97) Riesling Smaragd Hochrain 2015
94 Riesling Smaragd Hochrain 2014
Pale green-yellow with silver highlights. Fresh apricot and notes of peach with a touch of orange zest. Juicy and delicately fruity with a firm, balaced acidity structure. Sweet fruit extract lingers long on the finish. Very good potential for further development; will benefit from further bottle maturation.
96 Riesling Smaragd Hochrain 2013

(94–96) Riesling Smaragd Setzberg 2015
93 Riesling Smaragd Setzberg 2014
93 Riesling Smaragd Setzberg 2013

(90–92) Riesling Federspiel Steinterrassen 2015
90 Riesling Federspiel Steinterrassen 2014
91 Riesling Federspiel Steinterrassen 2013

(93–95) Grüner Veltliner Smaragd Honivogl 2015
94 Grüner Veltliner Smaragd Honivogl 2014
Medium greenish-yellow hue with silver highlights. Attractive mouthfilling fruit with notes of yellow apple and mango, elegant spice and nuances of tobacco and orange zest. A fine extract sweetness is wonderfully balanced with an elegant acidity structure. A note of honey is on the lengthy finish. Plenty of finesse and a marvellous accompaniment to food.
97 Grüner Veltliner Smaragd Honivogl 2013

(92–94) Grüner Veltliner Smaragd Axpoint 2015
93 Grüner Veltliner Smaragd Axpoint 2014
95 Grüner Veltliner Smaragd Axpoint 2013

(92–94) Grüner Veltliner Smaragd
        Kirchweg 2015
93 Grüner Veltliner Smaragd Kirchweg 2013
94 Grüner Veltliner Smaragd Kirchweg 2012

(92–94) Grüner Veltliner Smaragd
        Rotes Tor 2015
92 Grüner Veltliner Smaragd Rotes Tor 2014
94 Grüner Veltliner Smaragd Rotes Tor 2013

91 Grüner Veltliner Federspiel Rotes Tor 2015
90 Grüner Veltliner Rotes Tor 2014
91 Grüner Veltliner Federspiel Rotes Tor 2013

(91–93) Grauburgunder Smaragd Pluris 2015
93 Grauburgunder Smaragd Pluris 2014
94 Grauburgunder Smaragd Pluris 2013

(92–94) Weißburgunder Smaragd
        Steinporz 2015
93 Weißburgunder Smaragd Steinporz 2014
93 Weißburgunder Smaragd Steinporz 2013

(93–95) Neuburger Smaragd 2015
93 Neuburger Smaragd 2013
93 Neuburger Selection 2012

(92–94) Chardonnay Smaragd
        Schlossgarten 2015
92 Chardonnay Smaragd Schlossgarten 2014
93 Chardonnay Smaragd Schlossgarten 2013

★ ★ ★ ★

Weingut Högl

3620 Spitz/Donau, Viessling 31
T: +43 (2713) 8458, F: +43 (2713) 8458 4
office@weingut-hoegl.at, www.weingut-hoegl.at

Winemaker and Contact Person: Josef Högl
Production: 55.000 bottles (100 % white)
Hectares: 8
Fairs: Prowein, VieVinum
Distribution partners: J, NL, USA

This winery is situated in a little side valley of the Wachau, called the "Spitzergraben" "Terraces only" answered an English-speaking journalist when Josef Högl asked how he would describe the place. A visitor truly does get the feeling that a giant stone wall is going to fall down on him in this incredibly steep and narrow gorge. Hundreds of stone terraces climb 300 to 450 metres above sea level; dry stone walls that were painstakingly stacked by hand centuries ago and have been maintained for generations. The Schön vineyard alone has 57 terraces; half of this vineyard has been acquired over the past ten years and new terraces have been built and vines planted. The massive mica-schist in this site is a guarantee for Grüner Veltliner with depth and intense mineral character. The Brück vineyard also has mica-schist, but this is interspersed with pockets of sandstone. This meagre foundation is perfect for Riesling with extraordinary ageing potential. Josef Högl loves the challenge of getting the very most out of the extraordinary terroir that he has in his hands. His profound understanding of the microclimate allows him to choose the perfect picking time for ideal physiological ripeness. The numerous terraces are like musicians in an orchestra - each alone is an artist, yet combined together correctly, precision and exquisite complexity can be achieved in the wines. "Less is more," when it comes to vinification. Perfection in the fruit, achieved through multiple passages at harvest, is the foundation for the superb Högl wines.

(93–95) **Riesling Smaragd Vision 2015**
94 **Riesling Smaragd Vision 2014**
Medium green yellow. A highly refreshing bouquet features crisp greengage plum, white vineyard peach and attractive mineral components. Juicy and elegant with pleasant extract sweetness nicely balanced by a light and perky acidity play. Citrus notes appear on the lengthy finish. A promising future.
93 **Riesling Smaragd Vision 2013**

(94–96) **Riesling Smaragd Bruck
Alte Parzellen 2015**
94 **Riesling Smaragd Bruck
Alte Parzellen 2013**
95 **Riesling Smaragd Bruck
alte Parzellen 2012**

(92–94) **Riesling Smaragd Bruck 2015**
92 **Riesling Smaragd Bruck 2014**
93 **Riesling Smaragd Bruck 2013**

91 **Riesling Federspiel Bruck 2014**

(92–94) **Grüner Veltliner Smaragd
1000-Eimerberg 2015**
92 **Grüner Veltliner Smaragd
1000-Eimerberg 2014**
Brilliant green-yellow. Refreshing herbs and spice with white apple fruit, mango, and a touch of orange zest in the background. Compact and crisp with vibrant acidity. Subtle, pleasant vegetal components and plenty of fresh fruit mingle with salty minerals on the finish. This still needs a little time in the bottle to come together.
92 **Grüner Veltliner Smaragd
1000-Eimerberg 2013**

(93–95) **Grüner Veltliner Smaragd Schön 2015**
93 **Grüner Veltliner Smaragd Schön 2013**
94 **Grüner Veltliner Smaragd Schön 2012**

(94–96) Grüner Veltliner Smaragd Schön
    Alte Parzellen 2015
94 Grüner Veltliner Smaragd Schön
    Alte Parzellen 2013
95 Grüner Veltliner Smaragd Schön
    alte Parzellen 2012

(91–93) Grüner Veltliner Smaragd Dürnsteiner
    Kaiserberg G&G 2015
92 Grüner Veltliner Smaragd Dürnsteiner
    Kaiserberg 2013

89 Grüner Veltliner Federspiel Schön 2014

(92–94) Gelber Muskateller Smaragd Bruck 2015

(91–93) Chardonnay Smaragd Bruck 2015

★ ★ ★

Weingut Holzapfel

3610 Weißenkirchen, Prandtauerplatz 36
T: +43 (2715) 2310, F: +43 (2715) 2310 9
weingut@holzapfel.at, www.holzapfel.at

Winemaker and Contact Person: Karl Holzapfel
Production: n. a. (95 % white, 5 % red)
Hectares: 14
Fairs: ProWein, VieVinum
Distribution partners: J, CH, LV, DE, T, NZ, CZ, NL, N, USA, PL

The Holzapfel winery is found in an old harvest house that belonged to the Canons of St. Pölten 700 years ago. Jakob Prandtauer, the architect of the imposing Melk Monastery, later renovated the building in a baroque style. Most of the vineyards in the Wachau were once in the hands of the church and belonged to neighbouring abbeys and monasteries. This harvest house once served not only for vinification, but also as a centre for trade. The 14 hectares of vines continue to be cultivated in traditional methods. Plots are distributed in superb vineyards such as Achleiten, Vorderseiber, Weitenberg, Klaus, and Kollmitz. Grapes ripen on soils that are rocky and mineral with varying degrees of chalk and schist. Not only the excellent sites and low yield volumes are responsible for the uniqueness of the fruit – significant diurnal temperature fluctuations preserve the acidity that lends the wines freshness and light-footed elegance. Karl Holzapfel strives to produce crystal clear, fine, fruity wines with character and vibrancy for everyday enjoyment. His assortment, though, also includes concentrated Smaragd wines with complex aromas and outstanding ageing potential. After fermentation the wines remain on the fine lees. Each wine is given individual attention and the resulting wines display the inimitable stamp of their origin with splendid balance between minerality and freshness. Grüner Veltliner, Riesling and Weissburgunder (Pinot Blanc) are produced in all three of the Wachau quality categories Steinfeder, Federspiel and Smaragd. The series called "Selektion Hippolyt" impresses with its mellifluous creaminess and finesse.

(92–94) Riesling Smaragd Vorderseiber 2015
93 Riesling Smaragd Vorderseiber 2014
Pale green-yellow. Ripe peach with notes of lavender, wild herbs, and delicate mineral nuances. Juicy acidity nicely lifts papaya and apricot fruit. Long finish and plenty of finesse are found in this unique accompaniment to food.
93 Riesling Smaragd Vorderseiber 2013

92 Riesling Federspiel Zehenthof 2015
88 Riesling Federspiel Zehenthof 2014
90 Riesling Federspiel Zehenthof 2013

(93–95) Grüner Veltliner Smaragd Achleiten 2015
93 Grüner Veltliner Smaragd Achleiten 2014
Medium green-yellow with silver highlights. The complex nose features smoky, flinty notes, mango, floral components and dark minerals. Concentration and finesse are revealed through a complex array of fruit notes and a backbone of acidity and minerals. Subtle cayenne pepper notes are on the lengthy finish. Good ageing potential.
94 Grüner Veltliner Smaragd Achleiten 2013

(92–94) Grüner Veltliner Smaragd Kollmitz 2015
91 Grüner Veltliner Smaragd Kollmitz 2014
93 Grüner Veltliner Smaragd Kollmitz 2013

91 Grüner Veltliner Federspiel Zehenthof 2015
88 Grüner Veltliner Federspiel Zehenthof 2014
89 Grüner Veltliner Federspiel Zehenthof 2013

92 Grüner Veltliner Federspiel Achleiten 2015
89 Grüner Veltliner Federspiel Achleiten 2014
90 Grüner Veltliner Federspiel Achleiten 2013

91 Grüner Veltliner Hippolyt 2012

92 Weißburgunder Hippolyt 2012

Weingut Hutter Silberbichlerhof

3512 Mautern an der Donau, St.-Pöltner-Straße 385
T: +43 (2732) 83004, F: +43 (2732) 83004 4, M: +43 (664) 73543143
info@hutter-wachau.at, www.hutter-wachau.at

Winemaker: Friedrich Hutter III.
Contact Person: Friedrich Hutter III.
Production: 90.000 bottles (97 % white, 2 % red, 1 % sweet)
Hectares: 13
Fairs: VieVinum, ProWein
Distribution partners: CH, B, L, DE, EST, CZ, NL, GB, USA

The Hutter family winery cultivates 12.5 estate vineyards on the both sides of the Danube River – in the communities of Mautern on the right bank, and Loiben and Dürnstein on the left. The Hutter family is a member of the "Vinea Wachau" vintner association and produces wines in all three of the Wachau categories – Steinfeder, Federspiel and Smaragd – from the grape varieties Grüner Veltliner, Riesling and Grauburgunder (Pinot Gris).

94 Riesling Smaragd Hollerin 2014
Medium yellow with silver highlights. The attractive bouquet displays peach and apricot with candied orange peel and floral nuances. Complex and deep with subtle extract sweetness elegantly paired with juicy acidity. Orange comes in on the long finish. Plenty of finesse and superb ageing potential.

93 Riesling Smaragd Hollerin 2013
92 Riesling Smaragd Hollerin 2012

93 Riesling Smaragd Loibenberg 2014
93 Riesling Smaragd Loibenberg 2012
93 Riesling Smaragd Loibenberg 2011

90 Riesling Federspiel Riparum 2015
91 Riesling Federspiel Riparum 2014

90 Riesling Alte Point Federspiel 2014
89 Riesling Federspiel Alte Point 2013

92 Grüner Veltliner Smaragd Süssenberg 2013
92 Grüner Veltliner Smaragd Süssenberg 2014

(92–94) Grüner Veltliner Smaragd Alte Point 2015
92 Grüner Veltliner Smaragd Alte Point 2012

92 Grüner Veltliner Smaragd Kreutles 2013
91 Grüner Veltliner Smaragd Kreutles 2012

90 Grüner Veltliner Federspiel Süssenberg 2015
90 Grüner Veltliner Federspiel Süssenberg 2014
90 Grüner Veltliner Federspiel Süssenberg 2013

89 Grüner Veltliner Federspiel Alte Point 2015
90 Grüner Veltliner Federspiel Alte Point 2014
89 Grüner Veltliner Federspiel Alte Point 2013

88 Grüner Veltliner Steinfeder Silberbichl 2014

★ ★ ★ ★

Weingut Jamek

3610 Joching, Josef Jamek-Straße 45
T: +43 (2715) 2235, F: +43 (2715) 2235 22
info@weingut-jamek.at, www.weingut-jamek.at

Winemaker: Volker Mader
Contact Person: Dr. Herwig Jamek
Production: n. a. (85 % white, 14 % red, 1 % sweet)
Hectares: 25
Fairs: VieVinum, ProWein
Distribution partners: I, J, S, CH, B, LV, SLO, L, E, DE, FIN, CZ, F, NL, N, GB, H, USA, PL, P

The name Josef Jamek is inseparable from the cultural landscape of Wachau and the renaissance of Austrian wine culture. The estate was a leading influence in establishing a regional identity for the Wachau in the 1950s with its production of dry, unadulterated white wines. Jamek also provided the ideas that inspired the establishment of the esteemed "Vinea Wachau" vintner association. The winery possesses 25 hectares of largely contingent vineyards in the best primary rock sites and is among the most reputed private wineries in Wachau. The Ried Klaus vineyard is a synonym for Jamek wine culture, a prototype for Wachauer Riesling sourced from over one hundred steeply climbing stone terraces. This single-vineyard jewel has been bottled each vintage since 1959 and is testament to Josef Jamek's life vocation. Other famous Jamek sites include Achleiten, Stein am Rain, and Hochrain. The traditions of the winery and the adjacent gourmet restaurant have continued with the same ambition in the hands of Josef Jamek's daughter, Jutta, and her husband, Hans Altmann, since 1996. In recent years, they have been actively supported by their son in-law, Dr. Herwig Jamek, and his son, Johannes. Superb regional specialties can be enjoyed with the complete assortment of Jamek wines by the glass in the cosy atmosphere of the winery restaurant. A visit to the Jamek-Altmann estate is an obligatory appointment for every connoisseur that travels to the Wachau.

(92–94) Riesling Smaragd Ried Klaus 2015
93 Riesling Smaragd Ried Klaus 2014
Medium green-yellow with silver highlights. Delicate nuances of yellow peach and mandarin zest with a touch of honey and minerals. Complex and tautly textured with a vibrant acidity structure. Greengage plum and apricot linger elegantly on the finish. Already quite approachable.
94 Riesling Smaragd Ried Klaus 2013

(92–94) Riesling Smaragd Freiheit 2015
92 Riesling Smaragd Freiheit 2013

91 Riesling Federspiel Ried Klaus 2015
90 Riesling Federspiel Ried Klaus 2014
90 Riesling Federspiel Ried Klaus 2013

90 Riesling Federspiel Ried Pichl 2015
89 Riesling Federspiel Jochinger Pichl 2014
91 Riesling Federspiel Jochinger Pichl 2013

90 Jochinger Riesling Federspiel 2015
88 Riesling Federspiel Jochinger Riesling 2014
89 Riesling Federspiel Jochinger Berg 2013

**(92–94) Grüner Veltliner Smaragd
Ried Achleiten 2015**
93 Grüner Veltliner Smaragd Ried Achleiten 2014
Pale green-yellow with silver highlights. Nuances of fresh Golden Delicious apple with notes of fresh herbs and peppery spice. Subtle litchi and a touch of orange zest come in on the juicy, elegantly textured palate. Very round an approachable. Sweetly extracted fruit on the finish. A very versatile wine.
93 Grüner Veltliner Smaragd Ried Achleiten 2013

**(91–93) Grüner Veltliner Smaragd
Ried Liebenberg 2015**
92 Grüner Veltliner Smaragd Ried Liebenberg 2014
**92 Grüner Veltliner Smaragd
Ried Liebenberg 2013**

(90–92) Grüner Veltliner Smaragd
      Ried Kollmitz 2015

92 Grüner Veltliner Federspiel
    Ried Achleiten 2015
91 Grüner Veltliner Federspiel
    Ried Achleiten 2014
90 Grüner Veltliner Federspiel
    Ried Achleiten 2013

90 Grüner Veltliner Federspiel
    Stein am Rain 2015
89 Grüner Veltliner Federspiel
    Stein am Rain 2014
89 Grüner Veltliner Federspiel
    Stein am Rain 2013

(90–92) Weißer Burgunder Smaragd
      Ried Hochrain 2015
93 Weißburgunder Smaragd Ried Hochrain 2013

91 Weißburgunder Federspiel
    Ried Hochrain 2014
91 Weißburgunder Federspiel
    Ried Hochrain 2013

91 Gelber Muskateller Vierblattl 2014
90 Gelber Muskateller 2013
89 Gelber Muskateller Federspiel 2012

89 Chardonnay Federspiel Zweikreuzgarten 2014
89 Chardonnay Federspiel Zweikreuzgarten 2013

93 Riesling Trockenbeerenauslese
    Ried Klaus 2012

93 Riesling Beerenauslese Ried Klaus 2012

92 Grüner Veltliner Beerenauslese
    Ried Kollmitz 2012

Weingut Knoll

3601 Dürnstein, Unterloiben 132
T: +43 (2732) 79355, F: +43 (2732) 79355 5
weingut@knoll.at, www.loibnerhof.at

Winemaker and Contact Person: Emmerich Knoll
Production: n. a. (98 % white, 1 % red, 1 % sweet)
Hectares: 16
Fairs: VieVinum, ProWein
Distribution partners: AUS, I, J, S, B, CDN, CH, SGP, LV, SK, LT, DK, L,
E, DE, EST, FIN, T, F, NZ, CZ, NL, GB, N, USA

This winery has produced so many cult wines in recent decades, that it would not be a problem to fill an entire book with their tasting notes. Emmerich Knoll is not a fan of meaty, overly voluptuous wines. Like a Swiss watchmaker, Knoll tinkers uncompromisingly at details to bring terroir and finesse in the bottle. The Knoll winery in Unterloiben breathes tradition, and its inhabitants are straightforward, charming, and accommodating. Emmerich Knoll Jr. has travelled far and wide to gain international practical experience. Still, he enthusiastically supports his father. Together, they cultivate the famed sites Schütt, Loibenberg, Kellerberg, Kreutles, and Pfaffenberg. The vineyards are planted primarily with Riesling and Grüner Veltliner, which make up 45% each of the total vineyard area. The remaining 10% is planted with Chardonnay, Gelber Muskateller (Muscat Blanc à petits grains), Rivaner (Müller Thurgau), Blauburgunder (Pinot Noir), and Gelber Traminer (a rare local clone of Gewürztraminer). Each year's wine list comprises approximately 30 different wines, which include several versions of Grüner Veltliner and Riesling as well as other varietal wines. When the vintage brings botrytized grapes, they are selected by hand to produce noble sweet wines. The Knolls practice the admirable policy of waiting until September of the year following harvest to release their Smaragd and dessert wines, allowing them time to rest and mature in the cellar over the summer months. The Knoll wines are often considered late bloomers (not true) and to be worthy of ageing (very true). If one were to reduce the essence of Knoll, "Schütt" would be the quintessential vineyard and "Vinothekfüllung" the very best quality Grüner Veltliner and Riesling possible.

(95–97) Riesling Smaragd Vinothekfüllung 2015
95 Riesling Smaragd Vinothekfüllung 2014
Pale green-yellow with silver highlights. Honey-laced peach fruit with subtle candied orange peel and fresh mandarin. Complex; racy acidity is wonderfully bedded in sweet juicy peach and apricot. Dark mineral and salty elements add further complexity to the pleasant yellow fruit on the extremely long finale. Dependable potential for extended bottle maturation.
96 Riesling Smaragd Vinothekfüllung 2013

(94–96) Riesling Smaragd Ried Schütt 2015
94 Riesling Smaragd Schütt 2014
95 Riesling Smaragd Schütt 2013

(92–94) Riesling Smaragd Ried Loibenberg 2015
93 Riesling Smaragd Loibenberg 2014
93 Riesling Smaragd Loibenberg 2013

(93–95) Riesling Smaragd Ried Kellerberg 2015
93 Riesling Smaragd Kellerberg 2014
94 Riesling Smaragd Kellerberg 2013

(93–95) Riesling Ried Pfaffenberg
Selection 2015
94 Riesling Pfaffenberg Selection 2014
Pale green-yellow with silver highlights. Exotic yellow fruit reminiscent of pineapple and passion fruit with an undertone of dark minerals. Crisp and taut with pronounced mineral character. Litchi and lime come in on the long finish.
94 Riesling Pfaffenberg Selection 2013

(91–93) Riesling Kabinett Ried Pfaffenberg 2015
92 Riesling Kabinett Pfaffenberg 2014
91 Riesling Kabinett Pfaffenberg 2013

92 Riesling Federspiel Ried Loibenberg 2015
90 Riesling Federspiel Loibenberg 2014
90 Riesling Federspiel Loibenberg 2013

91 Loibner Riesling Federspiel 2015
89 Loibner Riesling Federspiel 2014
89 Riesling Federspiel 2013

(94–96) Grüner Veltliner Smaragd
         Vinothekfüllung 2015
96 Grüner Veltliner Smaragd
   Vinothekfüllung 2013
95 Grüner Veltliner Smaragd
   Vinothekfüllung 2012

(92–94) Grüner Veltliner Smaragd
         Ried Schütt 2015
93 Grüner Veltliner Smaragd Schütt 2014
Medium green-yellow with silver highlights. Yellow apple
and apricot interchange with notes of white pepper and
fresh meadow herbs. Finesse, concentration and an elegant
structure. White apple and honeydew melon remain on the
finish.
94 Grüner Veltliner Smaragd Schütt 2013

(92–94) Grüner Veltliner Smaragd
         Ried Loibenberg 2015
93 Grüner Veltliner Smaragd Loibenberg 2014
94 Grüner Veltliner Smaragd Loibenberg 2013

93 Grüner Veltliner Smaragd Ried Kreutles 2015
93 Grüner Veltliner Smaragd Kreutles 2013
93 Grüner Veltliner Smaragd Ried Kreutles 2012

96 Grüner Veltliner Loibenberg Reserve 2012

91 Loibner Grüner Veltliner Federspiel 2015
89 Loibner Grüner Veltliner 2014
89 Grüner Veltliner Federspiel 2013

92 Grüner Veltliner Federspiel
   Ried Kreutles 2015
91 Grüner Veltliner Federspiel Kreutles 2014
90 Grüner Veltliner Federspiel Kreutles 2013

91 Grüner Veltliner Federspiel Schütt 2014

90 Loibner Grüner Veltliner Steinfeder 2015
89 Grüner Veltliner Steinfeder 2013
88 Loibner Grüner Veltliner Steinfeder 2012

(91–93) Loibner Gelber Traminer Smaragd 2015
92 Gelber Traminer Smaragd 2013
92 Loibner Gelber Traminer Smaragd 2012

(91–93) Loibner Gelber Muskateller
         Smaragd 2015

90 Loibner Gelber Muskateller Federspiel 2015
90 Gelber Muskateller Federspiel 2014

(91–93) Loibner Chardonnay Smaragd 2015
92 Chardonnay Smaragd 2014
91 Chardonnay Smaragd 2013

93 Gelber Traminer Auslese 2014
94 Loibner Traminer Auslese 0,5l 2012

(93–95) Loibner Gelber Traminer
         Beerenauslese 2015

(93–95) Loibner Gelber Muskateller
         Beerenauslese 2015

(93–95) Loibner Grüner Veltliner
         Beerenauslese 2015

(94–96) Loibner Grüner Veltliner
         Trockenbeerenauslese 2015

(92–94) Loibner Riesling Auslese 2015

(94–96) Loibner Riesling Beerenauslese 2015

(96–98) Loibner Riesling
         Trockenbeerenauslese 2015

★ ★ ★ ★ ★

Weingut F. X. Pichler

3601 Dürnstein, Oberloiben 57
T: +43 (2732) 85375, F: +43 (2732) 85375 11
weingut@fx-pichler.at, www.fx-pichler.at

Winemaker: Lucas Pichler
Contact Person: Johanna Pichler
Production: n. a. (100 % white)
Hectares: 20
Fairs: VieVinum, ProWein
Distribution partners: AUS, I, RUS, J, S, CDN, CH, B, HR, SGP, SK, SLO, RC, L, E, DK, DE, MV, FIN, NZ, CZ, F, NL, GR, N, UA, GB, USA, IRL, PL, P, IL

The F.X. Pichler family winery has been one of the leading stars of the Wachau Valley for decades. Franz Xaver merits acknowledgement for an inimitable signature style of world-class wines. His son Lucas and daughter-in-law Johanna now manage the estate and succeed in further enhancing the F.X. Pichler reputation. When one speaks of the Pichler Rieslings and Grüner Veltliners, one also speaks of the most famous vineyards of Loiben and Dürnstein distributed between Steinertal in the east to Kellerberg in the west. The declared goal of the producer is to produce wines that are an authentic expression of the vintage, the soil, and the unique microclimate of the Wachau vineyards. One should be able to taste and feel the unique complexity and subtle nuances of each vineyard. Independent of their ripeness category, the wines also always exhibit the depth and precision sought by the producer. Anyone attempting to assess these wines must also consider the factor of time. The substantial Smaragd wines require seven to eight years in the bottle to fully develop and the wines under the "M" and the "Unendlich" labels need even longer to reach their peak. Since 2009, Lucas Pichler has a stunning facility in the middle of the vineyards between Dürnstein and Oberloiben. Finally, there is enough space for the winemaker to realize his oenological ideas.

(95–97) Riesling Smaragd
    Dürnsteiner Kellerberg 2015
94 Riesling Smaragd
    Dürnsteiner Kellerberg 2014
Pale green-yellow. Elegant vineyard peach and nuances of blossom honey, pineapple and orange. Clear and fresh as an alpine mountain stream: pineapple and stone fruits are highlighted by a racy, citrus acidity structure. Salty mineral elements come in on the long, refreshing finish. Already marvellous, but will still benefit from further bottle maturation.
97 Riesling Smaragd
    Dürnsteiner Kellerberg 2013

(97–99) Riesling Smaragd Unendlich 2015
98 Riesling Smaragd Unendlich 2013
97 Riesling Smaragd Unendlich 2012

(94–96) Riesling Smaragd
    Loibner Steinertal 2015
93 Riesling Smaragd Loibner Steinertal 2014
Pale green-yellow. Fresh pineapple and a touch of passion fruit mingle with attractive floral nuances. Tautly woven and with a cool character. Citrus and mineral notes combine with tropical fruit tones and play all the way through the long finale.
95 Riesling Smaragd Loibner Steinertal 2013

93 Riesling Smaragd Loibner Oberhauser 2015
92 Riesling Smaragd Loibner Oberhauser 2014
93 Riesling Smaragd Loibner Oberhauser 2013

(94–96) Riesling Smaragd
    Loibner Loibenberg 2015
93 Riesling Smaragd Loibner Loibenberg 2014
95 Riesling Smaragd Loibner Loibenberg 2013

(95–97) Riesling »M« Reserve 2015
96 Riesling »M« Reserve 2013

93 Riesling Smaragd Loibner Burgstall 2015
91 Riesling Federspiel Loibner Burgstall 2014
91 Riesling Federspiel Loibner Burgstall 2013

(95–97) Grüner Veltliner Smaragd Dürnsteiner
Kellerberg 2015
94 Grüner Veltliner Smaragd Dürnsteiner
Kellerberg 2014
Pale green-yellow with silver highlights. An inviting bouquet displays papaya, a touch of mandarin zest, honeydew melon, peppery spice and dark minerals. This continues on the complex full body where notes of white vineyard peach and fresh meadow herbs join in. The balanced acidity and mineral backbone demonstrate plenty of finesse. A complex, lingering finish.
95 Grüner Veltliner Smaragd
Dürnsteiner Kellerberg 2013

(93–95) Grüner Veltliner Smaragd
Dürnsteiner Liebenberg 2015
93 Grüner Veltliner Smaragd
Dürnsteiner Liebenberg 2014
94 Grüner Veltliner Smaragd
Dürnsteiner Liebenberg 2013

(93–95) Grüner Veltliner Smaragd
Loibner Loibenberg 2015
93 Grüner Veltliner Smaragd
Loibner Loibenberg 2014
94 Grüner Veltliner Smaragd
Loibner Loibenberg 2013

(93–95) Grüner Veltliner Smaragd
Loibner Steinertal 2015
92 Grüner Veltliner Smaragd
Loibner Steinertal 2014
94 Grüner Veltliner Smaragd
Loibner Steinertal 2013

93 Grüner Veltliner Smaragd
Urgestein Terrassen 2015
93 Grüner Veltliner Smaragd
Urgestein Terrassen 2013
93 Grüner Veltliner Smaragd
Urgestein Terrassen 2012

(94–96) Grüner Veltliner Smaragd »M« 2015
97 Grüner Veltliner Smaragd »M« 2013
95 Grüner Veltliner Smaragd »M« 2012

92 Grüner Veltliner Federspiel
Loibner Klostersatz 2015
90 Grüner Veltliner Federspiel
Loibner Klostersatz 2014
92 Grüner Veltliner Federspiel
Loibner Klostersatz 2013

(91–93) Grüner Veltliner Federspiel
Loibner Frauenweingarten 2015
91 Grüner Veltliner Federspiel
Loibner Frauenweingarten 2014
91 Grüner Veltliner Federspiel
Loibner Frauenweingarten 2013

94 Gelber Muskateller Smaragd
Loibner Loibenberg 2015
93 Gelber Muskateller
Loibner Loibenberg Smaragd 2013

(94–96) Riesling Beerenauslese
Loibner Loibenberg 2015

(96–98) Riesling Trockenbeerenauslese
Loibner Loibenberg 2015

★ ★ · ★ ★

Weingut Rudi Pichler

3610 Wösendorf, Marienfeldweg 122
T: +43 (2715) 2267
weingut@rudipichler.at, www.rudipichler.at

Winemaker and Contact Person: Rudi Pichler
Production: 70.000 bottles (100 % white)
Hectares: 15
Fairs: VieVinum, ProWein
Distribution partners: AUS, I, RUS, J, S, B, CDN, CH, SGP, BG, SK, DK, L, E,
DE, FIN, NZ, CZ, NL, N, HK, USA

Rudi Pichler certainly counts among the most successful vintners of the Wachau. His vineyards are distributed between Joching, Wösendorf, Weissenkirchen, and Mautern. White wines of character in astounding diversity for such a small winery are produced. Next to Grüner Veltliner and Riesling, Rudi Pichler cultivates Burgundian varieties as well. Pichler understands how to breathe character into wines of every category. His Grüner Veltliner Federspiel is always a favourite among insiders because it combines easy-drinking enjoyment with the classic varietal expression of the Wachau. Terroir is brilliantly defined in this vintner's Smaragd wines. After a few years' maturation in the bottle, these powerful wines develop their full splendour. Pichler continues to practice extended skin contact, yet abstains from his earlier philosophy of prolonging fermentation to better achieve the style that he seeks. The results are nuanced premium wines with an inimitable expression. The opening of the new winery building was celebrated in 2004, and not only is the architecture stunning, but it also provides the committed vintner optimal conditions for crafting his stunning wines. Mineral brilliance, taut structure and depth of aroma distinguishes Rudi Pichler's outstanding new series of wines. The differing terroirs are expressed with superb precision. It is a joy to taste these wines and the Grüner Veltliner and Riesling from the Achleithen vineyard are particularly fascinating. Falstaff awarded Rudi Pichler as Vintner of the Year in 2010.

96 Riesling Smaragd
Weissenkirchner Achleithen 2015
95 Riesling Smaragd
Weissenkirchner Achleithen 2014
Pale yellow with silver highlights. The multifaceted bouquet displays candied mandarin, dark minerals, a touch of yellow peach and citrus zest. Medium bodied and incredibly racy and salty. Litchi fruit is highlighted by a taut acidity structure. A very pure and crystalline finish features abundant minerals and notes of Fleur de Sel. Extraordinary ageing potential.
97 Riesling Smaragd
Weissenkirchner Achleithen 2013

95 Riesling Smaragd Wösendorfer Hochrain 2015
94 Riesling Smaragd Wösendorfer Hochrain 2014
95 Riesling Smaragd Wösendorfer Hochrain 2013

94 Riesling Smaragd
Wösendorfer Kirchweg 2015
94 Riesling Smaragd
Wösendorfer Kirchweg 2014
95 Riesling Smaragd
Wösendorfer Kirchweg 2013

95 Riesling Smaragd
Weissenkirchner Steinriegl 2015
93 Riesling Smaragd
Weissenkirchner Steinriegl 2014
94 Riesling Smaragd
Weissenkirchner Steinriegl 2013

93 Riesling Smaragd Terrassen 2015
93 Riesling Smaragd Terrassen 2014
93 Riesling Smaragd Terrassen 2013

91 Riesling Federspiel 2015
92 Riesling Federspiel 2014
92 Riesling Federspiel 2013

95 Grüner Veltliner Smaragd
  Weissenkirchner Achleithen 2015
95 Grüner Veltliner Smaragd
  Weissenkirchner Achleithen 2014

Pale green-yellow with silver highlights. Vineyard peach, subtle notes of mandarin zest and nuances of white pepper and dark minerals. Complex structure with a well-integrated acidity backbone embedded with sweet fruit notes. Pineapple comes in on the very convincing length. Already quite harmonious, but certainly not lacking in potential for ageing.

97 Grüner Veltliner Smaragd
  Weissenkirchner Achleithen 2013

94 Grüner Veltliner Smaragd
  Wösendorfer Hochrain 2015
94 Grüner Veltliner Smaragd
  Wösendorfer Hochrain 2014
95 Grüner Veltliner Smaragd
  Wösendorfer Hochrain 2013

94 Grüner Veltliner Smaragd
  Wösendorfer Kollmütz 2015
93 Grüner Veltliner Smaragd
  Wösendorfer Kollmütz 2014
94 Grüner Veltliner Smaragd
  Wösendorfer Kollmütz 2013

93 Grüner Veltliner Smaragd Terrassen 2015
93 Grüner Veltliner Smaragd Terrassen 2013
92 Grüner Veltliner Smaragd Terrassen 2012

92 Grüner Veltliner Federspiel Terrassen 2014

91 Grüner Veltliner Federspiel 2015
92 Grüner Veltliner Federspiel 2014
92 Grüner Veltliner Federspiel 2013

95 Roter Veltliner Smaragd 2015
95 Roter Veltliner Smaragd 2013
93 Roter Veltliner Smaragd 2012

93 Weißburgunder Smaragd
  Wösendorfer Kollmütz 2015
93 Weißburgunder 2014
94 Weißburgunder Smaragd
  Wösendorfer Kollmütz 2013

95 Grüner Veltliner Auslese Achleithen 2015

Weingut Prager

3610 Weißenkirchen, Wachaustraße 48
T: +43 (2715) 2248, F: +43 (2715) 25 32
prager@weissenkirchen.at, www.weingutprager.at

Winemaker: DI Toni Bodenstein
Contact Person: DI Ilse Bodenstein
Production: n. a. (100 % white)
Hectares: 17,5
Fairs: VieVinum
Distribution partners: AUS, I, RUS, J, S, B, SK, DK, T, CZ, NL, GB, N, USA

Vom Stein zum Wein" (from rocks to wine) is the motto. Toni Bodenstein's aim is to coax the ultimate quality potential of each of his vineyard sites in order to produce unique, archetypical wines that embody the character of their specific origin. Dubbed the "Terroirist of the Wachau," Toni Bodenstein also served as mayor of Weissenkirchen for several years. He has a complex philosophy, which fuses history with the future and sustainability with non-intervention. Thus, he cultivates his vineyards and makes his wines in a traditional way, employing innovation where necessary while always striving for the best possible quality. A holistic concept with sustainable measures results in authentic wines inspired by dedication to nature. Through his deep respect for the environment and responsibility to future generations, Bodenstein creates wines that unite elegance and finesse with expressiveness and power. These wines demonstrate that the great growths of the Wachau are some of the best in the world. Numerous international accolades validate the philosophy of Ilse and Toni Bodenstein, who together operate one of the most famous wine estates in Austria. The winery resembles a summer palace and was once a part of the old hamlet of Ritzling. This historic building was cited as the "Haus am Chling" .in a document dating to 1302, and further manuscripts from 1366 and 1715 identify the vineyards Ritzling, Hinter der Burg and Leber as belonging to the estate - as they still do today. The estate's extended vineyards are partly in Weissenkirchen (Steinriegl, Zwerithaler, Klaus and Achleiten), partly in Dürnstein (Kaiserberg, Hollerin and Liebenberg). The "Wachstum Bodenstein" is also worthy of attention, a Riesling that owes its filigree finesse to elevated sites (460 metres, or 1,500 feet).

With Grüner Veltliner it is the "Stockkultur" that is most remarkable: an ancient patch of post-trained vines in the Achleiten site provides wines of profound depth and concentrated mineral character. In contrast, another post-trained plot in the Achleiten that is only 20 years old is the source for the Grüner Veltliner "Wachstum Bodenstein". The Bodensteins cultivate 18 vineyard hectares and, for the most part, on extremely steep terraces. For Ilse and Toni Bodenstein, being vintners in the inimitable Wachau wine-growing area means both a privileged heritage and an inspiring challenge.

**(94–96) Riesling Smaragd Wachstum
Bodenstein 2015**
**95 Riesling Smaragd Wachstum
Bodenstein 2014**
Deep yellow with discreet green highlights. Nuances of peach, honey, and orange zest over a background of mango. Compact and concentrated with sweet fruit elegantly carried by balanced acidity. White vineyard peach, lemony nuances and plenty of minerals remain on the extremely long finish.
**94 Riesling Smaragd Wachstum
Bodenstein 2013**

(95–97) Riesling Smaragd Klaus 2015
94 Riesling Smaragd Klaus 2014
Medium green-yellow. Aromas and flavours of fresh vineyard peach and a touch of orange zest are bedded in abundant minerals. Juicy, tautly woven, precisely focused fruit. Sweet extract and white vineyard peach linger elegantly on the long finish. Excellent ageing potential.
93 Riesling Smaragd Klaus 2013

(93–95) Riesling Smaragd Steinriegl 2015
93 Riesling Smaragd Steinriegl 2013
93 Riesling Smaragd Steinriegl 2012

(94–96) Riesling Smaragd Achleiten 2015
93 Riesling Smaragd Achleiten 2014
93 Riesling Smaragd Achleiten 2013

91 Riesling Smaragd Kaiserberg 2013

93 Riesling Federspiel Steinriegl 2015
92 Riesling Federspiel Steinriegl 2014
90 Riesling Federspiel Steinriegl 2013

(95–97) Grüner Veltliner Smaragd Achleiten
          Stockkultur 2015
94 Grüner Veltliner Smaragd Achleiten
    Stockkultur 2014
Brilliant medium yellow with delicate green highlights. Inviting aromas of yellow tropical fruit reminiscent of pineapple and mango mingle with nuances of honey and candied
orange peel. Complex with sweetly extracted fruit highlighted by a vibrant acidity structure. Highly mineral on the per-
sisent finish. Very good potential for further developement.
94 Grüner Veltliner Smaragd Achleiten
    Stockkultur 2013

(94–96) Grüner Veltliner Smaragd Wachstum
          Bodenstein 2015
93 Grüner Veltliner Smaragd Wachstum
    Bodenstein 2014
93 Grüner Veltliner Smaragd Wachstum
    Bodenstein 2013

(93–95) Grüner Veltliner Smaragd
          Achleiten 2015
92 Grüner Veltliner Smaragd Achleiten 2014
93 Grüner Veltliner Smaragd Achleiten 2013

(92–94) Grüner Veltliner Smaragd
          Zweritaler 2015
92 Grüner Veltliner Smaragd Zwerithaler 2013
93 Grüner Veltliner Smaragd Zwerithaler 2012

91 Grüner Veltliner Smaragd Liebenberg 2013

91 Grüner Veltliner Federspiel
    Hinter der Burg 2015
90 Grüner Veltliner Federspiel
    Hinter der Burg 2014
91 Grüner Veltliner Federspiel
    Hinter der Burg 2013

Weingut Familie Schmelz

3610 Joching, Weinbergstraße 14
T: +43 (2715) 2435, F: +43 (2715) 2435 4
info@schmelzweine.at, www.schmelzweine.at

Winemaker and Contact Person: Johann and Thomas Schmelz
Production: n. a. (100 % white)
Hectares: 10 + 5
Fairs: VieVinum, ProWein
Distribution partners: AUS, I, RUS, S, CH, RC, L, DE, FIN, CZ, NL, GB, PL

The Schmelz family winery is situated in the heart of the Wachau in the little wine hamlet of Joching. It is operated by Johann and Monika together with their sons, Thomas and Florian, and Florian's wife, Bianca. Their vineyard plots are scattered over an eight-kilometre stretch from Wösendorf to Unterloiben, putting a variation of soil and microclimates at their disposal. Grüner Veltliner is the main variety followed by Riesling. The small remaining vineyard area is planted with Gelber Muskateller (Muscat blanc à petits grains), Sauvignon Blanc, and Weissburgunder (Pinot blanc). The care lavished on tending the vines and meticulous manual selection at harvest ensures healthy grapes. This pristine fruit is gently vinified in a modern cellar. The resulting wines offer inimitable drinking pleasure with their signature mellifluous fruit. The Schmelz family winery was a founding member of the "Vinea Wachau" vintner association. Their wines have won numerous national and international accolades. Hans Schmelz was awarded Falstaff Vintner of the Year in 2005. The Schmelz family wines can be tasted in their modern tasting room with an idyllic view of the surrounding vineyards.

(92–94) Riesling Smaragd Steinriegl 2015
93 Riesling Smaragd Steinriegl 2014
Pale green-yellow with silver highlights. Peach, litchi and lime over herbal spice and tobacco notes. The racy, well-integrated acidity highlights the juicy stone fruit flavours. The long fruity finish also features light salty mineral notes. Excellent ageing potential.
93 Riesling Smaragd Steinriegl 2013

(93–95) Riesling Smaragd
Dürnsteiner Freiheit 2015
91 Riesling Smaragd Dürnsteiner Freiheit 2014
91 Riesling Smaragd Dürnsteiner Freiheit 2013

(94–96) Riesling Smaragd Best Of 2015
93 Riesling Best Of 2013

90 Riesling Federspiel
Wachauer Weingebirge 2015
89 Riesling Wachauer Weingebirge 2014
90 Riesling Federspiel
Wachauer Weingebirge 2013

90 Riesling Federspiel TOM 2014
91 Riesling Federspiel TOM 2013
90 Riesling Federspiel TOM 2012

89 Riesling Federspiel Stein am Rain 2014
90 Riesling Federspiel Stein am Rain 2013

(92–94) Grüner Veltliner Smaragd
Höhereck 2015
92 Grüner Veltliner Smaragd Höhereck 2014
Pale green-yellow with silver highlights. Yellow apple, papaya nuance and a touch of orange zest with discreet wild herb notes in the background. Juicy, elegant, multifaceted structure. Ripe apple and mango mingle with abundant minerals on the finish. A versatile accompaniment to food.
92 Grüner Veltliner Smaragd Höhereck 2013

(92–94) Grüner Veltliner Smaragd
Steinertal 2015
92 Grüner Veltliner Smaragd Steinertal 2013
93 Grüner Veltliner Smaragd Steinertal 2012

(91–93) Grüner Veltliner Smaragd
Pichl Point 2015
92 Grüner Veltliner Smaragd Pichl Point 2014
91 Grüner Veltliner Smaragd Pichl Point 2013

(92–94) Grüner Veltliner Smaragd
    Loibenberg 2015
92 Grüner Veltliner Smaragd Loibenberg 2013
92 Grüner Veltliner Smaragd Loibenberg 2012

(93–95) Grüner Veltliner Smaragd Best Of 2015
93 Grüner Veltliner Smaragd Best Of 2013
95 Grüner Veltliner Best of 2012

90 Grüner Veltliner Federspiel Pichl Point 2015
90 Grüner Veltliner Federspiel Pichl Point 2014
91 Grüner Veltliner Federspiel Pichl Point 2013

91 Grüner Veltliner Federspiel Ried Klaus 2015

89 Grüner Veltliner Federspiel
    Loibner Gärten 2014
89 Grüner Veltliner Federspiel
    Loibner Gärten 2013
89 Grüner Veltliner Federspiel
    Loibner Gärten 2012

89 Grüner Veltliner Federspiel Steinwand 2014
90 Grüner Veltliner Federspiel Steinwand 2013
88 Grüner Veltliner Federspiel Steinwand 2012

89 Grüner Veltliner TOM 2014
91 Grüner Veltliner Federspiel TOM 2013
88 Grüner Veltliner Federspiel TOM 2012

90 Grüner Veltliner Federspiel
    Wachauer Terrassen 2015

88 Loibner Grüner Veltliner Federspiel 2015

91 Weißburgunder Smaragd Postaller 2014
91 Weißburgunder Smaragd Postaller 2013
93 Weißburgunder Smaragd Postaller 2012

90 Gelber Muskateller Postaller 2014
90 Gelber Muskateller Federspiel Postaller 2013
90 Gelber Muskateller Postaller 2012

(92–94) Weißer Burgunder Auslese 2015

★ ★ ★

Tegernseerhof – Mittelbach

3601 Dürnstein, Unterloiben 12
T: +43 (2732) 85362, F: +43 (2732) 85362 20
office@tegernseerhof.at, www.tegernseerhof.at

Winemaker and Contact Person: Martin Mittelbach
Production: n. a. (88 % white, 10 % red, 2 % sweet)
Hectares: 23
Fairs: VieVinum, ProWein
Distribution partners: AUS, I, S, CDN, CH, B, SGP, SK, DK, DE, T, FIN, CZ, F, N, GB, H, USA, PL, IS

The history of the Tegernseerhof stretches back one thousand years when Emperor Henry II gave the "zwei Huben Land" property in the Wachau to the Benedictine Abbey of Tegernsee. In 1176, the winery was built and given the name of the abbey that owned it. Today, many centuries later, the Tegernseerhof is in the hands of the Mittelbach family, who have been the owners now for six generations. The name Tegernseerhof has been passed from generation to generation just as has winemaking knowledge. The estate plots are distributed among some of the best vineyards of the Wachau. The sites are predominantly steep, terraced primary rock that benefit from good air circulation and exposure to sunshine. The Smaragd wines harvested from these vineyards exhibit astounding concentration of aroma and intense expression of their individual origins. Whether Grüner Veltliner or Riesling, each wine has its own personality and character. New in the assortment of wines this year is the Riesling Bergdistel Smaragd!

(93–95) Riesling Smaragd Kellerberg 2015
94 Riesling Smaragd Kellerberg 2014
Pale green-yellow with silver highlights. Yellow peach, a touch of mandarin and orange zest with dark minerals. Juicy and tightly woven with nuances of pineapple and passion fruit brightened with vibrant acidity. Citrus and saline notes linger in the aftertaste.
94 Riesling Smaragd Kellerberg 2013

(92–94) Riesling Smaragd Steinertal 2015
93 Riesling Smaragd Steinertal 2014

94 Riesling Smaragd Steinertal 2013
(93–95) Riesling Smaragd Loibenberg 2015
93 Riesling Smaragd Loibenberg 2014
92 Riesling Smaragd Loibenberg 2013

(92–94) Riesling Smaragd Bergdistel 2015

91 Riesling Steiner Pfaffenberg 2014

89 Riesling Federspiel Terrassen 2014
90 Riesling Federspiel Terrassen 2013

(93–95) Grüner Veltliner Smaragd Höhereck 2015
93 Grüner Veltliner Smaragd Höhereck 2014
Pale green-yellow with silver highlights. Still quite closed and the dark mineral, white apple fruit, orange zest, and elegant white pepper notes require some coaxing. Concentrated and elegant with a taut acid structure that lends light-footedness to the sweetly extracted fruit. The finish is long, delicious and crystalline. Good aging potential.
93 Grüner Veltliner Smaragd Höhereck 2013

(92–94) Grüner Veltliner Smaragd Loibenberg 2015
93 Grüner Veltliner Smaragd Loibenberg 2014
92 Grüner Veltliner Smaragd Loibenberg 2013

(91–93) Grüner Veltliner Smaragd Bergdistel 2015
92 Grüner Veltliner Smaragd Bergdistel 2014
92 Grüner Veltliner Smaragd Bergdistel 2013

(92–94) Grüner Veltliner Smaragd Schütt 2015

90 Grüner Veltliner Federspiel Superin 2014
90 Grüner Veltliner Federspiel Superin 2013
90 Grüner Veltliner Federspiel Superin 2012

92 Grüner Veltliner Federspiel Loibenberg 2014

91 Grüner Veltliner Federspiel Kreutles 2014
91 Grüner Veltliner Federspiel Kreutles
   Wallsé-Edition 2013

90 Grüner Veltliner Federspiel
   Frauenweingarten 2014
89 Grüner Veltliner Federspiel
   Frauenweingarten 2013

(91–93) Neuburger Smaragd Elsarner
        Brandstatt 2015
91 Neuburger Smaragd Brandstatt 2013

(92–94) Smaragd Weissenkirchner
        Zwerithaler 2015
92 Weissenkirchner Zwerithaler Smaragd 2013
   (Gemischter Satz)
91 Weissenkirchner Zwerithaler 2012

A mighty loess bank and deep, spicy wines

The Wagram gets its name from the magnificent loess bank that stretches along the left bank of the Danube River for over 30 km. 2,151 hectares of the Wagram vineyards are planted here. The remaining vineyard area (300 ha) is located in the vicinity of Klosterneuburg on the south side of the Danube River.

© ÖWM/Lehmann

The uniform geological features coupled with consistent weather and climatic patterns make the Wagram a model wine region. A deep layer of loess was deposited on the shore of a prehistoric sea forming a unique landscape with soils that are high in fossils and mineral content (the name Wagram comes from "Wogenrain" meaning "shore"). The influence of the Pannonian climate provides very warm sunny days that alternate with cool nights. This combination creates wines with pronounced fruit and elegant, creamy texture. This unique terroir is exquisitely expressed with the region's main grape variety, Grüner Veltliner. The indigenous speciality Roter Veltliner provides unique, long lasting wines. Leading producers will also cultivate some of the most opulent, full-bodied red wines in Niederösterreich especially from the Zweigelt and Pinot Noir varieties. The village of Grossriedenthal rounds off the range of wines with some outstanding Eiswein (ice wines). The success and confidence of the top producers has infused the entire Wagram region. Wine quality has soared to new heights with vintners not only inspiring one another, but also tourism and the culinary scene. Wagram is no longer considered an insider's tip. A new modern regional wine shop with a restaurant has been established in Kirchberg and offers the possibility to taste numerous wines from the Wagram.

The wineries of Klosterneuburg cover a wide range of viticultural activities, from the small, family owned heurige (winery taverns) to traditional estates of impressive magnitude. The Bundeslehranstalt für Wein und Obstbau (Federal Institute for Viticulture and Pomology), the world's first viticultural and oenology school (founded in 1860), is a leading wine institution with internationally recognised standards for future generations of Austrian winegrowers.

wine-growing area

© OEWM, 1040 Wien
www.TOURISVIS.COM

◆ Weingut Anton Bauer,
Feuersbrunn

◆ Weingut Familie Bauer – Naturnaher
Weinbau, Grossriedenthal

◆ Weingut Stefan Bauer,
Königsbrunn/Wagram

◆ Weingut Ecker – Eckhof,
Kirchberg/Wagram

◆ Weingut Josef Ehmoser,
Grossweikersdorf

◆ Weinhof Ehn, Engelmannsbrunn

◆ Weingut Fritsch, Kirchberg/Wagram

◆ Weingut Josef Fritz, Zaussenberg

◆ Weingut Heiderer-Mayer,
Baumgarten

◆ Weingut Stift Klosterneuburg,
Klosterneuburg

◆ Weingut Kolkmann, Fels/Wagram

◆ Weingut Leth, Fels/Wagram

◆ Weingut Nimmervoll, Kirchberg/Wagram

◆ Weingut Bernhard Ott, Feuersbrunn

◆ Weingut Urbanihof – Paschinger,
Fels/Wagram

◆ Weinhof Waldschütz, Sachsendorf

◆ Weingut Gerald Waltner,
Engelmannsbrunn

Weingut Anton Bauer

3483 Feuersbrunn, Neufang 42
T: +43 (2738) 2556, F: +43 (2738) 2556 60
office@antonbauer.at, www.antonbauer.at

Winemaker and Contact Person: Anton Bauer
Production: n. a. (54 % white, 45 % red, 1 % sweet)
Hectares: 29
Fairs: ProWein, VieVinum
Distribution partners: S, CH, B, DK, DE, CZ, GB, USA

When Anton Bauer takes something on, then he does so .wholeheartedly. At the time he took over the winery from his parents, in 1992, it had just 3.2 hectares of vines. The quality fanatic now cultivates around 30 hectares of vineyards in and around Feuersbrunn. He learned his craft at the viticultural high school in Krems, which he followed with an apprenticeship in Burgundy – a wine region that he continues to admire. Bauer also collected experience as a winemaker at various renowned wine estates in Lower Austria over a period of four years before he felt ready to begin his life's great adventure and take over the family estate. His path since then has been straight, steady and filled with enthusiasm. Anton Bauer's work is defined by the combination of a deeply rooted commitment to tradition and openness for new methods. This vintner's thoughts and actions have been visionary from the beginning. Next to the classic Wagram grape varieties Grüner Veltliner, Riesling and Roter Veltliner, he has also increased efforts in red wine production - something that was initially met with skepticism. Despite this, his Pinot Noir, Cabernet Sauvignon, and aptly named "Cuvée Legendär" (means legendary blend) now count among Austria's top red wines. The white wines play in the same league and express superb varietal and regional character. Rosenberg, Spiegel, Berg, and Gmörk are the names of his best vineyards from which single vineyard wines "with soul" are produced.

92 Grüner Veltliner Private Selection 2015

(92–94) Grüner Veltliner Grande Reserve 2015
94 Grüner Veltliner Grande Reserve 2014
Medium green-yellow with silver highlights. Mango and honeydew melon with an undertone of tobacco, herbs, minerals and peppery spice. Full-bodied with a mild acidity structure. Dark minerals and sweet extract of yellow fruit on the finish. Will benefit from bottle ageing.
93 Grüner Veltliner Grande Reserve 2013

(90–92) Grüner Veltliner Rosenberg Alte Rebe 2015
93 Grüner Veltliner Rosenberg Alte Reben 2014
91 Grüner Veltliner Rosenberg Alte Reben 2013

(90–92) Grüner Veltliner Spiegel 2015
92 Grüner Veltliner Spiegel 2014

(91–93) Riesling Alte Rebe 2015
91 Riesling Alte Reben 2013

(88–90) Pinot Blanc Rosenberg 2015

(90–92) Chardonnay Rosenberg 2015

(93–95) Legendär 2013 CS/ME/BF
94 Legendär 2012 CS/ME/BF
Deep dark ruby with an opaque core, purple highlights, and a thin transparent rim. An attractive bouquet features blueberry jam, nuances of fresh blackberry, liquorice, and a touch of sandalwood. Complex and full-bodied with abundant spicy tannins. Black cherry and minerals linger on the chocolaty finish. Will benefit from bottle ageing.
93 Legendär Limited Edition 2011 CS/ME/BF

(92–94) Cabernet Sauvignon Reserve
Limited Edition 2014
92 Cabernet Sauvignon Reserve
Limited Edition 2012
93 Cabernet Sauvignon Reserve Limited Edition 2011

(92–94) Blaufränkisch Reserve
      Limited Edition 2013
93 Blaufränkisch Reserve Limited Edition 2012

(91–93) Merlot Reserve Limited Edition 2014
91 Merlot Reserve Limited Edition 2012

(91–93) Wagram Reserve 2015 CS/BF/ZW/ME/SY
91 Wagram Reserve 2013 CS/BF/ZW/ME/SY
91 Wagram Reserve 2012 BF/CS/ZW/ME/SY

★★
Familie Bauer
3471 Großriedenthal, Hauptstraße 68
T: +43 (2279) 7204, F: +43 (2279) 2204 4
info@familiebauer.at, www.familiebauer.at

─── ORGANIC ───

Winemaker and Contact Person: Josef Bauer
Production: n. a. (60 % white, 35 % red, 5 % sweet)
Hectares: 25
Fairs: VieVinum, ProWein
Distribution partners: CH, B, DE, CZ, NL, USA

With a share of 45 percent, Grüner Veltliner is this 18-hectare estate's predominant grape variety, representing 45% of the vineyards. But due to the red tertiary gravel and deep loess deposits, the Wagram region is ideal also for the rare autochton variety Roter Veltliner, which is gaining importance here. Because the Wagram soils are so diverse, it is possible to find optimal sites for several different grape varieties. The Burgundian varieties are planted on calcareous loess while Riesling thrives on sandy-gravelly loess. Grüner Veltliner finds an ideal home on deep loess and red gravel. Four different Grüner Veltliner wines are produced, not including the ice wine that is made in suitable vintages. The Bauer family cultivates their vineyards according to certified organic regulations. Their diligent efforts brought them an environmental prize quite early. Also worthy of mention is an ice wine made from Blauer Burgunder (Pinot Noir) – a rarity that the family Bauer is justifiably quite proud.

91 **Roter Veltliner Hinterberg 2015**
91 **Roter Veltliner Hinterberg 2014**
Pale green-yellow. Pear and subtle honeydew melon with nuances of blossom honey and hedgerow flowers. Plenty of finesse and a juicy structure. Yellow apple and salty mineral compotes linger on the finish. A versatile accompaniment to food.
89 **Roter Veltliner Hinterberg 2013**

89 **Roter Veltliner Wagramterrassen 2015**
88 **Roter Veltliner Wagramterrassen 2014**

(90–92) **Grüner Veltliner Hinterberg 2015**
91 **Grüner Veltliner Hinterberg 2014**
92 **Grüner Veltliner Hinterberg 2013**

90 **Grüner Veltliner Goldberg 2015**
89 **Grüner Veltliner Goldberg 2014**
91 **Grüner Veltliner Goldberg 2012**

89 **Riesling Hinterberg 2015**
89 **Riesling Hinterberg 2014**
89 **Riesling Hinterberg 2013**

90 **Weißburgunder Reserve 2013**
92 **Weißburgunder Reserve 2011**

92 **Weißburgunder 2015**
89 **Weißburgunder 2014**
91 **Weißburgunder 2012**

93 **Blauburgunder Eiswein 2011**

92 **Grüner Veltliner Eiswein 2011**

88 **Zweigelt Reserve 2009**

Weingut Stefan Bauer

3465 Königsbrunn am Wagram, Rathausplatz 19
T: +43 (2278) 2771, F: +43
stefan@weingutbauer.at, www.weingutbauer.at

Winemaker and Contact Person: Stefan Bauer
Production: 60.000 bottles (90 % white, 9 % red, 1 % sweet)
Hectares: 12
Fairs: ProWein, VieVinum
Distribution partners: on request

Stefan and Karin Bauer have united the past and future with imagination in each of their wines as well as in the winery's architecture. The Bauers have no appreciation for aggressive wines that shout in your face. They rely on the natural virtues of regional varieties and strive for a classic, understated style that enhances the attributes of their leading varieties Grüner Veltliner and Roter Veltliner. The sensitive straightforwardness, the complete abstinence from fashionable allures as well as the rejection of the mainstream are what makes this winery and its wines special. "I don't chase after any short term trends," says Stefan Bauer. The entry level Grüner Veltliner is called "Wagram" and is followed by the single vineyard wines "Bromberg" and "Steinagrund". Bauer has named his flagship wine in honour of the foresight and adventurousness of his grandparents, Josef and Mathilde Hutzler. The "Hutzler" is sourced from the oldest and best vines in the vineyards surrounding Koenigsbrunn. Its great potential, complex fruit, and harmonious power are derived from the Wagram loess soils. It is a complex, vibrant wine with ageing potential that is first released on the market in the autumn following the harvest.

93 Grüner Veltliner Hutzler Reserve 2014
93 Grüner Veltliner Hutzler Reserve 2013
Pale golden yellow. Passion fruit and ripe yellow apple with delicate nuances of smoked lapsang souchong tea and wild herbs. Full bodied and elegantly structured with sweetly extracted fruit elegantly laced with abundant minerals. Yellow apple and salty mineral compnents linger on the finish. A versatile accompaniment to food.
93 Grüner Veltliner Hutzler Reserve 2012

91 Grüner Veltliner Steinagrund 2015
92 Grüner Veltliner Steinagrund 2013
91 Grüner Veltliner Steinagrund 2012

90 Grüner Veltliner Bromberg 2015
91 Grüner Veltliner Bromberg 2014
Pale green yellow with silver highlights. Aromas and flavours of apple, blossom honey, wild herbs and floral notes highlighted by a juicy, fine acidity structure. Pear, pepper and minerals linger on the finish of this versatile food wine.
90 Grüner Veltliner Bromberg 2013

88 Grüner Veltliner Wagram 2015
89 Grüner Veltliner Wagram 2014
89 Grüner Veltliner Wagram 2012

92 Roter Veltliner Reserve 2014
92 Roter Veltliner Reserve 2013

89 Roter Veltliner 2015
90 Roter Veltliner 2014
89 Roter Veltliner 2013

90 Riesling 2014
90 Riesling 2012

89 Weißburgunder 2014
88 Weißburgunder 2012

91 Roter Veltliner Reserve 2012

★★★

Weingut Ecker – Eckhof

3470 Kirchberg am Wagram, Mitterstockstall 25
T: +43 (2279) 2440, F: +43 (2279) 2440 50
weingut@eckhof.at, www.eckhof.at

Winemaker and Contact Person: Bernhard Ecker
Production: n. a. (80 % white, 20 % red)
Hectares: 24
Fairs: VieVinum, ProWein
Distribution partners: IL, B, FIN, NL, USA

The vineyards of the 400-year-old Ecker-Eckhof wine estate are located on the loess slopes of the idyllic hamlet Mitterstockstall. Bernhard Ecker, born 1977, strives uncompromisingly for the very highest qualities possible. A very diversified assortment, lead by Grüner Veltliner, is sourced from 24 hectares of vines. Other varieties grown are Riesling, Weissburgunder (Pinot Blanc), Roter Veltliner, Gelber Muskateller (Muscat Blanc á petits grains), St. Laurent, Zweigelt, and Blauburgunder (Pinot Noir). The top vineyards are Mordthal, Steinberg, Schlossberg and Hundsberg. The vineyards are cultivated sustainably using environmentally friendly techniques. Various styles of wines are produced ranging from classic light and fruity summer wines to more powerful premium wines. Sweet wines are produced in suitable years. The family's goal is to produce white wines with typical regional character and concentrated, harmonious red wines.

The winery made a significant achievement at the Lower Austrian Fair where, out of 1500 wine entries, Ecker wines won the two hotly contended Grüner Veltliner categories. The wines are available throughout the year either directly from the winery (appointment recommended) or from selected partners in Austrian and abroad. The wines can also be enjoyed at the wine tavern with tasty regional specialties.

(92–94) Roter Veltliner Steinberg Große Reserve 2015

92 Roter Veltliner Steinberg 2015
92 Roter Veltliner Steinberg 2014
Pale green-yellow. Litchi, wild meadow herbs, blossom honey and orange zest. Sweetly extracted fruit is nicely structured with juicy, well integrated acidity. Elegant ripe tropical fruit lingers on the finish of this versatile food wine. Good potential for further development.
92 Roter Veltliner Steinberg 2013

89 Roter Veltliner Wagram 2015
89 Roter Veltliner Wagram 2014
89 Roter Veltliner Wagram 2013

92 Grüner Veltliner Mordthal 2015
92 Grüner Veltliner Mordthal 2014
Pale green yellow. Tropical yellow fruit reminiscent of mango, ripe apple, blossom honey and floral notes. The multifaceted structure features juicy acidity that elegantly lifts the sweet extract with honeydew melon and passion fruit notes. Tropical nuances and minerals linger on the finish. Good potential.
91 Grüner Veltliner Mordthal 2013

92 Grüner Veltliner Steinberg Große Reserve 2013

89 Grüner Veltliner Steinberg 2015
89 Grüner Veltliner Steinberg 2014
89 Grüner Veltliner Steinberg 2013

90 Grüner Veltliner Schloßberg 2015
90 Grüner Veltliner Schlossberg 2014
90 Grüner Veltliner Schloßberg 2013

88 Grüner Veltliner von Stokstal 2015
89 Grüner Veltliner von Stokstal 2014
88 Grüner Veltliner von Stokstal 2013

88 Riesling 2015
88 Riesling Wagram 2014
89 Riesling 2013

91 Weißer Burgunder Schloßberg 2015
90 Weißburgunder Schlossberg 2014

91 Eckhof Weiße Reserve 2013 GV/SB
93 Eckhof 2011 SB/GV

★ ★ ★
Weingut Josef Ehmoser

3701 Tiefenthal, Tiefenthal 9
T: +43 (2955) 70442, F: +43 (2955) 70442
office@weingut-ehmoser.at, www.weingut-ehmoser.at

Winemaker: Josef Ehmoser
Contact Person: Josef and Martina Ehmoser
Production: n. a. (80 % white, 20 % red)
Hectares: 15,5
Fairs: ProWein, VieVinum
Distribution partners: on request

The wines of Josef Ehmoser tell of fertile soils and hard labour, from hot sun and deep loess. The expressive assortment of wines from this Wagram vintner is no longer a secret insider tip after years of consistently high quality. Full-bodied finesse is the style for which Josef Ehmoser is best known. Grüner Veltliner plays the leading role at this Wagram winery. "Von den Terrassen" is a spicy classic version while "Hohenberg" is the powerful expression of the unique terroir of the vineyard of the same name. The winery's top Grüner Veltliner stems from handpicked grapes from the prime vineyard "Georgenberg" in the wine village of Grossweikersdorf. This single vineyard wine is fermented partially in large oak casks. Josef Ehmoser demonstrates that Riesling from a pure loess site can also develop wonderful piquancy. The red wine program includes a Zweigelt and an expressive St. Laurent – both matured in large oak casks. Josef Ehmoser strives to enhance the potential of the wines and highlight their unique personalities without manipulating them to fit a certain recipe. The will of nature should remain undisturbed. And it provides plenty of drinking pleasure – even years later!

93 Grüner Veltliner Grossweikersdorfer Ried Georgenberg 2014
93 Grüner Veltliner Georgenberg 2013
Pale yellow hue with silver highlights. Yellow apple and pepper spice underscored by blossom honey and floral components. Sweet fruit extract is structured with elegant minerals and juicy acidity. Passion fruit and minerals on the finish. A versatile food wine with good potential to develop further.
93 Grüner Veltliner Georgenberg 2012

(90–92) Grüner Veltliner Grossweikersdorfer Ried Hohenberg 2015
91 Grüner Veltliner Hohenberg 2014
91 Grüner Veltliner Hohenberg 2013

89 Grüner Veltliner Von den Terrassen 2015
89 Grüner Veltliner Von den Terrassen 2014
88 Grüner Veltliner Von den Terrassen 2013

(90–92) Riesling Vom gelben Löss 2015
91 Riesling Vom gelben Löss 2014
Pale green yellow with silver highlights. Peach and mango laced with blossom honey and wild herbs. Refreshing acidity lends an elegant juiciness to the tropical fruit and apricot notes. Ripe stone fruit and mineral tones linger long on the finish. A versatile food accompaniment.
90 Riesling Vom gelben Löss 2013

(88–90) Weißer Burgunder 2015
89 Weißer Burgunder 2014
89 Weißer Burgunder 2013

Weinhof Ehn

3470 Engelmannsbrunn, Kapellenberg 47
T: +43 (2279) 27377, F: +43 (2279) 27377
office@weinhofehn.at, www.weinhofehn.at

Winemaker and Contact Person: Gerhard Ehn
Production: n. a. (85 % white, 15 % red)
Hectares: 10
Fairs: VieVinum
Distribution partners: on request

The versatile plateaus and slopes of the Wagram offer ideal preconditions for Gerhard Ehn to produce high quality wines in conscientious respect of the environment. The young vintner took over the family wine estate in 2003 and modernized it step by step and now has even built a new cellar. The wine labels have also been changed to a simple, but memorable design. The vinification is practiced as gently as possible by using the force of gravity to move grapes, must and wine with minimal use of pumps. Wines are fermented in stainless steel, large wooden casks, or partially in small oak barrels according to what is suitable for the variety and the vintage. The main focus of the vintner is Grüner Veltliner. With four different variations he has succeeded in creating a high quality series of wines that range from a light, spritzy summer wine called "Swing" all the way up to an impressive full-bodied example called "Sonnleitn". The grape varieties Weissburgunder (Pinot Blanc), Chardonnay, Riesling and Gelber Muskateller complete the assortment of white wines. Representing the red wines are two Zweigelts – one is fruit-driven and the other is matured in small oak barrels. The goal of this ambitious enterprise is to combine modern vinification with environmental conscientiousness to produce wines that bring abundant unadulterated enjoyment.

91 Grüner Veltliner Sonnleitn 2015
91 Grüner Veltliner Sonnleitn 2014
Medium green-yellow. Yellow apple and papaya with subtle floral notes, wild herbs and blood orange zest. Multifaceted and concentrated with a tightly woven structure. Refreshing acidity highlights the fruit on the palate and the mineral finish. Good ageing potential.
92 Grüner Veltliner Sonnleitn 2013

90 Grüner Veltliner Ried Satz 2015
90 Grüner Veltliner Ried Satz 2014
90 Grüner Veltliner Ried Satz 2013

89 Grüner Veltliner Hochrain 2015
89 Grüner Veltliner Hochrain 2014
89 Grüner Veltliner Hochrain 2013

88 Grüner Veltliner Swing 2014
88 Grüner Veltliner Swing 2013
89 Grüner Veltliner Swing 2012

91 Weißer Burgunder 2015
90 Weißburgunder 2014
91 Weißburgunder 2013

89 Chardonnay 2015
88 Chardonnay 2014
89 Chardonnay 2013

90 Gelber Muskateller 2015

★★★★
Weinbau Karl Fritsch

3470 Oberstockstall, Schlossbergstraße 9
T: +43 (2279) 5037, F: +43 (2279) 50 37 19, M: +43 (664) 9254470
info@fritsch.cc, www.fritsch.cc

——— ORGANIC ———

Winemaker and Contact Person: Karl Fritsch
Production: n. a. (75 % white, 25 % red)
Hectares: 25
Fairs: VieVinum, ProWein, MillesimeBio, Foodex Japan
Distribution partners: I, J, S, CDN, CH, ROK, SGP, CZ, NL, GB, USA

For Karl Fritsch, making wine in the new millennium means having a positive foundation and tradition on which to build. It is only when traditional values and experience are paired with modern inspiration that a cultural good can be preserved and further enhanced. Two thirds of the 21 hectares of vineyards are planted with white wines with the main focus on Grüner Veltliner and Riesling. The remaining third of the vineyard area is dedicated to the production of red wine. The Wagram offers exceptional conditions for Grüner Veltliner due to the superb symbiosis of climate and soil. If seeking the core competency of this estate, then one should best examine its examples of this variety. Grüner Veltliner is produced as a light summer wine as well as in the form of sublime single vineyard wines such as the "Steinberg" and "Schlossberg". Among the red wines, the juicy Pinot Noir possesses an excellent reputation and the "Foggathal" blend counts among the best and most renowned red wines of Austria. Karl Fritsch is manager of the estate as well as the winemaker. He enjoys a very good reputation among his colleagues due to his innovative spirit. His sensitive hand makes it possible to create a versatile assortment of wines from the endless possibilities provided by nature. This is confirmed not only by the growing number of customers, but also the numerous accolades for his wines. Karl Fritsch places priority on the preservation of nature and its resources with the conversion to biodynamic viticulture in January of 2006. He sees it not as a duty, but as a privilege to work with nature. Karl Fritsch was accepted into the prestigious vintners' association "Österreichischen Traditionsweingüter" in 2007, which further highlights the importance of his role as a leader in the Wagram wine region.

94 Grüner Veltliner Schlossberg 1 ÖTW 2014
93 Grüner Veltliner Schlossberg 1 ÖTW 2013
Brilliant yellow with silver highlights. Ripe, inviting tropical fruit reminiscent of pineapple and mango with subtle blossom honey in the background. Juicy and round with a delicate acidity structure lending elegance to the sweet fruit extract. This charming accompaniment to food is ready to enjoy.
94 Grüner Veltliner Schlossberg 1 ÖTW 2012

93 Grüner Veltliner Mordthal 1 ÖTW 2014
93 Grüner Veltliner Mordthal 1 ÖTW 2013
92 Grüner Veltliner Mordthal 1 ÖTW 2012

91 Grüner Veltliner Steinberg 2015
90 Grüner Veltliner Steinberg 2014
90 Grüner Veltliner Steinberg 2013

89 Grüner Veltliner Wagram 2015
89 Grüner Veltliner Wagram 2014
88 Grüner Veltliner Wagram 2013

89 Grüner Veltliner Donaulöss 2014
88 Grüner Veltliner Donaulöss 2013

92 Riesling Mordthal 1 ÖTW 2014
91 Riesling Mordthal 1 ÖTW 2013
93 Riesling Mordthal 1 ÖTW 2012

92 Riesling Kapuzinerberg 1 ÖTW 2013
91 Riesling Kapuzinerberg 1 ÖTW 2012

90 Riesling Wagram 2015
90 Riesling Wagram 2014
89 Riesling Wagram 2013

91 Roter Traminer Materia Prima 2014

94 Tausendweiss 2012 GV/WB/CH
94 Tausendweiss 2010 GV/WB/CH
Medium green-yellow with silver highlights. Wild meadow

herbs, delicate yellow apple, subtle greengage plum, nuances of orange zest and a touch of minerality. Tautly structured with highly elegant acidity supporting a pleasant pear tone. The tremendously long finish is very harmonious. A superb wine to pair with food.

95 Tausend Weiss 2009 GV/WB/CH

92 Burgunder Cuvée 2013 WB/CH
92 Weißburgunder Chardonnay 2012 WB/CH

92 Pinot Noir »P« 2013
93 Pinot Noir »P« 2012

90 Pinot Noir Exlberg 2014
89 Pinot Noir Exlberg 2013

93 Cabernet Sauvignon »P« 2011

92 Foggathal Nr. 20 2012 ZW/CS
92 Foggathal No. 19 2011 ZW/CS

89 Red Soil 2012 ZW/SY
90 Red Soil 2011 ZW/SY

92 Riesling Beerenauslese 2014

★ ★ ★
Weingut Josef Fritz

3701 Zaußenberg, Ortsstraße 3
T: +43 (2278) 2515, F: +43 (2278) 2515 4
office@weingut-fritz.at, www.weingut-fritz.at

Winemaker: Josef Fritz
Contact Person: Josef and Irene Fritz
Production: n. a. (80 % white, 19 % red, 1 % sweet)
Hectares: 15
Fairs: ProWein, VieVinum
Distribution partners: I, CH, B, SK, DK, DE, NL, GB, USA, PL

Fritz is a traditional wine estate with modern understanding. The union of the tried and true with innovation at the highest international standard is the goal of the Fritz family. Numerous national and international accolades confirm their efforts.

Ecological balance is a core value of the Fritz's holistic concept. Fertilization with homemade compost and reduction of plant protection sprays help to preserve the environment. Yield restricting methods help provide vines with optimal nourishment even in difficult years. Selective manual harvest and cautious fruit transport are a matter of course in ensuring the highest possible quality. Gentle processing of the grapes with movement exclusively with power of gravity and perfect fermentation are important factors in creating wines with plenty of character. Varietal character and easy drinking pleasure are the most valued attributes for the light wines and for this, temperature-controlled fermentation in stainless steel is a prerequisite. The Wagram terroir – the interplay of soil and cool climate – lend the wines unique regional expression and character. The best grapes are fermented spontaneously for the premium wines. Oak is used judiciously to lend wines the winemaker's unique signature. A total of 15 vineyard hectares are cultivated, with 80% of production made up of white wines. The most important varieties are Roter Veltliner, Grüner Veltliner, Chardonnay, and Roter Traminer (a local variation of Gewürztraminer).

95 Roter Veltliner Steinberg Privat 2014
95 Roter Veltliner Steinberg Privat 2013
Medium yellow green. Apricot and delicate tropical fruit nuances reminiscent of mango mingle with orange zest and a touch of blossom honey. A tightly woven structure features juicy acidity elegantly paired with sweetly extracted papaya. This versatile food wine has good length and potential for further development.
94 Roter Veltliner Steinberg Privat 2012

93 Roter Veltliner Steinberg 2015
92 Roter Veltliner Steinberg 2014
92 Roter Veltliner Steinberg 2013

89 Roter Veltliner Wagramterrassen 2015
89 Roter Veltliner Wagramterrassen 2014
89 Roter Veltliner Wagramterrassen 2013

92 Roter Veltliner Gondwana 2013

92 Grüner Veltliner Schlossberg 2014
92 Grüner Veltliner Schlossberg 2013
Medium green-yellow. Papaya, honeydew melon, baked apple and delicate wild herbs. Juicy and elegantly structured with plenty of finesse. Ripe, tropical fruit and sweet extract linger on the finish. Good ageing potential.
92 Grüner Veltliner Schloßberg 2012

91 Grüner Veltliner Himmelreich 2015
91 Grüner Veltliner Im Himmelreich 2014
91 Grüner Veltliner Im Himmelreich 2013

88 Grüner Veltliner Sandstein 2015
89 Grüner Veltliner Sandstein 2014
89 Grüner Veltliner Sandstein 2012

91 Chardonnay Steinberg 2013

91 Chardonnay Steinberg Große Reserve 2014

93 Roter Traminer Trausatz Große Reserve 2014
93 Roter Traminer Trausatz Grande Reserve 2013
92 Roter Traminer Trausatz Grande Reserve 2012

89 Sankt Laurent 2013

★
Weingut Heiderer-Mayer

3701 Großweikersdorf, Baumgarten am Wagram 25
T: +43 (2955) 70368, F: +43 (2955) 70368 4
office@heiderer-mayer.at, www.heiderer-mayer.at

Winemaker and Contact Person: Helmut Mayer
Production: n. a. (56 % white, 44 % red)
Hectares: 26
Fairs: ProWein, Alles für den Gast Salzburg, Intervino
Distribution partners: B, DE, NL, PL

Always in harmony with nature and striving to bring the highest quality from the vine into the bottle is family Mayer's motto. This member of the "Wagramer Selektion" marketing association cultivates 15 hectares of vineyards in Baumgarten in Wagram. The south-facing loess terraces are predestined for white wine, particularly Grüner Veltliner. Fruit-driven Chardonnays and elegant Rieslings also convince with their crystal clear structure. Special attention is given to the red wines that are sourced from a convex sloped bowl with ideal soils. Along with the Zweigelt and St. Laurent, a small amount of Cabernet Sauvignon is vinified. The emphasis is on powerful, fruity red wines with velvety tannins and good colour intensity. The oak matured blend "Legat" will be presented to the European Wine Knights. The sparkling wine Esprit completes a versatile range of wines. By sampling the wines in the winery tasting room one can not only be convinced of the longevity of the wines, but also their enjoyable drinkability and optimal value for price.

(90–92) Grüner Veltliner Silberberg 2015
91 Grüner Veltliner Ried Silberberg 2014
Green-yellow with silver highlights. Delicate apple with elegant notes of citrus and a touch of tobacco. Full-bodied and elegantly structured with light extract sweetness nicely paired with refreshing acidity. Ripe Golden Delicious apple on the long finish. Good ageing potential.
91 Grüner Veltliner Ried Silberberg 2013

89 Grüner Veltliner Wagramer Selektion 2015
89 Grüner Veltliner Wagramer Selektion 2014
88 Grüner Veltliner Wagramer Selektion 2013

88 Chardonnay Wagramer Selektion 2015
88 Chardonnay Wagramer Selektion 2014

89 Sauvignon Blanc Wagramer Selektion 2015
89 Sauvignon Blanc Wagramer Selektion 2013
87 Sauvignon Blanc Wagramer Selektion 2012

88 Sauvignon Blanc Ried Hohenberg 2013

88 Gelber Muskateller Wagramer Selektion 2012

89 Cabernet Sauvignon Barrique 2013
89 Cabernet Sauvignon Barrique 2012
89 Cabernet Sauvignon Barrique 2011

88 Legat Barrique 2012 ZW/CS/RÖ
88 Legat Barrique 2011 ZW/CS/RÖ

89 Traminer Beerenauslese 2013

★★★
Weingut Stift Klosterneuburg

3400 Klosterneuburg, Stiftsplatz 1
T: +43 (2243) 411 522, F: +43 (2243) 411 550
weingut@stift-klosterneuburg.at, www.stift-klosterneuburg.at

Winemaker: Günther Gottfried
Contact Person: Dr. Wolfgang Hamm
Production: n. a. (45 % white, 55 % red)
Hectares: 108
Fairs: ProWein, VieVinum
Distribution partners: AUS, I, J, S, B, CDN, SRB, RC, FIN, F, CZ, NL, GB, N, USA, IRL, PL

The Klosterneuburg Monastery has been growing grapes and making wine ever since it was founded in 1114, which makes it one of the oldest, largest and most famous wine estates in Austria. The vineyards are located in prime sites in Klosterneuburg, Vienna, Gumpoldskirchen and Tattendorf. Grüner Veltliner, Riesling and Sauvignon Blanc are cultivated on 23 hectares (57 acres) in Klosterneuburg, while Burgundian varieties dominate in the Viennese vineyards. Pinot Blanc, Chardonnay and Pinot Noir are supplemented by Traminer, Riesling and Grüner Veltliner on the 25 hectares (62 acres) on the Viennese vineyard slopes Kahlenberg, Leopoldsberg and Nussberg. The extremely rare autochthon specialties Zierfandler and Rotgipfler are cultivated in Gumpoldskirchen. The estate's famous red wines are grown in Tattendorf and its Ried Stiftsbreit is the largest contiguous vineyard area of St. Laurent in the world and comprises 42 hectares (104 acres). The estate also grows Zweigelt, Blaufränkisch, Cabernet Sauvignon, Cabernet Franc and Merlot there. The estate offers two ranges of wines. The Stiftsweine (abbey series) are fruit-driven in style and express typical varietal and regional character. The Lagenweine (single-vineyard series) come from the best vineyards and are unique, concentrated, long-lived wines from physiologically ripe grapes. You can taste the wines, including the bottle-fermented sparkling wine Mathäi Sekt, in the monastery's own wine shop. Wine lovers of a cultural bent will enjoy the tours through he monastery's vast premises, impressive cellars and exhibitions. The St. Laurent Reserve 2013 was champion of its variety at the Falstaff Red Wine Premier in autumn 2015.

(91–93) Grüner Veltliner Reserve 2015
92 Grüner Veltliner Reserve 2014
91 Grüner Veltliner Reserve 2013

(89–91) Grüner Veltliner Hengsberg 2015
90 Grüner Veltliner Hengsberg 2014
90 Grüner Veltliner Hengsberg 2013

89 Grüner Veltliner 2015
88 Grüner Veltliner 2013
88 Grüner Veltliner 2012

(90–92) Weißburgunder Jungherrn 2015
91 Weißburgunder Jungherrn 2014
92 Weißburgunder Jungherrn 2013

(91–93) Weißburgunder Reserve 2015

90 Weißburgunder 2015
90 Weißburgunder 2014
89 Weißburgunder 2013

(89–91) Riesling Franzhauser 2015
90 Riesling Franzhauser 2014

88 Riesling 2015

90 Gewürztraminer 2015
89 Gewürztraminer 2014
90 Gewürztraminer 2013

88 Sauvignon Blanc 2015

89 Zierfandler Rotgipfler 2015 ZF/RG
89 Zierfandler Rotgipfler 2014 ZF/RG
89 Zierfandler-Rotgipfler 2013 ZF/RG

88 Wiener Gemischter Satz DAC 2015
88 Wiener Gemischter Satz DAC 2014
88 Wiener Gemischter Satz DAC 2013

89 Mathäi 2013
90 Mathäi 2012
89 Mathäi 2011

93 St. Laurent Reserve 2013
Dark ruby with purple highlights and a transparent rim. Sandalwood and blackberry fruit with delicate herbal notes and a touch of nougat. Complex and juicy with well integrated tannins. Blackberry jam and salty notes on the long chocolaty finish. A nicely concentrated accompaniment to food.
92 St. Laurent Reserve 2012
91 Sankt Laurent Reserve 2011

91 St. Laurent Ausstich 2013
93 St. Laurent Große Reserve 2009
89 St. Laurent Ausstich 2012

90 Pinot Noir Reserve 2012

88 Pinot Noir 2011

89 Jubiläumswein 900 Jahre 2011 SL/ZW/ME

89 Patronis 2012 ZW/SL/ME

91 Chorus 2012 CS/ME/CF/SL
89 Chorus 2011 CS/ME/SL/CF

90 Escorial 2011 SL/ZW/CS/ME

92 Chardonnay Eiswein 2011

91 Welschriesling Eiswein 2011

★★★
Weingut Kolkmann

3481 Fels/Wagram, Kremser Straße 53
T: +43 (2738) 2436, F: +43 (2738) 2436 4
office@kolkmann.at, www.kolkmann.at

Winemaker: Ing. Daniel Schön
Contact Person: Gerhard and Horst Kolkmann
Production: n. a. (60 % white, 39 % red, 1 % sweet)
Hectares: 40
Fairs: ProWein, VieVinum
Distribution partners: RUS, B, LT, DE, NL, PL

The Kolkmann wine estate brings four generations of a family under one roof. They all live and work for wine, and cultivate 42 vineyard hectares in the best sites of Fels am Wagram. Horst and Gerhard Kolkmann's unerring dedication allow them to get the most out of their terroir each year. The vineyards are cultivated sustainably according to ecological principles with the goals of preserving natural balance and producing with great vitality and depth. In an exciting portfolio of white wines with typical varietal character and powerful red wines, Grüner Veltliner and Roter Veltliner play the leading roles. The Grüner Veltliner Brunntal and the Grüner Veltliner Brunntal Reserve convince each year with finesse and complexity. The family estate has six hectares of vines in south-facing terraces in the prime vineyard Brunnthal that are based 100 % on deep loam-loess soils. The Scheiben vineyard in Fels am Wagram also counts among the top sites of the region. It is from here that the Roter Veltliners, another specialty of the house, stem. The Roter Veltliner Scheiben is the classic varietal example while the Roter Veltliner Scheiben Reserve is a very aristocratic rendition with extraordinary ageing potential.

In honour of the 50-year anniversary of the Kolkmann winery, the vintners created a special wine. The Roter Veltliner VVision matured for one year in 500-litre oak barrels and one year in a large acacia wood cask. A very unique character that is derived from the deep loess soils of the Wagram wine region distinguishes this wine. Wine enthusiasts are invited to come and "feel the Wagram" in the modern sales and tasting studio. Delicious wines can be tasted while enjoying a marvellous view of the surrounding vineyards.

90 Roter Veltliner Scheiben Reserve 2014
91 Roter Veltliner Scheiben Reserve 2013
Medium green-yellow. Aromas and flavours of delicate papaya, blossom honey, subtle orange zest, candied apple, and soft smoky nuances wonderfully structured with juicy acidity. Tobacco and light salty notes come in on the medium long finish. Plenty of finesse and versatility at the table.
90 Roter Veltliner Scheiben Reserve 2012

89 Roter Veltliner Scheiben 2015
89 Roter Veltliner Scheiben 2014
88 Roter Veltliner Scheiben 2013

92 Roter Veltliner VVision 2013

93 Grüner Veltliner Brunnthal Reserve 2014

91 Grüner Veltliner Brunnthal 2015
90 Grüner Veltliner Brunnthal 2014
91 Grüner Veltliner Brunnthal 2013

87 Grüner Veltliner Fruchtspiel 2015
87 Grüner Veltliner Fruchtspiel 2014
87 Grüner Veltliner Fruchtspiel 2013

88 Grüner Veltliner Lössmann 2015
88 Grüner Veltliner Lössmann 2014
89 Grüner Veltliner Lössmann 2013

89 Riesling Fumberg 2015
89 Riesling Fumberg 2013

88 Burgunder vom Löss 2015 CH/WB
89 Burgunder vom Löss 2014 CH/WB
90 Burgunder vom Löss 2012 CH/WB

90 Pinot Noir Reserve 2011

Weingut Leth

3481 Fels am Wagram, Kirchengasse 6
T: +43 (2738) 2240, F: +43 (2738) 2240 17
office@weingut-leth.at, www.weingut-leth.at

Winemaker: Franz Leth
Contact Person: Franz and Erich Leth
Production: n. a. (80 % white, 20 % red)
Hectares: 50
Fairs: VieVinum, ProWein
Distribution partners: I, J, S, CDN, CH, B, SGP, LV, LT, L, DK, MAL, DE, EST, FIN, CZ, NL, N, GB, H, RI, USA, PL

The Leth family wine estate is located directly in the loess terraces of the Wagram. Loess lends the wines truly unique regional character and Grüner Veltliner in particular gains extraordinary spice, concentration and balance in this terroir. It is no coincidence that this variety makes up more than half of the estate's 50 vineyard hectares. Five different Grüner Veltliners are sourced from the south-facing terraces. The most outstanding wines are the single vineyard renditions from Brunnthat and Scheiben, both vineyards classified as "Erste Lagen" (grand cru) by the Österreichische Traditionsweingüter. It is not superficial primary fruit that is in the foreground of these wines, but rather aroma complexity, fine mineral character and superb ageing potential. First place at the Falstaff Grüner Veltliner Grand Prix in 2011 and 2013; SALON champion for "Scheiben" in 2011, and the Regional Trophy at the Decanter World Wine Awards in 2013 – again for "Scheiben" – all confirm that Grüner Veltliners from Leth count among the very best of Austria.

Another specialty of the Leth wine estate is the old traditional Wagram variety Roter Veltliner. An exceptional combination of juicy fruit and creaminess distinguishes the wines of the Scheiben vineyard and exemplifies the great quality potential of this increasingly popular variety. A couple of new parcels have been recently purchased and planted with Roter Veltliner to fulfil increasing consumer demand.

The Wagram is certainly primarily a white wine region, which makes the Leth red wine competence all the more astounding. Franz Leth junior has brought fresh impulse and the necessary knowledge for this with him. He took over responsibility for vinification at the age of 22. Red wines are strictly confined to the cool climate varieties Zweigelt, Pinot Noir and St. Laurent. Franz Leth Jr. certainly proves his red wine talents with "Gigama", an exceptional Zweigelt that became varietal champion at the Falstaff Red Wine Premier in 2010 and has won numerous other accolades. The Leth family wine estate not only sets quality standards domestically. Two thirds of the wines are successfully exported all over Europe and overseas and even find their way to the Far East.

94 Grüner Veltliner Gigama Grande Reserve 2013
Medium green-yellow with silver highlights. Inviting aromas of ripe stone fruit, such as apricot and mango, and a pleasant mineral character and a lemony touch. Full-bodied and complex with a silky texture. Sweet extract and salty minerals remain long on the finish. Very good ageing potential.
93 Grüner Veltliner Gigama Grande Reserve 2012

(92–94) Grüner Veltliner Scheiben 1 ÖTW 2015
93 Grüner Veltliner Scheiben 1 ÖTW 2014
Brilliant green-yellow with silver highlights. The attractive bouquet displays subtle apricot, ripe pear and mango with a delicate note of blossom honey. Complex and juicy with superb acidity structure. White pepper and yellow fruit on the finish. Plenty of finesse.
92 Grüner Veltliner Scheiben 1 ÖTW 2013

(91–93) Grüner Veltliner Brunnthal 1 ÖTW 2015
92 Grüner Veltliner Brunnthal 1 ÖTW 2014
91 Grüner Veltliner Brunnthal 1 ÖTW 2013

91 Grüner Veltliner Schafflerberg 2015
91 Grüner Veltliner Schafflerberg 2014
90 Grüner Veltliner Schafflerberg 2013

90 Grüner Veltliner Steinagrund 2014
90 Grüner Veltliner Steinagrund 2012

92 Roter Veltliner Wagram 2015

93 Roter Veltliner Scheiben 2014
92 Roter Veltliner Scheiben 2013
92 Roter Veltliner Scheiben 2012

91 Roter Veltliner Hofweingarten 2014
92 Roter Veltliner Hofweingarten 2012

91 Riesling Wagramterrassen 2015
92 Riesling Wagramterrassen 2014
91 Riesling Wagramterrassen 2013

91 Riesling Felser Weinberge 2014
91 Riesling Felser Weinberge 2012

93 Weißer Burgunder Reserve 2015

93 Weißer Burgunder Scheiben 2013
93 Weißburgunder Scheiben 2012

92 Sauvignon Blanc Brunnthal 2013
91 Sauvignon Blanc Brunnthal 2012

92 Chardonnay Floss 2014
92 Chardonnay Floss 2013
91 Chardonnay Floss 2012

(91–93) Simply Wow! 200 United 2015
92 Simply Wow! 2013
92 Simply Wow! 2012

90 Pinot Noir Reserve 2013
90 Pinot Noir Reserve 2012
91 Pinot Noir Reserve 2011

90 Cabernet Sauvignon Reserve 2013
90 Cabernet Sauvignon Reserve 2012
91 Cabernet Sauvignon Reserve 2011

92 Zweigelt Gigama Grande Reserve 2013
92 Zweigelt Gigama Grande Reserve 2012

90 Riesling »S« 2013

Weingut Gregor Nimmervoll

3470 Engelmannsbrunn, Steingassl 30
T: +43 (676) 9503682
office@nimmervoll.cc, www.nimmervoll.cc

Winemaker: Gregor Nimmervoll
Contact Person: Claudia Nimmervoll
Production: n. a. (85 % white, 13 % red, 2 % sweet)
Hectares: 11 + 3
Fairs: VieVinum, ProWein, Weinmesse München
Distribution partners: SK, DE, CZ

Memorable. This is certainly a word that describes the 2015 vintage at the Nimmervoll family winery quite well.. An unusual hailstorm hit nearly all of the estate's vineyards during a night in May, but hope soon returned, thankfully, as the harvest in autumn would eventually prove. The yield from the damaged vineyards was small, but the vines invested all their vitality in the remaining grapes. Ripening in autumn was delayed by cool temperatures, which proved advantageous for wine balance. Volumes from the usual vineyards are small from the 2015 vintage, but the resulting wines are all the more interesting. It is only the great reserve growths that fell victim to the hail and were not produced. For the first time this year, there is a tiny quantity of Roter Veltliner. "Our young vines in the Eisenhut vineyard brought their first fruit," says Gregor Nimmervoll. New plantings will continue in the next years, so that after this first taste from 2015, a larger quantity of this specialty will become available in the future. The newly founded family enterprise continues to evolve nd grow. New vineyard sites with impressive terroir have been purchased in the village of Grossriedenthal. Claudia Nimmervoll says: "Each one of our wines has its own unique character. Challenging years like 2015 make it possible to further enhance this."

93 Grüner Veltliner Große Reserve 2013
Medium green-yellow. Yellow apple, mango, and wild meadow herbs mingle with notes of tobacco and orange zest. Full-bodied, sweet fruit extract combined with juicy acidity in a complex structure. Apple and papaya remain long on the finish of this versatile accompaniment to food. Good ageing potential.

92 Grüner Veltliner Schafberg 2015
92 Grüner Veltliner Schafberg 2014
93 Grüner Veltliner Schafberg 2013

91 Grüner Veltliner Wagram 2015
90 Grüner Veltliner Wagram 2014
91 Grüner Veltliner Wagram 2013

90 Roter Veltliner Eisenhut 2015

91 Riesling Weißer Schotter 2015
89 Riesling Weißer Schotter 2014
90 Riesling Weißer Schotter 2013

92 Weißburgunder Große Reserve 2013
92 Weißburgunder Große Reserve 2011

89 Weißburgunder Mittersteig 2015
89 Weißburgunder Mittersteig 2014
89 Weißburgunder Mittersteig 2013

90 Traminer Fuchsberg 2014
91 Traminer Fuchsberg 2013
89 Traminer Fuchsberg 2012

91 Weißburgunder Beerenauslese 2011

Weingut Bernhard Ott

3483 Feuersbrunn, Neufang 36
T: +43 (2738) 2257, F: +43 (2738) 2257 22
bernhard@ott.at, www.ott.at

—— ORGANIC ——

Winemaker: Günter Weisböck
Contact Person: Bernhard Ott
Production: n. a. (100 % white)
Hectares: 40
Fairs: ProWein, VieVinum
Distribution partners: AUS, I, J, S, CDN, CH, B, ROK, SK, L, DE,
FIN, CZ, NL, N, GB, USA, IRL, PL

Bernhard Ott has dedicated himself nearly completely to the leading local grape variety Grüner Veltliner, which makes up 90 % of his wine production. A small quantity of Sauvignon Blanc and Riesling are also grown at higher elevations in gravelly soils. Two elegant Rieslings are included in the assortment of wines: the dry "Riesling Feuersbrunn" and the semi-dry German-style "Rheinriesling", which exhibits great finesse.

The most important wine of the house is the "Fass 4" Grüner Veltliner. Bernhard Ott likes to call this wine the golden middle, the wine that combines elegance with easy-drinking pleasure. A spicy, full-bodied Grüner Veltliner is called "Der Ott", and it does indeed honour its producer. Grapes for this wine stem from young vines in the prime vineyards Spiegel, Stein and Rosenberg. The old vines deliver the fruit for the single-vineyard wines. Spiegel, Stein and Rosenberg are first released each year in September.

The most recent international success are: 1st place for the Grüner Veltliner "Tausend Rosen" 2003 at the "Grand Jury Européen" that took place in the Loisium in 2006, Champion for "Der Ott" 2014 at the "Falstaff Grüner Veltliner Grand Prix 2014", and 3rd place for "Fass 4" 2013 at the "Falstaff Grüner Veltliner Grand Prix 2015". Bernhard Ott was honoured for his achievements as "Falstaff Vintner of the Year 2008".

Ott produced the Grüner Veltliner "Qvevre" for the first time in 2009 according to antique methods in large amphorae that were buried in Wagram loess. This is perhaps a taste of Wagram in its purest form.

95 Grüner Veltliner Tausend Rosen 2012

94 Grüner Veltliner Qvevre 2013
Brilliant golden yellow. Ripe quince and orange marmalade over a background of delicate blossom honey and smoked lapsang souchong tea. Pleasant, sweet peach fruit and mild acid structure provide a juicy, creamy texture. Elegant honey and caramel nuances come in on the long finish. Dependable ageing potential.

93 Grüner Veltliner Qvevre 2012
93 Grüner Veltliner Qvevre 2011

(94–96) Grüner Veltliner Feuersbrunner Rosenberg 1 ÖTW 2015
94 Grüner Veltliner Feuersbrunner Rosenberg 1 ÖTW 2013
94 Grüner Veltliner Feuersbrunner Rosenberg 1 ÖTW 2012

(93–95) Grüner Veltliner Feuersbrunner Spiegel 1 ÖTW 2015
93 Grüner Veltliner Feuersbrunner Spiegel 1 ÖTW 2013
94 Grüner Veltliner Feuersbrunner Spiegel 1 ÖTW 2012

(92–94) Grüner Veltliner Engabrunner Stein 1 ÖTW 2015
93 Grüner Veltliner Engabrunner Stein 1 ÖTW 2013
93 Grüner Veltliner Engabrunner Stein 1 ÖTW 2012

(91–93) Grüner Veltliner Der Ott 2015
92 Grüner Veltliner Der Ott 2014
Medium green-yellow. Apple, orange jelly and mandarin zest with a hazelnut nuance. Juicy and elegantly textured with a well balanced, Chablis-like character. Yellow fruit and fine salty notes on the finish. Ready to drink.

92 Grüner Veltliner Der Ott 2013

91 Grüner Veltliner Fass 4 2015
91 Grüner Veltliner Fass 4 2014
91 Grüner Veltliner Fass 4 2013

90 Grüner Veltliner Am Berg 2015
90 Grüner Veltliner Am Berg 2014
90 Grüner Veltliner Am Berg 2013

(91–93) Riesling Feuersbrunn 2015

92 Sauvignon Blanc 2013

92 Rheinriesling 2013

★ ★

Weingut Urbanihof – Familie Paschinger

3481 Fels/Wagram, St.-Urban-Straße 3
T: +43 (2738) 2344 12 und 13, F: +43 (2738) 2344 4, M: +43 (664) 3915577
weingut@urbanihof.at, www.urbanihof.at

Winemaker: Peter Reiter
Contact Person: Dipl.-HLFL-Ing. Franz Paschinger
Production: n. a. (70 % white, 30 % red)
Hectares: 26
Fairs: ProWein, VieVinum
Distribution partners: B, DE, NL

Franz and Sonja Paschinger's enterprise is one of the most historic wine estates in Wagram and can look back on 400 years of wine tradition. The Paschinger family has owned the Urbanihof estate since 1598 and is now in its 11th generation there. Wines are produced with much dedication and attention to detail. Franz Paschinger strives to produce the most authentic wines possible and choses his methods according to the potential of the grapes. As a member of the vintner association "Wagramer Selektion", the main focus is on the varieties Grüner Veltliner and Zweigelt. Grüner Veltliner leads the assortment of wines and the spectrum of styles range from the light "4U" to the classic "Wagramer Selection" to the "Alten Reben" sourced from old vines. Prolonged contact with the fine lees and delayed bottling yield a fine fruity, concentrated wine called "1598" that always exhibits good aging potential. "Barrique No. 5" is the premium Zweigelt that excels with an appetizing and well-balanced tannin structure.

The Paschingers signed the contract for certified organic production in 2013. They make their own compost from grape mash and horse dung, use plant protection methods that preserve beneficial insects, and have green cover between the vine rows. This ecological foundation, combined with conscientious canopy management and rigorous yield restrictions, help ensure high quality wines.

92 Grüner Veltliner »1598« 2015
91 Grüner Veltliner »1598« 2014
91 Grüner Veltliner »1598« 2013

91 Grüner Veltliner Alte Reben 2015
90 Grüner Veltliner Alte Reben 2014
90 Grüner Veltliner Alte Reben 2013

92 Grüner Veltliner Dorner Alte Reben 2012

92 Grüner Veltliner Fahn »1598« 2012

88 Grüner Veltliner Scheiben Wagramer Selektion 2015
88 Grüner Veltliner Scheiben 2014
88 Grüner Veltliner Scheiben Wagramer Selektion 2013

92 Cuvée Wagram Reserve 2013 GV/CH/SB
Medium green-yellow. Apple, apricot, orange zest, blossom honey and light floral nuances on the nose and in the mouth. Juicy and refreshing acidity structure. Mango and delicate, smoky oak spice come in on the finish. Good potential for further development.

89 Roter Veltliner 2015
89 Roter Veltliner Zeiselleiten 2012

88 Riesling Mitterweg 2014
88 Riesling Mitterweg 2013

90 Gelber Muskateller 2015

87 Rosé vom Merlot 2015
88 Rosé vom Merlot Hammer 2013
87 Rosé vom Merlot 2012

89 Blauer Zweigelt Barrique No.5 »1598« 2012

★ ★
Weinhof Waldschütz
3474 Sachsendorf, Sachsendorf 17
T: +43 (2738) 2387, F: +43 (2738) 2387 19, M: +43 (664) 3874076
wein@waldschuetz.at, www.waldschuetz.at

Winemaker: Anton Waldschütz
Contact Person: Anton and Elfriede Waldschütz
Production: n. a. (58 % white, 40 % red, 2 % sweet)
Hectares: 15
Fairs: VieVinum, ProWein, Vinobile Feldkirch
Distribution partners: on request

Family, tradition and experience are the bywords of the Waldschütz winery, which has existed in its present form since 1992. The vineyards cover an area of 15 hectares (37 acres) on sunny slopes in the two well-known wine regions of Kamptal and Wagram. The grapes for the fruity, elegant Waldschütz wines grow on primary rock, sandy loam and loess-gravel soils as well as on deep loam-loess. The quality and individual character of the wines are the result of meticulous care of each individual vine, canopy management, green harvesting and hand-picking. A broad assortment of high quality wines is offered. The light, mild wines are labelled "Classic" or "Kabinett", while the premium series is labelled "Reserve", of which some are fermented or matured in oak. The Waldschütz family has a heurigen (wine tavern) in the village of Obernholz where they serve delicious homemade food to complement their wines. They recently opened a modern, tastefully designed salesroom at their headquarters in Sachsendorf. It is best to phone for an appointment to taste and purchase the wines.

92 Grüner Veltliner Brunnthal Wagram Reserve
   Wagramer Selektion 2014
92 Grüner Veltliner Brunnthal Wagram Reserve
   Wagramer Selektion 2013
Pale golden yellow. Ripe apple, mango and subtle candied fruit elements combine with delicate smoky notes and peppery spice on the nose and in the mouth. A multifaceted structure with layers of concentrated fruit, sweet extract and spice in a full body. Good length and potential for further development.

(90–92) Grüner Veltliner Scheiben Reserve
        Wagramer Selektion 2015
90 Grüner Veltliner Scheiben Reserve
   Wagramer Selektion 2014
90 Grüner Veltliner Scheiben Reserve
   Wagramer Selektion 2013

88 Grüner Veltliner Kamptal DAC classic 2015
88 Grüner Veltliner Kamptal DAC Classic 2014
87 Grüner Veltliner Kamptal DAC Classic 2013

(91–93) Riesling Anzenthal Reserve
        Wagramer Selektion 2015
90 Riesling Anzenthal Reserve
   Wagramer Selektion 2014
89 Riesling Anzenthal Reserve
   Wagramer Selektion 2013

89 Riesling Kamptal DAC classic 2015

(88–90) Weißer Burgunder Schaflerberg
        Reserve Wagramer Selektion 2015
89 Weißer Burgunder Schaflerberg
   Reserve Wagramer Selektion 2014
89 Weißer Burgunder Schaflerberg
   Reserve Wagramer Selektion 2013

91 Grüner Veltliner Eiswein Scheiben 2013
93 Grüner Veltliner Eiswein 2012

Weingut Gerald Waltner

3470 Engelmannsbrunn, Am Berg 18
T: +43 (2279) 2471, F: +43 (2279) 2471
info@weingutwaltner.at, www.weingutwaltner.at

Winemaker and Contact Person: Gerald Waltner
Production: n. a. (80 % white, 20 % red)
Hectares: 10
Fairs: ProWein
Distribution partners: B, CH, DE, NL, IRL

Gerald Waltner has successfully restructured the family enterprise. In just ten years, he has metamorphosed from a grapegrower to become one of the leading producers in the Wagram. His main focus is the Grüner Veltliner, which finds ideal preconditions the unique terroir of the region. Gerald Waltner vinifies diverse styles of the variety from different vineyards: the fruity, easy-drinking GV Hochrain, the spicy, mineral GV Steinberz, and the full-bodied, mellifluous GV Dorner. The Grüner Veltliner Reserve from the top site, Dorner, is allowed to mature on the fine lees and is first bottled in September the year after the harvest. Also included in the assortment are Weissburgunder (Pinot Blanc), Chardonnay, Riesling, and Gelber Muskateller (Muscat Blanc à petits grains). Two versions of Zweigelt are produced: the Halterberg matures in large used casks while the Marienberg is matured in small oak barrels. The high share of Waltner wines in export is notable. Next to sales in Austria, over 65% of the production is sold in Germany, Ireland, Switzerland and the Netherlands. Numerous accolades in the last few years and inclusion in diverse wine guides confirm this dynamic vintner's efforts and testify to the high quality of his wines.

91 Grüner Veltliner Dorner 2015
91 Grüner Veltliner Dorner 2014
Pale green-yellow. Mango, yellow apple, subtle peppery spice and delicate notes of tobacco. Pear and minerals with a juicy acidity structure on the palate. Plenty of finesse, length and potential for further development.
90 Grüner Veltliner Dorner 2013

(91–93) Grüner Veltliner Dorner Reserve 2015
92 Grüner Veltliner Dorner Reserve 2013

88 Grüner Veltliner Hochrain 2015
88 Grüner Veltliner Hochrain 2014
88 Grüner Veltliner Hochrain 2013

91 Grüner Veltliner Steinberz 2015
89 Grüner Veltliner Steinberz 2014
89 Grüner Veltliner Steinberz 2013

91 Weißburgunder 2015
91 Weißburgunder 2014
90 Weißburgunder 2013

88 Gelber Muskateller 2015
88 Gelber Muskateller 2014
88 Gelber Muskateller 2012

89 Riesling 2013

88 Zweigelt Marienberg 2013
88 Zweigelt Marienberg 2011

WEINVIERTEL DAC
Romantic cellar alleys and peppery Grüner Veltliner

Expansive, rolling vineyard hills, cornfields waving in the wind, romantic cellar alleys – the Weinviertel is an open, inviting, and very versatile agricultural and cultural landscape. Nearly half of the region's 13,356 vineyard hectares are planted with the key to its success. Peppery Grüner Veltliner is synonymous for Weinviertel DAC.

© ÖWM/Weinkomitee Weinviertel, Haiden Baumann

This vast wine region sprawls from the Danube River in the south to the Czech border in the north, and from Manhartsberg in the west to the border of Slovakia in the east. With 6,221 vineyard hectares, Grüner Veltliner is the regional darling that excels with pronounced peppery character and crisp, refreshing acidity. This specific character profile inspired Austria's first protected geographic designation of origin (DAC), which was established in 2002.

Grüner Veltliner is grown throughout, but other varieties also thrive in the Weinviertel and they appear under the Niederösterreich protected geographical indication. Pinot Blanc, known locally as Weissburgunder, thrives in the area surrounding the wine village of Wolkersdorf. Riesling, is at home on the slopes of Bisamberg. In Mannersdorf an der March, optimal conditions prevail for Riesling, Traminer (Gewürztraminer) and Burgundian varieties, thanks to the influence of the warm Pannonian climate. The winemakers in the northeast part of the Weinviertel, particularly around Poysdorf, produce mainly Welschriesling in addition to the local hero "GV". At the area's northern border, Falkenstein is a focal point for fruit-driven white wines. Between Retz and Röschitz, in western Weinviertel, Riesling yields wines of exquisite mineral finesse and a deep spiciness. Due to its dry climate, the red wine enclave of Haugsdorf is an ideal location for rich, fruity Zweigelt and Blauer Portugieser.

© OEWM, 1040 Wien
www.TOURISVIS.COM

wine-growing area

- ◆ Weingut Ebner-Ebenauer, Poysdorf

- ◆ Weingut Frank, Herrnbaumgarten

- ◆ Weingut Gruber Röschitz, Röschitz

- ◆ Weingut Gschweicher, Röschitz

- ◆ Schlossweingut Graf Hardegg, Seefeld-Kadolz

- ◆ Weingut Ludwig Hofbauer, Unterretzbach

- ◆ Weingut Hofbauer-Schmidt, Hohenwarth

- ◆ Hofkellerei des Fürsten von Liechtenstein, Wilfersdorf

- ◆ Weingut R. & A. Pfaffl, Stetten

- ◆ Weingut Prechtl, Zellerndorf

- ◆ Weingut Schuckert, Poysdorf

- ◆ Weingut Schwarz, Schrattenberg

- ◆ Weingut Seifried, Oberstinkenbrunn

- ◆ Weingut Georg Toifl, Kleinhöflein

- ◆ Weingut Walek, Poysdorf

- ◆ Weingut Weinrieder, Kleinhadersdorf-Poysdorf

- ◆ Weingut Phillip Zull, Schrattenthal

★★★

Weingut Ebner-Ebenauer

2170 Poysdorf, Laaer Straße 5
T: +43 (2552) 2653, F: +43 2552/26 53
office@ebner-ebenauer.at, www.ebner-ebenauer.at

Winemaker: Manfred Ebner-Ebenauer
Contact Person: Marion Ebner-Ebenauer
Production: 70.000 bottles (85 % white, 15 % red)
Hectares: 15
Fairs: ProWein, VieVinum, MondoVino
Distribution partners: S, CH, B, SK, RC, L, DK, DE, CZ, NL, GB, USA

Marion Ebner and Manfred Ebenauer set the foundation for their joined efforts in the year 2007. First they married, then they joined Marion's négociant enterprise and Manfred's winery into one business, thus exponentially combining both their winemaking talents. Ebner-Ebenauer was born – and this has borne well: from the very beginning, their wines have counted among the best of what the Weinviertel has to offer. Individuality with all its edges and corners are certainly allowed, but what is not allowed is mediocre, mainstream wine. The heart of the assortment of wines is the single-vineyard wine series that is sourced from vines with a minimum of 30 years age. The oldest vines (Grüner Veltliner, Pinot Blanc, and Riesling) are between 50 and 65 years old and are thus titled on the wine labels. They abstain from a lot of technology in the cellar, preferring instead to rely on simply giving wine the time that it needs to mature in the cask. Grapes in the estate's 15 vineyard hectares are all exclusively hand-picked. The grapes are sorted directly in the vineyard and placed into 35 kg crates. Most wines are allowed a brief maceration and are then fermented spontaneously in wood or in stainless steel before they are matured on the fine lees. The Ebenauers do not view themselves as winemakers, but rather more as mediators. Manfred Ebenauer says: "Our wines are unadulterated and need time to develop. They are not flashy wines, but make a memorable impression and are capable of ageing. Nature writes the script; we simply direct the show!"

(92–94) Grüner Veltliner Black Edition 2015
93 Grüner Veltliner Black Edition 2014
Medium green-yellow with silver highlights. Fresh apple and crisp greengage plum with nuances of herbs and mineral. Complex with oak spice integrated in a creamy texture and refreshed with an elegant play of acidity. This substantial accompaniment to food exhibits superb balance and length.
94 Grüner Veltliner Black Edition 2013

(90–92) Grüner Veltliner Alte Reben 2015
92 Grüner Veltliner Alte Reben 2014
93 Grüner Veltliner Alte Reben 2013

(90–92) Grüner Veltliner Bürsting 2015
91 Grüner Veltliner Bürsting 2014
90 Grüner Veltliner Bürsting 2013

(88–90) Grüner Veltliner Hermannsschachern 2015
90 Grüner Veltliner Hermanschachern 2014
89 Grüner Veltliner Hermannschachern 2013

(91–93) Grüner Veltliner Sauberg 2015
92 Grüner Veltliner Sauberg 2014
90 Grüner Veltliner Sauberg 2013

(91–93) Riesling Alte Reben 2015

(90–92) Weißer Burgunder Alte Reben 2015
92 Weißer Burgunder Alte Reben 2013

(92–94) Chardonnay Black Edition 2015
92 Chardonnay Black Edition 2013

92 Blanc de Blancs Zero Dosage 2008
Medium golden yellow with a fine persistent mousse. A mature bouquet displays subtle baked apple with notes of herbs, dried fruit, and sea buckthorn nectar. Juicy and elegant with very fine bubbles. Ripe yellow tropical fruit, a salty mineral touch and citrus notes linger on the finish of this elegant food partner.
93 Blanc de Blancs Zero Dosage 2007

91 Pinot Noir Black Edition 2011

★ ★
Weingut Frank

2171 Herrnbaumgarten, Kellergasse 5 & 11
T: +43 (2555) 2300, F: +43 (2555) 2300 4
frank@weingutfrank.at, www.weingutfrank.at

Winemaker and Contact Person: DI Harald Frank
Production: n. a. (75 % white, 25 % red)
Hectares: 21
Fairs: VieVinum, ProWein
Distribution partners: RUS, S, B, DK, DE, FIN, NL, N, USA, PL

The Frank Winery is located in the most northerly part of the Weinviertel. The family is well known for deep, powerful Grüner Veltliners that excel with finesse rather than opulence. The single vineyard Grüner Veltliners from the Johannesbergen and Hoher Weg sites are of particular mention. Next to these, one also finds fruity, refreshing classic wines that carry the Weinviertel DAC label of origin. Riesling, Burgundian varieties and red wines round out the assortment of wines for which attention is always given the particular microclimates. This winery has recognized that the future belongs to elegant wines that express a unique place of origin. The high share of export sales confirms their chosen path.

**(90–92) Grüner Veltliner Hoher Weg
Reserve 2015**
90 Grüner Veltliner Hoher Weg Reserve 2014
91 Grüner Veltliner Hoher Weg 2013

89 Grüner Veltliner Johannesbergen 2015
89 Grüner Veltliner Johannesbergen 2014
90 Grüner Veltliner Johannesbergen 2013

91 Riesling Alte Reben 2013
Pale golden yellow. Inviting aromas of apricot and green-gage plum with notes of pineapple and blossom honey. Juicy, elegant acidity provides pleasant structure to the sweet fruit. The finish is quite mineral.
92 Riesling Alte Reben 2012

89 Riesling 2015
89 Riesling 2014

(91–93) Weißer Burgunder Adamsbergen 2015

90 Chardonnay Alte Reben 2013
89 Chardonnay Alte Reben 2012

88 Pinot & Co. 2015 WB/CH/GV
88 Pinot & Co. 2013 WB/CH/GV

89 Zweigelt Wachtberg 2012
89 Zweigelt Wachtberg 2011

89 M.C.S. 2012 ME/CS/SL

91 Hannbuch 2011 ME/CS

Weingut Gruber Röschitz

3743 Röschitz, Winzerstraße 46
T: +43 (2984) 2765, F: +43 (2984) DW 25
office@gruber-roeschitz.at, www.gruber-roeschitz.at

Winemaker: Ewald Gruber
Contact Person: Maria Gruber
Production: n. a. (70 % white, 30 % red)
Fairs: VieVinum, ProWein and other international fairs
Distribution partners: I, RUS, J, S, CH, SGP, DK, DE, T, CZ, N, USA, PL

Family business at its best! They are young, energetic, and competent – and they are here to make a difference. The sibling trio Maria, Ewald and Christian Gruber add a little more spice to Grüner Veltliner in the Weinviertel. The unique character of the individual vineyards is highlighted in their wines. Because creativity should never come too short, playful "helpers" in the vineyard and cellar adorn the labels and awaken the curiosity and appetite for the bottle contents. Röschitz is, after all, well known for its appetizing, mineral, spicy white wines. The western Weinviertel terroir is a guarantee for typicity and longevity. The three siblings are not really new to the business. They grew up in the midst of it all and their parents allow the space and time to find a suitable and fitting place. This included them collecting experience abroad and in other branches as well. Ewald has been responsible for winemaking for over ten years now. This affords him the experience and practice necessary for persistent reliability in wine style and quality. Maria has expanded distribution and exports and her playful critter labels have found a welcome reception. International wine lovers appreciate the unique character of this estate's Grüner Veltliner and Riesling. The mineral character derived from granite and the spice and fruit from loess are inimitable expressions of the region. The third sibling, Christian, has dedicated his efforts to the vineyard. His current project is converting the estate's vineyard to certified organic viticulture. And with beneficial insects in mind, we return again to the "helpers" depicted on the labels.

(93–95) Weinviertel DAC Reserve Mühlberg 2015
93 Weinviertel DAC Reserve Mühlberg 2013
Medium green-yellow. The multi-layered bouquet offers mineral nuances, crisp apple and stone fruit notes with an dash of apricot. Firmly structured with a dark, mineral-laced texture. Pleasant extract sweetness, yellow apple and delicious salty notes linger in the finish.
92 Weinviertel DAC Reserve Mühlberg 2012

92 Weinviertel DAC Hundspoint 2015
91 Weinviertel DAC Hundspoint 2014
91 Weinviertel DAC Hundspoint 2013

91 Weinviertel DAC Reipersberg 2015
91 Weinviertel DAC Reipersberg 2014
89 Weinviertel DAC Reipersberg 2013

91 Weinviertel DAC Röschitz 2015
90 Weinviertel DAC Klassik 2014

92 Riesling Königsberg 2015
89 Riesling Königsberg 2013

90 Riesling Röschitz 2015

89 Gelber Muskateller Röschitz 2015

89 Zweigelt Lauschen 2012

(87–89) Sankt Laurent Galgenberg 2015

90 Galgenberg 2013 SL/PN

(89–91) Cuvée Royale 2013 ZW/ME

93 Chardonnay Trockenbeerenauslese 2013
Brilliant yellow with golden highlights. Ripe tropical fruit reminiscent of pineapple is laced with botrytis spice and accompanied by notes of apple and honey. Complex with racy acidity integrated in lusciously sweet, juicy fruit. Yellow fruit lingers on the sweet, well balanced finish. Will benefit from further bottle maturation.
93 Chardonnay Eiswein 2012

Weingut Gschweicher

3743 Röschitz, Winzerstraße 29
T: +43 (2984) 3800, F: +43 (2984) 3800 4
weingut.stift@gschweicher.at, www.gschweicher.at

Winemaker: Gerhard and Bernhard Gschweicher
Contact Person: Bernhard Gschweicher
Production: n. a. (100 % white)
Hectares: 13
Fairs: VieVinum, ProWein
Distribution partners: on request

Soil vitality, old vines, and exceptional wines – this is for what the name Gschweicher from Röschitz stands. The Gschweicher family winery produces a unique style of wines that are distinguished by a precise structure and varietal character. This winery has always been a white wine producer specialized in Grüner Veltliner and diverse aromatic varieties. The leading "Weinviertel Plus" producer also makes three different Rieslings. Without much technological expense, the conditions of the site and different degrees of ripeness are used to create different wine categories. Soil vitality is the most essential factor for the style of the wines. Three quarters of the Grüner Veltliner vines are over 50 years old. The premium wine of the house is the powerful, mineral "Primary Rocks", a Grüner Veltliner from 80-year-old vines that grow on meagre metamorphic rock near Röschitz.

92 Grüner Veltliner Primary Rocks 2013
92 Grüner Veltliner Königsberg 2015
91 Grüner Veltliner Königsberg 2014

91 Grüner Veltliner Galgenberg 2015
90 Grüner Veltliner Galgenberg 2014
91 Grüner Veltliner Galgenberg 2013

(91–93) Weinviertel DAC Reserve Kellerberg 2015
92 Weinviertel DAC Reserve Kellerberg 2014
Brilliant green-yellow with silver highlights. Restrained aromas of delicate apricot and greengage plum with nuances of orange and subtle blossom honey. Full-bodied and juicy with subtle extract sweetness. Pineapple, mango, and soft spicy notes linger on the finish. Will benefit from further bottle maturation.
91 Weinviertel DAC Reserve Kellerberg 2013

89 Weinviertel DAC GrooVee 2015
89 Weinviertel DAC GrooVee 2014
90 Weinviertel DAC GrooVee Klassik 2013

(88–90) Riesling Reipersberg Urgestein 2015
92 Riesling Reipersberg Urgestein 2013
89 Riesling Reipersberg Urgestein 2012

91 Riesling Reipersberg Reserve 2012

(91–93) Riesling Mühlberg Reserve 2015

90 Sauvignon Blanc Reipersberg 2015
89 Sauvignon Blanc Reipersberg 2014
89 Sauvignon Blanc Reipersberg 2013

(92–94) Grüner Veltliner Primary Rocks 2015
93 Grüner Veltliner Primary Rocks 2014
Medium green-yellow with silver highlights. Delicate peach with mineral nuances, subtle blossom honey and a touch of tobacco spice. Complex and full-bodied with a firm texture. Very good length culminates in a mineral, salty finale. A great Grüner Veltliner from a difficult vintage that demonstrates dependable ageing potential.

Schlossweingut Graf Hardegg

2062 Seefeld-Kadolz, Großkadolz 1
T: +43 (2943) 2203, F: +43 (2943) 2203 10
office@hardegg.at, www.grafhardegg.at

ORGANIC

Winemaker: Andreas Gruber
Contact Person: Maximilian Hardegg and Andreas Gruber
Production: n. a. (65 % white, 33 % red, 2 % sweet)
Hectares: 35
Fairs: VieVinum, ProWein
Distribution partners: J, B, CDN, BR, DK, CZ, NL, USA, PL

Maximilian Hardegg's mission is to continue the nearly 400 years of family tradition of sustainable wine cultivation. The castle estate and its 35 hectares of vineyards is located in the Pulka Valley – the northern Weinviertel – near the border of the Czech Republic. The baroque cellar is from 1640 and its labyrinth of tunnels and impressive vaulted ceilings are still used by the aristocratic family for the maturation of their outstanding wines. The innovative Maximilian Hardegg and team have solidly positioned the historic castle winery among the leading producers in Austria. A continental climate with little precipitation and hot days and cool nights combine with interesting soils comprised of sand and marine limestone with abundant chalk to comprise a unique terroir. This terroir finds authentic expression through organic cultivation. The resulting wines are true classics, with firm acidity and plenty of elegance and finesse. Maximillian Hardegg describes his wines as having a "cool-climate style" and they certainly do express the northern geographic location of the estate. The fundamental wine ranges are "Veltlinsky", "Graf Hardegg", "Weine vom Schloss" and the single-vineyard reserves from the 14-hectare Steinbügel vineyard. A superb series of sparkling wines with extraordinarily fine mousse has been created by allowing them to mature for several years on the yeast. With their elegance and structure, these wines now count among the best grower-sparklings in Austria. Cult wines among connoisseurs are the Viognier "V" and the unique fortified Merlot "Forticus" made in the style of a vintage port.

(90–92) Grüner Veltliner Steinbügel 2015
91 Grüner Veltliner Steinbügel 2014
Medium green-yellow. Ripe tropical fruit nuances reminiscent of mango and papaya with a hint of orange zest. Full-bodied and powerful with pleasant extract sweetness nicely integrated with juicy acidity. Very good length with a mineral aftertaste.
91 Grüner Veltliner Steinbügel 2013

(89–91) Grüner Veltliner vom Schloss 2015
89 Grüner Veltliner vom Schloss 2014
89 Grüner Veltliner vom Schloss 2013

88 Grüner Veltliner Veltlinsky 2015
88 Grüner Veltliner Veltlinsky 2014
88 Grüner Veltliner Veltlinsky 2013

88 Grüner Veltliner Graf Hardegg 2015
88 Grüner Veltliner Graf Hardegg 2014
88 Grüner Veltliner Graf Hardegg 2013

(91–93) Riesling Steinbügel 2015

(88–90) Riesling vom Schloss 2015
89 Riesling vom Schloss 2014
89 Riesling vom Schloss 2013

(88–90) Riesling Spätlese 2015

93 Viognier »V« 2014
89 Viognier »V« 2013
93 Viognier »V« 2012

90 Chardonnay Steinbügel 2013

90 Graf Hardegg Brut 2011
91 Graf Hardegg Brut 2010

91 Graf Hardegg Brut Rosé 2011
91 Graf Hardegg Brut Rosé 2010

90 Pinot Noir vom Schloss 2013
90 Pinot Noir vom Schloss 2011
89 Pinot Noir vom Schloss 2010

92 Pinot Noir Steinbügel 2011
Pale cherry red with violet highlights and a broad transparent rim. Forest berry jam and nuances of fresh blackberry and wild cherry with a subtle undertone of tobacco and minerals. Complex with fine fruit nuances and subtle extract sweetness nicely integrating the oak. Good length and ageing potential.
91 Pinot Noir Steinbügel 2010
92 Pinot Noir Steinbügel 2009

93 Forticus 2006 ME

★ ★

Weingut Ludwig Hofbauer

2074 Unterretzbach, Hauptstraße 1
T: +43 (2942) 2505, F: +43 (2942) 20708, M: +43 (664) 4245052
office@weingut-hofbauer.at, www.weingut-hofbauer.at

Winemaker and Contact Person: Ludwig Hofbauer
Production: 90.000 bottles (73 % white, 25 % red, 2 % sweet)
Hectares: 20
Fairs: ProWein
Distribution partners: SK, DK, DE, FIN, CZ, GB, PL

Ludwig Hofbauer is the specialist for Burgundian varieties in the Weinviertel. His Weissburgunder (Pinot Blanc) counts among the very best examples of the variety in Austria's largest wine region. He repeatedly makes achievements at the Austrian Wine Salon and state championships with his Chardonnay. Hofbauer was once even awarded varietal champion with his Pinot Blanc at the Austrian Wine Salon. Pinot Noir also thrives well in the vineyards that border the Czech Republic. A vertical tasting of the Hofbauer Blauburgunder reaching all the way back to vintages in the 1950s was all convincing testimony of this winery's tradition for the Pinot Noir variety at their estate in Unterretzbach. The historic estate was first mentioned in written documents dating from 1615 and has been owned by the family for many generations. In 1931, Ludwig Hofbauer Sr. had already begun to plant vineyards with a single variety, which was then a novelty in the region. Edwin Hofbauer was the first to bottle the estate wines in 1949, thus continuing the family tradition of innovation and visionary thinking. Ludwig Hofbauer has been responsible for the family winery since 2000. He recently built a new crush facility where grapes are gently processed and vinified with the most modern technologies. Next to the Burgundian varieties, Hofbauer also naturally produces Grüner Veltliner in several different categories. A new addition to the assortment is the "Gemischter Satz Ludwig II". The grapes are sourced from an old vineyard that is planted with six different varieties. An excellent grappa completes the array of products.

91 Grüner Veltliner Heiliger Stein 2015
Pale green-yellow with silver highlights. Inviting fragrance of passion fruit and mango with subtle nuances of blossom honey, lemon balm and orange zest. Fine, sleek acidity lends good structure to the juicy fruit. Yellow apple and minerals linger on the finish of this very good accompaniment to food.

91 Grüner Veltliner Heiliger Stein 2013
91 Grüner Veltliner Heiliger Stein 2012

90 Weinviertel DAC Halblehen 2015
89 Weinviertel DAC Halblehen 2013
89 Weinviertel DAC Halblehen 2012

89 Weinviertel DAC Eisenköpfen 2015

90 Traminer Sandgrube 2013

89 Chardonnay Sandgrube 2015
90 Chardonnay Sandgrube 2012

88 Ludwig II. 2015

90 Pinot Noir In Feldern 2011

89 Zweigelt Selection 2011

93 Sauvignon Blanc Trockenbeerenauslese 2013

93 Sauvignon Blanc Ausbruch 2011

Weingut Hofbauer-Schmidt

3472 Hohenwarth, Hohenwarth 24
T: +43 (2957) 221, F: +43 (2957) 221 4, M: +43 (664) 1123989
weingut@hofbauer-schmidt.at, www.hofbauer-schmidt.at

Winemaker: Leopold and Ing. Johannes Hofbauer-Schmidt, BSc
Contact Person: Petra, Leopold and Ing. Johannes Hofbauer-Schmidt, BSc
Production: n. a. (85 % white, 15 % red)
Hectares: 15 + 10
Fairs: VieVinum
Distribution partners: S, CH, B, DE, CZ, NL

Wine was cultivated in the wine village of Hohenwarth, in southwestern Weinviertel, 50 km west of Vienna, already in the 10th century. Pebbles, sand and clay from the ancient Danube riverbed were subsequently partially covered with loess and loam. The high temperature fluctuations between day and night are ideal for the inimitable fruitiness and piquancy of the local wines. Petra, Leopold, and son Johannes are three people who work, decide, and laugh together, while always treating one another respectfully. Their shared passion is wine, in particular their leading varieties Grüner Veltliner and the rare local Roter Veltliner. The resulting wines are quite tasty. Year for year top qualities are produced in in four categories from their 25 hectares of vines. The four categories are "leicht & fruchtig" (light and fruity), "klassik" (classic), "lagenweine" (single-vineyard) and "alte reben & reserven" (old vines and reserves). Sustainability is practiced and the environment is treated with sensitivity and respect. The family philosophy is to "take the best from our region and carry it out into the world with enthusiasm". The cooperation between the generations is a great advantage because it provides a good mix of many years of experience and new ideas with youthful energy. Leopold and Johannes, the two winemakers, recently fulfilled their dream of a new crush facility. "We want to provide ideal vinification conditions for every individual charge of top quality, healthy grapes that arrive from our vineyards," says Leopold. "The soil and site should become tangible." Father and son achieve this well, and after barrel maturation in the old vaulted cellar, the waiting finally comes to an end. Age-worthy wines of great character leave the cellar each year and embark on their journey to carry the message of the Weinviertel region into the world.

92 Roter Veltliner Alte Reben 2014
Pale green-yellow. Tangerine zest, light floral nuances and an elegant touch of blossom honey. Yellow apple, sweet extract and juicy acidity combine to comprise a complex structure with plenty of finesse. Ripe tropical fruit on the long, pleasant mineral finish. A very appetizing style.
91 Roter Veltliner Alte Reben 2013
92 Roter Veltliner Alte Reben 2012

89 Roter Veltliner Ried Hochstrass 2015
89 Roter Veltliner Hochstrass 2014
88 Roter Veltliner Hochstrass 2012

89 Weinviertel DAC Ried Hochstrass 2015
89 Weinviertel DAC Hochstrass 2014
90 Weinviertel DAC Hochstrass 2013

(91–93) Weinviertel DAC Reserve 2015
92 Weinviertel DAC Reserve 2013
92 Weinviertel DAC Reserve 2011

89 Weinviertel DAC Klassik 2013

(90–92) Grüner Veltliner Alte Reben 2015
91 Grüner Veltliner Alte Reben 2014
92 Grüner Veltliner Alte Reben 2013

(89–91) Riesling Alte Reben 2015
90 Riesling Alte Reben 2014
89 Riesling Alte Reben 2012

88 Grüner Sylvaner Ried Kögl 2015

88 Sauvignon Blanc Mühlweg 2014
88 Sauvignon Blanc Mühlweg 2013

★
Hofkellerei des Fürsten von Liechtenstein

2193 Wilfersdorf, Brünner Straße 8
T: +43 (2573) 2219 27, F: +43 (2573) 2219 47
office@hofkellerei.at, www.hofkellerei.com

Winemaker and Contact Person: Josef Weinmeyer
Production: n. a. (50 % white, 50 % red)
Hectares: 35
Fairs: VieVinum, ProWein
Distribution partners: RUS, J, CH, RC, EST, CZ, USA

The Hofkellerei of the Prince of Liechtenstein has vineyards in two locations; the Austrian Domäne Wilfersdorf is 50 kilometres north of Vienna while the Domäne Vaduz is in Liechtenstein. Both are distinguished by a century-old tradition of viticulture and are simultaneously respected for a modern and innovative philosophy. The interesting combination of two wine production facilities that are over 700 kilometres apart make this winery truly unique. Included in the assortment of wines are rarities from the superb Pinot Noir vineyard in Vaduz as well as classic Grüner Veltliner and other white wine specialties such as Riesling Reserve or Traminer Amato from the traditional Weinviertel wine region in Austria. Among the red wines, the oak matured wines "Anberola Merlot", "Profundo Zweigelt" and "Principatus Zweigelt/Merlot" are worthy of special mention. Responsible interaction with natural resources in the vineyard and minimal intervention in the cellar are the pillars of the winery's philosophy. The construction of a new vinification facility in Wilfersdorf in 2011 and the opening of a wine shop in the Alsergrund district of Vienna in November 2012 are now followed by the next step of modernisation. In 2014, the winery introduced a new winery business identity, which fuses revitalized youth into centuries of history and tradition. Aristocratic elegance is reflected in all areas of marketing and distribution, from the company logo, to the labels, to the website, etc. The new location in Wilfersdorf now offers on-premise sales and an event venue for festivities of all kinds. The entire assortment of the Hofkellerei wines can be tasted in the wine shop in Vienna located near the picturesque garden palace.

91 Grüner Veltliner Reserve
   Selektion Karlsberg 2014
91 Grüner Veltliner Reserve
   Selektion Karlsberg 2012

88 Weinviertel DAC Clos Domaine 2015
88 Weinviertel DAC Clos Domaine 2014
88 Weinviertel DAC Clos Domaine 2013

90 Riesling Reserve Selektion Karlsberg 2014

88 Riesling Clos Domaine 2015
88 Riesling Clos Domaine 2014
89 Riesling Clos Domaine 2013

89 Traminer Clos Domaine 2015

92 Traminer Amato 2013
Brilliant golden yellow. Intense fragrance of rose oil and marshmallow with subtle oaky notes. Full-bodied and concentrated with complex layers of peach, tropical fruit, honey, flowers and apricot jam that continue to linger on the finish.

90 Traminer Auslese Amato
   Selektion Karlsberg 2011

91 Pinot Noir Abt AOC Liechtenstein Barrique 2012

89 Principatus Selektion Karlsberg 2012 ZW/ME
89 Principatus Selektion Karlsberg 2011 ZW/ME

90 Merlot Anberola Selektion Karlsberg 2011
89 Merlot Anberola Selektion Karlsberg 2009

87 Veramo Clos Domaine 2011 ZW/ME

88 Zweigelt Profundo Selektion Karlsberg 2011

87 Zweigelt Clos Domaine 2011

★★★★
Weingut R. & A. Pfaffl

2100 Stetten, Schulgasse 21
T: +43 (2262) 673423, F: +43 (2262) 673423 21
wein@pfaffl.at, www.pfaffl.at

Winemaker: Roman Josef Pfaffl
Contact Person: Pfaffl family
Production: n. a. (70 % white, 30 % red)
Hectares: 100
Fairs: VieVinum, ProWein
Distribution partners: on request

Grüner Veltliner belongs to Weingut R. & A. Pfaffl like Wiener Schnitzel does to Vienna. This variety has played the leading role at the estate from the very beginning. Roman Pfaffl realized the potential of this variety more than 30 years ago and was not only one of the first in the region to bottle it as a quality wine, but he did so in a number of variations, including oak fermented. Excited murmurs went through the Austrian wine scene and the Pfaffl assortment of Grüner Veltliners continues to hold its head above the crowd. Winemaker Roman Josef Pfaffl and his father Roman also prove master skill with Riesling: crisp and dry or mineral from the rocky Terrassen Sonnleiten (unique in the region) or fruity and off-dry or even sweet and sourced from a sandy knoll. The family also proves that the Weinviertel is a suitable terroir for international varieties. Chardonnay and Sauvignon Blanc achieve great finesse and must not shy from international comparison. Roman Josef Pfaffl is also one of the best in the red wine sector. The vineyards in the Stammersdorf district of Wien (Vienna) offer optimal preconditions for marvellous Pinot Noir with exquisite varietal character. He also found a plot with calcareous sand – where Merlot can become particularly round, making it a perfect partner for spicy Cabernet Sauvignon in the estate's top red wine blends "Heidrom" and "Excellent". The indigenous St. Laurent is a favoured child of the young winemaker. The single vineyard St. Laurent Altenberg is matured in small oak barrels and year for year is one of the best red wines in Austria. The expansive assortment of wines is based on the diversity of soils on which the Pfaffls cultivate their vines. They are scattered between eleven different wine villages with soils ranging from areas with metres-deep loess near the Marchfeld region to the calcareous flysch zone of the Bisam Mountains to the sandy-stony vineyards of Wolkersdorf and Wien (Vienna). Each area naturally has its own unique microclimate and is a logical explanation for such a diverse assortment of wines. Roman Josef Pfaffl has set very strict quality criteria. His founding principle is that quality must first grow in the vineyard because mistakes made there can no longer be corrected in the cellar – and even if that means a lot of sweat and toil in the summer heat.

95 Weinviertel DAC Reserve Hommage 2015
95 Weinviertel DAC Reserve Hommage 2013
Medium yellow with silver highlights. Juicy apricot and yellow apple with nuances of blossom honey and orange zest over a background of herbs and peppery spice. Full bodied and creamy with juicy, silky sweet fruit in an elegant cloak of acidity. Delicious apricot joins in on the very long finish. Superb ageing potential.
94 Weinviertel DAC Reserve Hommage 2012

92 Weinviertel DAC Reserve Hundsleiten 2015
92 Weinviertel DAC Reserve Hundsleiten 2014
92 Weinviertel DAC Hundsleiten 2013

93 Weinviertel DAC Reserve Goldjoch 2015
93 Weinviertel DAC Reserve Goldjoch 2014
93 Grüner Veltliner Goldjoch 2013

90 Weinviertel DAC Zeiseneck 2015
90 Weinviertel DAC Zeiseneck 2014
88 Weinviertel DAC Zeiseneck 2013

91 Weinviertel DAC Haidviertel 2015
91 Weinviertel DAC Haidviertel 2014

90 Weinviertel DAC Haidviertel 2013
89 Grüner Veltliner Vom Haus 2015

93 Riesling Passion Reserve 2015

92 Riesling Am Berg Grand Reserve 2013

91 Riesling Terrassen Sonnleiten 2015
91 Riesling Terrassen Sonnleiten 2014
91 Riesling Terrassen Sonnleiten 2013

90 Weißburgunder Nussern 2015
89 Weißburgunder Nussern 2013

88 Sauvignon Blanc Seiser am Eck 2015
88 Sauvignon Blanc Seiser am Eck 2014
88 Sauvignon Blanc Seiser am Eck 2013

90 Gelber Muskateller Sandlern 2015
90 Gelber Muskateller Sandlern 2014
89 Gelber Muskateller Sandlern 2013

92 Chardonnay Rossern Grand Reserve 2013
91 Chardonnay Rossern Grand Reserve 2011

91 Chardonnay Exklusiv 2015
91 Chardonnay Exklusiv 2014
90 Chardonnay Exklusiv 2013

88 Ganz Zart 2015 GV/SB

89 Gemischter Satz Symphonie 2015
89 Symphonie 2014
89 Gemischter Satz Symphonie 2013

89 Wien 1 2015 RR/WB/GV
89 Wien 1 2014 RR/WB/GV
88 Wien 1 2013 RR/GV/WB

89 Zweigelt Rosé 2015
88 Zweigelt Rosé 2012

93 Heidrom Grand Reserve 2012 ME/CS
94 Heidrom Grand Reserve 2011 CS/ME
Dark ruby with a deep core, purple highlights and a thin
transparent rim. The inviting bouquet displays blackberry, a
hint of chocolate and subtle herbal spice with soft vanilla
and tobacco notes in the background. Elegant lingonberry
nuances with well integrated oak refreshingly structured
with vibrant acidity. Minerals join in on the appetizing finish.
Dependable ageing potential.
91 Heidrom 2009 ME/CS

93 Excellent Reserve 2013 ZW/ME/CS
93 Excellent Reserve 2012 ZW/ME/CS
88 Excellent Reserve 2011 ZW/CS/ME

89 Wien 2 2015 ZW/PN
88 Wien 2 2012 ZW/PN

92 Pinot Noir Reserve 2013
92 Pinot Noir Reserve 2012
90 Pinot Noir Reserve 2011

91 Sankt Laurent Altenberg Reserve 2013
92 St. Laurent Altenberg Reserve 2012
91 Sankt Laurent Altenberg 2011

(90–92) Sankt Laurent Waldgärten 2015
91 St. Laurent Waldgärten 2013
89 St. Laurent Waldgärten 2012

92 Zweigelt Burggarten Reserve 2013
92 Zweigelt Burggarten Reserve 2012
90 Zweigelt Burggarten Reserve 2011

90 Zweigelt Sandstein 2015
90 Zweigelt Sandstein 2013
90 Zweigelt Sandstein 2012

89 Zweigelt Vom Haus 2015

Weingut Prechtl

2051 Zellerndorf, Zellerndorf 12
T: +43 (2945) 2297, F: +43 (2945) 2297 40, M: +43 (676) 3238470
weingut@prechtl.at, www.prechtl.at

Winemaker: DI Franz Prechtl
Contact Person: Franz and Petra Prechtl
Production: n. a. (90 % white, 10 % red)
Hectares: 14
Fairs: VieVinum, ProWein
Distribution partners: on request

Austrian Wine Salon Champion 2013 for "Weinviertel DAC Längen" was quite a confirmation for the oenologist Franz Prechtl, who is specialized in Grüner Veltliner. He gained profound knowledge of soil vitality and viticulture during his studies at the University of Natural Resources and Life Sciences, Vienna (BOKU). The assortment of wines comprises six different Grüner Veltliners from metamorphic rock, loess, and marine sediment. The wines are exported to six different countries. The winery is open to visitors every Saturday and it is possible to tour the new vinification facility with its barrique cellar and wine shop. Petra Prechtl, a WSET diploma holder, also welcomes guests in their "Sommerladen & Café" in the adjacent old farmhouse with a beautiful courtyard. Guests are pampered with delicious regional specialties and homemade baked goods.

92 Weinviertel DAC Reserve Äußere Bergen 2013
Pale yellow with silver highlights. Wild herbs, yellow apple, notes of mango, and a touch of tobacco. Juicy, sweet fruit extract is supported by elegant acidity. Apricot and minerals linger on the aftertaste. Good ageing potential.
92 Weinviertel DAC Reserve Äußere Bergen 2012

**92 Weinviertel DAC Reserve
 Leitstall von Molasse 2013**
Deep yellow with gold highlights. An inviting fragrance of yellow apple, mango, subtle orange zest and a touch of blossom honey. A taut acid structure frames white apple and pear fruit and provides a streamlined texture. Racy and appetizing with lemony nuances on the finish.
92 Weinviertel DAC Reserve Leitstall 2012

91 Weinviertel DAC Längen 2015
91 Weinviertel DAC Längen vom Löss 2014
91 Weinviertel DAC Längen vom Löss 2013

90 Weinviertel DAC Altenberg 2015
**89 Weinviertel DAC Altenberg
 vom Urgestein 2014**
**89 Weinviertel DAC Altenberg
 vom Urgestein 2013**

90 Weinviertel DAC Alte Reben 2015
90 Weinviertel DAC Alte Rebe vom Löss 2014
92 Weinviertel DAC Alte Rebe 2013

88 Riesling Wartberg 2015
89 Riesling Wartberg vom Urgestein 2014
88 Riesling Wartberg vom Urgestein 2013

88 Sauvignon Blanc Altenfeld 2015
88 Sauvignon Blanc Altenfeld 2013
89 Sauvignon Blanc Altenfeld 2012

89 Burgundercuvée 2015 WB/CH

★ ★

Weingut Schuckert

2170 Poysdorf, Wilhelmsdorfer Straße 40
T: +43 (2552) 2389, F: +43 (2552) 29389
weingut@schuckert.com, www.schuckert.com

Winemaker and Contact Person: Rainer Schuckert
Production: n. a. (72 % white, 25 % red, 3 % sweet)
Hectares: 20
Fairs: VieVinum, ProWein
Distribution partners: CH, RC, DE, CZ, NL

Weingut Schuckert counts among the most ambitious producers in the aspiring wine region of Weinviertel. The family has always produced good wines from their 20 estate hectares, but went largely unnoticed by wine lovers until recently. This has provided insiders with the advantage of superb wines for very reasonable prices. This is particularly true of Grüner Veltliner, which plays a central role at the Schuckert winery as well as in the entire Weinviertel. Rainer Schuckert's work with the leading variety exhibits the diversity that is possible to achieve from this old autochthon grape variety.

(91–93) Grüner Veltliner Novemberlese 2015
92 Grüner Veltliner Novemberlese 2013
91 Grüner Veltliner Novemberlese 2012

88 Grüner Veltliner Ried Nestelbächer 2015
88 Grüner Veltliner Ried Nestelbächer 2014
88 Grüner Veltliner Nestelbecher 2013

91 Grüner Veltliner Ried Hermannschachern 2014
Pale green-yellow with silver highlights. Yellow apple, pineapple, and orange zest with wild meadow herbs. Juicy elegant acidity provides a fine structure for tropical yellow fruit. Appetizing fruit and minerals linger on this stylish wine.

88 Weinviertel DAC 2015
89 Weinviertel DAC Classic 2014
89 Weinviertel DAC Classic 2013

91 Weißer Burgunder 2014
91 Weißburgunder 2013

90 Riesling Steinberg 2015
89 Riesling Steinberg 2014
89 Riesling Steinberg 2013

(88–90) Chardonnay 2015
88 Chardonnay 2012

89 Zweigelt Exklusiv 2012
89 Zweigelt Exklusiv 2011

92 Grüner Veltliner Eiswein 2012

Weingut Schwarz

2172 Schrattenberg, Kleine Zeile 8
T: +43 (2555) 2544, F: +43 (2555) 2544 4
office@schwarzwines.com, www.schwarzwines.com

— ORGANIC —

Winemaker: Alois and Reinold Schwarz
Contact Person: Schwarz family
Production: n. a. (23 % white, 76 % red, 1 % sweet)
Hectares: 22
Fairs: Gast Salzburg
Distribution partners: S, CH, DE, CZ, NL

The Schwarz family winery is located in Schrattenberg, one of the oldest and most significant wine villages of Austria. High-quality red wines, fine white wines and elegant sweet wines are produced here. The focus is on the organic cultivation of the vineyards. Quality oriented pruning, green cover appropriately selected for the region, compost for fertilization, intense canopy management including green harvesting and grape bunch division, and manual harvest are the labour intensive methods applied. Attention is given the gentle transportation grapes to the crush house in small crates. Vinification interventions are reduced to the minimum and the wine left to more or less make itself and thus preserve its unique inherent character. Inimitable wines are produced year for year in all categories: red, white, rosé, sweet and sparkling.

91 **Cabernet Sauvignon Premium 2013**
89 **Cabernet Sauvignon Premium 2012**
90 **Cabernet Sauvignon Premium 2011**

90 **Syrah Premium 2013**
90 **Syrah Premium 2012**
90 **Syrah Premium 2011**

89 **Zweigelt Premium 2013**
88 **Zweigelt Premium 2012**
89 **Zweigelt Premium 2011**

88 **Zweigelt 2013**

89 **Blaufränkisch 2013**

88 **Sankt Laurent 2013**

89 **Tradition 2013 ZW/BF/SL**
88 **Tradition 2012 BF/ZW/SL**
88 **Tradition 2011 BF/ZW/SL**

91 **Grande Reserve 2012 SY/ME**

91 **Chardonnay Premium 2014**
91 **Chardonnay Premium 2013**
89 **Chardonnay Premium 2012**

88 **Weinviertel DAC 2015**

92 **Chardonnay Trockenbeerenauslese 2013**
Brilliant yellow with silver highlights. Intense tropical fruit reminiscent of banana and litchi with candied orange and a honeyed botrytis touch. Medium complexity with luscious sweetness paired with fine, elegant acidity. Pineapple comes in on the sweet finish.

90 **Riesling Beerenauslese 2011**

Weingut Seifried

2023 Oberstinkenbrunn, Oberstinkenbrunn 43
T: +43 (2953) 2339, F: +43 (2953) 2339
office@weinbau-seifried.at, www.weinbau-seifried.at

Winemaker: Stefan Seifried
Contact Person: Hannes & Stefan Seifried
Production: n. a. (85 % white, 15 % red)
Hectares: 19
Fairs: VieVinum
Distribution partners: on request

This family estate was founded in 1849 and is now operated by the fifth (Christa and Josef) and sixth (Hannes, Stefan, Lisa, and Eva) generations. "It is a great joy and privilege for us to be able to cultivate grapes in such advantageous natural conditions," says Josef Seifried. Loess and weathered primary rock mark the wines with inimitable spice, fruit, and mineral character. Their vineyards in the wine village Oberstinkenbrunn south of the historic wine town of Retz enjoy a cool continental climate moderated by warm Pannonian influences. Warm days promote the ripening of grapes whilst the pronounced fluctuations between day and night temperatures enhance character. It is this vintner family's declared goal, with or despite all technological perfection, to preserve the inherent character of the variety and terroir. With this, they continue the old Weinviertel tradition of honest, natural wines – wines for pure enjoyment.

90 Grüner Veltliner Altenberg 2015
90 Grüner Veltliner Altenberg 2013

(91–93) Grüner Veltliner Alte Reben 2015
Brilliant green-yellow with silver highlights. Aromas and flavours of yellow apple laced with blossom honey, subtle stone fruit notes, and a touch of orange zest. Juicy with a well balanced acid structure. White vineyard peach and wild meadow herbs on the aftertaste. Good potential.
92 Grüner Veltliner Alte Reben 2012

88 Grüner Veltliner Lange Haide 2013
90 Grüner Veltliner Lange Haide 2012

89 Weinviertel DAC 2015
88 Weinviertel DAC 2013
88 Weinviertel DAC 2012

91 Riesling Zwei Gärten 2015
89 Riesling Zwei Gärten 2013

89 Gelber Muskateller 2015
88 Gelber Muskateller 2013
87 Gelber Muskateller 2012

88 Sauvignon Blanc 2015
89 Sauvignon Blanc 2013
89 Sauvignon Blanc 2012

★
Weingut Georg Toifl

2074 Kleinhöflein, Untere Hauptstraße 15 und 17
T: +43 (676) 6142074, F: +43 (2942) 2680 4
office@weingut-toifl.at, www.weingut-toifl.at

Winemaker and Contact Person: Georg Toifl
Hectares: 12
Fairs: VieVinum, ProWein
Distribution partners: on request

The Toifl winery is located in the village of Kleinhöflein near Retz in the western Weinviertel. Georg Toifl, the youngest son of the family, has managed the ten-hectare estate since spring of 2009. The vineyards are located primarily on the plateau surrounding Retz and on the slopes of the Buchberg Mountain near Obritz in Pulkautal. The wine assortment is divided into the following categories: "G" stands for crystal clear, streamlined enjoyment for everyday; "GEO" is the inimitable result of the play between geology, geography, the vines and Georg; "GE.ORG" is Georg's signature line of unique, experimental wines that test boundaries. The unique stamp of a specific site combined with the highest possible degree of physiological ripeness and personality mark the character of this series of wines.

(90–92) Grauburgunder Schatzberg GE.ORG 2015
91 Grauburgunder Schatzberg GE.ORG 2013
Pale salmon colour with golden highlights. Inviting peach and pair with orange zest and a touch of blossom honey. Juicy and complex with sweetly extracted apple fruit and nicely integrated oak components. Refreshing and citrus on the finish. Will benefit from further bottle maturation.

(90–92) Grüner Veltliner Wolfsthal GE.ORG 2015
92 Grüner Veltliner Wolfsthal GE.ORG 2013

89 Weinviertel DAC Grüner Veltliner GEO 2015
89 Weinviertel DAC Grüner Veltliner GEO 2014
89 Grüner Veltliner GEO 2013

88 Grüner Veltliner grünes G 2015

89 Gelber Muskateller GEO 2015
88 Gelber Muskateller GEO 2013

(89–91) Weißburgunder Seeleiten GE.ORG 2015
89 Weißburgunder Seeleiten GE.ORG 2013
88 Weißburgunder Seeleiten GE.ORG 2011

89 Riesling Siebzehnlehen GE.ORG 2013
88 Riesling Siebzehnlehen GE.ORG 2012

91 Pinot Noir Berghangen GE.ORG 2013
91 Pinot Noir Berghangen GE.ORG 2011

88 St. Laurent Wolfsthal GE.ORG 2013
89 Sankt Laurent Wolfsthal GE.ORG 2011

90 Zweigelt Seeleiten GE.ORG 2011

92 Sämling 88 Trockenbeerenauslese GE.ORG 2011

Weingut Walek

2170 Poysdorf, Gewerbepark 3
T: +43 (2552) 2354, F: +43 (2552) 2354 8
walek@reben.at, www.reben.at

Winemaker and Contact Person: Wolfgang Walek
Production: n. a. (65 % white, 35 % red)
Hectares: 25
Distribution partners: on request

The Walek family's success begins with their choice of vines. All of their vineyards are planted with vines that they have raised in their vine nursery. Each member of the family has their own specialized tasks, yet they work together with the precision of a Swiss watch. Harmonious perfection is for what they strive and this begins with soil and vine balance in the vineyard. Biodiversity is provided with fruit trees, blooming hedgerows for bees, and versatile green cover between vine rows. The resulting ecosystem is vital and provides a healthy, well-balanced environment for vines. The vines are in turn also vital and well balanced and deliver healthy, high-quality fruit. Grapes are processed as gently as possible and minimal intervention is practiced in order to produce wines that are as unadulterated and authentic as possible.

90 Weinviertel DAC Reserve 2012
Medium yellow with golden highlights. Yellow apple, nuances of lime, mango and wild herbs over a note of hazelnut. Juicy, elegant acidity is harmoniously integrated in the full body. Delicate pear fruit on the medium long finish. Ready to enjoy.
90 Weinviertel DAC Reserve 2011

**90 Weinviertel DAC Reserve
Hermannschachern 2012**
**88 Weinviertel DAC Reserve
Hermannschachern 2011**

**89 Weinviertel DAC Hermannschachern
Nr°113 2013**
88 Weinviertel DAC Nr°67 2012

89 Weinviertel DAC 2015
89 Weinviertel DAC 2014

90 Grüner Veltliner Freiberg 2015

88 Grüner Veltliner Poysdorfer Saurüssel 2015
88 Grüner Veltliner Poysdorfer Saurüssel 2014
88 Grüner Veltliner Poysdorfer Saurüssel 2013

88 Sauvignon Blanc 2015
88 Sauvignon Blanc 2014
87 Sauvignon Blanc 2013

87 Müller-Thurgau 2015
88 Müller-Thurgau 2013

86 Chardonnay 2015

89 Grauburgunder 2013

88 Welschriesling 2014

★★★

Weingut Weinrieder

2170 Kleinhadersdorf/Poysdorf, Untere Ortsstraße 44
T: +43 (2552) 2241, F: +43 (2552) 3708
office@weinrieder.at, www.weinrieder.at

Winemaker and Contact Person: Friedrich Rieder
Production: n. a. (95 % white, 5 % sweet)
Hectares: 20
Fairs: ProWein, VieVinum
Distribution partners: I, RUS, J, S, CDN, CH, B, RC, DK, DE, EST, CZ, NL, N, GB, H, USA, IRL, PL

Genius is often just a millimetre away from catastrophe" is a statement that dictates a lucid direction for the Weinrieder estate. Whether it is the work in the vineyard, the vinification of the wines or their marketing, the vintner unerringly seeks a method that is outside the norm. Even his concept of a final product is too unique to fit into a standard mould. He views a wine's attributes as an accompaniment to food as what puts it into the very top class. For this, it must possess finesse, power, character and superb ageing potential. It is also these attributes that place the Weinrieder wines on the wine lists of international top restaurants around the world. Friedrich Rieder sees the foundation for these attributes in the vineyard. Weinrieder focuses on natural cycles and has his own parameters for planning the vineyard work accordingly. Late harvest and long maturation on the fine lees help achieve the desired longevity, wines that will continue to fascinate with unique vitality for many years.

92 Grüner Veltliner Alte Reben 2013
Brilliant green-yellow with silver highlights. Yellow apple, a hint of mango, and delicate notes of wild herbs and fresh citrus zest. Full-bodied and powerful with elegant, sweetly extracted peach and mango. Peppery spice lingers on the long finish. Will benefit from further bottle maturation.
90 Grüner Veltliner Alte Reben 2012

91 Grüner Veltliner Privat 2013

(89–91) Grüner Veltliner Reserve 2014
91 Grüner Veltliner Reserve 2013
91 Grüner Veltliner Reserve 2011

(88–90) Grüner Veltliner Schneiderberg 2015
89 Grüner Veltliner Schneiderberg 2013

89 Chardonnay Hohenleiten 2014

89 Riesling Kugler 2013
90 Riesling Kugler 2012

(90–92) Riesling Schneiderberg 2015

92 Weißburgunder Kugler Lagenreserve 2013
92 Weißburgunder Kugler Lagenreserve 2011

89 Weißburgunder Birthal 2014
90 Weißburgunder Birthal 2012

(91–93) Riesling Grande Reserve 2015
90 Riesling Grande Reserve 2011

94 Riesling Eiswein Schneiderberg 2013
94 Riesling Eiswein Schneiderberg 2012
Brilliant yellow-green with silver highlights. The highly attractive bouquet features pineapple and papaya with floral nuances over layers of blossom honey and peach. Vibrant, well integrated acidity lends juiciness and silky texture to lusciously sweet fruit. The long finish features pleasant honey notes. Elegant and well balanced, this wine already offers abundant drinking pleasure.
93 Riesling Eiswein Schneiderberg 2011

92 Welschriesling Eiswein Hölzler 2011

Weingut Zull

2073 Schrattenthal, Schrattenthal 9
T: +43 (2946) 8217, F: +43 (2946) 8217 4
office@zull.at, www.zull.at

Winemaker and Contact Person: Phillip Zull
Production: n. a. (65 % white, 33 % red, 2 % sweet)
Hectares: 18
Fairs: VieVinum, ProWein
Distribution partners: J, CH, B, SK, DE, CZ, CY

As far as the eyes can reach, one sees picturesque rolling vineyard hills – this is the Weinviertel. In the middle of this idyllic landscape close to the Czech border, is Schrattenthal, Austria's smallest wine village. Here one also finds the Zull winery. Although its size of 18 hectares is not great, great wines are produced here. Everything at this winery is focused on family. At the beginning of the 1980s, Werner Zull was just about ready to begin his studies at the university when his brother was tragically killed in an accident. The family stuck together in those difficult times and Werner Zull sacrificed his studies for work in the vineyards. From that time on, the Zull winery began bottling their wines and concentrating on high quality. In the meantime this small winery has long become known for its wines. This is due to the unique microclimate that provides enough sun and warmth for optimal ripening while the Manhart Mountain shields from harsh weather that could harm the grapes. Deeply rooted vines find the nourishment they need from the soil. The Zulls rely on a sensitive hand rather than exaggerated technology for the vinification of their elegant and complex wines. Perseverance and courage for experimentation has been a key to the success at the Zull winery. Son Phillip now furthers the vision of his father and strives for brilliant wines of character and longevity. The top wines are the "Grüner Veltliner Äussere Bergen", "Riesling Innere Bergen" and the rare and popular Pinot Noir.

93 Weinviertel DAC Reserve Äußere Bergen 2015
92 Weinviertel DAC Reserve Äußere Bergen 2014
Pale green-yellow with silver highlights. Fresh apple fruit over a delicate background of meadow herbs and subtle notes of mango in the background. Good complexity with bright acidity elegantly balancing the sweet fruit extract. A touch of minerals join in on the finish of this pleasant accompaniment to food.
92 Weinviertel DAC Reserve Äußere Bergen 2013

91 Weinviertel DAC 2015
90 Weinviertel DAC 2014
90 Weinviertel DAC 2013

89 Grüner Veltliner Lust & Laune 2015
89 Grüner Veltliner Lust & Laune 2014
89 Grüner Veltliner Lust & Laune 2013

91 Riesling Innere Bergen 2015
91 Riesling Innere Bergen 2014
Pale green-yellow. Pleasant fragrance of stone fruit reminiscent of peach with a touch of pineapple, blossom honey, and mandarin. Nicely concentrated with vibrant acidity highlighting greengage plum. Subtle sweetness lingers on the aftertaste. Easy-drinking pleasure with good ageing potential.
91 Riesling Innere Bergen 2013

90 Chardonnay 2015
89 Chardonnay 2013
91 Chardonnay 2012

89 Lust & Laune Rosé 2015

92 Pinot Noir 2013
92 Pinot Noir 2011

91 Schrattenthal 9 2013 ZW/ME/CS
91 Schrattenthal 9 2011 ZW/ME/CS

89 Zweigelt 2015
89 Zweigelt 2013

88 Lust & Laune Rot 2015 ZW/PN

Steep, rolling hills and a cool climate, crisp and aromatic wines; the epitome of freshness

Aromatic, refreshing varietal wines from 4,240 vineyard hectares – and standing out from the crowd, classy Sauvignon Blanc. From the light and fruity wine of the latest vintage called "Junker" to the elegant, light-bodied classic wines and the late-harvest, single-vineyard wines, winemakers play out the regional strengths. All three sub-regions offer their own specialties and are located in the southern part of this federal province.

© Österreich Werbung/Himsl

In the Weststeiermark, one finds a picturesque, hilly landscape where a brisk, spicy rosé called "Schilcher" reigns the terroir. In Südsteiermark, the idyllic wine route meanders through vineyards planted with aromatic Sauvignon Blanc and Muskateller (Muscat Blanc à petits grains). These two varieties also thrive in Südoststeiermark, but here it is in particular the Traminer (Gewürztraminer) that thrives in the volcanic soils as a glittering jewel for connoisseurs. The most abundant varietal wine of Steiermark is Welschriesling and with its lovely green apple bouquet and refreshing, quaffable style, it has far more fans than wine pundits can even begin to imagine. Those seeking fuller bodied wines are in good hands with the Pinot family in Steiermark. The Weissburgunder (Pinot Blanc) achieves a refined minerality and distinguished character in calcareous soils. Chardonnay is known by its old local name "Morillon" and attains weighty firmness and power without sacrificing its pristine freshness. Like Morillon, Grauburgunder (Pinot Gris) from this region also benefits from extended bottle maturation.

Each new vintage in Steiermark is traditionally celebrated with the initiation of the light "Junker" wine, which debuts at the beginning of November. The dry "classic" wines enter the market in spring. The cognoscenti must remain patient, for the great single-vineyard wines are given more time to mature before they are released.

The vintners of Steiermark lavish these wines with attentive care and respect to ensure that the distinctive regional character is recognized for what it truly is: world class.

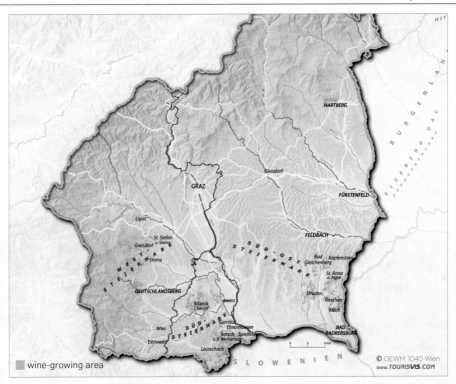

wine-growing area

© OEWM, 1040 Wien
www.TOURISVIS.COM

AUSTRIA ALTOGETHER: 45,900 ha

Wine-growing area Styria — 4,240 ha (9 %)

SPECIFIC WINE-GROWING AREA:

Southeast Styria	1,400 ha
South Styria	2,340 ha
West Styria	500 ha

White wine altogether:	**3,225 ha (76 %)**	**Red wine altogether:**	**1,017 (24 %)**
Welschriesling:	793 ha (19 %)	Blauer Wildbacher:	450 ha (11 %)
Weissburgunder:	513 ha (12 %)	Zweigelt:	441 ha (10 %)
Sauvignon Blanc:	513 ha (12 %)	Blauburger:	30 ha (0,7 %)
Chardonnay:	331 ha (7 %)	Blaufränkisch:	17 ha (0,4 %)
Müller-Thurgau:	314 ha (7 %)	Pinot Noir:	17 ha (0,4 %)

Volcanic terroir

Castles and fortresses perched on basalt cliff tops and tiny wine farms on the slopes of extinct volcanoes imbue special flair to the Südoststeiermark landscape. Affectionately called "Vulkanland" (Volcano Land) by the locals, this wine area's unique soils and Illyrian climate yield wines of inimitable spice and mineral character.

© ÖWM/Armin Faber

The extensive, standard range of regional Styrian grape varieties thrives in the 1,400 hectares of vineyards here, but Traminer is a specialty found predominantly around the area of Klöch.

This was a heavily disputed borderland for centuries as the many fortresses and castles perched high on basalt cliff tops evidence. Today, the borders are open and Riegersburg, Schloss Kapfenstein and other remarkable residences have become venues for an array of cultural events, many of which are related to food and wine. This wine-growing area, unlike any other, offers a particularly wide range of international grape varieties. White varieties are the most important and the predominant ones are Welschriesling, Morillon (Chardonnay), Weissburgunder (Pinot Blanc), Grauburgunder (Pinot Gris), Gelber Muskateller (Muscat Blanc à petits grains), the Traminer (Gewürztraminer) family, Sauvignon Blanc, and Riesling. Red wines feature Zweigelt as well as other grapes, including St. Laurent and Blauburgunder (Pinot Noir). All of

these varieties are able to express the unique geological conditions of the area through an inimitable spicy, mineral note. Four wine routes lead through charming landscape of rolling hills. A regional wine shop providing a view over the entire region is situated in St. Anna am Aigen and along the volcanic fault line, luxurious spas are popular vacation destinations. Apart from the few large estates, viticulture is generally part of a farm with mixed agriculture and livestock and theses products can be consumed in the numerous heuriger (winery taverns) of the region. The most important wine-growing villages are Bad Radkersburg, Feldbach, Gleisdorf, Hartberg, Kapfenstein, Klöch, Riegersburg, St. Peter, Straden, Tieschen, and Weiz. In the north at the Ringkogel near Hartberg, are some of Austria's most elevated vineyards, at 650 meters above sea level. The weather reflects the contrast between a warm, dry Pannonian climate and humid, warm Mediterranean conditions. Many of the vines grow in warm soils comprising volcanic earth, basalt, sand, clay and weathered stone.

wine-growing area

© OEWM. 1040 Wien
www.TOURISVIS.COM

◆ Weingut Frauwallner, Straden

◆ Weingut Krispel, Hof bei Straden

◆ Wein von Ploder-Rosenberg,
   St. Peter/Ottersbach

Weingut Frauwallner

8345 Straden, Karbach 7
T: +43 (3473) 7137, F: +43 (3473) 20057, M: +43 (676) 6036911
weingut@frauwallner.com, www.frauwallner.com

Winemaker and Contact Person: Walter Frauwallner
Production: n. a. (90 % white, 8 % red, 2 % sweet)
Hectares: 22
Fairs: ProWein, VieVinum
Distribution partners: CH, DE, NL, PL

Just like their winemaker, the wines of vintner Walter Frauwallner in Straden speak a clear and honest language. Each variety, each wine is given its unique voice. It is a true joy to taste this series of wines - a potpourri of unique characters, each with pronounced regional typicity and an inimitable signature. "There should be plenty of expression in the glass and the terroir should be clearly recognizable without ever losing the ease of enjoyment," philosiphizes the young father of two. And indeed he does achieve this quite impressively. The traditional varietal wines are fermented in stainless steel and prove to be cheerful while maintaining elegance and complexity. The single vineyard wines from the calcareous Hochrosenberg and from the mineral-rich Buch (an outstanding site for the Burgundian varieties) exhibit great depth and finesse. Those seeking to discover the true taste of the Styrian "Vulkanland" simply cannot ignore this producer. His Weissburgunder (Pinot Blanc) Grauburgunder (Pinot Gris), Morillon (Chardonnay), Sauvignon Blanc and Traminer are established in the domestic market as some of the top wines of the region. Manual vineyard work, which includes meticulous canopy management, yield restriction and the selective harvesting of grapes, is obligatory for Frauwallner. Patience and time are the virtues of his vinification philosophy. In the practical-focused cellar, an exciting assortment of wines is produced without pomp or circumstance. The wines can be tasted at the winery shop in Karbach.

93 Morillon vom Buch Eruption weiss 2013
93 Morillon vom Buch Eruption weiss 2012
Brilliant yellow hue with silver highlights. Delicate toasted components nicely integrated with papaya, hazelnut and candied orange zest. With length and ageing potential, this makes an elegant and harmonious culinary partner.
92 Morillon vom Buch Eruption weiß 2011

92 Morillon vom Buch Reserve 2011

92 Morillon Vulkanland 2015

89 Gelber Muskateller Vulkanland 2015
90 Gelber Muskateller "f" 2014

92 Grauburgunder
    Stradner Rosenberg 2014
92 Grauburgunder Hochrosenberg 2013
92 Grauburgunder Hochrosenberg 2011

91 Grauburgunder Vulkanland 2015

89 Welschriesling Vulkanland 2015

90 Weißburgunder Vulkanland 2015
89 Weißburgunder "f" 2014
89 Weißburgunder »f« 2013

92 Weißburgunder vom Buch 2013
91 Weißburgunder vom Buch 2012
91 Weißburgunder vom Buch 2011

92 Weißburgunder vom Buch
    Reserve 2011

93 Traminer Stradner Rosenberg 2015
92 Traminer Hochrosenberg 2014
89 Traminer Hochrosenberg 2013

93 Traminer Fabian Privat 2012

92 Sauvignon Blanc vom Buch 2014
93 Sauvignon Blanc vom Buch 2013
Soft yellow hue with silver highlights. Fresh orange fruit and mandarin zest with yellow peach and subtle oak spice. Complex and elegant with oak components nicely integrated with a white vineyard peach note in a very long finish.
92 Sauvignon Blanc vom Buch 2012

91 Sauvignon Blanc Stradner Rosenberg 2015
91 Sauvignon Blanc Hochrosenberg 2014
91 Sauvignon Blanc Hochrosenberg 2013

93 Sauvignon Blanc Privat 2013

89 Sauvignon Blanc Vulkanland 2015
89 Sauvignon Blanc "f" 2014
89 Sauvignon Blanc »f« 2013

90 Blauer Wildbacher vom Buch 2013

91 Eruption rot 2013 ZW/ME
91 Eruption rot 2012 ZW/ME
91 Eruption rot 2011 ZW/ME

Weingut Krispel

8345 Hof bei Straden, Neusetz 29
T: +43 (3473) 7862, F: +43 (3473) 7862 4
office@krispel.at, www.krispel.at

Winemaker: Stefan Krispel
Contact Person: Krispel family
Production: n. a. (90 % white, 10 % red)
Hectares: 34
Fairs: VieVinum, ProWein
Distribution partners: on request

The Krispel estate nestled at the foot of the Rosenberg in Straden is one of the most noteworthy epicurean addresses in Austria. The estate includes a winery, accommodation and a restaurant featuring Mangalitsa pork specialties. Winemaker Stefan Krispel produces classic regional wines in this little paradise, wines that reflect the many facets of the Styrian "Vulkanland". "Getting to know the character of our sites well was my goal from the very beginning. Only when my winemaking harmonizes with nature am I able to produce something great. Now I am perceiving the complete cycle."

The volcanic soil of the Hochstrandl and Neusetzberg vineyards together with the local microclimate provide outstanding preconditions for first class, authentic wines with plenty of substance. The skin-fermented "Basalt B1" can be considered Stefan Krispel's masterpiece. It is an exciting, intense wine with pronounced terroir character. The maturation in basalt vessels, a process that Stefan studied for years, mellows the tannins and enhances the inherent mineral character perfectly.

The Krispel estate is overall a unified vinophile-culinary work of art that focuses on the most valuable treasure of every epicurean: quality of life.

92 B1 Basalt Der Wein aus dem Stein 2012 SB/PG

(92–94) Grauburgunder Hochstrandl 2015
93 Grauburgunder Hochstrandl 2013
Moderate yellow hue with copper highlights. Ripe pear and orange zest front notes of hazelnut and dried fruit. Full-bodied and structured with a pleasant juicy acidity. Yellow apple and honey on the long finish. A nicely concentrated food wine that would pair well even with hotly spiced dishes.
93 Grauburgunder Hochstrandl 2012

92 Grauburgunder Hochstrandl Reserve 2012

91 Grauburgunder Vulkanland 2015
90 Grauburgunder Straden 2014
89 Grauburgunder Straden 2013

(91–93) Weißburgunder Straden 2015
91 Weißburgunder Rosenberg 2013
89 Weißburgunder Rosenberg 2012

(92–94) Sauvignon Blanc Neusetzberg 2015
92 Sauvignon Blanc Neusetzberg 2013
90 Sauvignon Blanc Neusetzberg 2012

93 Sauvignon Blanc Neusetzberg Reserve 2013

89 Traminer Neusetzberg 2012

91 Gelber Muskateller Stradner Rosenberg 2015

(91–93) Chardonnay Straden 2015

92 Chardonnay Königsberg 2013

91 Chardonnay Eruption weiß 2012

★★★
Wein von Ploder-Rosenberg

8093 St. Peter/Ottersbach, Unterrosenberg 86
T: +43 (3477) 3234, F: +43 (3477) 3234 4
office@ploder-rosenberg.at, www.ploder-rosenberg.at

──── ORGANIC ────

Winemaker: Manuel and Alfred Ploder
Contact Person: Alfred Ploder
Production: n. a. (85 % white, 14 % red, 1 % sweet)
Hectares: 12
Fairs: ProWein, Millésime Bio
Distribution partners: on request

The Ploder-Rosenberg winery is located in the "Vulkanland" region in Südoststeiermark (Southeast Styria). Maria, Lydia, Fredi and Manuel and their hardworking employees cultivate a total of 12.5 hectares of vines biodynamically. "Because we embark, the horizon opens," is their motto. Their passion, competence and consistency have placed them firmly in the league of top biodynamic vintners. All vineyards have been cultivated according to biodynamic principles for ten years and the wines have been certified organic for the past seven years. Since 2015, the estate has been a member of Demeter Austria. "At Ploder-Rosenberg, we have chosen a holistic philosophy for biodynamic cultivation," says Alfred Ploder. "This is a spiritual approach that considers earthly and astral forces in contributing value to the world socially and environmentally." Three lines of wines are produced to give consumers a choice of wine styles. The "Feine Linie" makes up 60% of production and is comprised of dry, fruity wines with easy-drinking finesse. The premium "Linea A" are the flagship wines, distinguished by prolonged contact with the lees and years of maturation in tasted 600-litre Startin barrels. These wines impress with depth, minerality and expressive complexity as well as longevity. The Reserve wines are produced occasionally - and met with much enthusiasm: Linea Chardonnay Reserve, Linea Sauvignon Blanc Reserve Magnum and Linea Blauer Zweigelt Reserve have a long, long life potential. Original "orange" wines - fermented on the skins, unfiltered and amber-coloured - are called "gewordene Weinwerke". These are fermented in 600-liter Startins and are released in Blanca, Ruga and Rose. Further wines are fermented long and slowly on the lees in amphorae and custom-made clay eggs - and only in preferred vintages. The resulting wines, with their intense colour, are multi-dimensional creations with names such as Aero, Tero, Fejro and Maro.

93 Pinot Gris Linea 2012
Medium greenish-yellow hue. Caramel, mango, pear, and subtle herbal spice mingle with a touch of brioche. Complexly structured with plenty of juicy acidity and refreshing, ripe tropical fruit. Impressive finesse continues on the finish with peppery nuances and salty minerlity adding to the array of flavours. Very good potential for more development in the bottle.

92 Pinot Gris Linea 2010

92 Pinot Gris Fejro 2011

92 Gelber Muskateller 2015
90 Gelber Muskateller Klassik 2014

91 Grüner Veltliner Linea 2013
91 Grüner Veltliner LINEA 2012

93 Sauvignon Blanc Linea 2013
92 Sauvignon Blanc Linea 2012
93 Sauvignon Blanc Linea 2010

90 Sauvignon Blanc 2015
90 Sauvignon Blanc Klassik 2014
90 Sauvignon Blanc 2012

90 Weißburgunder 2015
88 Weißburgunder 2013
92 Morillon Eruption W 2013

92 Chardonnay Eruption Weiss 2012
Brilliant yellow with silver highlights. Subtle herbal and curry spice notes underscore the pear fruit and mineral tones. Juicy and elegant with a multi-faceted structure. Sweet extract lingers on the finish.

92 Morillon Eruption 2011

92 Chardonnay LINEA Reserve 2009

92 Ruländer Fejro 2011

92 Blanca 2013

94 Aero 2012 SB/TR/GM/MS
93 Aero 2011 TR/SB/GM

94 Magnum 2012 WB/SB/PG/CH

91 Zweigelt Eruption R 2013

92 Blauer Zweigelt Linea Reserve 2007

BRAND NEW!

falstaff
RESTAURANT
GUIDE

DIE BESTEN RESTAURANTS EUROPAS
2016

FOR
FREE!

Discover Europe's best restaurants

With the Falstaff Restaurant App you have access to
Europe's **best restaurants**. Save your favourite restaurants on your
personal bucket list and comment on your experience!

This is how it works: the app is on the Google Play Store or in the app
store – enter the word »Falstaff«, download it for free.

GENIESSEN WEIN ESSEN REISEN

Lush green, romantic hillsides, zesty Sauvignon Blanc

Südsteiermark is known for its classy, crisp, highly aromatic wines, especially Sauvignon Blanc and Muscat. But the 2,340 hectares of vineyards provide splendid opportunities for a broad range of other varieties to grow as well. The steep, rolling vineyards may make this the most charming wine landscape in all of Europe, but grape growing here requires painstaking labour.

© Österreich Werbung/Himsl

Just as varied as the grape varieties in Südsteiermark are its soils. Sandstone, schist, marl, and limestone vary intermittently between the individual sites. The warm, humid Mediterranean climate determines the vegetation cycle. Cool nights enhance nuanced aromatic intensity and the noblesse of the white wines.

Sleek, fruity young wines called "Junker" herald each new vintage with their early release in November. These are followed by the elegant, "classic" wines that are so representative for the area. Vintners demonstrate the true potential of the region in the mature, richly extracted single-vineyard wines. Sauvignon Blanc from Südsteiermark has achieved international recognition as one of the world's very best examples of the variety thanks to continual development of a unique, terroir-driven style. Open-minded winegrowers ensure that the high standards and quality are maintained by bringing home knowledge and know-how from trips and work experience abroad.

There is also an excellent vinicultural school in Silberberg, which continues to equip new winegrowers with skills and experience through theoretical and practical courses.

No matter the season, it is always well worth getting to know Südsteiermark. Highly recommended is an autumn journey along the wine routes that hug the Slovenian border, wind through the Sausal Valley, and continue west of Leibnitz. Be sure to leave sufficient time for visiting the towns of Ehrenhausen, Gamlitz, Leutschach, and Kitzeck. Vineyard sites including Czamillonberg, Grassnitzberg, Kittenberg, Nussberg, Obegg, Sernauberg, and Zieregg are just as impressive to see as their wines are to drink. Not only have these wines established a fixed place on the tables of regional restaurants, but they have gained international favour as well. Archduke Johann of Austria, a visionary winegrowing pioneer would be proud of the spirit that continues in "his" winegrowers in Südsteiermark.

wine-growing area

- ◆ Weingut Fuchs, Leutschach/Weinstrasse
- ◆ Weingut Georgiberg, Berghausen
- ◆ Weingut Gross, Ratsch/Weinstrasse
- ◆ Weingut Hannes Harkamp, Leibnitz
- ◆ Weingut Hirschmugl – Domaene am Seggauberg, Leibnitz
- ◆ Weingut Lackner-Tinnacher, Gamlitz/Steinbach
- ◆ Meinhardt Hube, Kitzeck
- ◆ Domäne Müller Gutsverwaltung – Gut am Ottenberg, Groß St. Florian
- ◆ Weingut Muster.Gamlitz, Gamlitz/Grubtal
- ◆ Weingut Erich and Walter Polz, Spielfeld
- ◆ Weingut Regele, Berghausen

- ◆ Weingut Erwin Sabathi, Leutschach/Pössnitz
- ◆ Weingut Hannes Sabathi, Gamlitz/Kranachberg
- ◆ Weingut Sattlerhof, Gamlitz/Sernau
- ◆ Weingut Peter Skoff – Domäne Kranachberg, Gamlitz/Kranachberg
- ◆ Weingut Skoff Original, Gamlitz/Eckberg
- ◆ Weingut Walter Skoff, Gamlitz/Eckberg
- ◆ Weingut Karl & Gustav Strauss, Gamlitz/Steinbach
- ◆ Weingut Tement, Berghausen
- ◆ Weingut Wohlmuth, Fresing/Kitzeck im Sausal

Adolf & Heinrich Fuchs

8463 Leutschach a.d. Weinstraße, Glanz 6
T: +43 (3454) 387, F: +43 (3454) 70087
office@fuchs-weine.at, www.fuchs-weine.at

Winemaker and Contact Person: Heinrich Fuchs
Production: n. a. (70 % white, 30 % red)
Hectares: 15
Fairs: ProWein
Distribution partners: CDN, NL, GB, USA, UAE, CY

The Fuchs winery is nestled in the romantic hillside landscape of Südsteiermark (South Styria). This family winery was founded in 1920 and is now in its third generation, but the family's vinous history stretches back even further, to its beginning in Germany over 200 years ago. The Fuchs brothers now manage the estate with Adolf taking responsibility for the vineyards, Heinrich for administration, and the two of them sharing winemaking duties. Their success lies in the philosophy of producing refreshing, fruity wines that offer abundant drinking pleasure. White wines are vinified in stainless steel; red wines mature either in stainless steel or in small oak barrels.

90 Sauvignon Blanc Roßberg 2015

88 Sauvignon Blanc 2015
90 Sauvignon Blanc 2014
Pale greenish-yellow hue. Delicate floral aromas and subtle gooseberry and greengage plum notes. Vibrant and juicy on the palate with litchi and lemon flavours. Subtle fruit sweetness in the minerally aftertaste.
90 Sauvignon Blanc 2013

88 Chardonnay 2015
88 Morillon 2014
89 Morillon 2013

90 Gelber Muskateller Roßberg 2015

89 Gelber Muskateller 2015
89 Gelber Muskateller 2014
89 Gelber Muskateller 2013

89 Gewürztraminer 2013

90 Gewürztraminer Spätlese 2012

88 Weißburgunder 2015
90 Weißburgunder 2014
87 Weißburgunder 2013

88 Welschriesling 2014
87 Welschriesling 2013
87 Welschriesling 2012

89 Pinot Noir 2012

Weingut Georgiberg

8461 Berghausen, Wielitsch 54
T: +43 (3453) 20243, F: +43 (3453) 20243 4
office@weingut-georgiberg.at, www.weingut-georgiberg.at

Winemaker: Matthias Vormeier
Production: n. a. (70 % white, 25 % red, 5 % sweet)
Hectares: 25 + 3
Fairs: ProWein, VieVinum
Distribution partners: on request

The Georgiberg estate has been considered one of the best vineyard sites in South Styria for centuries. It is nestled in the romantic landscape of the valley of the Wielitsch Creek near the village of Berghausen where it is set among rolling hills, forests and peaceful ponds. The unique soil and the warm Illyrian climate provide the ideal preconditions for exceptional wines. The estate is particularly famed for its high share of red wines, which are of outstanding quality and unique in the Steiermark. The story of the estate goes back to 1777, when it was established by Johann and Juliana Schilcher. It was purchased in the 20th century by the Wagner family, who initially planted red grape varieties sourced from the nursery belonging to the Italian car producer Ferruccio Lamborghini and selected varieties imported from France. Family Trierenberg took over the 17-hectare estate in 2008. Despite Styria being considered white wine territory, the estate succeeds in producing very high quality Zweigelt, Pinot Noir, Merlot, and Cabernet Sauvignon. The Brut Rosé is a sparkling wine specialty made of the Black Muscat variety and fermented, via traditional method, in the bottle. In addition to the red wines and other sparkling wines, there are distillates, juice and wine vinegar produced as well. The newest addition to their product line is a local delicacy, a dry cured ham called "Vulkano Schinken".

91 Sauvignon Blanc Wielitsch 2015
90 Sauvignon Blanc Wielitsch 2014
Pale greenish-yellow hue with silver highlights. Gooseberry, cassis and nettles with grapefruit zest with a fine spice and nut undertone. Full-bodied and concentrated with ripe gooseberry and delicate roasted notes on the palate. Long and minerally finish. Complex partner with food. Good ageing potential.

92 Sauvignon Blanc Wielitsch "Grosses Holz" 2012

91 Sauvignon Blanc Ciringa (Slowenien) Alegriá Silber 2010

92 Pinot Gris Ciringa Secreto Silber 2011
92 Grauburgunder Ciringa Secreto Silber 2010

89 Pinot Blanc Wielitsch 2015
88 Weißburgunder Wielitsch 2014
89 Weißburgunder Wielitsch 2011

91 Pinot Blanc Wielitsch "Grosses Holz" 2012

90 Morillon Obegg "Grosses Holz" 2012
90 Morillon Obegg Großes Holz 2011

90 Gelber Muskateller Primavera 2015

91 Cuvée Wielitsch 2012 TR/PG

90 Merlot Cabernet Wielitsch Barrique 2011

89 Pinot Noir Wielitsch Barrique 2011

90 Zweigelt Wielitsch Barrique 2011

92 Traminer Eiswein Wielitsch 2011

92 Grauburgunder Auslese Wielitsch 2011

Weingut Gross

8461 Ratsch, Weinstraße 26
T: +43 (3453) 2527, F: +43 (3453) 2728
weingut@gross.at, www.gross.at

Winemaker: Johannes Gross
Contact Person: Alois and Michael Gross
Production: 300.000 bottles (93 % white, 6 % red, 1 % sweet)
Hectares: 45
Fairs: VieVinum, ProWein
Distribution partners: B, SGP, BG, RC, GB, USA, PL

The Gross winery is nestled on the slope of the Ratscher Nussberg, one of the very best sites in Südsteiermark (South Styria). The vines thrive on the steep slopes at altitudes between 300 and 600 metres above sea level. They are influenced both by the Alps and their exposure towards the Adriatic Sea. The soils of this charming hilly landscape on the border of Austria and Slovenia are diverse and range from limestone to gravel to slate and even soils of volcanic origins. The origin of each wine is the decisive factor for every task that Johannes and Michael undertake. The macroclimate and soil of each vineyard lend to the Gross wines unique character attributes that are consistently recognizable through the vintages. There are also challenges that the terroir presents to the vintner: knowing which grape variety is right for each vineyard parcel; how to care for the vines on the steep slopes, and how to strengthen the resiliance of the ecological system all require years of experience and persistent inquisitiveness. Two generations work together at the Gross winery to produce wines of prime quality that speak of their origins. "Meticulous work by hand, from pruning to grape harvesting, followed by careful vinification with minimal intervention" is the philosophy uniting Alois, James and Michael. The typical regional assortment of grape varieties is predominantly white, and includes Welschriesling, Weissburgunder (Pinot Blanc), Gelber Muskateller (Muscat Blanc à petits grains) and Sauvignon Blanc. The wines are vinified according to their origins either as crisp, fruity "Steirische Klassik" wines, as village wines, or as single-vineyard (cru) wines. The prime vineyards of the estate are Nussberg, Kittenberg, Perz, and Sulz. Also included in the assortment is a Sauvignon Blanc called "Jakobi" that carries a label with weather and viticulture symbols that tell the story of the most important events of the wine year. The Gross family also cultivates vines in neighbouring Slovenia or, more specifically, the Štajerska Slovenija wine region. Here again, the flagship wine is a Sauvignon Blanc; "Colles" completes the array of impressive wines from the Gross winery. Visitors can enjoy the currently available wine vintages directly in the Nussberg vineyard with a spectacular view of the rolling hills of the South Styrian landscape.

94 Gewürztraminer Nussberg 2013
94 Gewürztraminer Nussberg 2012
93 Gewürztraminer Nussberg 2011

96 Sauvignon Blanc Nussberg Fassreserve G STK 2006
Pale greenish-yellow. A multifaceted bouquet shows litchi and papaya notes laced with coconut and honey and a touch of wild herbs and delicate spice. Powerful, full-bodied and an elegant texture nicely integrated with a pleasant hint of oak. Abundant dark minerals and grapefruit line the refreshing, slightly salty aftertaste.

94 Sauvignon Blanc Nussberg G STK 2014
95 Sauvignon Blanc Nussberg G STK 2013
Medium greenish-yellow hue with silver highlights. Golden currant, gooseberry and lime mingle with herbs & spices and a touch of greengage plum. Complex and concentrated with fine extract sweetness dancing with lemony nuances in a filigree-toned acidity structure. Persistent mineral finish and long ageing potential.
94 Sauvignon Blanc Nussberg G STK 2012

93 Sauvignon Blanc Sulz 1 STK 2014
93 Sauvignon Blanc Sulz 1 STK 2013
93 Sauvignon Blanc Sulz 1 STK 2012

94 Sauvignon Blanc
Witscheiner Herrenberg 2013

92 Sauvignon Blanc Colles 2013
92 Sauvignon Blanc Colles
Stajerska Slovenija 2012
92 Sauvignon Blanc Colles
Stajerska Slovenija 2011

92 Ratscher Sauvignon Blanc 2014
92 Sauvignon Blanc Ratsch 2013
91 Sauvignon Blanc Ratsch 2012

92 Sauvignon Blanc Steirische Klassik 2015
91 Sauvignon Blanc Steirische Klassik 2014
89 Sauvignon Blanc Steirische Klassik 2013

90 Sauvignon Blanc Jakobi 2015
89 Sauvignon Blanc Jakobi 2014
88 Sauvignon Blanc Jakobi 2013

92 Ratscher Morillon Startin 2014
92 Morillon Ratsch Startin 2013
92 Morillon Ratsch Startin 2012

(92–94) Chardonnay 2014
93 Chardonnay 2013

(92–94) Gelber Muskateller Perz 1 STK 2015
92 Gelber Muskateller Perz 1 STK 2013
93 Gelber Muskateller Perz 1 STK 2012

91 Gelber Muskateller Steirische Klassik 2015
90 Gelber Muskateller Steirische Klassik 2014
89 Gelber Muskateller Steirische Klassik 2013

(91–93) Gamlitzer Gelber Muskateller 2015

94 Weißburgunder Nussberg G STK 2011
96 Weißburgunder Nussberg G STK
(Magnum) 2007

92 Weißburgunder Kittenberg 1 STK 2013
92 Weißburgunder Kittenberg 1 STK 2012

92 Weißburgunder Steirische Klassik 2015
90 Weißburgunder Steirische Klassik 2014
90 Weißburgunder Steirische Klassik 2013

90 Sämling 88 Steirische Klassik 2015
89 Sämling 88 Steirische Klassik 2014
88 Sämling 88 Steirische Klassik 2013

90 Welschriesling Steirische Klassik 2015
90 Welschriesling Steirische Klassik 2014
89 Welschriesling STK 2013

92 Grauburgunder 2013

92 Furmint Stajerska Slovenija 2013

90 Riesling Spätlese 2013

88 Blauer Zweigelt 2012

(95–97) Furmint Trockenbeerenauslese SJI 2013

93 Gewürztraminer Beerenauslese 2013

93 Chardonnay Trockenbeerenauslese 2012

Weingut Hannes Harkamp

8430 Leibnitz, Seggauberg 75
T: +43 (3452) 76420, M: +43 (660) 3449599
weingut@harkamp.at, www.harkamp.at

Winemaker: Hannes Harkamp
Contact Person: Petra and Hannes Harkamp
Production: n. a. (90 % white, 10 % red)
Hectares: 17
Fairs: VieVinum, ProWein, Fancy Food NY
Distribution partners: on request

The Harkamp winery is located on the Flamberg in the Sausal Mountains of Südsteiermark. The vineyard terraces climb so steeply up the mountainside that this place is often locally referred to as "Himmelreich", which translates to "kingdom of heaven". The vineyard slope is so exposed that it offers an expansive view that sweeps from the Koralpe Mountains to the edge of the Great Hungarian Plain and to Slovenia. Südsteiermark is internationally famed for its crisp, refreshing, fruity wines. Yet here on the slope of the Flamberg in the most northerly part of Südsteiermark, the sensitivity of Hannes and Petra Harkamp allow them to accomplish so much more. There is hardly another winery that achieves more aristocratic elegance and finesse in such refreshing wines. The top vineyards of the Harkamp estate count among the best sites of Südsteiermark. The vines of the Oberburgstall site are rooted in the marine limestone soils directly on the Flamberg Mountain. The Kogelberg vineyard is farther south and its schist soil is the foundation for subtle, fine-tuned wines. Hannes Harkamp certainly understands how to bring the full potential of these steep sites into the bottle. He vinifies classic varietal wines that are distinguished by crisp fruit and the typical Styrian character. Grapes from the Oberburgstall and Kogelberg are the source for elegant single vineyard wines that express their terroir with great finesse and sensitivity. Hannes Harkamp can no longer hide his secret passion: he has been revealed as a talented sparkling wine producer, which his Brut Reserve so aptly demonstrates. Like everything else, the craft of making sparkling wine is self-taught – typical for this quiet, thoughtful vintner. The Harkamp wine estate can be best described as "an experience for all the senses". Besides the elegant wines, also to be enjoyed is the authentic regional cuisine in the Harkamp family's restaurant, and the comfort of their charming hotel – all featuring a breathtaking view of the undulating Südsteiermark landscape.

93 Brut Reserve 2012
93 Brut Reserve 2011
Brilliant yellow-green and a very fine mousse. Subtle lime and melon, a touch of spicy tobacco, fresh herbs, and subtle brioche notes. Juicy, elegant, and tightly woven. Delicate apple and minerals on the finish. A sparkling wine with international appeal. Well-structured finesse and good ageing potential.
92 Brut Reserve 2010

92 Zero Dosage 2012
91 Zero Dosage 2011
92 Brut Reserve Zero 2010

93 Sauvignon blanc Extra Brut

91 Gelber Muskateller Brut
91 Gelber Muskateller Brut
91 Gelber Muskateller Sekt

92 Harkamp Brut Reserve 2009 PN/WB/CH

92 Brut Rosé
91 Brut Rosé
90 Brut Rosé PN/WB

89 Sauvignon Blanc Flamberg 2015
91 Sauvignon Blanc Flamberg 2014
91 Sauvignon Blanc Flamberg 2013

92 Sauvignon Blanc Kogelberg 2014
93 Sauvignon Blanc Kogelberg 2013
93 Sauvignon Blanc Kogelberg 2012

90 Sauvignon Blanc Schiefer Terrassen 2015
92 Sauvignon Blanc Schiefer Terrassen 2014

93 Grauburgunder Oberburgstall 2014
94 Grauburgunder Oberburgstall 2013
Brilliant yellow-green hue. The complex bouquet displays tropical yellow fruit reminiscent of carambola and papaya, a touch of pear, and subtle oak spice in the background. The palate is juicy and elegant with a finely woven structure. Yellow apple and abundant minerals linger long on the finish. Plenty of finesse and tremendous potential for further development.
94 Grauburgunder Oberburgstall 2012

91 Gelber Muskateller Flamberg 2015
89 Gelber Muskateller Flamberg 2014
89 Gelber Muskateller Flamberg 2013

91 Morillon Flamberg 2015
91 Morillon Flamberg 2014
91 Morillon Flamberg 2013

92 Riesling Alte Reben 2014

Hirschmugl – Domaene am Seggauberg

8430 Leibnitz, Seggauberg 41
T: +43 (3452) 86300, F: +43 (3452) 8443818
toni@hirschmugl-domaene.at, www.hirschmugl-domaene.at

ORGANIC

Winemaker and Contact Person: Alexander Scherübl
Production: n. a. (80 % white, 20 % red)
Hectares: 12
Fairs: VieVinum, Millésime Bio
Distribution partners: CH, D

Toni and Astrid Hirschmugl purchased this estate in Seggauberg on Götterberg several years ago. An organic fruit orchard had already been cultivated here for two decades, and the decision for sustainable viticulture was logical. It was a long road until the dream of "living and working with nature" became a reality. The Styrian Seggauberg has long been the source not only for still and sparkling wine, but also for vinegar specialties and honey from the estate's apiculture. The grapes ripen on sedimentary rock with high mineral content. The goal is to work in harmony with nature to produce high-quality food products. Compassion, respect, innovation and consistency are the daily working values instilled in the team at Domaene Hirschmugl by the organic wine consultant Christoph Sturm. The minerality of the soil, the warmth of the day and the coolness of the night are the microclimatic attributes that contribute to the regional varietal character found in the wines. In the hands of the creative winemaker Alexander Scherüble, outstanding wines of great finesse are produced. Considering the broad spectrum of products, it is truly astounding what the Hirschmugls have achieved with their young, ambitious team in such a short time. An abundance of various species of colubridae thrive in the Seggauberg vineyards and these nonvenomous snakes are dependable signs of an intact environment. To communicate this, the natter serves as the estate's mascot.

90 Sauvignon Blanc Trinkvergnügen 2015
90 Sauvignon Blanc Trinkvergnügen 2014
90 Sauvignon Blanc Trinkvergnügen 2013

92 Cabernet Blanc SMC 2014
91 Cabernet Blanc Seggauberg Nobilis 2013
Brilliant yellow with silver highlights. Ripe mango, honey and candied orange zest with pleasant oxidative notes. The full body with a peach fruit tone is highlighted by juicy acidity. Delicate nutty sherry-like touch on the mineral finish.
88 Cabernet Blanc Nobilis 2012

88 Cabernet Blanc Seggauberg
   Trinkvergnügen 2014
87 Cabernet Blanc Steirisches
   Trinkvergnügen 2013
89 Cabernet Blanc Steirisches
   Trinkvergnügen 2012

92 Chardonnay SMC 2013

89 Chardonnay Seggauberg
   Trinkvergnügen 2013
88 Morillon Steirisches Trinkvergnügen 2012

90 Morillon Aurum 2011

89 Muscaris Trinkvergnügen 2015
89 Muscaris Seggauberg Trinkvergnügen 2014
87 Muscaris Steirisches Trinkvergnügen 2013

92 Muscaris SMC 2015

91 Traminer Aurum 2013
90 Traminer Aurum 2012

91 Traminer Nobilis 2012
92 Traminer Nobilis 2011

★★★★
Weingut Lackner-Tinnacher

8462 Gamlitz, Steinbach 12
T: +43 (3453) 2142, F: +43 (3453) 4841
weingut@tinnacher.at, www.tinnacher.at

Winemaker: Dipl. Ing. Katharina Tinnacher
Contact Person: Katharina Tinnacher
Production: 110.000 bottles (92 % white, 6 % red, 2 % sweet)
Hectares: 27
Fairs: ProWein
Distribution partners: I, S, CH, SK, DK, DE, CZ, F, USA

The Lackner-Tinnacher winery is nestled between vines and orchards on a chain of hills in Steinbach near Gamlitz. Vines have been cultivated here for centuries. Four vineyards of this winery were described in detail in the Josephine land register of 1787. Fritz and Wilma Tinnacher and their daughter Katharina presently operate the winery. Twenty-seven hectares of vineyards thrive at an ideal elevation of 400 to 500 meters on the best steep slopes of Steinbach and Eckberg. The vines are Fritz Tinnacher's central focus. The vineyards are surrounded on three sides by meadows and forests in a protected microclimate. Vines are thinned four times and the shoots carefully positioned by hand to enhance physiological ripeness. The harvest usually takes place late and is done manually at a carefully chosen degree of ripeness. All of the winery's grapes are sourced from their own vineyards with quite varying geological conditions. The Tinnacher family makes a special effort at amplifying these soil differences in their wines. The winery's main wine variety is Sauvignon Blanc, with the "Klassik" version stemming from predominantly loamy soils and the "Steinbach" rooted in sandy, gravelly soils. The Sauvignon Blanc "Welles" is from rocky mineral-rich conglomerate with topsoil comprised of red and grey sand. Since 2007, a late harvest "Welles Reserve" has been part of the wine roster. Another focus has long been the Burgundian varieties. Weissburgunder (Pinot Blanc) "Eckberg" and Morillon (Chardonnay) "Eckberg" grow on calcareous marl while Weissburgunder "Steinbach", Morillon "Steinbach" and Grauburgunder (Pinot Gris) "Steinbach" thrive on sandy gravelly soils. Welschriesling, Gelber Muskateller (Muscat Blanc à Petits Grains) and Roter Traminer are further varie-

ties that are cultivated. Young vine Gelber Muskateller from the Gamitz site appears as the first time as "Steirische Klassik" while the nearly 50-year-old vines are the source for the single-vineyard Gelber Muskateller "Gamitz". Riesling is preferred for the sweet predicated wines. The winery's vineyard holdings were expanded at the beginning of 2008 to include new sites in the village of St. Nikolai in the Sausal Valley. These five hectares form a south- to southwest-facing amphitheatre. Sauvignon Blanc and Pinot Blanc thrive here on marine limestone and offer an interesting and exciting contrast to the terroir in Steinbach. It is understandable why Flamberg receives so much attention from Katharina Tinnacher; the interaction of vines with their soil and climate was already her specialty during her studies at the University of Natural Resources and Applied Life Sciences Vienna. Next to the nurturing of valuable old vines, she places her focus on the cultivation of Sauvignon Blanc and the Pinot varieties in the Flamberg vineyard.

95 Sauvignon Blanc Welles Reserve 2011
Pale yellow with silver highlights. Litchi and apricot with wild meadow herbs in the background. Impressive complexity is demonstrated by power and depth that are harmoniously balanced with superb vitality. Gooseberry and pineapple linger on the finish, marked with sweet extract. Wonderful ageing potential.

94 Sauvignon Blanc Welles G STK 2014
95 Sauvignon Blanc Welles 2013
Medium greenish-yellow with silver highlights. The multifaceted bouquet reveals smoky and spicy notes with nuances of cassis, anise and wild meadow herbs. Full body with sweet extract and a lively acidity structure. Grapefruit and a

fine salty minerality linger in the finish. Very good ageing potential.

94 Sauvignon Blanc Welles G STK 2012

93 Sauvignon Blanc Steinbach 1 STK 2014
93 Sauvignon Blanc Steinbach 1 STK 2013
93 Sauvignon Blanc Steinbach 1 STK 2012

93 Sauvignon Blanc Flamberg 2014
94 Sauvignon Blanc Flamberg 2013
93 Sauvignon Blanc Flamberg 2012

92 Sauvignon Blanc Steirische Klassik 2015
91 Sauvignon Blanc Steirische Klassik 2014
92 Sauvignon Blanc Steirische Klassik 2013

94 Grauburgunder Reserve 2011

93 Grauburgunder Steinbach 1 STK 2014
93 Grauburgunder Steinbach 2013
92 Grauburgunder Steinbach 1 STK 2012

92 Weißburgunder Steinbach 1 STK 2014
92 Weißburgunder Steinbach 2014
92 Weißburgunder Steinbach 1 STK 2013

92 Weißburgunder Eckberg 2015
90 Weißburgunder Eckberg 2014
89 Weißburgunder Eckberg 2013

92 Morillon Steinbach 1 STK 2014
90 Morillon Steinbach 1 STK 2013
90 Morillon Steinbach 1 STK 2012

93 Morillon Eckberg 2015
91 Morillon Eckberg 2014
91 Morillon Eckberg 2013

92 Morillon Flamberg 2013
92 Morillon Flamberg 2012

(92–94) Welschriesling Franz Lackner 2015

90 Welschriesling Steirische Klassik 2015
91 Welschriesling Steirische Klassik 2014
87 Welschriesling Steirische Klassik 2013

91 Gelber Muskateller Steirische Klassik 2015
91 Gelber Muskateller Steirische Klassik 2014
88 Gelber Muskateller Steirische Klassik 2013

90 Gelber Muskateller Gamitz 1 STK 2013
91 Gelber Muskateller Gamitz 1 STK 2012

(92–94) Roter Traminer Türken 1 STK 2015
89 Roter Traminer Türken 2012

(95–97) Riesling Trockenbeerenauslese 2013

92 Welschriesling Trockenbeerenauslese Demibouteille 2009

★ ★
Meinhardt Hube

8441 Kitzeck, Fresing 24
T: +43 (3456) 2303, F: +43 (3456) 2121
office@meinhardthube.com, www.meinhardthube.com

Winemaker and Contact Person: Gerhard Wohlmuth
Production: 60.000 bottles (100 % white)
Hectares: 11
Fairs: VieVinum, ProWein
Distribution partners: B, CH, DK, DE, NL, IRL

The Meinhart Hube estate is one of the oldest wineries in the region and was first documented in 1574. The 12 hectares of vineyards enjoy a south- or south-west-facing position and are planted with vines up to 50 years-old. Wines of the highest standards and enormous finesse that express a unique sense of place are produced here. A very specific Styrian terroir is ensured by a unique microclimate and soil. During the ripening phase, evenings cool drastically and diurnal temperature differences can be as much as 25° Celsius, which enhances the development of fine fruit aromas. The resulting wines are highly ripe and fruity and their finess is highlighted by an intense mineral character. Soil type vary from calaceous sand and limestone to chalk-free loamy sand to Kreuzberg gravel and marine sediments. These allow for a wonderful differentiation of sites and a terroir study for connoisseurs. The wines of Meinhardt Hube are vinified in a well-equipped cellar by their owner, the experienced and highly regarded vintner Gerhard Wohlmuth. The Wohlmuth family places importance on the terroir expression here - it is quite unique and different from the terroir define the well-known Wohlmuth wines from Kitzeck.

93 Sauvignon Blanc Kisl 2015
92 Sauvignon Blanc Kisl 2014
Pale green-yellow with silver highlights. Nuances of gooseberry, orange and grapefruit with subtle oak, hazelnut, and yeast notes comprise a complex bouquet. Concentrated and spicy with refreshing acid structure. The long finish features pleasant grassy notes and spice. Dependable potential for further development.
93 Sauvignon Blanc Kisl 2013

91 Sauvignon Blanc Steinbachberg 2014
91 Sauvignon Blanc Steinbachberg 2013
90 Sauvignon Blanc Steinbachberg 2012

91 Gamlitzer Sauvignon Blanc 2015
90 Sauvignon Blanc Klassik 2014
90 Sauvignon Blanc Klassik 2013

92 Chardonnay Steinbachberg 2015
91 Chardonnay Steinbachberg 2014
91 Chardonnay Steinbachberg 2013

92 Gelber Muskateller Steinbachberg 2015
90 Gelber Muskateller Steinbachberg 2014
90 Gelber Muskateller Steinbachberg 2013

91 Weißer Burgunder Steinbachberg 2015
90 Pinot Blanc Steinbachberg 2014
91 Pinot Blanc Steinbachberg 2013

90 Welschriesling Klassik 2015
89 Welschriesling Klassik 2014
89 Welschriesling Klassik 2013

Domäne Müller Gutsverwaltung – Gut am Ottenberg

8522 Groß St. Florian, Grazer Straße 71
T: +43 (3464) 2155, F: +43 (3464) 211625
office@mueller-wein.at, www.domaene-mueller.com

Winemaker: Yves-Michel Müller
Contact Person: Eva R. and Yves-Michel Müller
Production: 140.000 bottles (51 % white, 48 % red, 1 % sweet)
Hectares: 26,5
Fairs: ProWein, Alles für den Gast Salzburg, Foodex Japan,
fafga Innsbruck, ÖGW Zürich, ProWein China
Distribution partners: BY, J, S, B, CH, HR, RC, SLO, DK, DE, EST, N, HK

The wines of Domäne Müller reflect a trinity of values: family harmony, community and care for the environment. This philosophy is the foundation from which Eva and Günter Müller and their children Marie Yvette and Yves Michel constantly evolve and strive for perfection. Two wineries are united in their hands: the Gut am Ottenberg in South Styria and the "Ehemalige Prinz Liechtenstein'sche Weingut" in Deutschlandsberg in West Styria. The Müller family has been an importer of fine wines for many years and has a close, historic bond with French culture. From the broad spectrum of wines they produce in both wineries, it is the wines from the classic French varieties that most prolifically excel. All wines are sourced exclusively from 35 hectares of estate fruit sourced from outstanding vineyards. A classic line of wines is offered without vineyard designation and a "Gut am Ottenberg" range is consecutively broadened with single vineyard bottlings as the vineyards mature. Astute attention was given to the selection of cultivar and rootstock to match each terroir in the 26 hectares of Gut am Ottenberg vineyards. Chardonnay clones were sourced from California while Sauvignon blanc stems from the Loire Valley. Pinot blanc, Welschriesling, Cabernet Sauvignon, Cabernet Franc, Merlot and Zweigelt have also been planted. The share of red wine varieties is unusually great for the region, but the quality produced certainly justifies the choice. "Der Sauvignon Blanc" from Domäne Müller is such an outstanding wine that it has become a flagship for the estate. It is quite a unique growth of pedigree that is predestined to capture attention. This wine has won a dedicated following in the Austrian fine dining scene and has become a much demanded export. Domäne Müller draws attention to their best wines by adding the article "Der" in front of the name of the variety. Recent vineyard purchases of the Gut am Ottenberg include a small plot in the famous Zieregg vineyard. After lying barren for many years, the parcel was replanted by Yves-Michel Müller in 2010 according to the estate's demanding standards – with a special Sauvignon Blanc clone. A further new plot in the Ottenberg vineyard was created to reap the advantages of a very unusual South Styria microclimate. This parcel is a mini-paradise for grapevines, heirloom apples and rare fauna. Michael Müller has been working together with his father in the vineyards and wine cellar since 2007. There now appears to be a gradual return to the old traditional style of vinification with a focus on micro-vinification that was perhaps influenced by his working experience with Stephane Derenoncourt in Bordeaux. The first vintage of a new Muskateller (Muscat Blanc à Petits Grains) – from 2014 – entered the market in 2015 in a very small quantity.

93 Der Sauvignon Blanc Ried Deutsche Weingärten – Berghausen 2013
93 Der Sauvignon Blanc Ried Deutsche Weingärten - Berghausen 2012
Medium yellow with silver highlights. Ripe gooseberry, carambola a touch of pineapple and a subtle orange zest note. Full-bodied, complex on the palate with elegant acidity and dark minerals framing the apricot fruitiness. An extremely long finish abundant in spice, salty minerality and an elegant note of grapefruit.

94 Der Sauvignon Blanc Private Reserve Ried Zieregg – Spielfeld 2013

93 Der Sauvignon Blanc Private Reserve Ried
   Deutsche Weingärten 2010
(92–94) Der Sauvignon Blanc Wielitsch 2015

92 Der Sauvignon Blanc Grassnitzberg 2015

90 Sauvignon Blanc Ottenberg Gutswein 2015

92 Der Chardonnay Ried Deutsche Weingärten –
   Berghausen 2011

(91–93) Der Chardonnay Grassnitzberg 2015
92 Der Morillon Grassnitzberg - Spielfeld 2013

90 Chardonnay Wielitsch Gutswein 2015

89 Gelber Muskateller Ottenberg Gutswein 2015

90 Gelber Muskateller Gut am Ottenberg -
   Ratsch - Erste Lese 2014

93 Der Cabernet Sauvignon Private Reserve
   Michel Ried Untere Ranz – Ratsch 2011
92 Der Cabernet Sauvignon Private Reserve
   Michel Müller 2009
90 Der Cabernet Sauvignon Private Reserve 2007

92 Der Cabernet Sauvignon Untere Ranz
   Ried Ratsch 2012
Dark ruby and violet hue with a transparent rim. An
attractive bouquet displays cassis and blackberry with elegant nuances of tobacco, spice, herbs and sandalwood.
Complex with abundant firm tannins that still require some
time. Juicy dark berries and minerals linger sweetly on the
long finish.
89 Cabernet Sauvignon Untere Ranz
   Ried Ratsch 2008

93 Cabernet Sauvignon Ottenberg Privat 2013

92 Cabernet Franc Untere Ranz
   Ried Ratsch 2012

91 Merlot Ried Deusche Weingärten –
   Berghausen 2011

92 Der Riunterra Ottenberg 2011 CS/ME

92 Riunterra Ried Untere Ranz –
   Ratsch 2011 ME/CF

93 Sauvignon Blanc Eiswein Grassnitzberg
   Ironie 2011 (Lesedatum 2012)

Weingut MUSTER.gamlitz

8462 Gamlitz, Grubtal 14
T: +43 (3453) 2300, F: +43 (3453) 2300 4
weingut@muster-gamlitz.at, www.muster-gamlitz.at

Winemaker: Reinhard Muster
Contact Person: Muster family
Production: n. a. (90 % white, 7 % red, 3 % sweet)
Hectares: 40
Fairs: VieVinum, ProWein, ÖGW Zürich
Distribution partners: S, CH, DE, FIN, USA

Up until 1973, this estate was operated as a mixed-agriculture farm. In 1974, the two families, Muster and Dreisiebner, decided to specialize in the cultivation of vineyards and orchards, and thus lay the foundation for the present estate. This unique partnership continued for 26 years during which the vineyards were extended to eight hectares and wines were bottled on the premises. A Buschenschank (wine tavern) was opened and wines were sold on the premises. This long and fruitful partnership ended in 2000 due to health reasons and it is now a one-family estate. A year of reassessment ensued and a new brand MUSTER.gamlitz was initiated in 2002. The classic line of wines comprises light, aromatic varietal wines. The range of "Reverenz" wines exhibits power, depth and terroir-driven mineral character. Both small oak barrels and large wooden casks are employed for these wines – sometimes in combination, sometimes pure. MUSTER.gamlitz would like these extraordinary wines to define standards for a serious point of difference in the central European wine landscape. The wines are divided into three lines: "Klassik", "Reverenz", and single vineyard varietal wines from the Grubthal site. The "Private Reserve Grubthal" is one of the most highly valued wines from this prime vineyard. A unique combination of soil and microclimate is given expression. In extraordinary vintages, the best grapes are hand-selected from bunches to produce this extravagant wine, which is matured in barrel until it reaches the peak of its drinking maturity.

93 Sauvignon Blanc Grubthal 2013
Pale green-yellow with silver highlights. Subtle smoky nuances, delicate oak spice, white vineyard peach, grapefruit zest and mineral accents. Firm and tautly woven with plenty of tropical yellow fruit laced with salty minerals. The finish is long and appetizingly lemony. Dependable ageing potential.

92 Sauvignon Blanc Grubthal 2011

92 Sauvignon Blanc Reverenz 2014
92 Sauvignon Blanc Reverenz 2013
91 Sauvignon Blanc Reverenz 2012

(93–95) Sauvignon Blanc Grubthal
　　Privat Reserve 2013

91 Sauvignon Blanc Klassik 2015
89 Sauvignon Blanc Klassik 2013
92 Sauvignon Blanc Klassik 2012

91 Grauburgunder Rieglbauer 2013
91 Grauburgunder Rieglbauer 2012

93 Grauburgunder Rieglbauer
　　Privat Reserve 2011
Medium green-yellow with silver highlights. Distinct oak spice, hazelnut, mango, apricot and pear with a soft smoky undertone. Full-bodied and elegantly polished with well integrated oak. The long, silky-sweet finish features abundant ripe apricot.

90 Weißburgunder Reverenz 2013
89 Weißburgunder Reverenz 2011

91 Gelber Muskateller Grubthal 2013
92 Gelber Muskateller Grubthal 2011

90 Gelber Muskateller Klassik 2015

91 Chardonnay Marienkreuz 2015

93 Chardonnay Grubthal 2013
93 Chardonnay Grubthal 2012

★★★★
Weingut Erich & Walter Polz

8471 Spielfeld, Grassnitzberg 54a
T: +43 (3453) 2301, F: +43 (3453) 2301 6
weingut@polz.co.at, www.polz.co.at

Winemaker: Christoph Polz
Contact Person: Mag. Peter Keller
Production: 650.000 bottles (90 % white, 10 % red)
Hectares: 70
Fairs: VieVinum, ProWein
Distribution partners: AUS, I, RUS, HR, NL, GB

The Erich and Walter Polz winery is situated in one of the very best wine regions of Styria. The geological attributes of the vineyards, the numerous hours of sunshine and well-distributed precipitation contribute to nearly ideal conditions for viticulture. Wine quality is not determined by nature alone; decades of experience, a sustainable philosophy and working ethic as well as uncompromising demands on quality and a good vintage all contribute to wines of truly great character. For many generations, the name Polz stands for a handcrafted terroir that makes all the passion and attention to detail tangible in the wine glass.

94 Sauvignon Blanc Hochgrassnitzberg
  Reserve G STK 2013
95 Sauvignon Blanc Hochgrassnitzberg
  G STK Jubiläumsedition 2012
Brilliant green with silver highlights. Intense aroma of gooseberry is followed by vanilla and floral notes. Litchi and a touch of minerals come in on the full, compact and tautly strung palate. The clear, vibrant, and extremely long finish features litchi, lemon notes and sweet gooseberry. Very polished and ideal for cellar ageing.
94 Sauvignon Blanc Hochgrassnitzberg
  Reserve G STK 2011

(91–93) Sauvignon Blanc Hochgrassnitzberg
  G STK 2014
94 Sauvignon Blanc Hochgrassnitzberg
  G STK 2013
Pale green-yellow with silver highlights. Pleasant herbal spice, a touch of orange zest, a hint of gooseberry and cassis, mandarin and mineral nuances. Full bodied and well concentrated with pleasant sweet extract and litchi fruit. Delicate notes of peach come in on the finish. Tremendous ageing potential.
93 Sauvignon Blanc Hochgrassnitzberg
  G STK 2012

93 Sauvignon Blanc Therese 1 STK 2015
92 Sauvignon Blanc Therese 1 STK 2014
90 Sauvignon Blanc Therese 1 STK 2013

(91–93) Sauvignon Blanc Czamilla 2015
92 Sauvignon Blanc Czamilla 2013

91 Sauvignon Blanc Steirische Klassik 2015
90 Sauvignon Blanc Steirische Klassik 2014
88 Sauvignon Blanc Steirische Klassik 2013

(90–92) Spielfelder Sauvignon Blanc 84/88 2015
89 Sauvignon Blanc 84/88 2013

88 Sauvignon Blanc Spiegel 2014
87 Sauvignon Blanc Spiegel 2013

95 Chardonnay Obegg G STK 2013
93 Chardonnay Obegg G STK 2012
93 Chardonnay Obegg G STK 2011

92 Chardonnay MOTH 1 STK 2014
91 Chardonnay MOTH 1 STK 2013
89 Chardonnay MOTH 1 STK 2012

92 Chardonnay Grassnitzberg 2013
92 Chardonnay Grassnitzberg 2012

92 Morillon Steirische Klassik 2015
90 Morillon Steirische Klassik 2014
88 Morillon Steirische Klassik 2013

92 Gelber Muskateller Grassnitzberg 1 STK 2012

90 Gelber Muskateller Steirische Klassik 2015
90 Gelber Muskateller Steirische Klassik 2014
89 Gelber Muskateller Steirische Klassik 2013

90 Weißburgunder Steirische Klassik 2015
89 Weißburgunder Steirische Klassik 2014
88 Weißburgunder Steirische Klassik 2013

93 Grauburgunder 2014
92 Grauburgunder 2013
90 Grauburgunder 2012

90 Welschriesling Steirische Klassik 2015
90 Welschriesling Steirische Klassik 2014
87 Welschriesling Steirische Klassik 2013

Weingut Regele

8461 Ehrenhausen an der Weinstraße, Ewitsch 34
T: +43 (3453) 2426, F: +43 (3453) 2426 10
office@regele.com, www.regele.com

Winemaker and Contact Person: Ing. Georg Regele
Production: n. a. (89 % white, 10 % red, 1 % sweet)
Hectares: 19
Fairs: VieVinum
Distribution partners: S, D

There is hardly another wine producer in Südsteiermark (South Styria) that can look back on a longer viticultural tradition than the Regele Winery. The winery has been family owned and operated since its establishment in 1830 and is now managed by Georg and Ingrid Regele, who are both WSET diploma holders. An interest in all that is unique and special distinguishes a first class Styrian wine assortment that is complemented by a selection of bottle-fermented sparkling wines. Manual remuage and dégorgement is practiced for the "Blanc de Blancs", a sparkling made from 100% Chardonnay. The motto "the best begins at the root" cannot be pushed off simply as lip service to some nebulous idea, as anyone who has had the opportunity to visit this idyllically located winery will confirm. Optimal development of premium wines is ensured by deep oenological knowledge and unerring dedication. The typical regional varieties are fermented and matured in the winery cellars. Welschriesling, Weissburgunder (Pinot Blanc), Grauburgunder (Pinot Gris), Sauvignon Blanc, Morillon (Chardonnay), Gelber Muskateller (Muscat Blanc à petits grains) and Traminer (Gewürztraminer) all thrive at the estate. The Sulz and Zoppelberg vineyards count among the very best sites in the region. The wines can be tasted in a modern tasting room that is bright and friendly and opens towards the garden and rows of vines that climb the slope. Wood and glass are combined with soft colours and eclectic artwork to achieve a cultivated atmosphere for wine connoisseurs.

(89–91) Sauvignon Blanc Sulztaler Zoppelberg 2015

91 Sauvignon Blanc Sulztaler Sulz 2014
Brilliant yellow with silver highlights. Pineapple, litchi, cassis and floral nuances on the nose. Grassy notes, litchi and edgy acidity with a touch of lime on the finish. A racy wine perfect with food.
89 Sauvignon Blanc Sulztaler Sulz 2013

91 Chardonnay Seggauberg 2012
90 Chardonnay Seggauberg 2013
90 Chardonnay Seggauberg 2011

89 Chardonnay Sulztaler Sulz 2013

(87–89) Morillon Privat 2015

91 Gelber Muskateller Oberglanz 2015
90 Gelber Muskateller Oberglanz 2014

89 Grauburgunder Sulztaler Sulz 2013
90 Grauburgunder Sulztaler Sulz 2012

90 Traminer Sulztaler Zoppelberg 2015

88 Welschriesling Kranachberg 2013

92 Brut Rosé Reserve 2013
90 Pinot Noir Rosé 2007

92 Blanc de Blancs 2006

Weingut Erwin Sabathi

8463 Leutschach a.d. Weinstraße, Pössnitz 48
T: +43 (3454) 265, F: +43 (3454) 265 6
weingut@sabathi.com, www.sabathi.com

Winemaker: Erwin Sabathi
Contact Person: Erwin Sabathi family
Production: n. a. (99 % white, 1 % sweet)
Hectares: 43
Fairs: VieVinum, ProWein
Distribution partners: CH, B, DK, DE, CZ, NL, USA

The roots of Erwin Sabathi's family winery in Pössnitz near Leutschach .an der Weinstrasse reach back to 1650. Erwin Sabathi and his brothers Gerd and Christoph represent the 10th generation of vintners. In recent years, the winery has invested heavily in expansion of its vineyard area, which continues to be mainly on the Pössnitzberg mountain. The brothers' grandfather purchased the first core plot on this site in the 1950s. Cultivation of this steep rocky site with a slope of up to 75% is extremely labour-intensive and can be achieved only by hand. The vineyards are cultivated sustainably with great respect for the environment; there are no herbicides, insecticides or systematic plant protection aids.

Sauvignon Blanc and Chardonnay enjoy not only international acclaim, but also being the mo st important varieties for Erwin Sabathi. The Sauvignon and Chardonnay wines from the prime "Großen STK Lagen" site are among the truly great white wines of the world. The growths from Pössnitzberg are marked by the meagre calcareous Opok marl soil; they are immensely mineral, nearly salty on the palate, and possess taut structure and tremendous ageing potential. The "Alte Reben" Chardonnay and Sauvignon Blanc wines are rarities sourced from meticulously selected fruit from the oldest vines on the Pössnitzberg. As required for all Große STK Lagen wines, the Alte Reben wines also mature for a minimum of 18 months before bottling.

Further single vineyard wines appear with the "Erste STK Lagen" classification (similar to premier cru). Poharnig is a monopole Sauvignon Blanc vineyard in Pössnitz. The Krepskogel is a parcel in the Pössnitzberg and the Jägerberg is found in Gamlitz. Beyond the single vineyard wines are also the village wines that express the typical regional character of Leutschach. These are usually matured in the traditional neutral large oak casks. Particularly pleasurable are the stainless steel fermented wines from the "Steirische Klassik" series, which offer refreshing, aromatic enjoyment with distinct varietal character.

94 Sauvignon Blanc Alte Reben Pössnitzberg G STK 2014
95 Sauvignon Blanc Alte Reben Pössnitzberg G STK 2013
Medium yellow with silver highlights. A multifaceted bouquet displays delicate herbs and spice with red gooseberry, minerals, pineapple and and mango. Plenty of finesse here with a firm, taut structure featuring extract sweetness carried by elegant acidity. A greengage plum nuance lingers in the finish.
93 Sauvignon Blanc Alte Reben 2012

93 Sauvignon Blanc Pössnitzberg G STK 2014
94 Sauvignon Blanc Pössnitzberg G STK 2013
92 Sauvignon Blanc Pössnitzberg G STK 2012

93 Sauvignon Blanc Poharnig 1 STK 2015
92 Sauvignon Blanc Poharnig 1 STK 2014
92 Sauvignon Blanc Poharnig 1 STK 2013

91 Sauvignon Blanc Steirische Klassik 2015
91 Sauvignon Blanc Steirische Klassik 2014
89 Sauvignon Blanc Steirische Klassik 2013

92 Leutschacher Sauvignon Blanc 2015

(92–94) Grauburgunder Jägerberg 1 STK 2015
92 Grauburgunder Jägerberg 1 STK 2013
92 Grauburgunder Jägerberg 1 STK 2012

92 Weißburgunder Jägerberg 1 STK 2015
91 Weißburgunder Jägerberg 1 STK 2013
91 Weißburgunder Jägerberg 1 STK 2012

91 Weißburgunder Steirische Klassik 2015
90 Weißburgunder Steirische Klassik 2014
89 Weißburgunder Steirische Klassik 2013

94 Chardonnay Alte Reben
   Pössnitzberg G STK 2014
96 Chardonnay Alte Reben
   Pössnitzberg G STK 2013

Brilliant green-yellow. An elegant bouquet is hauntingly Burgundian and displays slightly reductive notes of herbs, very fine oak spice, dark minerals and nuances of tropical fruit. Great complexity continues on the palate with pineapple and yellow apple mingling with perfectly integrated oak. Sweet extract and a very long finish. Extraordinary ageing potential and perfect for laying down.

96 Chardonnay Alte Reben
   Pössnitzberg G STK 2011

93 Chardonnay Pössnitzberg G STK 2014
93 Chardonnay Pössnitzberg G STK 2013
93 Chardonnay Pössnitzberg G STK 2012

92 Leutschacher Chardonnay 2015
91 Chardonnay Glanz 2014
89 Chardonnay Glanz 2013

94 Gelber Muskateller Krepskogel 1 STK 2015
91 Gelber Muskateller Krepskogel 1 STK 2014
92 Gelber Muskateller Krepskogel 1 STK 2013

92 Gelber Muskateller Steirische Klassik 2015
90 Gelber Muskateller Steirische Klassik 2014
89 Gelber Muskateller Steirische Klassik 2013

90 Welschriesling Steirische Klassik 2015
89 Welschriesling Steirische Klassik 2014
88 Welschriesling Steirische Klassik 2013

90 Sabathini 2015 WR/SB
88 Sabathini 2014 WR/SB
88 Sabathini 2013 WR/SB

91 Chardonnay Brut 2013

95 Sauvignon Blanc Trockenbeerenauslese 2014

94 Welschriesling Trockenbeerenauslese 2013
92 Welschriesling Trockenbeerenauslese 2011

Weingut Hannes Sabathi

8462 Gamlitz, Kranachberg 51
T: +43 (3453) 2900, F: +43 (3453) 2900 29
office@hannessabathi.at, www.hannessabathi.at

Winemaker and Contact Person: Hannes Sabathi
Production: n. a. (100 % white)
Hectares: 25
Fairs: VieVinum, ProWein
Distribution partners: on request

Hannes Sabathi ranks among the exceptional vintners in Südsteiermark (South Styria). The authentic regional character of his wines has won them many fans throughout the world. Sabathi conscientiously takes a course outside the mainstream of Styria and challenges wine lovers with wines that demand contemplation. Terroir and time are the decisive factors in Sabathi's wine making; there is hardly another vintner that allows his wines as much time to mature. The prime vineyards Kranachberg, Jägerberg and Steinbach offer the vintner more than a solid foundation for producing wines of exceptional character. The ideal synthesis of structure and aromas derived from soil and variety is what the dynamic winemaker seeks to express in each bottle of wine. In 2011, Sabathi captured attention with a new line of wines called "Gamlitz", which are released every May. With these wines, Sabathi introduced a French "village" principle for the first time in Südsteiermark. Not the vineyard, but the commune is in the foreground with this series of wine – something that he achieved impressively from the first vintage in 2011. Hannes Sabathi is one of the three new members of the renowned STK vintner association.

93 Sauvignon Blanc Kranachberg G STK 2014
94 Sauvignon Blanc Kranachberg G STK 2013
Medium green-yellow. Gooseberry, mango, and grapefruit mingle with pleasant notes of nettle and spicy bell pepper. Well structured finesse on the palate with wonderfully juicy, mango and apricot that continue all the way though the long mineral finish.
93 Sauvignon Blanc Kranachberg G STK 2012
94 Sauvignon Blanc Kranachberg Reserve G STK 2013

92 Sauvignon Blanc Gamlitz 2015
92 Sauvignon Blanc Gamlitz 2014
91 Sauvignon Blanc Gamlitz 2013

91 Sauvignon Blanc Steirische Klassik 2015
90 Sauvignon Blanc Steirische Klassik 2014
89 Sauvignon Blanc 2013

93 Grauburgunder Jägerberg 1 STK 2014
93 Grauburgunder Jägerberg 1 STK 2013
Pale yellow with delicate coppery highlights. Complex aromas and flavours of dark minerals, tobacco nuances, pear, candied orange peel, and spice. A taut, firm structure frames creamy fruit. Salty minerals linger on the spicy finish.
92 Grauburgunder Jägerberg 1 STK 2012

(91–93) Chardonnay Jägerberg 2015

92 Chardonnay Gamlitz 2015
92 Chardonnay Gamlitz 2013
91 Chardonnay 2012

92 Gelber Muskateller Gamlitz 2015

90 Gelber Muskateller Steirische Klassik 2015
90 Gelber Muskateller Steirische Klassik 2014
89 Gelber Muskateller 2013

91 Weißburgunder Steirische Klassik 2015
90 Weißburgunder Steirische Klassik 2014

90 Welschriesling Steirische Klassik 2015
89 Welschriesling Steirische Klassik 2014

90 Steirischer Mischsatz 2015
89 Steirischer Mischsatz 2014

★ ★ ★ ★ ★
Weingut Sattlerhof
8462 Gamlitz, Sernau 2
T: +43 (3453) 2556, F: +43 (3453) 5732
weingut@sattlerhof.at, www.sattlerhof.at

Winemaker: Willi Sattler and Andreas Sattler
Contact Person: Willi and Maria Sattler
Production: n. a. (95 % white, 3 % red, 2 % sweet)
Hectares: 40
Fairs: VieVinum, ProWein
Distribution partners: I, J, S, CDN, CH, B, ROK, HR, SGP, SK, L, E, DK, DE, FIN, CZ, F, NL, N, USA

Sensitivity, sustainability and courage for innovation are the cornerstones that enhance the development of the character and uniqueness of the wines of Maria and Willi Sattler. The continuity of quality and the untiring search for perfection mark the handcraft of this vintner family. Their two sons Alexander and Andreas now bring youthful esprit to the family operation. Vineyards in prime sites, the "soft pruning" method, the long-term conversion to organic viticulture, meticulous hand selection of the grapes and plenty of patience and integrity are the means. The results are inimitable wines that sweep national and international awards (particularly the Sauvignon Blanc wines) and serve as first class ambassadors of Austrian wine culture. A pilgrimage to the Sattlerhof estate is worth it not only for the top class wines, but also for the four new chapels that have been built in the vineyards for giving thanks to the wonderful fruits of nature. Each of the four chapels has a view of one of the four famous vineyards of the estate: Sernauberg, Kranachberg, Pfarrweingarten and Kapellenweingarten.

As of the 2015 vintage, the long term goal of defining wines according to their origin has been made. The wines are now organized in three groups: regional wines (Südsteiermark) with a new design with labels created by created by Ela and Lukas Sattler; village wines (Gamlitzer), and the famous single vineyard wines (Kapellenweingarten, Sernauberg, Pfarrweingarten and Kranachberg).

95 Sauvignon Blanc Pfarrweingarten G STK 2013
93 Sauvignon Blanc Pfarrweingarten G STK 2012
93 Sauvignon Blanc Pfarrweingarten 2011

(93–95) Sauvignon Blanc Kranachberg G STK 2014
94 Sauvignon Blanc Kranachberg G STK 2013
94 Sauvignon Blanc Kranachberg G STK 2012

(92–94) Sauvignon Blanc Sernauberg 1 STK 2015
92 Sauvignon Blanc Sernauberg 1 STK 2014
92 Sauvignon Blanc Sernauberg 1 STK 2013

95 Sauvignon Blanc Privat 2011
97 Sauvignon Blanc Privat 2007

94 Sauvignon Blanc Grassnitzburg 2013
94 Sauvignon Blanc Grassnitzburg 2012
93 Sauvignon Blanc Graßnitzburg 2011

92 Sauvignon Blanc Element 2013
93 Sauvignon Blanc Element 2012
92 Sauvignon Blanc Element 2011

92 Gamlitzer Sauvignon Blanc 2015
91 Gamlitzer Sauvignon Blanc 2014
91 Gamlitzer Sauvignon Blanc 2013

90 Sauvignon Blanc Südsteiermark 2015
90 Sauvignon Blanc Vom Sand 2014
89 Sauvignon Blanc Vom Sand 2013

96 Morillon Pfarrweingarten G STK 2013
Medium green-yellow. A multifaceted nose exhibits delicate herbal spice, reductive flinty notes, subtle hints of brioche and coconut, pineapple, and soft smoky nuances. Concentrated and tautly structured with plenty of finesse. Elegant notes of litchi, lime and salt linger on the finish. A wine of superb delicacy with tremendous ageing potential.
93 Morillon Pfarrweingarten G STK 2012

(92–94) Morillon Kapellenweingarten 2015
91 Morillon Kapellenweingarten 2014

92 Gamlitzer Morillon 2015
90 Gamlitzer Morillon 2014
91 Gamlitzer Morillon 2013

96 Weißburgunder Pfarrweingarten
Fassreserve 2007
Pale yellow with silver highlights. Delicate aromas of hazelnut, orange zest and white apple fruit wrapped in a flinty-mineral veil. Complex, finely structured and sweetly extracted with plenty of finesse. Wonderfully faceted with salty minerals and delicate yellow apple lingering on the exceedingly long finish. A monumental Pinot Blanc.

93 Weißburgunder Pfarrweingarten 2011

91 Gamlitzer Weißburgunder 2015
90 Gamlitzer Weißburgunder 2014
90 Gamlitzer Weißburgunder 2013

91 Welschriesling Südsteiermark 2015
90 Welschriesling Steirische Klassik 2014
89 Welschriesling Steirische Klassik 2013

(91–93) Welschriesling Alte Rebstöcke 2015

(93–95) Gelber Muskateller Sernauberg
1 STK 2015
93 Gelber Muskateller Sernauberg 1 STK 2012

92 Gamlitzer Gelber Muskateller 2015
91 Gamlitzer Gelber Muskateller 2014
91 Gamlitzer Muskateller 2013

95 Gelber Muskateller
Trockenbeerenauslese 2013

94 Morillon Trockenbeerenauslese 2013

96 Sauvignon Blanc Trockenbeerenauslese 2013

★★★

Weingut Peter Skoff – Domäne Kranachberg

8462 Gamlitz, Kranachberg - Sauvignonweg 50
T: +43 (3454) 6104, F: +43 (3454) 6104 4
weingut@peter-skoff.at, www.peter-skoff.at

Winemaker and Contact Person: Peter and Markus Skoff
Production: n. a. (96 % white, 3 % red, 1 % sweet)
Hectares: 23
Fairs: VieVinum, ProWein
Distribution partners: CH, B, D

The Peter Skoff winery is among the top addresses in South Styrian wine scene. Sauvignon Blanc is the leading variety of the estate, which continues to bring accolades consistently. Numerous awards and satisfied customers confirm the uncompromising quality efforts. The winery is located in the middle of the highest vineyard on Kranachberg and enjoys a stunning view of the South Styrian Wine Land Natural Park. Peter Skoff and his two sons, Markus and Peter junior, cultivate 25 hectares in one of the best vineyards of the country. The expressive, mineral wines offer harmonious drinking pleasure and versatile food pairing opportunities. Connoisseurs enjoy tasting the wines with delicious regional specialties prepared by Anna Skoff in their popular wine tavern where five cosy guestrooms are also available. As of the 2014 vintage, certified organic wines appear under the label "Peter Skoff – Gut Sernau".

92 Sauvignon Blanc Kranachberg 2015
92 Sauvignon Blanc Kranachberg 2014
Pale green-yellow with silver highlights. Grapefruit, ripe gooseberry, and papaya are bedded on herbs and spice. The firm full body is refreshingly structured with racy acidity. Blood orange, litchi, spice and abundant minerals linger long on the finish.
92 Sauvignon Blanc Kranachberg 2013

93 Sauvignon Blanc Finum 2012
92 Sauvignon Blanc Finum 2011

92 Sauvignon Blanc Gamlitz G. XV 2015
91 Sauvignon Blanc Gamlitz G. XIV 2014
89 Sauvignon Blanc Gamlitz G. XIII 2013

90 Sauvignon Blanc Klassik 2015
89 Sauvignon Blanc Klassik 2014
88 Sauvignon Blanc Klassik 2013

(90–92) Sauvignon Blanc Bio 2015
90 Sauvignon Blanc Bio 2014

93 Morillon Kranachberg Reserve 2012
91 Morillon Kranachberg Reserve 2011
92 Morillon Kranachberg Reserve 2009

91 Morillon Gamlitz 2015

(90–92) Morillon Bio 2015

95 Gewürztraminer Gamlitz 2015
92 Gewürztraminer Gamlitz 2013

92 Gewürztraminer Kranachberg Reserve 2011

93 Sauvignon Blanc Kranachberg Reserve 2012
93 Sauvignon Blanc Kranachberg Reserve 2011
Medium green-yellow. Delicate smoky aromas are woven with candied orange zest, delicate yellow peach, and spicy nuances. Complex with sweetly extracted fruit and well-integrated oak spice reminiscent of coconut. Yellow stone fruit joins in on the finish.
93 Sauvignon Blanc Kranachberg Reserve 2010

Weingut Skoff Original

8462 Gamlitz, Eckberg 16
T: +43 (3453) 4243, F: +43 (3453) 4243 17
weingut@skofforiginal.com, www.skofforiginal.com

Winemaker and Contact Person: Walter Skoff
Production: n. a. (88 % white, 10 % red, 2 % sweet)
Fairs: VieVinum, Vinexpo, ProWein, Igeho Basel
Distribution partners: RUS, J, S, SK, RC, CZ, NL

Walter Skoff, known among the pundits as "Mr. Sauvignon", and with 30 years of experience, is one of the top vintners in Südsteiermark (South Styria). Numerous highly unique sites and attentive employees that meticulously harvest physiologically ripe grapes during several passes though the vineyard are the foundation for SKOFF ORIGINAL wines of inimitable character. The exceptional quality is given worthy recognition both on a national and international level. The Royal Sauvignon Blanc, for example, won first place in the category "Sauvignon Blanc over 13% alcohol" at the Austrian Wine Challenge (AWC) in the Viennese Hofburg Palace and was a finalist at the Styrian State Wine Championship. Skoff can be rightfully proud of the one gold and two silver medals achieved at the International Wine Challenge (IWC) in London. The top wines of the estate are also listed in 2 and 3 Michelin star restaurants in Tokyo and are enjoyed at European royal residences. The SKOFF ORIGINAL wines are particularly fruity, lean and elegant. The family owns plots in a total of eleven different vineyards with varying soils and microclimates that are distributed within fifteen kilometres of the winery. The single vineyard wines of the estate are extraordinary. They represent a perfect combination of the mineral character of physiologically ripe grapes from superb sites and meticulous vinification with long maturation. Walter Skoff's passion and dedication for wine are greater than ever before. We can therefore look forward to a continuation of outstanding wines from SKOFF ORIGINAL.

93 Sauvignon Blanc 30 2012
94 Sauvignon Blanc Royal 2014
94 Sauvignon Blanc Royal 2013
Brilliant yellow green with silver highlights. Delicate toasty aromas, black currant, peach and litchi comprise quite an attractive bouquet. A touch of grapefruit and pleasant oak spice come in on the palate and are completed with a long mineral finish. Reminiscent of a white Bordeaux, this wine has very dependable potential for further development and ageing.
92 Sauvignon Blanc Royal 2012

93 Sauvignon Blanc Obegg 2014
93 Sauvignon Blanc Obegg 2013
Brilliant yellow green. Delicate litchi, cassis and blossom honey with nuances of grapefruit zest in the background. Full bodied and elegantly textured with delicate golden currant and highlighted by the refreshing acidity structure. Very well balanced and already offering plenty of drinking pleasure.
92 Sauvignon Blanc Obegg 2012

(91–93) Sauvignon Blanc Kranachberg 2015
92 Sauvignon Blanc Kranachberg 2014
93 Sauvignon Blanc Kranachberg 2013

(91–93) Sauvignon Blanc Hochsulz 2015
92 Sauvignon Blanc Hochsulz 2014
92 Sauvignon Blanc Hochsulz 2013

(91–93) Sauvignon Blanc Grassnitzberg 2015
91 Sauvignon Blanc Grassnitzberg 2014
91 Sauvignon Blanc Grassnitzberg 2013

90 Sauvignon Blanc Klassik 2015
89 Sauvignon Blanc Klassik 2014
90 Sauvignon Blanc 2013

93 Chardonnay Royal 2013
92 Chardonnay Royal 2012

92 Morillon Grassnitzberg 2013
92 Morillon Grassnitzberg 2011

91 Morillon Klassik 2015
89 Morillon Klassik 2014
89 Morillon Classique 2013

90 Gelber Muskateller Hohenegg 2015
90 Gelber Muskateller Hohenegg 2013

89 Gelber Muskateller Klassik 2015
89 Gelber Muskateller Klassik 2014
88 Gelber Muskateller 2013

92 Weißburgunder Grassnitzberg 2013
91 Weißburgunder Grassnitzberg 2012

90 Weißburgunder Klassik 2015
89 Weißburgunder Klassik 2014
89 Weißburgunder 2013

89 Welschriesling 2015
88 Welschriesling 2014
88 Welschriesling 2013

90 Riesling 2015

90 Grauburgunder 2015
90 Grauburgunder 2014
91 Grauburgunder 2013

89 Skoffignon 2015 WR/SB
88 Skoffignon 2014 WR/SB
88 Skoffignon 2013 WR/SB

89 Cuvée Walter 2015 SÄ/GM
89 Der Walter - Cuvée weiss 2014 SÄ/GM
89 Der Walter 2013 SÄ/GM

88 Zweigelt 2013

91 Zweigelt Reserve 2013

89 Zweigelt Barrique 2013
89 Zweigelt Barrique 2012
90 Zweigelt Barrique 2011

95 Sauvignon Blanc Trockenbeerenauslese 2014
89 Sauvignon Blanc Trockenbeerenauslese 2013

Weingut Walter Skoff

8462 Gamlitz, Eckberg 16
T: +43 (3453) 4243, F: +43 (3453) 4243 17
weingut@skofforiginal.com, www.skofforiginal.com

Winemaker and Contact Person: Walter Skoff
Production: n. a. (88 % white, 10 % red, 2 % sweet)
Hectares: 70
Fairs: VieVinum, Vinexpo, ProWein, Igeho Basel
Distribution partners: on request

Walter Skoff represents the fourth generation of the family to produce wines from vineyard slopes in Südsteiermark (South Styria). He feels a deep connection to his vines, which can be tasted in his wines. Each wine is vibrant and has its own unique character that reflects the inimitable signature of Walter Skoff, which is distinguished by a combination of fruit and terroir notes. The estate's vineyards are all found within 15 kilometres of the winery and yet exhibit a broad spectrum of differing soil structures and macroclimates. Each vineyard site brings a unique flavour profile to the grapes, which is further enhanced by attentive vinification of individual charges. Walter Skoff vinifies an excellent series of "Classique" wines that excel with intense fruit and mineral character. Because the grapes for these wines stem from various sites, they also reflect varying characteristics and offer respective fruit complexity. Walter Skoff places a special focus on the vinification of his two single vineyard wines "Sauvignon Blanc Aus den Lagen" and "Burgunder Grassnitzberg". Walter Skoff has been able to prove his talent and skill repeatedly in recent years at various comparative tastings on a national and international level.

92 Sauvignon Blanc Aus den Lagen 2015
91 Sauvignon Blanc Aus den Lagen 2013
Pale green-yellow with silver highlights. Delicate nuances of gooseberry and fresh grapefruit zest with wild meadow herbs on the nose. Juicy white apple and litchi are highlighted by crisp acid and a spicy texture. Cassis lingers on the mineral finish.

90 Sauvignon Blanc Klassik 2015
89 Sauvignon Blanc Klassik 2014
90 Sauvignon Blanc 2013

89 Weißburgunder Klassik 2015
89 Weißburgunder Klassik 2014
88 Weißburgunder 2013

89 Welschriesling 2014
88 Welschriesling 2013

88 Gelber Muskateller Klassik 2015
88 Gelber Muskateller Klassik 2014
88 Gelber Muskateller 2013

88 Chardonnay Klassik 2014
88 Chardonnay 2013

92 Grassnitzberg Burgunder Cuvée 2013 CH/WB
91 Grassnitzberg Burgunder 2013 WB/CH
90 Grassnitzberg Burgunder 2011 WB/CH

(88–90) Zweigelt Barrique 2014
89 Zweigelt Barrique 2013
89 Zweigelt Barrique 2012

88 Zweigelt 2013
87 Zweigelt 2012

Weingut Karl & Gustav Strauss

8462 Gamlitz, Steinbach 16
T: +43 (664) 4424128, F: +43 (3453) 3434
office@weingut-strauss.at, www.weingut-strauss.at

Winemaker: Gustav Strauss
Contact Person: Karl & Gustav Strauss
Production: 250.000 bottles (88 % white, 7 % red, 1 % sweet, 4 % rose)
Hectares: 23 + 23
Fairs: VieVinum, ProWein
Distribution partners: DE, USA

The wines of the brothers Karl and Gustav Strass from Gamlitz aptly express Südsteiermark: sometimes elegant and harmonious, then a little wild, intense and full of contrasts. What all the growths share is how they unite power with fruit, freshness with elegance, and they all excel with great drinkability. Every wine region in the world has its own allure and that is true of the Südsteiermark in particular. It is here that the brothers Karl and Gustav Strauss vinify a broad assortment of quality wines. Four lines of wines are produced. The Strauss Classic line is the light fruity wine with refreshing acidity and well-defined varietal character: Welschriesling, Weissburgunder (Pinot Blanc) Morillon (Chardonnay), Sauvignon Blanc, Sämling 88 (Scheurebe) and Gelber Muskateller (Muscat Blanc à petits grains). The Strauss Gamlitzberg line is sourced from selections of the most beautiful grapes from the Gamlitzberg vineyard and vinified in large neutral oak casks. In particularly good years, the Strauss Reserve line and the Strauss Steinbach from Hundsberg line are fermented matured in small and large oak barrels for up to 24 months: Sauvignon Blanc, Gelber Muskateller, Grauburgunder (Pinot Gris) and Chardonnay come with great potential in the bottle. The winery has been owned by the family since 1810 and offers enthusiastic visitors cellar tours and commentated tastings with a marvellous view of Gamlitzberg.

92 Sauvignon Blanc Gamlitzberg Reserve 2013
93 Sauvignon Blanc Gamlitzberg Reserve 2011
Pale green-yellow. Delicate, lingering nuances of litchi, gooseberry, grapefruit zest and elderflower. Complex with a pleasant, edgy acidity and minerals providing structure for juicy, discreetly sweet fruit. Pineapple and minerals linger on the finish of this harmonious accompaniment to food.

91 Sauvignon Blanc Gamlitzberg 2015
91 Sauvignon Blanc Gamlitzberg 2014

89 Sauvignon Blanc Classic 2015
89 Sauvignon Blanc Classic 2014

90 Gelber Muskateller Gamlitzberg Reserve 2013
92 Gelber Muskateller Gamlitzberg Reserve 2011

90 Gelber Muskateller Gamlitzberg 2014

92 Chardonnay Gamlitzberg Reserve 2013

88 Chardonnay Gamlitzberg 2015
89 Chardonnay Gamlitzberg 2014

Weingut Tement

8461 Berghausen, Zieregg 13
T: +43 (3453) 4101, F: +43 (3453) 4101 30
weingut@tement.at, www.tement.at

Winemaker: Manfred and Armin Tement
Contact Person: Armin Tement
Production: n. a. (97 % white, 2 % red, 1 % sweet)
Hectares: 80
Fairs: VieVinum, ProWein, Summa
Distribution partners: I, S, CH, B, SK, SLO, RC, DE, FIN, N, H, USA

The Tement family winery is situated on a small mountain plateau just above the impressive Zieregg vineyard. From here the visitor can enjoy a stunning view that reaches far into neighbouring Slovenia on one side and Southeast Styria on the other. The winery is now in its third generation with Armin and Stefan Tement in the starting blocks. The brothers intend to continue the same conscientiousness for quality and tradition. Selective cultivation, rigorous yield restrictions and sustainable handcraft are the cornerstones of their efforts and the foundation for elegant wines with authentic expression of origin. The estate vineyards have been vastly expanded over the past years and have now reached their culmination of 80 hectares in Austria. The estate owns a full 14 hectares in the prized vineyard, Zieregg. A further 20 ha in the Sulz vineyard and 10 ha in Grassnitzberg as well as smaller plots in Sernau (3 ha), Hochkittenberg (8 ha), Wielitsch, Ottenberg and Steinbach complete the impressive list of plots. Sixty percent of the vineyard area is planted with Sauvignon Blanc, making it the winery's most important variety. Other typical regional varieties vinified are Welschriesling, Gelber Muskateller (Muscat Blanc à petits grains), Morillon (Chardonnay), Weissburgunder (Pinot Blanc), and Gewürztraminer - listed according to their significance in surface area. Total production of white varieties is 96% while 3% is dedicated to red - Blauer Zweigelt and Pinot Noir. Predicated dessert wines round out the assortment. White wines are produced in three different categories: branded wines called Steirischen Klassik STK®, village wines, and STK®-Lagen (single vineyard) wines. The average yields are between 3500 and 5500 litres per hectare depending on variety.

Vinification is is practiced according to Stryian tradition. Whether fermented in steel tanks or large neutral oak casks, the wines are always defined more by their origins than their vinification. Steirischen Klassik wines are assembled from various Tement estate vineyards. To preserve the aroma and fruitiness of these wines, they are usually fermented in stainless steel. These single-varietal wines are representative of the region and vintage. The "Steirischen Klassik Sauvignon Blanc" is the most important wine of this producer and is followed by the Gelber Muskateller and the Weissburgunder. The village and single vineyard STK® are the third and highest category of wines in the Tement portfolio. Fully ripened grapes are harvested late from the best sites and fermented slowly, gently and spontaneously and they usually mature in large neutral oak casks until bottling. The single vineyard wines are expressive, complex, highly mineral and exhibit superb balance and elegance.

In recent years, the family winery has extended its top site, the Zieregg, by planting more vines just over the border in neighbouring Slovenia. The microclimatic conditions in the "Ciringa" (Slovenian for Zieregg) comprise ideal preconditions for authentic, elegant, highly mineral Sauvignon Blanc of astounding longevity. To reflect the unique origins of this wine, it carries the name "Domaine Ciringa" as producer. This expressive highly mineral Sauvignon Blanc is marketed since 2009 under the name Fosilni Breg (Fossile Mountain). As of the 2016 vintage, the Tement winery is undergoing conversion to certified organic cultivation.

95 Sauvignon Blanc Zieregg IZ Reserve 2008

95 Sauvignon Blanc Zieregg
  Vinothek Reserve 2012
95 Sauvignon Blanc Zieregg
  Vinothek Reserve 2011
94 Sauvignon Blanc Zieregg
  Vinothek Reserve 2008

95 Sauvignon Blanc Zieregg G STK 2014
96 Sauvignon Blanc Zieregg G STK 2013
Pale green-yellow. Delicate pear, cassis and gooseberry jam mingle with a touch of beeswax underscored by fresh kitchen herbs. The taut structure is complexly flavoured and precisely focused. White pear, pleasant lemon nuances and abundant minerals linger on the marvellously long finish. Multi-layered, refreshing and seductive with wonderful ageing potential.
95 Sauvignon Blanc Zieregg G STK 2012

94 Sauvignon Blanc Sernau G STK 2014
94 Sauvignon Blanc Sernau G STK 2013
94 Sauvignon Blanc Sernau G STK 2012

95 Sauvignon Blanc Grassnitzberg Reserve 2011

94 Sauvignon Blanc Grassnitzberg 1 STK 2015
93 Sauvignon Blanc Grassnitzberg 1 STK 2014
92 Sauvignon Blanc Grassnitzberg 1 STK 2013

93 Sausaler Sauvignon Blanc STK 2015
92 Sausaler Sauvignon Blanc 2014
93 Sausaler Sauvignon Blanc 2013

93 Sauvignon Blanc Berghausener Spätfüllung
  Weinbank Selektion 3 2011

93 Berghausener Sauvignon Blanc STK 2015
92 Berghausener Sauvignon Blanc 2014
92 Berghausener Sauvignon Blanc 2013

92 Sauvignon Blanc Fosilni Breg
  Domaine Ciringa 2015
91 Sauvignon Blanc Fosilni Breg
  Domaine Ciringa Slowenien 2014
91 Sauvignon Blanc Fosilni Breg
  Domaine Ciringa Slowenien 2013

92 Sauvignon Blanc Fosilni Breg Reserve
  Domaine Ciringa Slowenien 2011

92 Sauvignon Blanc Steirische Klassik STK 2015
91 Sauvignon Blanc Steirische Klassik 2014
92 Sauvignon Blanc Steirische Klassik 2013

96 Morillon Zieregg IZ Reserve 2005

94 Morillon Zieregg G STK 2014
95 Morillon Zieregg G STK 2013
Brilliant yellow with silver highlights. The multifaceted bouquet displays ripe golden currant and a hint of pineapple, subtle herbs and spice and a barely noticeable kiss of oak. Complex and tightly woven, the elegant texture is flavoured with apple and highlighted by refreshing, well integrated acidity. Mineral and subtle litchi nuances remain long on the finish. This wine is still youthful and will continue to benefit from further bottle maturation.
93 Morillon Zieregg G STK 2012

93 Morillon Sulz 1 STK 2014
93 Morillon Sulz 1 STK 2013
92 Morillon Sulz 1 STK 2012

93 Morillon Rossberg Weinbank Selektion 2 2013

(90–92) Morillon Muschelkalk STK 2014
90 Morillon Muschelkalk Gutswein 2013
90 Morillon Muschelkalk Gutswein 2012

(93–95) Gewürztraminer Wielitsch 1 STK 2015
90 Gewürztraminer Wielitsch 1 STK 2014
91 Gewürztraminer Wielitsch 1 STK 2013

92 Gelber Muskateller Steinbach 1 STK 2015
92 Gelber Muskateller Steinbach 1 STK 2014
92 Gelber Muskateller Steinbach 1 STK 2013

91 Gelber Muskateller
  Hochkittenberg 1 STK 2015
90 Gelber Muskateller
  Hochkittenberg 1 STK 2013
91 Gelber Muskateller
  Hochkittenberg 1 STK 2012

92 Gelber Muskateller Wielitsch Weinbank
  Selektion 1 2013

91 Gelber Muskateller Steirische Klassik
  STK 2015
90 Gelber Muskateller Steirische Klassik 2014
89 Gelber Muskateller Steirische Klassik 2013

92 Weißer Burgunder Sulz Pino.T 1 STK 2014
92 Weißburgunder Sulz Pino.T 1 STK 2013
91 Weißburgunder Sulz Pino.T 1 STK 2012

92 Weißburgunder Steirische Klassik STK 2015
90 Weißburgunder Steirische Klassik 2014
89 Weißburgunder Steirische Klassik 2013

93 Welschriesling Weinstock Alte Reben 2014
92 Welschriesling Weinstock Alte Reben 2013

91 Welschriesling Steirische Klassik STK 2015
90 Welschriesling Steirische Klassik 2014
89 Welschriesling Steirische Klassik 2013

90 Riesling Rossberg 2013

90 Temento Green Südsteiermark 2015
   WR/SB/WB/GM/CH
89 Temento Green Südsteiermark 2014 SB/WR
89 Temento Green 2013 SB/WR

92 Pinot Noir Alte Reben 2013
90 Pinot Noir 2012
92 Pinot Noir Blauburgunder 2011

90 Temento Rosé Südsteiermark 2015
89 Temento Rosé Südsteiermark 2014
88 Temento Rosé 2013

92 Sauvignon Blanc Beerenauslese Fosilni Breg
   Desertno Vino Slowenien 2013

98 Sauvignon Blanc Trockenbeerenauslese
   Zieregg Grand Reserve 2013

95 Gelber Muskateller Trockenbeerenauslese
   Hochkittenberg 2013
Medium golden yellow. A pleasantly restrained bouquet exhibits subtle botrytis spice, muscat and papaya. Subtle, well
integrated sweetness and concentration with a compact
core make an elegant impression on the palate. The long
finish seems to melt over the tongue with delicate spice and
ripe tropical fruit. A true rarity with potential for more than
a lifetime.

Weingut Wohlmuth

8441 Kitzeck im Sausal, Fresing 24
T: +43 (3456) 2303, F: +43 (3456) 2121
wein@wohlmuth.at, www.wohlmuth.at

Winemaker and Contact Person: Gerhard Wohlmuth
Production: 350.000 bottles (85 % white, 15 % red)
Hectares: 65
Fairs: VieVinum, ProWein
Distribution partners: I, RUS, S, B, CDN, CH, HR, SK, RC, LT, SLO, DK, L, DE, FIN, T, F, CZ, NL, GB, N, H, USA, IRL, PL, P

Exceedingly steep vineyards, minimal yields and 100% handcraft – these are just some distinguishing attributes of this leading producer. The Wohlmuth winery, located in the Sausal Valley, works in extreme conditions and succeeds in making wines of great finesse. Family Wohlmuth has been making wines in Austria's most highly elevated wine village, Kitzeck, since 1803, and their work in the vineyard has not changed much during that time. Now, just as then, the massive schist on the surface must be broken up with a hammer and each new vine thus meticulously placed into the meagre rocky soil. There is no irrigation here and the steepest sites, which have a slope incline of up to 90%, must be mown by hand with a scythe. The 65 vineyard hectares lying between 400 and 610 metres altitude are among the steepest vineyard slopes in Europe. Anyone who has stood between the rows of vines that rise vertically up the slope face understands why only manual harvesting is possible. Up to 1200 hours of labour are dedicated to these excruciatingly steep vineyards each year before the finished wine rests in the barrel.

According to tradition, the winery continues to be managed by the family. Father Gerhard and son Gerhard Josef share the work in the vineyard and cellar; mother Maria and daughter-in-law Marion are responsible for the office and business administration.

Site-specific character is the prime focus for all of the wines, just as the unique schist soils demand. The Altenberg, Anöd, Edelschuh, Gola, Sausaler Schlössel, and Steinriegl are the Wohlmuth's grand cru sites that are based on red, grey and blue-black schist or a conglomerate of these rock types.

Tremendous ageing potential, multi-layered complexity and impressive schist minerality distinguish the single vineyard and terroir wines. Next to the typical regional variety Sauvignon Blanc, which achieves notable minerality in the Sausal, the Wohlmuths also produce impressive Riesling, Gelber Muskateller (Muscat blanc à petits grains), Pinot Blanc, Chardonnay, and Pinot Noir. Welschriesling and Gewürztraminer round out the assortment of wines.

93 Sauvignon Blanc Ried Edelschuh 2014
94 Sauvignon Blanc Edelschuh 2013
94 Sauvignon Blanc Edelschuh 2012

95 Sauvignon Blanc Ried Hochsteinriegl 2015
94 Sauvignon Blanc Hochsteinriegl 2014
Pale green-yellow with silver highlights. Subtle pineapple and blossom honey mingle with mandarin and ripe yellow bell pepper and spice. Complex and juicy with highly elegant, pleasant extract sweetness laced with abundant dark minerals. Orange peel comes in on the long finish. Dependable ageing potential.
93 Sauvignon Blanc Hochsteinriegl 2013

94 Sauvignon Blanc Ried Steinriegl 2015
93 Sauvignon Blanc Steinriegl 2014
93 Sauvignon Blanc Steinriegl 2013

91 Sauvignon Blanc Klassik 2015
90 Sauvignon Blanc Klassik 2014
92 Sauvignon Blanc Klassik 2013

90 Sauvignon Blanc Südsteiermark 2015
89 Sauvignon Blanc Südsteiermark 2014
92 Kitzecker Sauvignon Blanc 2015

92 Kitzecker Sauvignon Blanc 2015
91 Kitzecker Sauvignon Blanc 2014
92 Kitzecker Sauvignon Blanc 2013

91 Sausaler Sauvignon Blanc 2015

94 Gelber Muskateller Ried Hochsteinriegl
Privat 2015

93 Gelber Muskateller Ried Steinriegl 2015
92 Gelber Muskateller Steinriegl 2014
92 Gelber Muskateller Steinriegl 2013

91 Gelber Muskateller Klassik 2015
90 Gelber Muskateller Klassik 2014
90 Gelber Muskateller Klassik 2013

93 Gewürztraminer Alte Reben 2015
93 Gewürztraminer Alte Reben 2013

93 Chardonnay Edelschuh 2013
93 Chardonnay Edelschuh 2012

92 Chardonnay Ried Gola 2015
92 Chardonnay Gola 2014
91 Chardonnay Gola 2013

93 Chardonnay Ried Sausaler Schlössl 2015

90 Chardonnay Klassik 2015
90 Chardonnay Klassik 2014
89 Chardonnay Klassik 2013

90 Chardonnay Südsteiermark 2015
89 Chardonnay Südsteiermark 2014

93 Pinot Blanc Sausaler Schlössl 2014
93 Pinot Blanc Sausaler Schlössl 2013
93 Pinot Blanc Sausaler Schlössl 2012

93 Pinot Blanc Ried Gola 2015
91 Pinot Blanc Gola 2014
92 Pinot Blanc Gola 2013

89 Pinot Blanc Klassik 2015
89 Pinot Blanc Klassik 2014
90 Pinot Blanc Klassik 2013

91 Pinot Blanc Südsteiermark 2015
88 Pinot Blanc Südsteiermark 2014

92 Welschriesling Quarzit 2015
93 Welschriesling Quarzit 2014

91 Welschriesling Klassik 2015
90 Welschriesling Klassik 2014

94 Pinot Gris Ried Gola Privat 2013
93 Pinot Gris Gola Privat 2013
94 Pinot Gris Gola Privat 2012

92 Pinot Gris Ried Gola 2015
92 Pinot Gris Gola 2014
92 Pinot Gris Gola 2013

94 Riesling Edelschuh 2015
94 Riesling Edelschuh 2014
Pale green-yellow. An incredibly complex bouquet displays delicate aromas of dried apricot, subtle blossom honey, yellow peach and nuances of beeswax. Full-bodied and concentrated, yet elegant with a refreshing acidity structure. The finish is very long and tremendous ageing potential is exhibited.
93 Riesling Edelschuh 2013

92 Kitzecker Riesling 2015
91 Kitzecker Riesling 2013
92 Kitzecker Riesling 2014

90 Semillon 2015

89 Sämling Südsteiermark 2015

90 Steirischer Panther 2015 RR/GM/PG/CH/SB
89 Steirischer Panther 2014 SB/GM/PG/CH/RR
90 Steirischer Panther 2013 SB/RR/PG/GM/CH

93 Ried Gola Alte Reben 2012 CH/PG/WB

89 Steirischer Panther Rosé Schilcher 2015

93 Blaufränkisch Rabenkropf Neckenmarkt 2013
93 Blaufränkisch Rabenkropf 2012
94 Blaufränkisch Rabenkropf 2011

95 Blaufränkisch Ried Rabenkropf Privat 2012
94 Blaufränkisch Rabenkropf Privat 2009

92 Blaufränkisch Red Nek Neckenmarkt 2015
89 Blaufränkisch Red Nek Neckenmarkt 2014
91 Blaufränkisch Red Nek 2013

90 Blaufränkisch Hochberg Neckenmarkt 2015
91 Blaufränkisch Hochberg Neckenmarkt 2014
90 Blaufränkisch Hochberg 2013

92 Aristos Neckenmarkt 2014 CS/BF
91 Aristos Neckenmarkt 2013 BF/CS
91 Aristos 2012 CS/BF

92 Pinot Noir Ried Altenberg 2013
89 Pinot Noir Altenberg 2012
91 Pinot Noir Altenberg 2011

Home of a rare viticultural treasure, Blauer Wildbacher and tart, pink Schilcher

Known are 10 hectares of Blauer Wildbacher in northern Italy, the other 400 hectares in the world are located in Weststeiermark (West Styria). Its racy acidity and appetizing herbal perfume have brought the local rosé called "Schilcher" international fame. The remaining 100 hectares in this region are dedicated to other wines equally worthy of discovery.

© ÖWM/Armin Faber

Austria's smallest wine-growing area, Weststeiermark, is also where the ancient Illyrians, Celts, and Romans cultivated vines. Blauer Wild-bacher is not the only eccentric thing about Weststeiermark. The geology is also quite different from its neighbouring regions with multiple variations of plattengneiss, partly pegmatitic gneisses and dyke rocks, but also areas with vineyards planted on garnet mica-schist, amphibolite, or marble. The climate is described as Illyrian, a meeting of warm, humid Mediterranean influences and warm air masses from southeast Europe. The vineyards climb steep inclines, some vines growing at a height of 600 metres above sea level, from the foothills of the Koralpe and the Reinischkogel mountains to the border with Slovenia in the south. The Blauer Wildbacher is small-berried and robust enough to cope with this terrain and climate.

Just as persistent as the predominant grape are the local vintners. Just two decades ago, Blauer Wildbacher was brushed off as a rustic peasant wine with harsh and aggressive acidity. Talented winemakers have slowly brought the best out of it and styles now range from wonderfully fruity, refreshing rosé and sparkling wines to succulent dessert wines, and even reds. The assortment of grape varieties goes beyond Blauer Wildbacher (Schilcher) to include other Austrian and international grapes that yield cool climate wines of astounding quality.

The road from Ligist in the north over St. Stefan ob Stainz and down to Deutsch-landsberg and Eibiswald in the south is dotted with quaint, tiny cellar huts between the vineyards. A drive through the pretty wine-growing villages of Greisdorf, Gundersdorf, Wildbach and Wies offers great views and tasty wines.

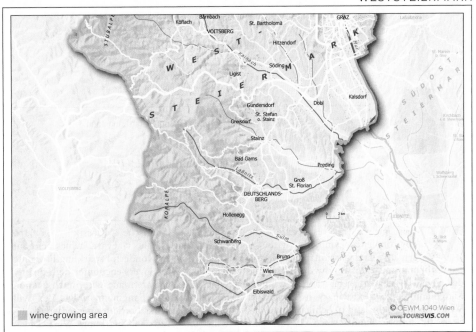

wine-growing area

© OEWM. 1040 Wien
www.TOURISVIS.COM

◆ Weingut Langmann,
   Sankt Stefan ob Stainz

◆ Müller Domäne Gutsverwaltung –
   Ehem. Prinz Liechtenstein'sches Weingut,
   Gross St. Florian

◆ Weingut Reiterer,
   Wies

◆ Weingut Thomas Strohmaier,
   Pölfing-Brunn

Weingut Langmann

8511 Sankt Stefan ob Stainz, Langegg 23
T: +43 (3463) 6100
weingut@l-l.at, www.weingut-langmann.at

Winemaker and Contact Person: Stefan Langmann
Hectares: 33
Fairs: ProWein, VieVinum
Distribution partners: CH, DE, CZ, N, USA

Wines grown in respect of the environment, vinified with a sensitive and passionate hand, and patiently matured – this is how drinkable joie de vivre is made. The award-winning Langmann vulgo Lex winery is located in Weststeiermark, the land of Schilcher, and has been in family hands since 1746. This producer stands for uncompromising quality and embodies tradition, modernity and a demanding wine culture. Every generation of the family invests incredibly dedicated passion in their work knowing that the engagement of each family member contributes significantly to the success of the winery. Their wines have it good: they are rooted in the best sun-pampered slopes of the Greisdorf, Langegg and Hochgrail vineyards in the picturesque, undulating landscape of Weststeiermark. The Langmann family cultivate their vines sustainably in harmony with nature here in the foothills of the Koralpe Mountains. For the past two years they have abstained completely from the use of herbicides and insecticides. The synthesis of an optimal climate, crystalline schist, perfectly ripened grapes, love of the product and the art of winemaking is the secret to the success of their excellent wines. Their Schilcher has been an essential part of regional wine history. This rosé wine specialty is made from one of the oldest autochthon grape varieties in Europe, Blauer Wildbacher. Easy-drinking Schilcher is justifiably considered a culinary benchmark of Weststeiermark. Langmann contributes significantly to this reputation and their love for Schilcher as the local hero inspires them to produce it in a broad spectrum of styles that are marked by its signature shiny, pale red colour and unique aroma and flavour profile.

Whether "Steirische Klassik" or the outstanding single vineyard wines, elegant sweet wines or wonderful sparkling Frizzante and Sekt. Wine lovers encounter high-quality wines here that are made with much passion and dedication. Langmann vulgo Lex will present their first bottle-fermented sparkling wine on "Austrian Sparkling Wine Day", October 22nd.

91 **Schilchersekt Brut 2015**
92 **Schilchersekt Brut**
Pale pink with a lively, fine mousse. Delicate raspberry jelly, cherry and red currant with subtle mandarin zest. Pleasant forest berry fruit is elegantly balanced with the juicy acid structure. Superb balance between discreet sweetness and refreshing acidity continues on the mineral finish. Outstanding summer drinking pleasure.

90 **Schilcher Frizzante 2015**

92 **Muskateller Sekt Brut 2015**

92 **Schilcher Hochgrail 2015**
91 **Schilcher Hochgrail 2014**

90 **Schilcher Greisdorf 2014**

91 **Gelber Muskateller Klassik 2015**
89 **Gelber Muskateller Klassik 2014**

92 **Sauvignon Blanc Greisdorf 2014**

90 **Sauvignon Blanc Greisdorf 2015**
89 **Sauvignon Blanc Klassik 2014**

★ ★ ★
Domäne Müller Gutsverwaltung –
Ehem. Prinz Liechtenstein'sches Weingut

8522 Groß St. Florian, Grazer Straße 71
T: +43 (3464) 2155, F: +43 (3464) 211625
office@mueller-wein.at, www.domaene-mueller.com

Winemaker: Yves-Michel Müller
Contact Person: Eva R. and Yves-Michel Müller
Production: 25.000 bottles (55 % white, 44 % red, 1 % sweet)
Hectares: 10
Fairs: ProWein, Alles für den Gast Salzburg, Foodex Japan, fafga Innsbruck,
ÖGW Zürich, ProWein China
Distribution partners: RUS, BY, J, B, CH, HR, RC, DK, DE, EST, CZ, NL, N, HK

The ten vineyard hectares of the "Prinz Liechtenstein'schen Weingutes" are spread beneath the imposing Landsberg Fortress in Weststeiermark (West Styria). Domäne Müller cultivates Welschriesling, Traminer (Gewürztraminer), Pinot Gris, and Zweigelt on the primary rock soils of the filet parcel of the Burgegg vineyard called "Fürstenstück". A rare specialty of West Steirmark, is the Blauer Wildbacher grape variety (also called Schilcher). A rosé wine is made from this ancient variety. Its robust nature and taut structure make it a refreshing thirst-quencher in the summer, and in winter it is an elegant accompaniment to salmon and shellfish. A red wine is also produced from the Blauer Wildbacher, and this is known as "Out of Red", which has received accolades continuously in Austria and captured fans far beyond the country's borders. Varietal wines are also produced from both wineries and their vineyards. Both classic, steel-fermented wines and oak-matured wines are made. The oaked wines are considered to be "Vins de Garde" and capable of increasing in aromatic finesse with extended bottle maturation. Professor Zweigelt personally planted the vines that carry his name in the Burgegg vineyard in the 1930s, making it one of the oldest existing Zweigelt vineyards in Austria. Yves-Michel Müller continues the old traditions of this estate. He vinifies a deep black-red Zweigelt of extraordinary quality that excels with depth and elegance. In spring of 2016 a new Zweigelt from the 2013 vintage will launch the label "Origo 34", which refers to the original year of its planting by Professor Zweigelt.

92 Der Schilchersekt Jahrgangsreserve brut 2013
90 Der Schilchersekt Jahrgangsreserve
extra brut 2010

91 Schilcher Seelenfreund Kabinett Burgegg -
Fürstenstück Hommage an Günter J. Müller
2015
90 Der Schilcher Seelenfreund Kabinett Ried
Burgegg – Fürstenstück 2014
91 Der Schilcher Seelenfreund Kabinett Ried
Burgegg – Fürstenstück 2013

90 Schilcher Gutswein Kabinett Burgegg 2015

92 Pinot Gris Burgegg Privat 2012

91 Grauburgunder Burgegg Gutswein 2015
91 Grauburgunder Ried Burgegg – Fürstenstück 2014
Brilliant yellow with silver highlights. Aromas and flavours of ripe pear, apple, and delicate blossom honey nuances. Juicy fruit and a lemony touch join in with abundant minerals on the palate. Sweet orange fruit and salty minerals linger on the appetizing finish.
89 Pinot Gris – Grauburgunder Ried Burgegg 2013

93 Der Pinot Gris vom Fürstenstück 2012
93 Der Pinot Gris vom Fürstenstück Relaunch 2007

92 Der Pinot Gris vom Fürstenstück Spätlese 2012

(90–92) Der Zweigelt »Origo 34« Burgegg 2013

89 Zweigelt Ried Burgegg – Deutschlandsberg
Alte Reben 2012
92 Der Zweigelt Alte Reben 2010

91 Der Zweigelt Ried Burgegg Alte Reben
Reserve 2007

89 Blauer Wildbacher Ried Burgegg 2010

Weingut Reiterer

8551 Wies, Lamberg 11
T: +43 (3465) 3950, F: +43 (3465) 3950 6
info@weingut-reiterer.com, www.weingut-reiterer.com

Winemaker and Contact Person: Christian Reiterer
Production: n. a. (10 % white, 90 % rosé)
Hectares: 50
Fairs: VieVinum, ProWein
Distribution partners: J, CH, DE, USA

The vintner Christian Reiterer was born and raised in Lamberg bei Wies in Weststeiermark (West Styria). After the untimely death of his father, his strong connection to his home and fascination for the Blauer Wildbacher grape variety inspired him to strive to realize his vision of a large and modern winery in Weststeiermark. Three hectares of farmland with only one hectare of vines on the Lamberg Mountain were his starting point. At that time, the end of the 1970s, Blauer Wildbacher usually appeared as a simple, rustic rosé called Schilcher, that was quaffed predominantly at regional farm taverns (Buschenschank). It was Reiterer's goal to further develop these wines and achieve international recognition for a unique regional specialty. On the one side, he saw possibilities in single vineyard Schilcher that would reflect a specific terroir. On the other side, he discovered that the piquant spice, crisp acidity, and marvellous fruit of the grape variety made it predestined for superb sparkling wines. So he began – in the early 1980s – to produce wines that would later become the winery's well known brands: Schilcher Rosé Frizzante and Schilcher Rosé Sekt. Today, Reiterer cultivates 60 hectares of vineyards in top sites in Weststeiermark and exports a large share of his wines to ten different countries in the world. In the meantime, Christian Reiterer is affectionately called "Mr. Schilcher".

92 **Schilcher Rosé Sekt 2015**
91 **Schilcher Sekt 2014**
Pale cherry hue with pink highlights, and a fine, persistent mousse. Nuances of red forest berry jam, red currant, grapefruit zest and strawberry. Racy acidity lifts the red berry and white apple fruit. Citrus notes line the salty mineral finish. Refreshing summer drinking pleasure.
91 **Schilcher Sekt 2013**

89 **Sauvignon Blanc Sekt Brut 2014**

89 **Schilcher Rosé Frizzante 2015**
89 **Schilcher Frizzante 2014**
89 **Schilcher Frizzante 2013**

91 **Schilcher Rosé Engelweingarten Alte Reben 2015**
90 **Schilcher Engelweingarten Alte Reben 2013**
90 **Schilcher Engelweingarten Alte Reben 2012**

90 **Schilcher Rosé Exklusiv 2015**
90 **Schilcher Exklusiv 2014**

89 **Schilcher Lamberg 2013**
88 **Schilcher Lamberg 2012**

88 **Schilcher Riemerberg 2013**
89 **Schilcher Riemerberg 2012**

90 **Sauvignon Blanc Lamberg 2015**
89 **Sauvignon Blanc 2014**
89 **Sauvignon Blanc 2012**

89 **Weißburgunder 2014**

88 **Steirercuvée 2014 SB/WB**

Weingut Thomas Strohmaier

8544 Pölfing-Brunn, Brunn 41
T: +43 (3465) 2322, F: +43 (3465) 2322, M: +43 (664) 4513945
weingut.strohmaier@aon.at, www.strohmaier.schilcher.com

Winemaker and Contact Person: Thomas Strohmaier
Production: n. a. (50 % white, 50 % red)
Hectares: 7,5
Fairs: VieVinum
Distribution partners: RUS, S, CH, DE, PL

The Strohmaier winery considers the symbiosis of nature and terroir and harmony with the phases of the moon to be the most important factors in creating unique, captivating wines. The aromatic varieties Sauvignon Blanc, Schilcher (Blauer Wildbacher) and Gelber Muskateller (Muscat Blanc à petits grains) grow on schist-gneiss rock and mature to multifaceted elegant wines. As Thomas Strohmaier says: "If one does everything right in the vineyard, and the grapes are top quality, then the road to extraordinary wines is easy."

89 Schilcher Frizzante 2015
90 Schilcher Frizzante 2014

90 Gelber Muskateller Sekt 2014

89 Schilcher Ried Aibl 2015
92 Schilcher Ried Aibl 2014
Pale onion skin colour with pink highlights. Subtle smoky-mineral components, nuances of cassis and red forest berries, and a touch of grapefruit on the nose. Taut and firm with a delicate red berry texture highlighted by a vibrant acid structure. Good length and classic style expression.

90 Schilcher Privat 2015
90 Schilcher Privat 2014

91 Sauvignon Blanc Schlossweingarten 2013
91 Sauvignon Blanc Schlossweingarten 2013

90 Chardonnay Luna 2015
89 Chardonnay Luna 2014

88 Gelber Muskateller 2014

Vigorous wines from the land of sunshine

Burgenland is famed for its trilogy of wine styles: spicy red wines, full-bodied white wines, and some of the world's most delicious noble sweet wines. Austria's cool climate is tempered in Burgenland by Lake Neusiedl and warm, arid Pannonian air masses sweeping in from the east. Huge variations in microclimate within the 13,840 hectares can also not be underestimated.

© Der Schlegel-Gergey Kovács

The huge variations in the soils and microclimates in Burgenland are the foundation for the establishment of protected designations of origin (abbreviated "DAC") in each of Burgenland's sub-regions. The indigenous Zweigelt variety dominates the sandy-loamy alluvial soils in the distinctly Pannonian climate of the Neusiedlersee DAC on the flat, low-lying east side of Lake Neusiedl. On the west side of Lake Neusiedl in the Neusiedlersee-Hügelland region, the Leitha Mountains are a prominent feature of the topography. Two very different parent rocks of vineyard soils meet: acidic schist and gneiss encounter calcareous Leitha limestone. Due to this unique geology, it is only natural that the Leithaberg DAC includes both a Blaufränkisch-based red wine and a white wine blend. Dense loam soils lend Mittelburgenland DAC Blaufränkisch particularly deep fruit and exceptional length. In Südburgenland, the Eisenberg and surrounding hills offer a unique mosaic of parent rock material and cool Styrian climatic influences. This provides optimal conditions for an inimitable style of Blaufränkisch that appears under the Eisenberg DAC protected designation of origin. Burgenland offers a plethora of other varieties and styles that do not fit under the present DACs, but are no lesser in quality.

These wines appear under the Burgenland protected geographical indication, or when appropriate, under Neusiedlersee-Hügelland or Südburgenland.

Lake Neusiedl in northern Burgenland covers 315 km² and is never deeper than 1.8 metres. Humidity and morning fog in the otherwise long, warm, sunny autumns promote desireable development of noble rot *(Botrytis cinerea)* – the prerequisite for the production of Burgenland's legendary sweet wines Beerenauslese, Trockenbeerenauslese, and Ruster Ausbruch.

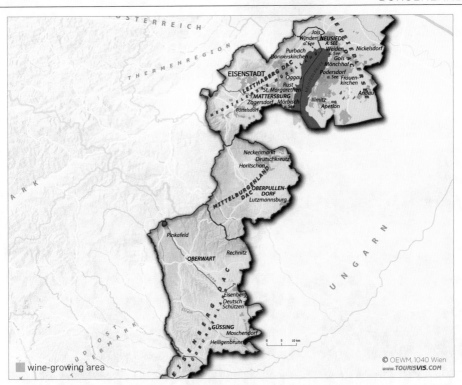

wine-growing area

© OEWM, 1040 Wien
www.TOURISVIS.COM

AUSTRIA ALTOGETHER: 45,900 ha

Wine-growing area Burgenland   **13,840 ha (30 %)**

SPECIFIC WINE-GROWING AREA:

Neusiedlersee	7,649 ha
Neusiedlersee-Hügelland	3,576 ha
Mittelburgenland	2,117 ha
Südburgenland	498 ha

White wine altogether:	**6,227 ha (45 %)**	**Red wine altogether:**	**7,615 ha (55 %)**
Grüner Veltliner:	1,473 ha (11 %)	Blaufränkisch:	3,053 ha (22 %)
Welschriesling:	1,422 ha (10 %)	Zweigelt:	2,649 ha (19 %)
Chardonnay:	566 ha (4 %)	St. Laurent:	406 ha (3 %)
Weissburgunder:	551 ha (4 %)	Merlot:	395 ha (3 %)
Müller-Thurgau:	376 ha (2 %)	Cabernet Sauvignon:	363 ha (3 %)

NEUSIEDLERSEE DAC
Pannonian climate and lake land, mild, velvety Zweigelt

The east side of the vast, shallow Lake Neusiedl is dominated by sandy-loamy alluvial soils predestined for soft, fruity red wines from Zweigelt. The region is also home to exquisite botrytized sweet wines of international acclaim.

© ÖWM/Lukan

The Neusiedlersee DAC is situated on the eastern shores of the 315 km² shallow Lake Neusiedl. This protected designation of origin stretches from the wine community of Gols in the north, over the flat Heideboden terrain, down to the Seewinkel adjacent to the Hungarian border. A wide variety of grapes flourish on its 7,649 hectares. 1,812 hectares are planted with the indigenous Zweigelt. Neusiedlersee DAC stands for fruity, mild, velvety red wines made from the indigenous Zweigelt variety that express the regional terroir. The Neusiedlersee DAC Reserve is a bit more robust and appears either as a pure Zweigelt or as a Zweigelt-dominated blend. The Neusiedlersee DAC region encompasses the political district of Neusiedl am See, except for the communities of Winden and Jois, which belong to the Leithaberg DAC.

In the northern part of the region, the Parndorf Plateau breaks off, forming a sloped escarpment in the vicinity of Gols. There is more gravel in the soil here and the evening breezes have a cooling effect.

There are a number of ambitious producers here that produce superb wines from black grape varieties like Blaufränkisch, St. Laurent, Merlot, Cabernet Sauvignon, and even Syrah that appear under the Burgenland protected geographical indication.

Also released under the Burgenland protected geographical indication are a number of dry white wines, ranging from the easy-drinking, crisp Welschriesling to rich, full-bodied Chardonnay, Pinot Blanc, and Neuburger.

Lake Neusiedl is the largest endorheic lake in Central Europe and makes a huge impact on the region's macroclimate. Where the lake makes a bend on the southeast side in the Seewinkel area, there are numerous tiny salt lakes scattered between the vineyards. Humidity and morning fog in the long sunny autumns provide ideal conditions for desirable noble rot (Botrytis cinerea), the basis for some of the world's most exquisite sweet wines made from a number of different grape varieties.

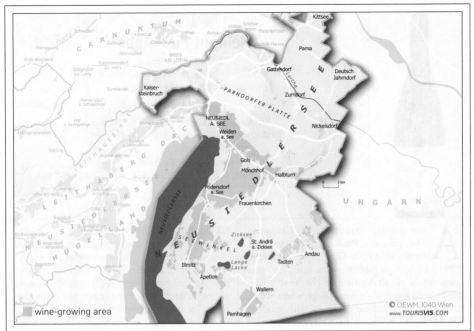

wine-growing area

© OEWM, 1040 Wien
www.TOURISVIS.COM

Lake Neusiedl and the Seewinkel National Park are a natural habitat for many birds and unique vegetation. A network of bicycle paths, water sports, and spa hotels provide numerous recreational opportunities.

◆ Weingut Paul Achs, Gols

◆ Weingut Markus Altenburger, Jois

◆ Winzerkeller Andau, Andau

◆ Weingut Haider, Illmitz

◆ Weingut Gernot and Heike Heinrich, Gols

◆ Weingut Keringer, Mönchhof

◆ Weingut Jacqueline Klein, Andau

◆ Weinlaubenhof Kracher, Illmitz

◆ Weingut Leitner, Gols

◆ Josef Lentsch – Dankbarkeit, Podersdorf

◆ Weingut Münzenrieder, Apetlon

◆ Weingut PMC Münzenrieder, Apetlon

◆ Weingut Pittnauer, Gols

◆ Weingut Claus Preisinger, Gols

◆ Weingut Hannes Reeh, Andau

◆ Weingut Erich Scheiblhofer, Andau

◆ Hans Tschida – Angerhof, Illmitz

◆ Weingut Velich, Apetlon

◆ Zantho, Andau

◆ Weingut Ziniel, St. Andrä/Zicksee

★ ★ ★ ★

Weingut Paul Achs

7122 Gols, Neubaugasse 13
T: +43 (2173) 2367, F: +43 (2173) 2367 7, M: +43 (699) 11897228
office@paul-achs.at, www.paul-achs.at

─── ORGANIC ───

Winemaker and Contact Person: Paul Achs
Production: 100.000 bottles (20 % white, 80 % red)
Hectares: 25
Fairs: ProWein, VieVinum
Distribution partners: AUS, CDN, CH, SGP, SK, RC, DK, DE, F, NL, USA

After gaining experience in California and abroad, Paul Achs joined the family winery in Gols as oenologist in 1991. Only four short years later, he was awarded "Falstaff Vintner of the Year". Formerly renowned for its excellent white wines and ability to combine tradition with modern vinification technology, the winery is now also famed for its red wines. The Achs wines are by no means "show wines," but rather are characterized by elegance and finesse. Red wine now makes up 90% of the total production. Not only the red wine specialties Pinot Noir, Blaufränkisch Ungerberg, and the "Pannobile" blend are matured in small French oak barrels, but also Chardonnay and Sauvignon Blanc. A maximum yield of 3,000 kilos fruit per hectare help ensure the high quality of the Achs wines, which are certainly among the very best that Austria has to offer. Just how well Blaufränkisch can be in a region otherwise dominated by Zweigelt was proven with the "Ungerberg 2003", which was awarded second place among 1700 wines in the Falstaff Red Wine Premier of 2005. In autumn 2012 the "Blaufränkisch Spiegel" 2010 won first place for the variety and third place in the total assessment in the Falstaff Red Wine Premier. The 2011 "Zweigelt Alte Reben" won the Zweigelt Grand Prix. At the Falstaff Red Wine Premier in 2013, the "Blaufränkisch Ungerberg" 2011 was awarded third place in its varietal category. The wines of Paul Achs are always among the very best of the country.

93 Blaufränkisch Ungerberg 2013
Deep dark ruby with an opaque core, purple highlights and a discreet transparent rim. The attractive bouquet displays ripe wild cherry, delicate plum compote, candied orange peel, and floral components. Sweetly textured, fine tannin and juicy acidity build the frame for fine cherry fruit on the palate. The elegant accompaniment to food exhibits good length and potential for the future.
92 Blaufränkisch Ungerberg 2012
94 Blaufränkisch Ungerberg 2011

93 Blaufränkisch Spiegel 2013
Dark ruby with an opaque core. Purple highlights, and a thin transparent rim. Ripe dark forest berry jam mingles with a touch of chocolate, herbal spice, and nuances of orange zest. Ripe wild cherry and pleasant sweet extract are elegantly structured with juicy acidity and well-integrated tannins. Long finish and possesses good ageing potential.
92 Blaufränkisch Spiegel 2012
95 Blaufränkisch Spiegel 2011

92 Blaufränkisch Altenberg 2013
93 Blaufränkisch Altenberg 2012
93 Blaufränkisch Altenberg 2011

90 Blaufränkisch Edelgrund 2014
91 Blaufränkisch Edelgrund 2013

(89–91) Blaufränkisch Heideboden 2015
89 Blaufränkisch Heideboden 2014

(92–94) Pinot Noir 2014
92 Pinot Noir 2013
92 Pinot Noir 2012

(91–93) Zweigelt Alte Reben 2015
90 Zweigelt Alte Reben 2014
91 Zweigelt Alte Reben 2013

89 Zweigelt 2014

92 Syrah 2013
92 Syrah 2012
92 Syrah 2011

(90–92) Sankt Laurent 2014
90 St. Laurent 2013
90 St. Laurent 2012

(92–94) Pannobile 2014 ZW/BF/SL
93 Pannobile 2013 BF/ZW
Dark ruby with purple highlights and a thin transparent rim.
The inviting bouquet displays blackberry, delicate sandalwood, and dark berry jam over chocolaty notes. Very elegant
on the palate with sweetly extracted red cherry refreshingly
structured with juicy acidity. An approachable and multifaceted accompaniment to food.
92 Pannobile 2012 ZW/BF/SL
94 Pannobile 2011 BF/ZW/SL

(90–92) Lust & Leben 2015 ZW/SL/BF

(91–93) Chardonnay Pannobile weiß 2014
92 Chardonnay Pannobile weiß 2013
93 Pannobile weiß 2012 CH

90 Chardonnay 2015
89 Chardonnay 2014
89 Chardonnay 2013

90 Sauvignon Blanc 2015
90 Sauvignon Blanc 2014
89 Sauvignon Blanc 2013

89 Neuburger 2011

89 Heideboden weiß 2015 WB/CH/GV

Weingut Markus Altenburger

7093 Jois, Untere Hauptstraße 62
T/F: +43 (2160) 71089
contact@markusaltenburger.com, www.markusaltenburger.com

Winemaker and Contact Person: Markus Altenburger
Production: n. a. (25 % white, 75 % red)
Hectares: 11
Fairs: VieVinum, ProWein
Distribution partners: on request

Markus Altenburger now has half of his vineyard area planted with Blaufränkisch. Upon his return to the family winery after several years at Schlossweingut Halbturn, the situation was quite different. The assortment of varieties was predominantly white and within just a few years this was changed in favour of red grapes. A few plots of the interesting old native white grape Neuburger remains, as does the Chardonnay in the Jungenberg vineyard. The main focus is on the plots of old Blaufränkisch vines. All of the estate's vineyards are in the wine village of Jois and are cultivated according to strict quality regulations coupled with significant yield reduction methods. Since the vintage 2007, the single-vineyard Blaufränkisch wines from the Jungenberg and from the Gritschenberg count among the best examples of the variety in the country. The flagship blend "Altenburger" has also secured a niche on the wine lists of esteemed restaurants in Austria and abroad. All of the wines are vinified in the family winery in Jois. The old vaulted cellar offers an ideal environment for gentle vinification techniques. The wines are matured predominantly in large used wooden casks, 500-litre barrels and 225-litre oak barrels. The winery joined the "Leithaberg" movement in 2010, which promotes the regional ideal of puristic, clearly structured and vibrant Blaufränkisch wines that express the unique marine limestone and schist geology of the Leitha mountains.

94 Leithaberg DAC rot Gritschenberg 2013
94 Leithaberg DAC rot Gritschenberg 2012
Dark ruby with purple highlights and a thin transparent rim.

The multifaceted bouquet exhibits dark forest berry jam, sweet spice reminiscent of juniper and cardamom, heather and nougat. Lingonberry and wild cherry are complexly structured with juicy acidity and well-integrated tannins. Pronounced mineral notes join in on the very long finale. Dependable potential for the future.

94 Blaufränkisch Gritschenberg 2011

95 Leithaberg DAC rot Jungenberg 2013
95 Leithaberg DAC rot Jungenberg 2012
Dark ruby with purple highlights and a discreet transparent rim. Attractive lingonberry jam, fresh blackberry and wild cherry mingle with delicate herbal spice and nougat. Good complexity is demonstrated with pleasant extract sweetness nicely countered by refreshing acid and tannin structure. Abundant minerals join in on the long finish. Dependable ageing potential.

94 Blaufränkisch Jungenberg 2011

92 Leithaberg DAC rot 2013
92 Leithaberg DAC rot 2012
92 Leithaberg DAC rot 2011

90 Blaufränkisch Ried Satz 2012

94 JOIS - Cuvée Altenburger 2012 BF/CS/ME
93 JOIS – Cuvée Altenburger 2011 BF/CS/ME

93 Leithaberg DAC weiß Jungenberg 2013
92 Chardonnay Jungenberg 2012
90 Chardonnay Jungenberg 2011

89 Chardonnay vom Kalk 2014
88 Chardonnay vom Kalk 2013
88 Chardonnay vom Kalk 2012

(89–91) Neuburger betont. 2015

92 Markus Altenburger weiß 2015 GV/NB/TR/WR

Winzerkeller Andau

7163 Andau, Dammweg 1
T: +43 (2176) 2181, F: +43 (2176) 2181 4
office@winzerkeller-andau.at, www.winzerkeller-andau.at

Winemaker: Christopher Eisinger
Contact Person: Heidi Pammer
Production: 100.000 bottles
Distribution partners: on request

Winzerkeller Andau is the oldest producer in Andau and, with approximately 700 vineyard hectares, it is also the largest producer in Burgenland. The vineyards are dispersed predominantly in and around Andau, but there are also a few selected parcels located in other villages that are still within the Seewinkel region. The wines produced thus all display the typical regional character of Seewinkel.

The main focus is on the production of red wines from indigenous varieties like Zweigelt, Blaufränkisch and Sankt Laurent. Further specialties include Grüner Veltliner, Sauvignon Blanc, and Welschriesling. Rigorous yield restriction, sustainable vineyard cultivation, and meticulous selection of grape material guarantee high wine quality. The goal is the production of elegant wines with good varietal and regional character that pair superbly with food.

(89–91) Blaufränkisch 2015
Medium yellow with gold highlights. Aromas and flavours of mango and pear mingle with nuances of hazelnut, herbs and spice. Honey-like sweetness is well integrated and refreshingly buffered with juicy acidity. Very good length and although already offering abundant drinking pleasure, there is still plenty of potential for the future.
89 Blaufränkisch 2011

88 Zweigelt Selection 2012
91 Zweigelt Selection 2011

(87–89) Zweigelt 2015
88 Zweigelt 2011

87 Grüner Veltliner 2015
87 Grüner Veltliner 2012

86 Sauvignon Blanc 2015
87 Sauvignon Blanc 2012

(91–93) Beerenauslese 2015 WR/WB/RR

★ ★ ★

Weingut Haider

7142 Illmitz, Seegasse 16
T: +43 (2175) 2358, F: +43 DW 4
office@weinguthaider.at, www.weinguthaider.at

Winemaker: Gerhard Haider
Contact Person: Gerhard Haider and Silvia Kast
Production: n. a. (20 % white, 40 % red, 40 % sweet)
Hectares: 13
Fairs: VieVinum, ProWein
Distribution partners: CH, SK, DE, NL, GB, PL

"You can defend yourself against criticism, but against praise one is powerless," is the motto of family Haider. They can say this in a fairly relaxed way due to their many successes on the Austrian and international wine stage. Standards have been set high for son Gerhard and daughter Silvia who now manage the estate in its fourth generation. One could say that everything is new except the wines and the quality, which the two siblings have taken over from their father Martin. Thirteen different varieties are planted on sand, gravel, and cambisol soils. The soil and the unique climate are the main capital for the production of equally unique wines. All white and noble sweet wines are vinified in stainless steel. "Traminer absolut" is the first wine in the "absolut" series of wines created by Gerhard Haider, which stand for "absolutely unique, absolutely my signature". The Traminer (Gewürztraminer) is sourced from 43-year-old vines that grow in pure sand – "the dry essence of the lake shore". The complete series of Haider wines excel with finesse, elegance, pure fruit and varietal character. Botrytis and honey notes accentuate the inimitable character of the region. The red wines of the house appear in two styles – one is easy-drinking and fruity, while the reserve wines are powerful and voluptuous with plenty of character.

95 Welschriesling Trockenbeerenauslese 2013
Medium yellow with gold highlights. Aromas and flavours of mango and pear mingle with nuances of hazelnut, herbs and spice. Honey-like sweetness is well integrated and refreshingly buffered with juicy acidity. Very good length and although already offering abundant drinking pleasure, there is still plenty of potential for the future.

94 Welschriesling Trockenbeerenauslese 2012
93 Welschriesling Trockenbeerenauslese 2011

92 Welschriesling Beerenauslese 2014
91 Welschriesling Beerenauslese 2013
92 Welschriesling Beerenauslese 2012

94 Sämling 88 Trockenbeerenauslese 2013
Medium yellow with gold highlights. Intense tropical yellow fruit reminiscent of passion fruit, papaya, and litchi mingle with notes of nutmeg and orange zest in the background. Refreshingly structured with juicy acidity that balances the luscious sweetness. Pineapple and white pepper linger long on the delicious finish. Superb ageing potential.
94 Sämling 88 Trockenbeerenauslese 2012
96 Sämling 88 Trockenbeerenauslese Nektaressenz 2010

93 Sauvignon Blanc Trockenbeerenauslese 2013
93 Sauvignon Blanc Trockenbeerenauslese 2012

93 Muskat Ottonel Trockenbeerenauslese 2013

88 Muskat Ottonel Spätlese 2015

94 Chardonnay Trockenbeerenauslese 2013
93 Chardonnay Trockenbeerenauslese 2012
94 Chardonnay Trockenbeerenauslese 2010

89 Traminer Spätlese 2015

91 Traminer absolut 2015

90 Traminer 2013

90 Mythos 2012 CS/BF/ME

90 Zweigelt Selection 2012

⭐⭐⭐⭐⭐

Weingut Gernot und Heike Heinrich

7122 Gols, Baumgarten 60
T: +43 (2173) 3176, F: +43 (2173) 3176 4
weingut@heinrich.at, www.heinrich.at

——— ORGANIC ———

Winemaker: Gernot Heinrich and Harald Lehner
Contact Person: Heike Heinrich
Production: n. a. (6 % white, 94 % red)
Hectares: 90
Fairs: VieVinum, Vinitaly, ProWein
Distribution partners: RO, RUS, J, S, B, CDN, ROK, HR, SK, RC, DK, L, T, GR, NL, GB, USA

Salzberg, Gabarinza, Alter Berg, Edelgraben – completely different worlds open in the grand vineyards of Gernot and Heike Heinrich, yet one single goal is shared: realizing full potential. The preconditions for this are cool limestone slopes of the Leitha Mountains and a gentler topography with a warmer climate in the vineyards surrounding the winery in Gols. Biodynamic cultivation, a handful of autochthon grape varieties led by Blaufränkisch, and gentle, conscientious vinification set the course. Handcraftsmanship and manual labour pave the path. Time takes the journey to its finish. Inquisitiveness is the foundation for continuing evolution. Lively exchange with friends and partners in the Pannobile and Respect vintner associations open additional perspectives. All of this is undertaken with the goal of bottling unique and authentic wines that express their place of origin while still allowing space for individual interpretations.

(95–97) Salzberg 2013 ME/BF
95 Salzberg 2012 ME/BF
Deep dark ruby with violet highlights and a thin transparent rim. The multifaceted bouquet displays attractive blackberry and plum fruit over layers of liquorice and sandalwood. Superb complexity with juicy acidity and firm, well integrated tannins lending impressive structure to intense cherry fruit. Chocolaty notes join in on the very long finish. This will benefit from further bottle maturation.
96 Salzberg 2011 ME/BF

93 Gabarinza 2013 ZW/ME/BF
Deep ruby with purple highlights and a discreet, slightly paler rim. Initially rather restrained, but with aeration elegant black berry jam, a touch of liquorice, wild cherry, heather and spice are revealed. This complexity continues on the palate and is accompanied by abundant, well-integrated tannin. A delicate touch of nougat joins the other flavours on the long finish. Good ageing potential.
94 Gabarinza 2012 ZW/ME/BF
94 Gabarinza 2011 ME/ZW/BF

(91–93) Pannobile 2014 ZW/BF
92 Pannobile 2013 BF/ZW
93 Pannobile Rot 2012 ZW/BF

(93–95) Blaufränkisch Alter Berg 2014
93 Blaufränkisch Alter Berg 2013
Deep dark ruby with purple highlights and a thin transparent rim. The attractive bouquet displays blackberry jam, juniper, cherry, peppery notes, and mineral accents. The abundant, wonderfully silky tannins are well integrated in the medium body. Juicy red berries and delicate spice linger on the very long finish. Dependable potential for further development.
93 Blaufränkisch Alter Berg 2012

(94–96) Leithaberg DAC rot 2014
92 Leithaberg DAC rot 2013
92 Leithaberg DAC rot 2012

92 St. Laurent Rosenberg 2014

93 Pinot Noir Leithakalk 2011

(92–94) Leithaberg DAC weiß 2014
91 Leithaberg DAC weiß 2013
92 Leithaberg DAC weiß 2012 WB

93 Roter Traminer 2012
93 Roter Traminer 2011

92 Neuburger Kurzberg 2012

Weingut Keringer

7123 Mönchhof, Wiener Straße 22a
T: +43 (2173) 80380, F: +43 (2173) 80380 40
weingut@keringer.at, www.keringer.at

Winemaker and Contact Person: Ing. Robert Keringer
Production: 150.000 bottles (20 % white, 75 % red, 5 % sweet)
Hectares: 14 + 14
Fairs: ProWein, VieVinum
Distribution partners: B, CH, ROK, RC, DK, DE, EST, F

Unusual creations with catchy names such as "Aviator", "Commander" and "Massiv" are just a few of the numerous popular wines from the young and ambitious vintner couple Robert and Marietta Keringer. After his job at a famous spirits merchant, and a detour of several years as a viticultural consultant, Robert returned to the family winery. Within just a few years after taking over management, gradually evolving from part-time to full-time vintner, he began collecting awards for his wines. Robert initiated another innovative wine series in 2011: the "100 Days" wines. These wines are produced using a special vinification technique. The best grapes from each variety macerate for 100 days on their pips and skins in the fermentation tank. During this period grape berry contents are gently extracted. The resulting wines are particularly complex. The vintner does not only impress with the constant quality of his red wines. His Welschriesling has been the international winner for the variety at the "Austrian Wine Challenge" three times. The "Chardonnay Classic" and the oak-fermented "Chardonnay Herrschaftswein" are often superb.

(93–95) Massiv 2013 BF/RA/ZW/CS
92 »MASSIV« 2012 BF/RA/ZW/CS
Deep ruby with an opaque core, purple highlights, and a thin, transparent rim. Complex aromas and flavours of blackberry, cassis, and nougat over notes of juniper and tobacco. Full-bodied and structured with well-integrated tannin. Elderberry juice and a touch of red berries remain on the finish. Will benefit from further bottle maturation.

92 Grande Cuvée 2011 RA/BF/ZW

93 Cabernet Sauvignon »100 Days« 2013

91 Merlot »100 Days« 2013

89 Sankt Laurent Commander 2013
89 St. Laurent Commander 2012

92 St. Laurent Commander Reserve 2011

91 Zweigelt »100 Days« 2013
91 Zweigelt 100 Days 2011

89 Zweigelt 2012

90 Shiraz »100 Days« 2013

88 Neusiedlersee DAC 2013

90 Blaufränkisch Aviator 2012

88 White Commander »Gleichgepresster« 2013 PN/SL/ZW

(88–90) Chardonnay Herrschaftswein 2015
89 Chardonnay Herrschaftswein 2014
89 Chardonnay Herrschaftswein 2013

88 Welschriesling 2014

Weingut Jacqueline Klein

7163 Andau, Baumhöhäcker 10
T/F: +43 (2176) 40555
info@klein-wein.at, www.klein-wein.at

— NEW —

Winemaker and Contact Person: Jacqueline Klein
Production: n. a. (30 % white, 70 % red)
Hectares: 20
Fairs: ProWein, VieVinum
Distribution partners: CH, DE, MV

Andau, a small village in the middle of the Pannonian Plain, offers ideal terroir for wine cultivation with its high number of sunshine hours and predominantly gravelly, mineral-rich, warm soils. This is the home of the winery of Jacqueline Klein. The dedicated young vintner jumped enthusiastically into the wine business and produced her first wine in 2010. Klein's parents have been grape growers from many years and contribute valuable experience and support to her young enterprise.

Quality is the golden rule. The young winemaker is convinced that the foundation for quality is decided in the vineyard with the production of the most perfect grapes possible. The white wines display finesse. For varieties like Gelber Muskateller (Muscat Blanc à petits grains) and Sauvignon Blanc, Klein places great value on clear structure, crisply pronounced fruit, and varietal character. The main focus though, is the production of classy red wines with depth and character. Zweigelt is the main and favourite grape variety of the vintner. Zweigelt is produced both as a varietal wine as well as an excellent partner in diverse red wine blends. Merlot, Cabernet Sauvignon, and Syrah complete the red wine assortment.

While the white wines are vinified in stainless steel, the red wines are matured in small oak barrels. The choice of oak barrel is made to enhance the expression of site and the character of each grape variety. Wines thus evolve their own unique nuances as well as the personal signature of the winemaker during maturation. Klein's passion for wine is enhanced by her youthful élan and creative thinking and supported by her vinophile knowledge in the production of quite distinctive wines.

93 Syrah 2013
Deep dark ruby with an opaque core, purple highlights, and a thin transparent rim. The attractive bouquet exhibits pronounced varietal character with aromas of blackberry, olive, and nougat. Complex with well-integrated tannins and juicy acidity lending refreshing structure. Sweet fruit with pleasant freshness and a subtle touch of chocolate linger on the finish. Already offering abundant drinking pleasure.

92 Alius 2013 SY/ME
89 Alius 2012 SY/ME

91 Mustum Nobilis 2013 ZW/SY
89 Mustum Nobilis 2012 ZW/SY

91 Zweigelt Exklusiv 2014
91 Zweigelt Exklusiv 2013

90 Neusiedlersee DAC 2015
87 Neusiedlersee DAC 2014

92 Sauvignon Blanc 2015

91 Chardonnay 2015

★ ★ ★ ★ ★

Weinlaubenhof Kracher

7142 Illmitz, Apetloner Straße 37
T: +43 (2175) 3377, F: +43 (2175) 3377 4
office@kracher.at, www.kracher.at

Winemaker and Contact Person: Gerhard Kracher
Production: n. a. (5 % white, 15 % red, 80 % sweet)
Hectares: 32
Fairs: ProWein, Vinexpo
Distribution partners: AUS, I, RUS, J, S, BY, CDN, CH, B, HR, SGP, LV, SK, BG, LT, SLO, RC, L, E, DK, DE, EST, T, FIN, NZ, CZ, F, NL, TR, GR, N, UA, GB, H, USA, IRL, PL, P, IL, RO

I n 1981, the very year that Alois Kracher's father passed on the reigns to him, Gerhard Kracher was born – the next promising generation of a Burgenland vintner family. Gerhard began working in the winery immediately following his studies in economics. He made many international contacts and contributed much with his own ideas and concepts. He planned and managed the remodelling of the winery together with his father and step by step took over responsibility for individual market segments and collected experience with distribution partners in the USA. His father's excellent contacts helped him to quickly find the right partners and allowed him to spread his wings internationally and discover budding trends in wine production and marketing. Gerhard Kracher quickly accumulated solid knowledge and also had the opportunity to taste and explore a vast array of different international wines and wine styles, thus educating his palate as well. He now manages the estate with the support of his wife Yvonne.

The name Kracher has long stood not only for some of the world's most extraordinary sweet wines, but numerous other gourmet products and joint ventures. It is quite an exciting and ambitious presence to which this 35-year-old is heir. Not only a world-famous winery and some of most highly sought wines in the world belong to this legacy, but also a visionary spirit and determination to fulfil potential that Gerhard has taken over from his father.

TBA COLLECTION 2013

93 **Rosenmuskateller Trockenbeerenauslese No. 1**
Nouvelle Vague 2013
92 **Zweigelt Trockenbeerenauslese No. 2**
Nouvelle Vague 2013
92 **Chardonnay Trockenbeerenauslese No. 3**
Nouvelle Vague 2013
93 **Welschriesling Trockenbeerenauslese No. 4**
Zwischen den Seen 2013
96 **Scheurebe Trockenbeerenauslese No. 5**
Zwischen den Seen 2013
94 **Trockenbeerenauslese Grande Cuvée No. 6**
Nouvelle Vague 2013 CH/WR
96 **Welschriesling Trockenbeerenauslese No. 7**
Zwischen den Seen 2013
97 **Scheurebe Trockenbeerenauslese No. 8**
Zwischen den Seen 2013
94 **Red Roses 2013**

TBA COLLECTION 2012

93 **Rosenmuskateller Trockenbeerenauslese No. 1**
Nouvelle Vague 2012
94 **Rosenmuskateller Trockenbeerenauslese No. 2**
Zwischen den Seen 2012
95 **Scheurebe Trockenbeerenauslese No. 3**
Zwischen den Seen 2012
95 **Chardonnay Trockenbeerenauslese No. 4**
Nouvelle Vague 2012
96 **Welschriesling Trockenbeerenauslese No. 5**
Zwischen den Seen 2012

Brilliant gold-yellow. Subtle stone fruit reminiscent of peach and ripe mango with nuances of wild meadow herbs, papaya, and blossom honey. Luscious sweetness is woven into the complex fruit and nicely buffered with juicy acidity. Pineapple and salty minerals join in on the extremely long finish. Still significant baby fat – requires more bottle maturation.

96 Trockenbeerenauslese Grande Cuvée No. 6
Nouvelle Vague 2012 CH/WR
97 Welschriesling Trockenbeerenauslese No. 7
Zwischen den Seen 2012

Brilliant yellow-gold. Fragrant honey, banana, and pineapple with nuances of orange zest and wild herbs. Simultaneously fresh and opulent with luxurious sweet, ripe peach flavour wrapped around a spicy core and buffered with juicy acidity. The tremendous length pairs a salty bite with sweet fruit. Promises a marvellous future with many years of drinking pleasure.

96 Chardonnay No. 8
Nouvelle Vague 2012
97 Muskat Ottonel No. 9
Zwischen den Seen 2012

Deep golden yellow. Intensely fragrant nose exhibits pronounced varietal character with fresh Muscat grapes, nutmeg, hibiscus, and spice. Despite all its concentration, crystal clear and bright on the palate – something achievable only in rare vintages. Luscious sweetness is very well integrated. A perfect fruity, drinkable dessert. Extraordinary enjoyment!

96 Scheurebe Trockenbeerenauslese No. 10
Zwischen den Seen 2012

TBA COLLECTION 2011

93 Traminer Trockenbeerenauslese No. 1
Nouvelle Vague 2011
94 Rosenmuskateller Trockenbeerenauslese No. 2
Nouvelle Vague 2011
93 Rosenmuskateller Trockenbeerenauslese No. 3
Zwischen den Seen 2011
95 Welschriesling No. 4
Zwischen den Seen 2011
94 Chardonnay Trockenbeerenauslese No. 5
Nouvelle Vague 2011
97 Trockenbeerenauslese Grande Cuvée No. 6
Nouvelle Vague 2011 WR/CH
96 Scheurebe Trockenbeerenauslese No. 7
Zwischen den Seen 2011
95 Scheurebe Trockenbeerenauslese No. 8
Zwischen den Seen 2011
96 Muskat Ottonel Trockenbeerenauslese No. 9
Zwischen den Seen 2011

90 Spätlese 2015 WB/CH/PG

92 Beerenauslese 2013 WR/CH
91 Beerenauslese Cuvée 2012 WR/CH

92 Zweigelt Beerenauslese 2012

92 Pinot Gris 2013
90 Pinot Gris 2011

92 Pinot Gris Reserve 2011

91 K 2013 WR/SÄ/CH

91 Grüner Veltliner St. Georg 2013

92 Blend 1 2012 CS/ZW/ME
92 Blend 1 2011 CS/ZW/ME

91 Blend 2 2012 ZW/ME/CS

90 Zweigelt 2011

90 Brut Rosé

★ ★ ★
Weingut Leitner
7122 Gols, Quellengasse 33
T: +43 (2173) 2593, F: +43 (2173) 21547
weingut@leitner-gols.at, www.leitner-gols.at

Winemaker and Contact Person: Gernot Leitner
Production: 65.000 bottles (18 % white, 82 % red)
Hectares: 10
Fairs: ProWein, VieVinum
Distribution partners: CH, SGP, DE, GB

The Leitner winery has been family owned and operated for generations. Melitta and Matthias Leitner took over the estate in 1975 and operated it as a second income until 1990. The decisive new orientation came in the early 1980s. National and international recognition from 1985 onwards inspired them to continue their successful strategy. The next big change came in 1991, as Matthias Leitner gave up his job as travelling salesman to dedicate himself completely to wine production. In the following years the vineyard area was increased to nearly ten hectares. Since January 1st, 2003, also son Gernot Leitner has been working full-time in the family winery and in 2010, he took over management of the estate. The core philosophy of the enterprise is to strive for quality wines that express the character of their terroir. To achieve this, the vineyards are cultivated sustainably. Whatever nature gives is treated with the utmost care in the cellar. The Altenberg, Ungerberg, Salzberg, and Schafleiten vineyards count among the very best sites in Gols and it is there that the Leitner family wines are sourced. The Leitner winery is a founding member of the "Pannobile" vintner association.

93 Blaufränkisch Ungerberg 2013
Deep ruby with purple highlights and a broad, slightly paler rim. Delicate notes of cherry and blackberry with subtle spice and liquorice comprise an inviting bouquet. Medium complexity with sweet red berry fruit laced with fine grained tannin. Wonderful mineral character joins in on the finish. Good ageing potential.
92 Blaufränkisch Ungerberg 2012
92 Blaufränkisch Ungerberg 2011

92 Zweigelt Altenberg 2013
92 Zweigelt Altenberg 2012

89 Zweigelt Heideboden 2012
90 Zweigelt Heideboden 2011

(92–94) Syrah Dorflagen 2014

92 Syrah Schafleiten 2013
92 Syrah Schafleiten 2012

(89–91) St. Laurent Dorflagen 2014

(92–94) Pannobile 2014 ZW/LE
91 Pannobile 2013 ZW/BF/SL
91 Pannobile rot 2012 ZW/BF

93 Pannobile Salzberg Pinot Blanc 2014
93 Pannobile weiß Salzberg 2013 WB
Brilliant gold-yellow. Nuances of ripe pineapple mingle with apricot on the nose. Juicy acidity refreshes the creamy texture. Good complexity with pineapple and mineral components on the finale. Good potential for further development.
92 Pannobile Salzberg 2012 WB

92 Pinot Blanc Salzberg 2015
91 Pinot Blanc Salzberg 2014

89 Gemischter Satz Breitenacker 2015

Josef Lentsch – Dankbarkeit

7141 Podersdorf/See, Hauptstraße 39
T: +43 (2177) 2223, F: +43 DW 4
office@dankbarkeit.at, www.dankbarkeit.at

Winemaker and Contact Person: Josef Lentsch
Production: 30.000 bottles (30 % white, 40 % red, 30 % sweet)
Hectares: 1,5 + 5
Distribution partners: CH, DK, DE, GB, PL

Two hearts beat in the chest of Josef Lentsch: one heart operates a restaurant that has been in the family for generations; the other loves the cultivation of wine with a passion. The "Gasthaus zur Dankbarkeit" is an important starting point in the region for hungry and thirsty epicureans. A decisive point is the use of delicious regional products that are found in the immediate vicinity. This also offers a very good possibility to gain an overview not only of the Lentsch wines, but also of those from all of Burgenland. Josef is an ambassador for his vintner colleagues and the numerous producers of gourmet delicacies in the region. Lentsch also offers guest accommodations since 2016.

The enterprising restaurateur always has an eye on his winery, which despite its small size of only two vineyard hectares always has a brave experiment or two going. Long-term contracted winegrowers help supplement the wine volume. Most interesting are the Pinot Gris and Pinot Noir, which in suitable years are also produced as noble sweet wines. The Karmarzik vineyard is Lentsch's favourite site and is situated directly on Lake Neusiedl facing the "Hölle", the deepest point in Austria. The soil is pure alluvial sand, which enhances the expression of fruit. Despite moderate acidity, the wines are harmonious and have good ageing capacity. All of the vineyards are located in the Neusiedler See – Seewinkel National Park. In addition to Pinot Gris and Pinot Noir, Welschriesling and Pinot Blanc also find ideal conditions. Josef Lentsch has received numerous accolades and honours for his dedicated efforts as a restaurateur and wine producer as well as for his achievements in serving all of Burgenland. Lentsch is a true family enterprise.

93 Welschriesling Trockenbeerenauslese 2009
Pale amber with gold highlights. Delicate layers of tobacco, herbs and spice are wrapped around a subtle core of dried pear and dried apricot. Silky texture with well-integrated sweetness. Pleasant mineral character, yellow peach and honey linger sweetly on the finish. Dependable ageing potential.

96 Welschriesling Trockenbeerenauslese Schrammel 2012
93 Welschriesling Beerenauslese Schrammel 2011

93 Pinot Noir 2012
92 Pinot Noir 2011
92 Pinot Noir 2010

89 Dankbarkeit rot 2013 ZW/PN/SL
89 Dankbarkeit rot 2012 ZW/PN/SL
90 Dankbarkeit rot 2011 ZW/PN/SL

89 Blaufränkisch Wachstum Christine Lentsch 2013

93 Pinot Gris 2013
Deep yellow with gold highlights. Ripe pear is found over a background of fine oak spice and nuances of tropical yellow fruit. Powerful and creamy with juicy acidity pleasantly lifting ripe pineapple flavour to the fore. Sweetly extracted fruit remains on the aftertaste. Dependable ageing potential.

91 Pinot Gris 2012
92 Pinot Gris 2011

88 Gelber Muskateller Muskat³ Wachstum Christine Lentsch 2015
89 Gelber Muskateller Muskat³ Wachstum Christine 2014
89 Dankbarkeit weiss 2014 PG/WB/NB
89 Dankbarkeit weiß 2012 PG/WB/NB

★ ★
Weingut Münzenrieder
7143 Apetlon, Wallerner Straße 27
T: +43 (2175) 2259, F: +43 (2175) 2259 6, M: +43 (676) 7014971
info@muenzenrieder.at, www.muenzenrieder.at

Winemaker and Contact Person: Johann and Johannes Münzenrieder
Production: n. a. (10 % white, 60 % red, 30 % sweet)
Hectares: 22
Fairs: VieVinum, Vinexpo, ProWein, Prodexpo Moskau
Distribution partners: J, S, B, CDN, CH, SGP, RC, DK, DE, FIN, NL, GB, USA, PL

The Münzenrieder winery is located in Apetlon amongst the numerous small salt ponds that are so typical for the Seewinkel area. This winery is famed first and foremost for their wonderfully balanced sweet predicated wines. Yet the typical terroir character is reflected in the entire assortment of this family's wines. When son Johannes joined the winery, he brought fresh new ideas and not only created a red wine blend called "Mavie", but remodelled the cave and the sales room. Due to their harmonious combination of sweetness, acidity and fruitiness, the white wine varieties Sämling (Scheurebe), Welschriesling and Grüner Veltliner are best suited for the production of their typical regional beerenauslese, trockenbeerenauslese and eiswein (ice wine). The winery can also show good qualities with Zweigelt and Blaufränkisch as well as blends from Zweigelt, Cabernet Sauvignon, and Merlot. Family Münzenrieder efforts are seen to increase with the dry white wines as well. International accolades and the frequent nominations in the Austrian Wine Salon as well as the success on the export market testify to the good qualities produced here.

93 Sämling 88 Trockenbeerenauslese 2013
Pale golden yellow. The attractive bouquet displays botrytis spice, dried pear, and pineapple over nuances of blossom honey and peach. Luxurious sweetness is elegantly buffered by juicy, well-integrated acid. Sweet fruit, nougat and salty piquancy linger on the finish.

94 Sämling 88 Trockenbeerenauslese 2011

(89–91) Sämling 88 Beerenauslese 2015
92 Sämling 88 Beerenauslese 2012

87 Sämling 88 Spätlese 2012

(93–95) Welschriesling Trockenbeerenauslese Siddartha 2015

90 Heideboden Spätlese 2015 SÄ/SB/BO

91 Cuvée Eiswein 2012 GV/WR

90 Zweigelt Beerenauslese 2013

(90–92) Blauer Zweigelt Illmitzerweg 2015
91 Neusiedlersee DAC Reserve Illmitzerweg 2013
89 Neusiedlersee DAC Reserve Illmitzerweg 2012

89 Heideboden Reserve 2014 ZW/BF/ME
90 Heideboden Reserve 2011 ZW/ME/BF/CS

92 Mavie 2013 ZW/ME/CS
89 Mavie 2012 ZW/CS/ME

(91–93) Chardonnay Reserve - C9 2015
91 Chardonnay Reserve C7 2013
91 Chardonnay C6 2011

89 Chardonnay Heideboden 2014

★ ★ ★
Weingut PMC Münzenrieder

7143 Apetlon, Triftgasse 31
T: +43 (2175) 26700, F: +43 (2175) 26701, M: +43 (699) 13311583
office@weingut-pmc.at, www.weingut-pmc.at

Winemaker: Christoph Münzenrieder
Contact Person: Peter Münzenrieder
Production: n. a. (15 % white, 55 % red, 30 % sweet)
Hectares: 20
Fairs: VieVinum, ProWein, Prodexpo
Distribution partners: RUS, J, RC, DE, NL

The winery of the brothers Peter and Christoph Münzenrieder is located right next to the Langen Lacke biotope in the heart of the Lake Neusiedl Seewinkel National Park. Standing in front of the winery, one recognizes the architectural interpretation from the memorable wine label. The tasting room offers a view into the impressive oak barrel cellar where the single vineyard wines mature at optimal temperature and humidity. The brothers' philosophy of single vineyard vinification for enhancing the expression of terroir serves their wines well. From the series, four wines are particularly worthy of mention: Pinot Noir, Chardonnay, Sauvignon Blanc and Zweigelt from the Neubruch vineyard, one of the best sites for Burgundian varieties in Apetlon. Zweigelt is the most important variety for this producer and it brings exceptional quality in Neusiedlersee where it obviously feels quite comfortable. The flagship blend "Diabolus" (the red devil) is made from the broad selection of small wine charges that were all harvested and vinified separately. "Auratum TBA" is the estate's liquid gold, which is blended and bottled after long maturation in small oak barrels. Some of the world's very best producers of botrytized sweet wines are found in the Seewinkel area of the Neusiedlersee wine region. With innumerable international gold medals and accolades for their sweet white and red predicated wines, the Münzenrieder brothers are among these fine producers. The PMC wines can be found on wine lists of prestigious restaurants around the world.

93 Trockenbeerenauslese Auratum 2013 CH/SÄ
Medium gold yellow. Aromas and flavours of delicate dried fruit, subtle botrytis spice, ripe peach, apricot jam, orange zest, and honey. Luxuriously sweet with juicy, tropical yellow fruit and a long finish. Will benefit from further bottle maturation.
94 Trockenbeerenauslese Auratum 2012 WR/CH

(92–94) Scheurebe Trockenbeerenauslese 2015
92 Scheurebe TBA 2012

93 Welschriesling TBA 2012

(92–94) Grüner Veltliner
     Trockenbeerenauslese 2015

(93–95) Chardonnay Trockenbeerenauslese 2015
93 Chardonnay Trockenbeerenauslese 2011

(91–93) Muskat Ottonel
     Trockenbeerenauslese 2015

92 Beerenauslese 2013 CH/SÄ/WR

89 Diabolus 2013 ZW/ME/BF
89 Diabolus 2012 ZW/ME/BF
90 Diabolus 2011 ZW/ME/BF

(88–90) Heideboden Reserve 2014 ZW/SL/BF

91 Merlot 2013
91 Merlot 2012
91 Merlot 2011

89 Sauvignon Blanc 2015
92 Sauvignon Blanc Neubruch 2013
Pale green-yellow. Mango, pineapple, and pear over a background of grass, herbs and delicate blossom honey nuances. Juicy acid lends an elegant, fine structure. White vineyard peach and tobacco notes join in on the long finish. Very good ageing potential.
90 Sauvignon Blanc Neubruch 2012

Weingut Pittnauer

7122 Gols, Neubaugasse 90
T: +43 (2173) 3407, F: +43 (2173) 20088
weingut@pittnauer.com, www.pittnauer.com

ORGANIC

Winemaker: Gerhard Pittnauer
Contact Person: Brigitte Pittnauer
Production: 160.000 bottles (3 % white, 97 % red)
Hectares: 15 + 10
Fairs: VieVinum, ProWein
Distribution partners: on request

There has been much discussion and philosophizing about the growing sameness of wines versus wines with a unique signature in recent years. It is the declared goal of many winemakers to produce wines that reflect their origin. This includes the soil in which vines root, the climate to which they are exposed and the people behind the scenes that make the wine. Gerhard and Brigitte Pittnauer achieved uniqueness at the very latest when they converted their vineyards to biodynamic cultivation. Unperturbed by fashions and trends, the vintner couple remains dedicated to the autochthon St. Laurent as their leading variety like no other producer in Gols. The "Pittis" are convinced of this variety's potential on the cool, well-aerated plateau on the south edge of the Parndorf Plain. The calcareous gravelly soils are also advantageous for this botrytis-susceptible variety. The St. Laurent Rosenberg 2011 convinced the jury of the "Falstaff Red Wine Guide 2014" and was champion for this variety.

The components for the "Pannobile" blend are sourced from the loamy southwest-facing slope above Gols and Weiden (Blaufränkisch) and from the humus-rich escarpment of the Parndorf Plateau as it slopes gently towards the Heideboden (Zweigelt). The Pittnauers have abstained from the use of cultivated yeasts, enzymes and massive use of new oak since 2006. Vinification decisions are not based on laboratory results, but on tasting and intuition. The results are vibrant wines with good aging potential and pronounced regional expression that have a unique style far beyond the mainstream. Gerhard Pittnauer was named "Falstaff Vintner of the Year 2014".

(94–96) Merlot Altenberg Reserve 2013
95 Merlot Altenberg Reserve 2012
Deep dark ruby with an opaque core, purple highlights and a discreet transparent rim. Blackberry jam with notes of sea buckthorn, rosehips and orange zest over a background of intense chocolate. Powerful and full-bodied with abundant firm tannins and attractive toasty notes bedded in fruit and flowers. A touch of nougat joins in on the finale and lingers long. Plenty of drinking enjoment guaranteed for many years.
95 Merlot Altenberg Reserve 2011

93 St. Laurent Altenberg 2013
Dark ruby with purple highlights and slightly paler rim. Blackberry jam, a touch of candied orange peel and subtle nougat over a background of herbs and spices. Ripe wild cherry flavours, silky tannins and pleasantly refreshed with juicy acidity. Red berries flavour the finale. A light-footed wine with good length.
92 St. Laurent Altenberg 2012
92 St. Laurent Altenberg 2011

92 St. Laurent Rosenberg 2013
94 Sankt Laurent Rosenberg 2012
94 Sankt Laurent Rosenberg 2011

(91–93) St. Laurent vom Dorf 2015
90 St. Laurent Dorflagen 2014
91 St. Laurent Dorflagen 2013

93 Pinot Noir Baumgarten 2012
94 Pinot Noir Baumgarten 2011

(90–92) Pinot Noir vom Dorf 2015

(92–94) Blaufränkisch Ungerberg 2014
92 Blaufränkisch Ungerberg 2013
93 Blaufränkisch Ungerberg 2012

92 Blaufränkisch Rosenberg 2013
93 Blaufränkisch Rosenberg 2012
93 Blaufränkisch Rosenberg 2011

92 Blaufränkisch Dogma 2013
93 Blaufränkisch Bühl 2013
95 Blaufränkisch Bühl 2011

(91–93) Pannobile 2014 ZW/BF
92 Pannobile 2013 BF/ZW/SL
92 Pannobile 2012 ZW/BF/SL

90–92) red pitt 2015 ZW/LE/ME
90 red pitt 2012 ZW/BF/ME
90 pitti 2012 BF/ZW

90 mash pitt 2014 CH/SB/GV

(90–92) Rosé Dogma 2015
89 Rosé 2014
90 Pittnauer Rosé 2013

Weingut Claus Preisinger

7122 Gols, Goldbergstraße 60
T: +43 (2173) 2592, F: +43 (2173) 20000
wein@clauspreisinger.at, www.clauspreisinger.at

ORGANIC

Winemaker and Contact Person: Claus Preisinger
Production: n. a. (15 % white, 85 % red)
Hectares: 18
Fairs: VieVinum, ProWein, RAW – The Artisan Wine Fair London, Millésime Bio
Distribution partners: AUS, I, S, CDN, CH, B, SGP, SK, LT, E, DK, DE, CZ,
F, NL, GB, H, USA, IRL, PL

Should one come knocking at Claus Preisinger's door as a friend or acquaintance, you'll first be served an incredibly good espresso – fragrant, dark, intense, multifaceted, organic, fair trade, freshly roasted, and of course without milk, sugar or other diluting substances. Just the real stuff. Only what is pure and authentic is interesting. And this is how Preisinger is with his vines, his life, his work, and of course, his wines. Manual labour in the vineyard and cellar, biodynamic cultivation, spontaneous fermentation, and little or no intervention in the cellar – everything is kept as natural as possible. It is all about the grape variety, the soil, the region, and the vintage. This naturally raises a few eyebrows, especially since his extremely puristic methods often result in wines beyond the mainstream. But what is for some a "no-go" is for others a "bring-it-on" and the fact is that his most exceptional and unique wines are reserved for purchase even before they are bottled.

Fortunately, you don't necessarily have to go that far to enjoy the wines of Claus Preisinger. Even the classic wines, for which Preisinger employs solid instinctive handcraftsmanship more than creative genius, are brilliant. From uncomplicated entry-level wines through the Burgenland varietal classics, Claus Preisinger's signature is recognisable not only in the bottle, but on the label and stands for naturalness, individuality, and strength of character. This is a signature that one enjoys "reading" repeatedly.

95 Pinot Noir 2014
94 Pinot Noir 2013
Medium ruby with garnet highlights and a broad transparent rim. Delicate raspberry jam, liquorice, mandarin zest, and floral components. Complex and red berried with medium bodied and silky tannin. The long finish features red fruit and salty-minerals. A delicate representative of the variety.
93 Pinot Noir 2012

(94–96) Blaufränkisch Bühl 2013
94 Blaufränkisch Bühl 2012
Deep ruby with an opaque core, purple highlights, and a thin transparent rim. Blackberry and elegant balsamic nuances with notes of cool smoke, tobacco, nougat and intense spice. Abundant chocolaty textured tannins lend a good frame to the complex, very spicy flavours. A powerful wine with very good length that will benefit from extended bottle maturation.
94 Blaufränkisch Bühl 2011

(91–93) Blaufränkisch Kalkstein 2015
89 Blaufränkisch Kalkstein 2014

90 Blaufränkisch 2013

94 St. Laurent 2012
93 Sankt Laurent 2011

(89–91) Zweigelt Kieselstein 2015
88 Zweigelt Kieselstein 2014
90 Zweigelt 2013

(91–93) Pannobile 2014 ZW/LE
92 Pannobile 2013 ZW/BF
93 Zweigelt Pannobile 2012

93 Paradigma 2013 BF/ME
93 Paradigma 2012 BF/ME
95 Paradigma 2011 BF/ME

91 Heideboden 2013 ZW/BF/ME
92 Heideboden rot 2012 ZW/BF/ME
91 Heideboden rot 2011 ZW/BF/ME

93 Weißer Burgunder
    ErDELuftGRAsundreBEN 2014
95 Weißburgunder maischevergoren
    Erdeluftgrasundreben 2012

(92–94) Kalkundkiesel 2015 GV/WB

93 Grüner Veltliner »gv« maischevergoren 2013
91 Grüner Veltliner 2012

92 Heideboden weiß 2014 WB/GV/CH
92 Heideboden weiß 2013 WB/CH
90 Heideboden 2012

Weingut Hannes Reeh

7163 Andau, Augasse 11a
T: +43 (2176) 27011, F: +43 (2176) 27011 40
wein@hannesreeh.at, www.hannesreeh.at

Winemaker: Hannes Reeh and Herbert Götzinger
Contact Person: Hannes Reeh and Kathrin Markl-Reeh
Production: n. a. (20 % white, 80 % red)
Hectares: 50
Fairs: VieVinum, ProWein
Distribution partners: RUS, J, S, CH, SGP, SK, RC, L, DK, DE, FIN, CZ, NL, N, GB, H, USA, PL

Hannes Reeh is an unconventional winemaker in Andau, Burgenland. He embodies a leisurely lifestyle, yet consequently strives towards his goals. He undertakes the winemaking duties personally. The estate is a reflection of Hannes Reeh himself – an interesting mixture of family tradition, New World experience, regional authenticity, unbridled belief in the future, and strong Burgenland roots. He works with uninhibited intuition, doing exactly what he loves most, and he is successful at it. Andau is the wine village on the far eastern edge of the Seewinkel sub-region of Neusiedlersee bordering Hungary. The vines thrive with 2,400 hours of sunshine in one of the sunniest and driest parts of Austria. The soils are predominantly gravel and yield wines of exceptional power, depth, and ripeness.The wines appear in three different ranges. The "Klassik" range comprises varietal wines that offer uncomplicated, everyday drinking pleasure. "Heideboden" is represented by two charming blends, one white and one red, which highlight the best attributes of the Seewinkel. "Unplugged" are the specialties of Hannes Reeh that are produced without much adornment, but with plenty of feeling. "Unplugged" is Andau pure – no fining enzymes nor cultivated yeasts are used.

(91–93) Zweigelt Unplugged 2015
91 Zweigelt Unplugged 2014
Dark ruby with purple highlights and a transparent rim. Wild forest berries, bright cherry and subtle oak spice, orange zest and nougat. Medium complexity, silky sweet fruit, pleasant tannins, and a subtle touch of chocolate on the finish.
92 Zweigelt Unplugged 2013

89 Neusiedlersee DAC 2015
89 Neusiedlersee DAC 2014
89 Neusiedlersee DAC 2013

91 Merlot Unplugged 2013
93 Merlot Unplugged 2012
92 Merlot Unplugged 2011

90 Cabernet Sauvignon Unplugged 2014
91 Cabernet Sauvignon Unplugged 2012

89 Heideboden Rot 2014 ZW/SL/CS/ME
90 Heideboden Rot 2013 ZW/SL/ME/CS
89 Heideboden Rot 2012 ZW/SL/ME/CS

93 Chardonnay Unplugged 2015
91 Chardonnay Unplugged 2014
91 Chardonnay Unplugged 2013

91 Heideboden Weiss 2015 SB/WB/CH
89 Heideboden Weiss 2014 SB/CH/WR
89 Heideboden weiß 2012 SB/WB/WR

★ ★ ★

Weingut Erich Scheiblhofer

7163 Andau, Halbturner Straße 1a
T: +43 (2176) 2610, F: +43 (2176) 2610 4
office@scheiblhofer.at, www.scheiblhofer.at

Winemaker: Erich Scheiblhofer
Contact Person: Erich and Harald Scheiblhofer
Hectares: 65
Fairs: VieVinum, ProWein
Distribution partners: on request

Erich Scheiblhofer is among the young garde of Burgenland that are receiving recognition for their excellent red wines. The young vintner travelled the world gathering experience from masters in the field in California and Australia before founding his own winery in 1999. His first vintage in 2000 brought him regional awards for his most important wine, the "Zweigelt Prädium". The following vintage brought him the national award, the Falstaff Grand Prix, for his Zweigelt, and the next year third place. Further premium wines from this young, dedicated vintner are Merlot and Shiraz, also from the Prädium vineyard. The Merlot 2002 and 2004, the Cabernet Sauvignon 2008 and 2010, and the Shiraz 2013 were Falstaff champions of their variety. The young winery receives high accolades not only nationally, but also wins either a regional or state championship nearly every year. He also breaks international records for Austrian wine: at the world's largest wine competition, the AWC, he won the title "Winery of the Year" in 7 of 9 years. The vintage 2011 has brought him the greatest international furore to date. Markus del Monego and Andreas Larsson awarded the blend "Big John" 94.5 points as the best wine of Austria with his blend "Legends" close on its heels with 93.5 points. No less spectacular are the 19/20 points from René Gabriel for the Cabernet Sauvignon and Blaufränkisch blend called "Jois".

(89–91) Shiraz Perfection 2014
92 Shiraz Perfection 2013
Deep ruby with an opaque core, purple highlights and a thin, transparent rim. Intense oak spice, black cherry, and a touch of liquorice over a background of olives, nougat, smoked bacon, and heather. Blackberry fruit and discreet extract sweetness are wonderfully structured with juicy acidity. Good length. The obvious oak notes will integrate with further bottle maturation.
91 Shiraz Perfection 2012

(91–93) Merlot Perfection 2014
91 Merlot Perfection 2013
92 Merlot Perfection 2012

(90–92) Cabernet Sauvignon Perfection 2014
91 Cabernet Sauvignon Perfection 2013
92 Cabernet Sauvignon Perfection 2012

(91–93) Blaufränkisch Jois 2014
90 Blaufränkisch Jois 2013
89 Blaufränkisch Jois 2012

(91–93) Blaufränkisch Mordor 2013

(91–93) Zweigelt Prädium 2015
90 Zweigelt Prädium 2014
92 Zweigelt Prädium 2013

(89–91) Legends 2014 ME/CS
91 Legends 2013 CS/ME
Deep ruby with an opaque core, purple highlights and a thin transparent rim. Sweet juniper spice, a touch of vanilla, and blackberry jam comprise an inviting bouquet. Fine-grained tannins are nicely woven into juicy, sweet fruit. Dried fruit and mineral notes linger on the finish.
90 Legends 2012 ME/CS

(90–92) Chardonnay Perfection 2015

★★★★
Hans Tschida – Angerhof

7142 Illmitz, Angergasse 5
T: +43 (2175) 3150, F: +43 (2175) 3150 4
weingut@angerhof-tschida.at, www.angerhof-tschida.at

Winemaker: Hans Tschida
Contact Person: Hans and Lisa Tschida
Production: n. a. (30 % red, 70 % sweet)
Hectares: 30
Fairs: VieVinum, ProWein, Vinexpo
Distribution partners: on request

One finds many of the world's best sweet wine makers in Burgenland and one of them is Hans Tschida from Illmitz. He consistently strives for the absolute best quality grapes in the vineyard and together with his sensitive hand in the cellar, he succeeds in making award-winning wines. Predicated sweet wines represent 70% of his production. The climate in the Seewinkel sub-region on the east shore of Lake Neusiedl is predestined for the production of botrytized wines. The timing could not be more perfect – just as grapes have accumulated enough sugar, autumnal morning fog appears and desirable noble rot affects the grapes nearly overnight. What is a nightmare for the red wine vintners in northern Burgenland, is a gift of nature for sweet wine specialists. As far as style goes, the Angerhof wines are distinguished by clear varietal character and elegance. They are vinified fairly reductivly and Hans Tschida prefers somewhat lower sugar content. Viscous, sticky essences are not his thing; the drinkability of his products is of utmost importance to him. Tschida is a fan of the Lüss vineyard because the wines from this site usually have one milligram per litre more acidity. Sämling is perhaps the variety that has won the winery the most fame. This producer also offers excellent spätlese and auslese, which are a wonderful introduction to the sweet wine theme. But once you try the higher predicates, you will never want to miss them.

97 Muskat Ottonel Schilfwein 2012
Medium yellow with silver highlights. A nearly Gewürztraminer-like nose exhibits intense floral notes of mallow and lily of the valley. Exotic fruit notes and luxurious sweetness are refreshed with good acidity. White pepper and nutmeg join in on the extraordinarily long finish. An explosion of aromas and flavours.

92 Muskat Ottonel Auslese 2015
93 Muskat Ottonel Auslese 2013

94 Chardonnay Beerenauslese 2013
90 Chardonnay Beerenauslese 2012

95 Sämling 88 Trockenbeerenauslese 2012
Deep yellow with gold highlights. Intense floral fragrance reminiscent of frangipani is accompanied by lemongrass and sweet pineapple. Juicy, refreshing acidity lends vibrance to the lusciously sweet, exotic fruit. Sweet honey and lime zest remain on the long finish.

92 Sämling 88 Beerenauslese 2013
94 Sämling 88 Beerenauslese 2012
93 Sämling 88 Beerenauslese 2011

93 Sauvignon Blanc Trockenbeerenauslese 2013

93 Sauvignon Blanc Beerenauslese 2013
92 Sauvignon Blanc Beerenauslese 2012
93 Sauvignon Blanc Beerenauslese 2011

92 Zweigelt Schilfwein 2012
93 Zweigelt Schilfwein 2011

93 Welschriesling Beerenauslese 2012
92 Welschriesling Beerenauslese 2011

95 Gelber Muskateller Eiswein 2012

92 Illmitzer Spätlese 2015 TR/NB/RR/SÄ/MO

91 Spätlese 2015 WR/WB/CH/SB

92 Auslese 2015 WR/TR/CH/SB
92 Auslese 2013 WB/TR/CH/WR

★★★★
Weingut Velich

7143 Apetlon, Seeufergasse 12
T: +43 (2175) 3187, F: +43 (2175) 3187 4, M: +43 (664) 4216843
weingut@velich.at, www.velich.at

Winemaker and Contact Person: Heinz Velich
Production: 50.000 bottles (80 % white, 20 % sweet)
Hectares: 12
Fairs: ProWein, Summa, VieVinum
Distribution partners: I, RUS, CH, B, SK, DK, DE, F, NL, H, USA, PL

The Velich family winery is situated in the heart of the wildlife preservation area in the Seewinkel district on Lake Neusiedl. Several small saltwater ponds surround Apetlon and contribute advantageously to the microclimate. Heinz Velich cultivates ten hectares of vineyards planted with white wine varieties. 45 % of the vineyard area is dedicated to Chardonnay, 25 % to Welschriesling, and the rest to Muskat Ottonel, Bouvier, and Sämling (Scheurebe). The light, fruity wines from Welschriesling and Muskat Ottonel are vinified in stainless steel. Concentrated, full-bodied Chardonnay is fermented in oak. The "Chardonnay Tiglat" is consistently one of the best examples of the variety in Austria. A second "Chardonnay Darscho", and a blend of Chardonnay, Welschriesling, and Sauvignon Blanc called "TO" (which means "lake" in Hungarian) are also produced. Sweet wines are produced in suitable vintages and partially vinified in small oak barrels. This winery pursues high physiological ripeness and typical regional character. Heinz Velich is the winner of Falstaff magazine's Vintner of the Year award in 2012.

94 Chardonnay Tiglat 2013
96 Chardonnay Tiglat 2012
Medium green-yellow. After aeration, the rather restrained nose displays subtle notes of mandarin zest, shaved almond, and floral components with chalky nuances and a touch of coconut. Elegantly structured with juicy acidity and a silky texture. Litchi and almond linger with salty minerals and blossom honey on the tremendously long finish. Displays impressive old vine character. Decanting recommended.
95 Tiglat 2011 CH

93 Chardonnay Darscho 2013
94 Chardonnay Darscho 2012
93 Darscho 2011 CH

95 Chardonnay The other side 2011

92 TO 2013 CH/SB/WR
92 TO 2012 CH/SB/WR
91 TO 2011 CH/SB/WR

(92–94) Welschriesling Trockenbeerenauslese 2007
100 Welschriesling Trockenbeerenauslese 2006
Deep mahogany colour with orange highlights and a reddish shimmer. Intense botrytis spice reminiscent of dried fig and honey mingles with lingonberry jam and candied orange peel. Juicy acidity structure lends finesse to sweet stone fruit; the raciness makes the significant residual sugar nearly disappear. An "old school" sweet wine in a most positive sense, drawing similarities to great German Riesling TBAs.

(92–94) Sämling 88 Trockenbeerenauslese 2007
97 Scheurebe Sämling TBA 2006

94 Seewinkel Beerenauslese 2010 CH/SÄ/WR
94 Beerenauslese Seewinkel 2009 WR/SÄ

★ ★ ★
Weingut Zantho
7163 Andau, Dammweg 1a
T: +43 (2176) 27077, F: +43 (2176) 27078
office@zantho.com, www.zantho.com

Winemaker: Wolfgang Peck and Christopher Eisinger
Contact Person: Thomas Gratzer
Production: 600.000 bottles (25 % white, 70 % red, 5 % sweet)
Hectares: 100
Fairs: VieVinum, ProWein, Vinexpo
Distribution partners: RO, I, RUS, J, S, B, CDN, CH, ROK, LV, SK, RC, DK, L, DE, EST, FIN, F, CZ, NL, GB, N, HK, H, USA, IRL, PL

Leading winemakers Josef Umathum and Wolfgang Peck embarked on a new venture in Burgenland quality wine with "Zantho". The project is a perfect symbiosis of many years of experience, best technology, and optimal environmental conditions. The wines are produced at the Winzerkeller Andau, one of the most modern vinification facilities in Austria. A small group of selected grape growers from the Winzerkeller Andau cooperative, trained and supervised by Josef Umathum, deliver the fruit that is destined specifically for "Zantho". Zantho, the historic name of the wine village Andau at the time of its first written documentation, is now the name for an established brand of wines that has a Pannonian lizard as its logo. Predominantly red wines are produced from regional varieties: "Zantho" Zweigelt, St. Laurent, Blaufränkisch, Pinot Noir, and Zweigelt Reserve. A sparkling wine produced from Pinot Noir and St. Laurent according to the traditional method of bottle fermentation joined the assortment last year. White wines include "Zantho" Muskat (Muscat), Sauvignon Blanc, Welschriesling and Grüner Veltliner and noble sweet wines are also made in suitable years. The goal is to produce wines from indigenous Austrian grape varieties in a relevant volume for international export. The wines are available in well-sorted specialty shops, restaurants, ex-cellar and the online shop.

90 Zweigelt Reserve 2013
Dark ruby with purple highlights and a transparent rim. Ripe plum fruit with traces of wild red berries and subtle herbal spice. Juicy fruit reminiscent of strawberry and cherry are nicely structured with refreshing acidity. Medium long finish.
90 Zantho Zweigelt Reserve 2011

(90–92) **Zweigelt 2015**
91 **Zweigelt 2013**
89 **Zweigelt 2012**

(88–90) **Sankt Laurent 2014**
89 **Sankt Laurent 2013**
89 **St. Laurent 2012**

89 **Sankt Laurent Reserve 2013**

(89–91) **Blaufränkisch 2015**
90 **Blaufränkisch 2013**
91 **Blaufränkisch 2012**

(87–89) **Pinot Noir 2015**
89 **Pinot Noir 2013**

87 **Pink 2015**

89 **Grüner Veltliner 2015**
88 **Grüner Veltliner 2012**

88 **Muskat Ottonel 2015**
89 **Muskat Ottonel 2014**
89 **Muskat Ottonel 2013**

87 **Sauvignon Blanc 2015**
88 **Sauvignon Blanc 2014**
88 **Sauvignon Blanc 2013**

89 **Welschriesling 2015**
89 **Welschriesling 2014**

(91–93) **Trockenbeerenauslese 2015 TR/RR**

92 **Trockenbeerenauslese 2013 SÄ/WR**

(91–93) **Scheurebe Beerenauslese 2015**

90 **Zantho Brut Rosé PN/SL**

Weingut Ziniel

7161 St. Andrä/Zicksee, Hauptstraße 47
T: +43 (2176) 2116, F: +43 (2176) 2116 4
office@ziniel.at, www.ziniel.at

Winemaker: Andreas Ziniel
Contact Person: Elisabeth, Andreas and Wolfgang Ziniel
Production: n. a. (50 % white, 45 % red, 5 % sweet)
Hectares: 18,5
Fairs: ProWein, VieVinum
Distribution partners: CH, SK, DE, PL

A cool and bold statement is being made in the heart of the Seewinkel with a line of wines that range from classic dry white wines to reds from the St. Laurent variety to exceptional sweet "Schilfwein". This is pure "coolness"! Not just casual cool, but edgy, like Cool Jazz. Not trendy, but consequent with handpicked grapes from traditional varieties from estate fruit. Taking into consideration that the Ziniels are newcomers rather than veterans, the question as to just where this self-confident lightness comes is legitimate. It could well be that the young winemaker Andreas gained this from apprenticing with legendary producers like "John" Nittnaus, Schäfer-Fröhlich in Germany, Baumann in Switzerland and De Trafford in South Africa. It is certainly also true that the Ziniels must be slaves to the market. Other than Andreas, the rest of the family has other occupations, which allow them the freedom of making no compromises. Father Alfred is an agriculturist and responsible for soil and vineyard management. Brother Wolfgang is a scientist and supports Andreas with vinification and style. Mother Elisabeth takes care of internal matters and everything that has to do with communication, distribution and generally keeping the family on track.

Above everything else, the Ziniel family is dedicated to sustainability. They value long term partnerships and do not readily throw things overboard. This is something that their loyal ex-cellar customers appreciate. This is a win-win situation for it allows the Ziniels direct feedback from their customers, which they can consider immediately in their work.

By the way, the tiny village of St. Andrä am Zicksee, where the Ziniels are located, is geographically exactly there where "Z" is located in the alphabet. At the very end. Or at the very beginning, depending on how you look at it. With this in mind, it is certainly worthwhile to broaden your horizon towards the most eastern end of Austria.

(89–91) St. Laurent St. Andräer Johannishöhe 2014
93 St. Laurent St. Andräer Johannishöhe 2013

91 Neusiedlersee DAC Reserve Hutweide 2013

(89–91) Zweigelt 2014

92 Zeta 2014 ZW/ME/CS
88 Zeta 2013 ME/ZW/CS

90 Zicksee Cuvée 2013 ME/CS/ZW

92 Chardonnay St. Andräer Heulage 2014
92 Chardonnay St. Andräer Heulage Reserve 2013

89 Weißer Burgunder 2015

96 Gelber Muskateller Schilfwein 2013
Pale golden yellow. White vineyard peach, litchi, lime and nutmeg comprise a fascinating and intense bouquet. Luscious, creamy sweetness is perfectly countered by juicy acidity, which lends plenty of vibrant appeal. Ripe peach and mineral remain on the extremely long finish. This wine seems to dance on the tongue and is an extraordinary liquid dessert.

93 Beerenauslese 2013 WR/GM

Fabulous quality in red, white and sweet wines

On the west side of Lake Neusiedl at the foot of the Leithagebirge (Leitha Mountains) is the Neusiedlersee-Hügelland region, home to Austria's trilogy of wine styles. A proud historic wine culture and very unique geology contribute to the strong regional identity.

The 3,576 vineyard hectares in Neusiedlersee-Hügelland offer a diversity of high-quality wine styles that is difficult to exceed. This is not surprising considering the region's geography and geology. The Leithagebirge (Leitha mountains) are the last foot hills of the Alps, a worn and weathered ridge of acidic crystalline schist and gneiss, that was also once the shore of an ancient sea that left marine limestone deposits, known locally as "Leithakalk". The Leitha Mountains are about 35 km long and face southeast towards Lake Neusiedl. Vineyard microclimates vary greatly not only according to their respective soils, but also to their proximity to the forested peaks of the mountains or the shores of the lake.

The Leithaberg DAC protected designation of origin encompasses the district of Eisenstadt as well as the communities Jois and Winden. Around 20 Leithaberg wine villages line the wine route from Jois in the northeast to Grosshöflein and Zagersdorf in the southwest. The grape varieties Pinot Blanc, Chardonnay, Neuburger, and Grüner Veltliner are permitted for "Leithaberg DAC weiss", either as a single varietal or as a blend. The "Leithaberg DAC rot" is vinified principally from Blaufränkisch with up to 15% Zweigelt, St. Laurent or Pinot Noir. The wines labelled as Leithaberg DAC exhibit restrained fruit, pronounced mineral character, appetizing acidity, and moderate alcohol levels. They are versatile culinary talents and often have very good ageing potential.

Closer to the lake, especially in Rust, exquisite botrytized sweet wines of legendary quality are produced. In 1681 the city of Rust purchased its right to self-govern from Emperor Leopold I. with 60,000 guilders and 500 buckets of the wine specialty Ruster Ausbruch. The sweet wines and dry wines that do not fit the style or varietal description for the Leithaberg DAC appear under the Neusiedlersee-Hügelland or Burgenland protected geographical indications. Due to the region's superb wines and thriving culinary scene, it has become a popular destination for gourmet travellers. Cultural programmes in Burgenland's capital city

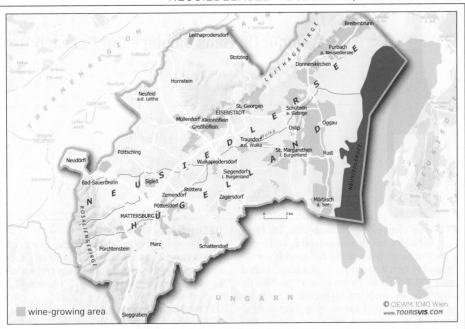

wine-growing area

© OEWM. 1040 Wien
www.TOURISVIS.COM

Eisenstadt with its famous Schloss Esterházy and the atmospheric musical festivals on the lake in Mörbisch and in the Sankt Margarethen quarry are additional attractions. The Austrian Wine Academy, Central Europe's leading wine education institution offers WSET courses in German and English and has its headquarters in the lively, historic little city of Rust.

◆ Weingut Dr. Hans Bichler – Gut Purbach, Purbach

◆ Esterházy Wein, Trausdorf

◆ Weingut Toni Hartl, Reisenberg

◆ Weingut Kollwentz, Großhöflein

◆ Weingut Mad – Haus Marienberg, Oggau

◆ Weingut Hans Moser, Eisenstadt

◆ Weingut Prieler, Schützen/Gebirge

◆ Weingut Sommer, Donnerskirchen

◆ Weingut Ernst Triebaumer, Rust

◆ Weingut Günter & Regina Triebaumer, Rust

◆ Weingut Wagentristl, Großhöflein

Weingut Dr. Hans Bichler – Gut Purbach

7083 Purbach, Sätzgasse 22
T: +43 (1) 71720, F: +43 (1) 71720 99
office@b-z.at, www.bichler-weinbau.eu

Winemaker: Thomas Schwarz
Contact Person: Dr. Hans Bichler
Production: 10.000 bottles (70 % white, 30 % red)
Hectares: 4
Distribution partners: on request

The Viennese economic lawyer, Dr. Hans Bichler, has owned vineyards and made wine in Burgenland for more than 20 years. He purchased a small vineyard planted with Pinot Gris in Purbach in 1986. Shortly after this, he made an arrangement with his vintner friend, Josef Leberl, who continues to function as vineyard manager today. The winery now owns four hectares of prime vineyards situated on the southeast-facing slopes of the Leitha Mountains. The focus is centred on Pinot Gris, Chardonnay and Pinot Noir. In addition to this, Blaufränkisch is also cultivated. After the early and tragic death of Josef Leberl's son, Gerald, in 2012, Thomas Schwarz (Kloster am Spitz, Purbach) now takes responsibility for vinification. Gentle processing of the fruit with minimal technical intervention and abstinence from additives are in the foreground. The red wines are fermented spontaneously and, after the malolactic fermentation, mature for around 15 months in small oak barrels. They are then allowed another six months bottle maturation before they enter the market. A similar regime is given the white wines. Only in certain years is the Pinot Gris fermented and matured in temperature-controlled stainless steel. The winery is a founding member of the "Leithaberg" vintners' association.

92 Chardonnay Reserve 2013
Pale golden yellow. Ripe Bartlett pear and baked apple with notes of tobacco, herbs, and spice. A juicy, fine acidity structure offers elegant refreshment to the palate. Yellow tropical fruit nuances join in on the long finish. Good potential for further development.
93 Chardonnay Reserve 2012
93 Chardonnay Reserve 2011

90 Leithaberg DAC weiß 2014
91 Leithaberg DAC weiß 2013 CH
91 Leithaberg DAC weiß 2012 CH

88 Neuburger Gut Purbach weiß 2014
88 Neuburger Gut Purbach weiß 2013
89 Neuburger Gut Purbach weiß 2012

92 Leithaberg DAC rot Thenau 2012

92 Blaufränkisch 2011

91 Blauburgunder Reserve 2012

90 Blauburgunder 2013
90 Blauburgunder 2012
92 Blauburgunder 2011

★★★
Weingut Esterházy

7061 Trausdorf an der Wulka, 1
T: +43 (2682) 63348, F: +43 (2682) 63348 16
wein@esterhazy.at, www.esterhazywein.at

Winemaker: Milan Arti, Alexander Wapp, Stéphane Derenoncourt
Contact Person: Stefan Tscheppe
Production: 500.000 bottles (30 % white, 69 % red, 1 % sweet)
Hectares: 65
Fairs: ProWein, The London International Wine & Spirits Fair, Vievinum
Distribution partners: J, S, B, CH, RC, LT, DK, DE, FIN, T, F, GB, N, H

The house of Esterházy has cultivated wine in the Pannonian region for more than 250 years. Soils are diverse and range from loamy gravel on the shores of Lake Neusiedl to the marine limestone of the Leitha Mountains. The cold winters and warm summers of the Pannonian climate are tempered by Lake Neusiedl and combine with these soils to create unique terroir. The state-of-the-art wine cellar was conceived for the ease of preserving the inimitable character of each individual vineyard site. The knowledge of many generations of grape growers and their knowledge of climate, site, terroir and autochthon grape varieties are paired perfectly with the expertise of the internationally renowned wine consultant Stéphane Derenoncourt. He and oenologist Milán Arti use particularly gentle vinification techniques to produce expressive wine personalities with aromatic depth and pronounced varietal character. The assortment of wines includes refreshing, fruity classic wines as well as characterful single-vineyard wines. The flagship wine is the "Tesero", a blend of Blaufränkisch and Merlot. The wines of the Esterházy estate are outstanding ambassadors of Austrian wine culture. Besides their presence on the domestic market they achieve consistent success in Europe, Asia, and North America. Esterházy counts among the largest organic producers in Austria. The Esterházy gourmet products can be purchased in the on-premise wine shop. Visitors are offered a diversified wine experience programme and opportunity to taste throughout the year.

91 Leithaberg DAC rot 2013
92 Leithaberg DAC rot 2012
Deep ruby with purple highlights and a thin transparent rim.

Blackberry jam, nuances of cassis and liquorice, and subtle sandalwood with an undertone of herbal spice and nougat. Juicy, refreshing acidity and fine tannins lend an elegant frame to the complex array of flavours and aromas. Salty minerals join in on the finish. Good ageing potential.
92 Leithaberg DAC rot 2011

92 Leithaberg DAC rot Schildten 2013

92 Leithaberg DAC rot Föllig 2013
93 Blaufränkisch Föllig 2012

92 Blaufränkisch Baumschule 2012

91 Merlot Schneiderteil 2013
93 Merlot Schneiderteil 2012
93 Merlot Schneiderteil 2011

93 Tesoro 2012 BF/ME
93 Tesoro 2011 BF/ME

(90–92) Estoras 2013 BF/ME/CS
91 Estoras 2012 BF/ME/CS
91 Estoras 2011 BF/ME/CS

91 Weißburgunder Tatschler 2013
Pale green-yellow. Golden Delicious apple, subtle wild meadow herbs, and a touch of orange zest with notes of passion fruit in the background. Complexly structured with juicy acid and elegant minerals. Pineapple joins in on the long finish of this very good accompaniment to food.
92 Pinot Blanc Tatschler 2012
91 Weißburgunder Tatschler 2011

90 Sauvignon Blanc 2014
90 Sauvignon Blanc Estoras 2013

93 Leithaberg DAC weiß Tatschler 2014
91 Leithaberg DAC weiß 2013
92 Leithaberg DAC weiß 2012 CH

Weingut Toni Hartl

2440 Reisenberg, Florianigasse 7
T: +43 (2234) 80636 0, F: +43 (2234) 80636 4
wine@toni-hartl.at, www.toni-hartl.at

ORGANIC

Winemaker and Contact Person: Toni Hartl
Production: n. a. (25 % white, 72 % red, 3 % sweet)
Hectares: 23
Fairs: VieVinum, ProWein
Distribution partners: B, PL

The Toni Hartl winery cultivates 25 vineyard hectares in two wine regions, Thermenregion in Lower Austria and Leithaberg/Neusiedlersee-Hügelland in Burgenland. Red varieties planted make up 75% of the vineyards; the remaining 25% are white. Profound knowledge of the very different microclimates and diversity of soils in Reisenberg and Purbach make it possible to find the optimal place for each grape variety. Expressing each individual origin and its uniqueness is the prime goal of vinification. New in Toni Hartl's wine assortment is a Pinot Noir Reserve from the Zwergsberg vineyard in Reisenberg; the old vines here grow in calcareous soil. This wine is produced only in exceptional vintages and is matured for three years before it enters the market. Also in the Reserve category is the Blaufränkisch "Eisner", which as the name implies, stems from vines in a prime iron-rich site. An optimal interplay between the soil and each microclimate is the foundation for producing physiologically fully ripe wines that clearly pronounce their origin. Under the motto, "everything has only been borrowed", Hartl works according to the most recent ecological findings. Gentle soil management and targeted preservation of beneficial insects are practiced to preserve ecological balance in the vineyard. The winery has been certified organic since 2010 and is a founding member of the Leithaberg Vintners' Association.

93 Blaufränkisch Eisner 2013
Dark ruby with an opaque core, purple highlights, and a thin, transparent rim. Pleasant sandalwood notes, ripe blackberry jam, and a hint of plum mingle with nougat and smoky mineral components on the nose and in the mouth. Juicy, elegant acidity refreshes the medium body. Subtle extract sweetness, ripe cherry, minerals and chocolate linger on the finish.

94 Blaufränkisch Eisner 2012

91 Blaufränkisch Edelgraben 2012
92 Blaufränkisch Edelgraben 2011

92 Leithaberg DAC rot Rosenberg 2013
92 Leithaberg DAC rot Rosenberg 2012
93 Leithaberg DAC rot Rosenberg 2011

93 Syrah Thenau 2013
Deep ruby with an opaque core, purple highlights and a thin, transparent rim. Intense herbs and spice with sweet blackberry jam, nougat, and black olive. Juicy, refreshing acidity structure and fine-grained tannins. Blackberry continues on the finish with subtle chocolate notes. An elegant style that offers plenty of drinking pleasure.

92 Syrah Thenau 2012

91 Pinot Noir Zwergsberg 2013
91 Pinot Noir Zwergsberg 2011

(92–94) Pinot Noir Goldberg 2014
89 Pinot Noir Goldberg 2012
90 Pinot Noir Goldberg 2011

92 Cabernet Sauvignon Felsenstein 2011

91 Inkognito 2013 BF/ZW/CS
92 Inkognito 2012 BF/CS/SY
92 Inkognito 2011 BF/ZW/CS/SY

92 Leithaberg DAC weiß 2014
91 Leithaberg DAC weiß 2013
92 Leithaberg DAC weiß 2012 CH

(91–93) Chardonnay Thenau 2014
92 Chardonnay Thenau 2013

★★★★★

Weingut Kollwentz

7051 Großhöflein, Hauptstraße 120, Büro und Verkauf: Gartengasse 4b
T: +43 (2682) 65158, F: +43 (2682) 65158 13, M: +43 (2682) 65158
kollwentz@kollwentz.at, www.kollwentz.at

Winemaker: Andi Kollwentz
Contact Person: Kollwentz family
Production: 90.000 bottles (37 % white, 62 % red, 1 % sweet)
Hectares: 23
Fairs: VieVinum, ProWein
Distribution partners: I, S, CDN, CH, SK, L, DK, DE, CZ, F, NL, USA, IS

What really separates the great vintners from the good is the ability to produce consistently high quality, whether in a good or difficult vintage. For two generations, the Kollwentz family has ranked among the great dependable vintners in Austria, no matter the style or the variety. The jury of tasters for the Falstaff Burgunder Barrique Trophy was in unanimous agreement with one wine·this last summer. Year for year, it is not only the unoaked Chardonnay from the Leitha Mountains that is among the best examples of the variety: the repeated champions of the Burgunder Barrique Trophy – the single-vineyard Chardonnays "Gloria" and "Tatschler" – are also always among the elite. It is no different with the red wines. The Cabernet Sauvignon won its category in the 2003 Falstaff red wine competition and the 2004 "Blaufränkisch Point" was awarded 94 points and second place in the reserve category. At the Falstaff Red Wine Premier 2009, the Kollwentz family proudly achieved three accolades; and in the 2010 championship, they won the correlating categories with their "Pinot Noir Dürr" and their flagship blend "Steinzeiler". Anton Kollwentz Sr. is considered the pioneer of Cabernet Sauvignon in Austria and, as Falstaff champion in 1984 and 1985, he sparked a veritable Cabernet boom in Austrian vineyards. Andi Kollwentz Jr. is the prize fighter among Austrian vintners and has perfected every discipline. His wines are among the best the country has to offer in every category. The indigenous varieties Blaufränkisch and Zweigelt dominate the red wine assortment. The spicy, powerful Blaufränkisch is the backbone for the "Steinzeiler" and "Eichkogel" blends. The "Blaufränkisch Vom Leithagebirge" and "Blaufränkisch Point" are also first-class. The dark berry fruit of Zweigelt lends elegant suppleness to the "Föllikberg" as well as comprising a harmonious element in blends. Special attention should be given the "Sauvignon Blanc Riede Steinmühle" as its flinty soil brings excellent spice to this variety. A small quantity of exquisite, noble sweet wines are produced from Sauvignon Blanc and Chardonnay each year and are archived in the winery cellars all the way back to the 1963 vintage. Because the top wines were not produced in 2010, there is particular excitement about the "Steinzeiler", "Cabernet Sauvignon" and "Point Blaufränkisch" from the 2011 vintage. There is one small change in wine names: the "Vom Leithagebirge" range of wines will be labelled "Leithakalk" (as of the 2014 vintage for the Chardonnay and 2013 for the Blaufränkisch).

(93–95) Chardonnay Tatschler 2014
94 Chardonnay Tatschler 2013
Medium yellow with silver highlights. Initially rather restrained, but then reveals ripe yellow fruit nuances reminiscent of peach with delicate blossom honey, subtle vanilla, and oak spice. Full bodied and tautly structured with white apple fruit and fine spicy notes. Salty mineral character on the long persistent finish. Good potential for further development.
94 Chardonnay Tatschler 2012

(94–96) Chardonnay Gloria 2014
93 Chardonnay Gloria 2013
95 Chardonnay Gloria 2012

(92–94) Chardonnay Neusatz 2014
92 Chardonnay Neusatz 2013
93 Chardonnay Neusatz 2012

(91–93) Chardonnay Leithakalk 2015
89 Chardonnay Leithakalk 2014
92 Chardonnay von den Rieden 2013

94 Sauvignon Blanc Steinmühle
Methusalemreben 2013
94 Sauvignon Blanc Steinmühle
Methusalemreben 2012
95 Sauvignon Blanc Steinmühle
Methusalemreben 2011

(91–93) Sauvignon Blanc Steinmühle 2015
92 Sauvignon Blanc Steinmühle 2014
92 Sauvignon Blanc Steinmühle 2013

(92–94) Blaufränkisch Setz 2013
94 Blaufränkisch Setz 2012
Dark ruby with purple highlights and a thin transparent rim.
The highly attractive bouquet displays sweet dark berry
jam, juniper and cardamom, and a touch of chocolate. Full
bodied and powerful, but by no means lacking elegance or
finesse. Delicate extract sweetness is harmoniously paired
with abundant, well-integrated tannins. Very good length. A
concentrated accompaniment to food with dependable potential for further development.
94 Blaufränkisch Setz 2011

(93–95) Blaufränkisch Point 2013
93 Blaufränkisch Point 2012
96 Blaufränkisch Point 2011

(91–93) Blaufränkisch Leithakalk 2014
92 Blaufränkisch Leithakalk 2013
92 Blaufränkisch von den Rieden 2012

(92–94) Cabernet Sauvignon 2014
93 Cabernet Sauvignon 2013
93 Cabernet Sauvignon 2012

(91–93) Pinot Noir Dürr 2014
93 Pinot Noir Dürr 2013
92 Pinot Noir Dürr 2012

91 Zweigelt Föllikberg 2014
92 Zweigelt Föllikberg 2013

(93–95) Steinzeiler 2013 BF/ZW/CS
94 Steinzeiler 2012 BF/ZW/CS
Dark ruby with purple highlights and a thin transparent rim.
Attractive wild forest berry jam over a background of ripe
wild cherry, sandalwood, sweet spices, and nougat. Juicy,
dark berries are elegantly bedded in abundant tannins that
have a chocolaty texture. Nougat lingers on the very long
finish. Will benefit from further bottle maturation.
95 Steinzeiler 2011 BF/ZW/CS

(91–93) Eichkogel 2014 BF/ZW
92 Eichkogel 2013 BF/ZW
92 Eichkogel Tradition 2012 BF/ZW

94 Scheurebe Trockenbeerenauslese 2014

93 Sämling 88 Beerenauslese 2012

93 Chardonnay Beerenauslese 2014

★★
Weingut Mad – Haus Marienberg

7063 Oggau, Antonigasse 1
T: +43 (2685) 7207, F: +43 (2685) 7207 4
office@weingut-mad.at, www.weingut-mad.at

Winemaker: Christian Händler and Tobias Siess
Contact Person: Matthias and Sebastian Siess
Production: n. a. (29 % white, 70 % red, 1 % sweet)
Hectares: 47
Fairs: VieVinum, ProWein
Distribution partners: CH, DE, NL

The Mad estate is essentially the united effort of three families. The Mads have been successful winegrowers in Oggau since 1786. Father Wilhelm Mad, father of Rafaela Händler and Maria Siess, is the patriarch of the family. He has accompanied the successful development of the winery with pride and enjoyment. Rafaela Händler is responsible for the back office while her husband Christian Händler is the winemaker. Maria's son, Tobias Siess, supports his uncle Christian in winemaking duties. Matthias Siess, Maria's husband, and Sebastian Siess, son of Matthias and Maria, are responsible for sales and marketing. Maria Siess operates a restaurant directly next to the winery, the award-winning "Zum Herztröpferl". Barbara Kölbl-Siess, Sebastian's wife, works together with her mother-in-law at the restaurant. The most important person in the entire enterprise is Maria Mad, wife of Wilhelm, and she cooks lunch for everyone. When visiting the estate, it is possible to taste the wines and match them with delicious regional specialties.

92 Leithaberg DAC rot Hochberg 2012
Dark ruby with purple highlights and a thin transparent rim. The inviting bouquet displays ripe lingonberry jam and cherry compote with subtle notes of heather and nougat. Juicy acidity and well-integrated tannin lend good structure to the medium body. Blackberry, wild cherry, and salty minerals linger on the finish.

90 Blaufränkisch Ambrosi 2015
89 Ambrosi rot 2012 BF

90 Blaufränkisch Altenberg 2012

(89–91) Zweigelt MAD Basis schwefelfrei & unfiltiert 2015

91 Cabernet – Merlot 2012 CS/ME

91 Pinot Blanc Isel 2015
89 Pinot Blanc Isel 2013
88 Pinot Blanc Isel 2012

91 Chardonnay Pratsche 2015
90 Chardonnay Pratsche 2013
89 Chardonnay Pratsche 2012

89 Ambrosi 2015 CH/WB/MT
88 Ambrosi weiß 2013 CH/WR/GV
87 Ambrosi weiß 2012 CH/WR/GV

89 Pink Bliss 2015

Weingut Hans Moser

7000 Eisenstadt, St. Georgener Hauptstraße 13
T: +43 (2682) 66607, F: +43 (2682) 66607 14
weingut@hans-moser.at, www.hans-moser.at

Winemaker: Hans Moser
Contact Person: Sabine and Hans Moser
Production: 100.000 bottles (48 % white, 50 % red, 2 % sweet)
Hectares: 14 + 6
Fairs: VieVinum, ProWein, Prodexpo Moskau
Distribution partners: RUS, J, S, CDN, RC, CZ, USA

Hans Moser unites varietal character with expression of site in his wines. Welschriesling, Gemischter Satz, Sauvignon Blanc and Chardonnay make up 55 % of wine production. Next to the autochthon grape varieties Blaufränkisch and Zweigelt, Cabernet, Syrah and Merlot are also cultivated. The basic line of wines is labelled "Classic" while the middle category appears as the "Leithakalk" series (Sauvignon Blanc, Chardonnay, Blaufränkisch, and Cabernet-Merlot). Single-vineyard wines represent the peak of the pyramid: Leithaberg DAC Scheibenberg Chardonnay, Leithaberg DAC Hummelbühel Blaufränkisch and Joachimstal Merlot. A semi-dry, fruity spätlese and a high quality Ausbruch round out the assortment of wines. Son Johannes brings a fresh breeze into the enterprise with a blanc de noir called "Harys-Syrah", which has been a hit since the 2012 vintage. New in the assortment of wines since spring of 2015 is "GEORGE", a cool climate style red wine from Sankt GEORGEn.

92 Merlot Joachimstal 2012
91 Merlot Joachimstal 2011
Deep ruby with purple highlights and a transparent rim. The nose is rather restrained, but exhibits discreet dark berry, tobacco and subtle oak aromas. Medium-bodied with a sweet plum tone and well-integrated tannins. Berry compote and chocolate on the finish.

91 Blaufränkisch Cigar reserva 2012
92 Blaufränkisch Cigar reserva 2011

88 Blaufränkisch Leithakalk 2013

93 Leithaberg DAC rot Hummelbühel 2012
91 Leithaberg DAC rot Hummelbühel 2011

90 Cabernet - Merlot Leithakalk 2013 CS/CF/ME
90 Cabernet – Merlot 2011 CS/CF/ME

89 V.T.S. – Vintage Top Select 2011 CS/CF/SY/BF/ZW/ME

87 Harys Syrah weißgepresst 2014
87 Syrah Harys (weißgepresst) 2013
88 Syrah Harys (weißgepresst) 2012

91 Leithaberg DAC weiß Scheibenberg 2013
89 Leithaberg DAC weiß Scheibenberg 2012

88 Gemischter Satz 2015

88 Sauvignon Blanc 2014
88 Sauvignon Blanc 2013

★ ★ ★ ★
Weingut Prieler

7081 Schützen/Gebirge, Hauptstraße 181
T: +43 (2684) 2229, F: +43 (2684) 2229 4
weingut@prieler.at, www.prieler.at

Winemaker and Contact Person: Georg Prieler
Production: 95.000 bottles (40 % white, 60 % red)
Hectares: 20
Fairs: VieVinum, ProWein
Distribution partners: B, CDN, DK, FIN, CZ, NL, GB, USA

Wine is poetry in the bottle." Nothing could better describe the wines of this superb, small family winery. The Prieler family main focus is the vineyards. The largest share of the vineyard area is found near the village of Schützen am Gebirge, but significant vineyards are also located in Oggau and Oslip. In each place there is a different soil composition, which is the explanation for various grape varieties finding an ideal place to thrive. Despite this, a sensitive and experienced hand is required to produce top white and red wines consistently each year. Georg Prieler, the young oenologist with overseas experience and Silvia Prieler, doctor of microbiology, possess these attributes. They are true all-rounders able to make good decisions intuitively. This is a good thing that results in memorable wines being made here. Terroir is not an empty word for Prielers. Just get Georg talking about this subject and watch his eyes light up. Chalky soils are found in the Seeberg and Sinner vineyards toward Lake Neusiedl and this is the source for the great white wines of the producer. Ungerbergen has sandy loam with pebbles, making it an ideal place for late ripening varieties like Cabernet Sauvignon. Goldberg, inarguably the best vineyard of the estate, offers meagre micha-schist soils and is predestined for Blaufränkisch, the most traditional and important variety for the producer. The Prieler family focuses their winemaking efforts on the terroir characteristics. For this reason the "Pinot Blanc Seeberg" ferments in stainless steel after extended maceration to preserve its refreshing delicacy. The "Blaufränkisch Johanneshöhe", on the other hand, is matured in wooden casks and the "Blaufränkisch Goldberg" achieves its incredible suppleness during its maceration – up to 26 months in 500-litre wooden barrels.

The Goldberg is an extraordinary wine and was the champion of the "Falstaff Reserve Trophy" in 2005 and 2008. The Prielers have also had repeated success with their Pinot Blanc wines in the "Falstaff Burgunder Trophy", winning two of four trophies with Pinot Blanc Seeberg 2004 and the extraordinarily matured Chardonnay Seeberg 2001. The Leithaberg wines were launched in the assortment of wines with enthusiastic public response and consistently receive top placements in blind tastings. It is no surprise that the family was recognized as Falstaff Vintner of the Year in 2009.

(93–95) Leithaberg DAC rot Goldberg 2013
93 Blaufränkisch Goldberg 2012
Brilliant dark ruby with purple highlights and a thin transparent rim. Aromas and flavours of blackberry jam, ripe wild cherry, and subtle herbal notes in the background. Juicy, delicate red berry nuances are hihglighted by a refreshing acidity structure. Abundant tannins are elegantly integrated. A light, refreshing citrus touch appears in the lengthy finish. Very good ageing potential.
95 Blaufränkisch Goldberg 2011

(89–91) Blaufränkisch Johanneshöhe 2014
91 Blaufränkisch Johanneshöhe 2013
90 Blaufränkisch Johanneshöhe 2012

93 Cabernet Sauvignon Ungerbergen 2012
93 Cabernet Sauvignon Ungerbergen 2011

(91–93) Leithaberg DAC rot 2014

89 Pinot Noir Hochsatz 2012
91 Pinot Noir Hochsatz 2011

92 Merlot Schützner Stein 2013
92 Merlot Schützner Stein 2012

93 Schützner Stein 2011 BF/ME

(92–94) Leithaberg DAC weiß Haidsatz 2015

(92–94) Leithaberg DAC weiß 2015
92 Leithaberg DAC weiß 2013
Medium green-yellow with silver highlights. Initially rather
restrained, but then reveals delicate pear notes, a touch of
apple, papaya, and subtle herbal spice in the background.
Complex with ripe pear fruit and discreet sweetness countered by a refreshing acidity structure. Notes of orange,
light honey and minerals linger on the finish.
93 Leithaberg DAC weiß 2012 WB

92 Pinot Blanc Seeberg 2015
91 Pinot Blanc Seeberg 2014
92 Pinot Blanc Seeberg 2013

91 Chardonnay Sinner 2015
90 Chardonnay Sinner 2014
91 Chardonnay Sinner 2013

★ ★ ★
Weingut Sommer

7082 Donnerskirchen, Johannesstraße 26
T: +43 (2683) 8504, F: +43 (2683) 8504 4
info@weingut-sommer.at, www.weingut-sommer.at

Winemaker and Contact Person: Ing. Leo Sommer
Production: 145.000 bottles (80 % white, 18 % red, 2 % sweet)
Hectares: 30
Fairs: ProWein, VieVinum
Distribution partners: CH, DE, NL, USA

The Sommer family wine estate has a long tradition for setting benchmarks. They produce a full array of mineral wines with an inimitable signature from vines that are deeply rooted in rocky, southeast-facing slopes of the Leitha Mountains. Leitha Mountain terroir makes it possible for the family to realise their wine vision and share it with others. Winemakers Leo and Leo junior are very conscientious of the uniqueness of each site and attentive in achieving optimal physiological ripeness of fruit. The Donnerskirchen microclimate allows the production of a broad spectrum of superb quality wines. The impressive white wine assortment includes refreshing, fruity wines as well as powerful, deep wines of distinct character. The vineyards on the west side of Lake Neusiedl provide not only ideal conditions for outstanding white wines, but also for great red wine growths that exhibit good substance and spice. The diversity and top class quality of the wines have made them a standard on the wine lists of Austrian restaurants. As a founding member of the Leithaberg Vintners' Association, the Sommer winery has been a strong impetus for the region in highlighting the very special and unique geology of the Leitha Mountains and its wines. New quality benchmarks combined with respect for tradition in both the vineyard and cellar is the Sommer family's secret to superb wines of character; wines that clearly express the schist soils of their vineyards.

92 Chardonnay Riefring Thal 2013
Brilliant yellow with golden highlights. Baby banana, pineapple, vanilla, and subtle oaky notes. Powerful body and fiery texture. Ripe stone fruit reminiscent of peach and mango join in on the on the minerally, subtly sweet finish. Good ageing potential.

92 Chardonnay Riefring 2011

90 Chardonnay Kreuzjoch 2015
88 Chardonnay Kreuzjoch 2014
89 Chardonnay Kreuzjoch 2013

89 Grüner Veltliner Bergweingarten M 2015
90 Grüner Veltliner Bergweingarten M 2014
91 Grüner Veltliner Bergweingarten M 2013

(92–94) Grüner Veltliner Himmelreich 2015
92 Grüner Veltliner Himmelreich 2013

91 Leithaberg DAC weiß 2014
91 Leithaberg DAC weiß 2013
92 Leithaberg DAC weiß 2011 GV

89 Riesling Bergweingarten 2015
89 Riesling Bergweingarten 2014
91 Riesling Bergweingarten 2012

91 Sauvignon Blanc Wolfsbach 2015
88 Sauvignon Blanc Wolfsbach 2014
89 Sauvignon Blanc Wolfsbach 2013

90 Leithaberg DAC rot 2013

91 Camer Reserve 2013 CS/ME
92 Camer Reserve 2011 ME/CS

92 Blauer Zweigelt Schieferstein 2011

91 Gewürztraminer Spätlese 2015

92 Traminer Handwerk 2014

92 Welschriesling Beerenauslese 2014

Weingut Ernst Triebaumer

7071 Rust, Raiffeisenstraße 9
T: +43 (2685) 528, F: +43 (2685) 60738
office@ernst.triebaumer.com, www.triebaumer.com

Winemaker: Herbert and Gerhard Triebaumer
Contact Person: Claudia and Stephanie Triebaumer
Production: 100.000 bottles (20 % white, 75 % red, 5 % sweet)
Hectares: 20
Fairs: VieVinum, ProWein
Distribution partners: J, CH, SK, DE, CZ, NL, GB, UAE

Herbert and Gerhard Triebaumer have taken over the complete responsibility for wine production step-by-step and in an unspectacular, but effective manner. The motto of their father, Ernst: "work hard in the vineyard and have less to do in the cellar" finds continuity here. Vine vigour is controlled more strictly than ever and the soil is worked mechanically less often to encourage smaller, more resistant and more aromatic grapes. A further positive side effect to the new methods is deeper rooting of the vines, which contributes to expression of character and longevity of the wine. The cornerstone of wine production is the protection and enhancement of soil vitality, which logically means no use of herbicides, no irrigation and reduced use of the tractor in the vineyard. Conscientious canopy management measures include shoot placement and leaf removal. Grapes are selected manually at harvest. Traditional regional varieties are preferred and half of the vineyards are planted with Blaufränkisch. The Triebaumers wish to fully express each vintage through selection of the time of harvest, choice of style and appropriate vinification methods. Judicious intervention is practiced in order to allow each wine to express its own individuality.

94 Blaufränkisch Mariental 2013
Dark ruby with an opaque core, purple highlights and a thin transparent rim. Lingonberry, wild cherry and orange zest with an undertone of herbs and spices. Full-bodied with abundant, well-integrated tannins bedded in red cherry fruit. Citrus and minerals in the long finish.
94 Blaufränkisch Mariental 2012
94 Blaufränkisch Mariental 2011

(90–92) Blaufränkisch Gmärk 2015
91 Blaufränkisch Gmärk 2013
91 Blaufränkisch Gmärk 2012

(92–94) Blaufränkisch Aus den Rieden 2014

93 Blaufränkisch Oberer Wald 2011

89 Blauburgunder Rusterberg 2012
92 Blauburgunder Rusterberg 2011

90 Cabernet Sauvignon Merlot 2013 CS/ME
93 Cabernet Sauvignon Merlot 2012 CS/ME

(89–91) Maulwurf 2014 BF/ME/CS
90 Maulwurf 2012 BF/ME/CS
89 Maulwurf 2010

89 Tridendron 2012 ME/CS/BF
89 Tridendron 2010 ME/CS/BF

88 Hauptsache Rot 2013 SY/ME/SL
89 Hauptsache Rot 2012 SL/SY/ME

91 Chardonnay Pandkräftn 2013
Pale green-yellow with silver highlights. Pear and subtle white vineyard peach over a delicate background of tobacco, herbs, and spice. Juicy, elegant acidity structure brings tropical fruit notes reminiscent of pineapple to the fore. Delicate oak spice joins in on the finish. Good ageing potential.
90 Chardonnay Pandkräftn 2011

88 Gelber Muskateller Greiner 2015
88 Gelber Muskateller Greiner 2014
89 Gelber Muskateller Greiner 2013

92 Ruster Ausbruch 2013 WR/TR/GV

★ ★ ★ ★
Weingut Günter und Regina Triebaumer

7071 Rust, Neuegasse 18
T: +43 (676) 4728288, F: +43 (2173) 200804
weingut@triebaumer.at, www.triebaumer.at

Winemaker: Günter Triebaumer
Contact Person: Günter and Regina Triebaumer
Production: 130.000 bottles (25 % white, 65 % red, 10 % sweet)
Hectares: 25 + 3
Fairs: ProWein, VieVinum
Distribution partners: CH, B, DK, DE, NL, GB, USA

"Low tech – high effort" is the strategy of Günter and Regina Triebaumer. Based on the local, traditional specialties of the historic royal free city of Rust, Blaufränkisch, Furmint, Gelber Muskateller and Ruster Ausbruch are produced with passion and dedication to authenticity. The Triebaumers produce wines that can be clearly categorized as being from Burgenland. The couple puts its many years of experience in the international wine and restaurant trade, import/export, education at the Austrian Wine Academy, and extensive wine travels to good use. The rather "Burgundian" structure of the enterprise with 25 hectares distributed between 45 different parcels is due to the history of the region. The conscientiousness of the diversity of sites is definitely astute. Eight hectares of Blaufränkisch makes it the sovereign king of their grape varieties. A classic, delicate cherry fruit version finds its place just as does a complex spicy Blaufränkisch Reserve. The very first harvest of their calcareous plot in the prime Oberer Wald vineyard in 2009 brought them the "Falstaff Reserve Trophy". The 2013 vintage inspires great expectations for a second "great growth" from the chalk-free Plachen vineyard. The Ruster Ausbruch is undoubtedly the oldest, uninterrupted wine origin in Austria. Triebaumer strives to produce this concentrated, noble sweet wine from the dependable Welschriesling each year. The Muscato, a light playful semi-sparkling wine made from Gelber Muskateller (Muscat blanc à petits grains), is produced according to the Asti method, and certainly deserves a special mention.

93 Blaufränkisch Plachen 2013
94 Blaufränkisch Plachen 2012
Intense ruby with purple highlights and a broad, slightly paler rim. Initially rather restrained with discreet lingonberry jam, a touch of fresh cherry, and blackberry jam with a touch of wild herbs. Juicy acidity brightens sweetly extracted fruit on the palate where abundant, silky tannins are harmoniously integrated. Already well developed, but still has dependable ageing potential.
96 Blaufränkisch Plachen 2011

93 Blaufränkisch Oberer Wald 2012
94 Blaufränkisch Oberer Wald 2011

(90–92) Blaufränkisch Reserve 2014
93 Blaufränkisch Reserve 2013
94 Blaufränkisch Reserve 2011

90 Blaufränkisch Klassisch 2015
92 Blaufränkisch 2012

90 Blauer Zweigelt 2012

94 Cabernet Franc Gillesberg 2013

(89–91) Blaufränkisch/Cabernet 2014 BF/CS
91 Blaufränkisch/Cabernet 2013 BF/CS/CF
91 Blaufränkisch/Cabernet 2012 BF/CS

93 Weite Welt 2011 CF/CS/SY

91 Chardonnay Geyerumriss 2014

90 Sauvignon Blanc 2015

89 Furmint 2015

90 Muscato 2015
90 Muscato 2014

94 **Ruster Ausbruch 2014 WR/FU**
93 **Welschriesling Ruster Ausbruch 2013**
Medium yellow with golden highlights. Refreshing mandarin zest with subtle banana and pineapple with delicate
honey and herb notes. Juicy, refreshing acidity elegantly
balances the luscious sweetness. Minerals and a lemony
touch join in on the long finish. A modern, internationally
styled sweet wine.
95 **Ruster Ausbruch 2012 CH/WR/RR**
97 **Welschriesling Ruster Ausbruch 2011**

90 **Traminer Spätlese 2015**
91 **Traminer Spätlese 2013**
91 **Traminer Spätlese 2012**

89 **Spätlese Cuvée 2015 CH/WR**

★ ★ ★
Weingut Wagentristl

7051 Großhöflein, Rosengasse 2
T: +43 (2682) 61415, F: +43 (2682) 61415
weingut@wagentristl.com, www.wagentristl.com

Winemaker: Rudolf Wagentristl
Contact Person: Wagentristl family
Production: 60.000 bottles (25 % white, 70 % red, 5 % sweet)
Hectares: 12
Fairs: VieVinum, ProWein
Distribution partners: CH, DE, NL

The cornerstone for the current Wagentristl winery was laid by the great-great grandparents, Johann and Julianna Wagentristl, in 1888. She brought the "Hof Nr. 135" in Grosshöflein with her into the marriage. In the following decades, the family increasingly practiced viticulture. Slowly but surely, the focus on animal husbandry and agricultural crops were abandoned in favour of wine grape cultivation. Over time, the "Hof Nr. 135" became the winery that now stands in the Rosengasse. The estate vineyards are located on the gentle slopes of the Leitha Mountains and its foothills. A unique combination of soils and the special macroclimate of the region form an incomparable terroir found nowhere else. "I am a fan of clear lines and I also follow this in the vinification of my wines," says vintner Rudi Wagentristl. "I strive to create wines with inimitable character, wines with both power and finesse. I want to provide pleasure to others as well as myself with these wines."

91 **Heulichin 2013 CS/BF/ZW**
93 **Heulichin 2012 CS/BF/ZW**
Dark ruby with purple highlights and a thin, transparent rim. The attractive bouquet displays blueberry jam and cherry with subtle nuances of orange and nougat. Good complexity with juicy acidity and well-integrated tannins pleasantly balancing the subtle extract sweetness. Fresh blackberry lingers on the finish of this versatile accompaniment to food.
93 **Heulichin 2011 ZW/BF/CS**

93 **Leithaberg DAC rot 2013**
91 **Leithaberg DAC rot 2012**
95 **Leithaberg DAC rot 2011 BF**

(88–90) **Föllikberg 2014**
90 **Föllikberg 2013 BF/ZW**
92 **Föllikberg 2012 BF/ZW**

91 **Pinot Noir Kreideberg 2013**
91 **Pinot Noir Kreideberg 2012**
93 **Pinot Noir Kreideberg 2011**

91 **Zweigelt Setzen 2014**

91 **Leithaberg DAC weiß 2014**
92 **Leithaberg DAC weiß 2013**
Medium green-yellow with silver highlights. Pineapple and a touch of peach with a slight undertone of mandarin zest. Tightly woven with fine, fruity sweetness supported by a firm acidity backbone. Plenty of finesse and good length with orange fruit and minerals on the finale. Good potential for further development.
91 **Leithaberg DAC weiß 2012 CH**

93 **Leithaberg DAC weiß Kreideberg 2014**

90 **Weißburgunder 2015**
89 **Weißburgunder 2014**

92 **Trockenbeerenauslese 2013 MO/GM**

© WM Egon Müller

MITTELBURGENLAND DAC
Blaufränkisch with the taste of wild berries

Blaufränkisch is the leading grape in the 2,117 hectares of vineyards of Mittelburgenland. The typical wild berry aroma of the Mittelburgenland DAC wines is derived from Blaufränkisch grown in clayey soils of the gentle rolling hills.

Austrians have affectionately called central Burgenland, south of Lake Neusiedl on the Hungarian border, "Blaufränkischland" for decades. It was logical that the predominant variety of the 2.117 hectares of vineyards be the basis for its protected designation of origin.

It was also logical that the regional name, which was already so strongly identified with Blaufränkisch, serve as the name for the region's DAC from the year 2005 onwards. The Mittelburgenland DAC comes in three categories. Mittelburgenland DAC stands for fruit-driven Blaufränkisch vinified in traditional large wooden casks or stainless steel tanks. Single-vineyard Mittelburgenland DAC wines also bear the name of the vineyard in which they grew and are often matured in used small oak barrels. The premium Blaufränkisch that are harvested late and are fuller in body, mature in small oak barrels and appear under the Mittelburgenland DAC Reserve protected designation of origin label. From a geological point of view, central Burgenland belongs to the Oberpullendorf Basin.

Its clayey marl, sand and gravel soils are occasionally interspersed with ancient coral banks. The protection of three mountain ranges in the north, south and west with an opening to the east, fully fosters the influence of the Pannonian climate. There are an average of over 300 sunny days and as little as 600 mm rainfall annually.

The regional soil's excellent capacity to store moisture has proved ideal for the late-ripening Blaufränkisch in such an arid climate.

Alongside Blaufränkisch, the red wine varieties Zweigelt, Cabernet Sauvignon and Merlot display ample body and supple structure, and perform very well both as varietal wines and blends. Dry white and rosé wines are also produced. These wines appear under the Burgenland protected geographical indication.

Mittelburgenland has become an attractive destination for tourists, not just for wine, but also for the thermal spas that have mushroomed in the past years. A varied recreational program for people of all ages adds to the appeal of this hospitable region.

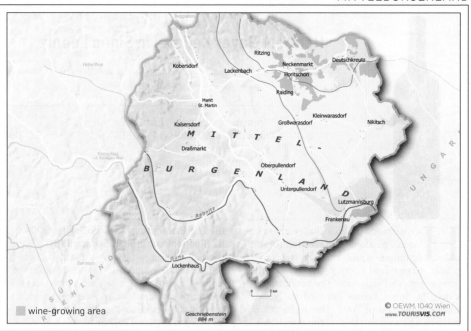

wine-growing area

© OEWM, 1040 Wien
www.TOURISVIS.COM

- ◆ Heribert Bayer Kellerei In Signo Leonis, Neckenmarkt

- ◆ Weingut Gager, Deutschkreutz

- ◆ Weingut Gesellmann, Deutschkreutz

- ◆ Weingut Silvia Heinrich, Deutschkreutz

- ◆ Weingut Anton Hundsdorfer, Neckenmarkt

- ◆ Rotweine Lang, Neckenmarkt

- ◆ Rotweingut Prickler, Lutzmannsburg

- ◆ Weingut Tesch, Neckenmarkt

- ◆ Weingut Wellanschitz, Neckenmarkt

Heribert Bayer Kellerei In Signo Leonis

7311 Neckenmarkt, Wirtschaftspark 5
T: +43 (2610) 42644, F: +43 (2610) 42644 4, M: +43 (664) 4349004
bayer@weinfreund.at, www.weinfreund.at

Winemaker and Contact Person: Patrick Bayer
Production: 70.000 bottles (5 % white, 95 % red)
Fairs: VieVinum, ProWein
Distribution partners: CH, B, DE, USA

Heribert and Patrick Bayer share the same passion: the creation of outstanding wines embody the variety, origin, terroir and vintage as well as their unique personal signature. The vinification facility "In Signo Leonis" opened in Neckenmarkt at the end of 2002. The architecture is modern and concentrates on the essential. The huge glass wall of the tasting room offers a stunning view of illuminated barrique barrels. The cellar was extended with the addition of a storage room with a capacity of up to 450,000 bottles, thus lending the possibility to hold back contingents of premium wine ready for delivery to their key customers. The Neckenmarkt Hochberg and its old Blaufränkisch parcels are the terroir from which a large share of the red wines originate. The blend "In Signo Leonis" is the flagship of the house and appears regularly on the best restaurant wine lists. On the same quality level is the Blaufränkisch called "In Signo Sagittarii" that was first produced in the 2002 vintage. The Bayers are négociants èleveures and source their wines from where they find the expression and typicity of grape varieties most exemplary.

(91–93) Blaufränkisch In Signo Sagittarii 2014
92 Blaufränkisch In Signo Sagittarii 2013
Dark ruby with purple highlights and a thin transparent rim. Delicate sandalwood, candied orange zest, chocolate and elegant blackberry jam with spicy herbal notes. Juicy, ripe wild cherry flavours and fine well integrated tannins. Discreet extract sweetness lingers on the finish.
93 In Signo Sagittarii 2012 BF

(90–92) Blaufränkisch EX·QUI·SIT 2014
91 Blaufränkisch »EXQUISIT« 2013

89 Blaufränkisch Zeitlos 2013

90 Zweigelt »EXQUISIT« 2013
89 Zweigelt Zeitlos 2013

92 Merlot »EXQUISIT« 2013

(91–93) In Signo Leonis 2014 BF/ZW/CS
93 In Signo Leonis 2013 BF/ZW/CS
Dark ruby with purple highlights and a thin transparent rim. Dark berry jam, pronounced cherry and nougat with a subtle smoky undertone with some cedar and vanilla. Fine tannin is bedded in cassis and succulent red berry nuances. This juicy food wine exhibits good length.
93 In Signo Leonis 2012 BF/ZW/CS

94 Herzblut (Magnum) 2009 BF/ME/ZW/CS

90 Sails Red 2012 BF
92 Sails Red 2011 BF

91 In Signo Tauri 2012

90 Weißburgunder 2013
89 Sails White 2012 WB

93 Albatros 2011 CH

Weingut Gager

7301 Deutschkreutz, Karrnergasse 2 und 8
T: +43 (2613) 80385, F: +43 (2613) 80385 15
info@weingut-gager.at, www.weingut-gager.at

Winemaker: Josef Gager, Horst Gager, Manuel Wieder
Contact Person: Josef and Paula Gager, Ing. Horst Gager, Daniela Dostal
Production: n. a. (100 % red)
Hectares: 38
Fairs: ProWein, VieVinum
Distribution partners: CH, RC, DE, NL

The successful story of the Gager wine estate began in 1984, when Josef Gager started growing his first vines and filled his first 800 bottles. It was clear from the very beginning that a terroir with very special attributes was at hand. This became the inspiration for the quality and character of the wines. "Our soils are heavy and fertile with plenty of nutrients, humus and vitality," says Josef Gager. "The climate is distinguished by abundant sunshine. We attempt to unite all of this in a liquid form." This explanation indeed summarizes Gager's philosophy well. In the very early years, the portfolio included what continues to be the producer's top wine: the blend called Quattro was born in 1988. It was one of the first red wine blends in Austria and became Gager's draught horse and trademark. This wine embodies not only the principles of the winery, but the label design also became the winery's logo. In the evolving success story, the operation had grown to a size that became difficult to manage alone and Josef's son Horst joined the operation. With the fresh breeze of youth and the know-how of the father, the winery was modernized between 2004 and 2006. The Gager wine estate now produces wine from 38 vineyard hectares planted with varieties like Blaufränkisch, Zweigelt, Cabernet Sauvignon, Cabernet Franc, Merlot, Syrah, and even the exotic Tannat. Independent of which of the Gager wines are in the glass "deep dark, concentrated and compact - wine with character" is always an apt phrase to describe them.

(94–96) Blaufränkisch Gager 2013
94 Blaufränkisch Gager V-Max 2012
Dark ruby with a black core, purple highlights, and a thin

transparent rim. The attractive bouquet displays ripe dark berry jam, pleasant herbal spice and candied orange zest over fine nougat notes. Refreshing acidity highlights juicy ripe cherry and sandalwood spice and carries this all the way through the long mineral finish. Very good ageing potential.
94 Blaufränkisch Gager 2011

(90–92) Blaufränkisch Ried Fabian 2013

**90 Mittelburgenland DAC Reserve
    Mitterberg 2013**
91 Blaufränkisch Mitterberg Reserve 2012

91 Blaufränkisch Vitikult 2014

93 Merlot 2012
93 Merlot 2011

(92–94) Tycoon 2013 BF/CS/TA
92 Tycoon 2012 BF/TA/CS
Dark ruby with a black, opaque core, purple highlights and a thin transparent firm. The dark, spicy bouquet features ripe elderberry and cassis with nuances of liquorice and nougat. Complex with blackberry fruit and extract sweetness mingling with herbal spice on the palate. A touch of bitter chocolate joins in on the yet rather hard finish.
92 Tycoon 2011 BF/CS/TA

(91–93) Quattro 2014 CS/BF/ZW/ME
91 Quattro 2013 CS/BF/ZW/ME
92 Quattro 2012 CS/BF/ZW/ME

(89–91) Q2 2014 BF/CS/SY
90 Q2 2013 BF/CS/SY
92 Q2 2011 BF/CS/SY

91 Cablot 2013 CS/ME
91 Cablot 2012 CS/ME
94 Cablot 2011 CS/ME

★ ★ ★ ★ ★

Weingut Gesellmann

7301 Deutschkreutz, Langegasse 65
T: +43 (2613) 80360 0, F: +43 (2613) 80360 15
weingut@gesellmann.at, www.gesellmann.at

— ORGANIC —

Winemaker: Albert Gesellmann
Contact Person: Albert and Silvia Gesellmann
Production: 230.000 bottles (9 % white, 90 % red, 1 % sweet)
Hectares: 45
Fairs: VieVinum, ProWein
Distribution partners: SLO, CZ, NL

The Gesellman estate was first documented in 1767 and since then, numerous generations have passed down their knowledge to be combined and newly defined with modern methods. With 45 vineyard hectares, it is not the producer's goal to supply the world market, but rather international wine lovers in limited quantities. Weingut Gesellmann places great value on autochthon grape varieties. The blend "Opus Eximum" unites the local varieties Blaufränkisch, Zweigelt and St. Laurent in a wine that is destined as an ideal accompaniment to food. Another premium wine is the "G" made from Blaufränkisch and St. Laurent, which stirs the senses with clarity and depth that originated in the 90-year-old vines. The "hochberc", made totally from Blaufränkisch, has been vinified since 2005 and embodies the finesse of the union of a special variety with region and vintner. Also among the top blends is the "Bela Rex" with which the vintner exhibits his abilities with the international varieties Merlot and Cabernet Sauvignon. The estate vineyards also offer ideal sources for tasty white wines. The "Chardonnay Steinriegel" is distinguished by an exciting array of aromas with fine mineral notes while the non-oaked Chardonnay allows the vintner to express his passion for varietal typicity. As of the vintage 2011, the assortment of wines also include a "hochberc weiss", which is a white field blend wine that offers appealing aromas, complexity and body. The Gesellmann white wines are expressive and complex wines for special moments that are matured in new and used small oak barrels or in stainless steel.

(93–95) Blaufränkisch hochberc 2013
95 Blaufränkisch hochberc 2012
Dark ruby with purple highlights and a thin transparent rim. The highly attractive bouquet offers elegant notes of sandalwood, vanilla, herbs, blackberry jam and tobacco nuances. Powerful body with sweet extract and fine tannins. Dark berries, orange, coconut, and a touch of chocolate linger on the exceedingly long finish.
96 Blaufränkisch hochberc 2011

(95–97) Blaufränkisch hochberc Stockkultur 2012
95 Blaufränkisch Hochberg Stockkultur 2011

(91–93) Blaufränkisch Creitzer Reserve 2014
92 Blaufränkisch Creitzer Reserve 2013
92 Blaufränkisch Creitzer Reserve 2012

(90–92) Mittelburgenland DAC Hochacker 2014
91 Mittelburgenland DAC Hochacker 2013
91 Blaufränkisch Hochäcker 2012

(95–97) Merlot 2012
95 Merlot 2011
Dark ruby with purple highlights and thin transparent rim. Ripe cherry, blackberry jam, sandalwood, subtle cassis, and a touch of minerals and spice. Full bodied with abundant, well integrated tannins and vibrant acidity lending a taut texture. Nicely focussed with red berries, minerals and salty components on the finish.

(94–96) G 2012 BF/SL
96 G 2011 BF/SL
Dark ruby with purple highlights and a thin transparent rim. Inviting aromas of sandalwood, blackberry, cassis and tobacco nuances. Juicy, fresh cherry and salty minerals are firmly framed in a fine cloak of tannin. A touch of lemon comes in on the long finish. Outstanding ageing potential.
96 G 2009 BF/SL

(91–93) Opus Eximium No 27 2014 BF/ZW
93 Opus Eximium No 26 2013 BF/ZW/SL
91 Opus Eximium No. 25 2012 BF/ZW/SL

94 Bela Rex 2013 ME/CS
93 Bela Rex 2012 ME/CS
96 Bela Rex 2011 ME/CS

93 Pinot Noir Siglos 2013
92 Pinot Noir Siglos 2012
92 Pinot Noir Siglos 2011

92 Syrah 2012
94 Syrah 2011

93 Chardonnay Steinriegel 2014
93 Chardonnay Steinriegel 2013
93 Chardonnay Steinriegel 2012

91 Chardonnay 2015
92 Chardonnay 2014
90 Chardonnay 2013

91 Sauvignon Blanc 2015
92 Sauvignon Blanc 2014

(91–93) hochberc weiss 2015
92 hochberc weiss 2014
92 hochberc weiß 2013

92 Sämling 88 Beerenauslese 2010

★★★★
Weingut Heinrich

7301 Deutschkreutz, Karrnergasse 59
T: +43 (2613) 89615, F: +43 (2613) 89615 4
office@weingut-heinrich.at, www.weingut-heinrich.at

Winemaker: Silvia Heinrich, Mario Felder
Contact Person: Silvia Heinrich
Production: n. a. (100 % red)
Hectares: 38
Fairs: VieVinum, ProWein, Hong Kong International Wine & Spirits Fair, Interwine China
Distribution partners: CH, SGP, SK, RC, DK, DE, NL, HK, PL

Silvia Heinrich expresses her passion well when she says: "The vineyards are like children to me. And as with children, I strive to accompany them, support them, and do my best for them. In this way I can help them develop their character and realize their potential." Silvia Heinrich grew up in the winery and it is not simply and eight-hour-per-day job; it is a lifestyle. The Heinrichs have specialized completely in red wine since 2009. In fact, the predominant grape variety of the region, Blaufränkisch, is planted to 80% of the Heinrich vineyards. This red variety was even referred to as "Austria's aristocratic grape variety" by the American wine magazine, "Wine & Spirits". Heinrich produces Mittelburgenland's emblematic variety in seven variations from different single vineyards. The interpretations range from elegant and mineral to intense and muscular. The soul of the 36-hectare vineyard area is the Goldberg vineyard, which is planted with eight hectares of Blaufränkisch, three of which were planted in 1947, the year that Judith's grandparents married. The authenticity of Blaufränkisch from this prime vineyard makes the wine count regularly among the very best in the country. Heinrich's motto is "less is more." Fewer varieties, sustainable viticulture, manual harvest, and spontaneous fermentation with native yeast are the pillars of her uncompromising quality – quality that receives much recognition. The extraordinary qualities of the Heinrich wines constantly reap new success at home and abroad. Besides the accustomed good assessment from Falstaff, the Heinrich "Mittelburgenland DAC" 2009 was awarded first place and 94 points out of 200 Austrian wines by Wine & Spirits magazine in April 2013. The "Blaufränkisch vom Weingebirge" was the only Austrian Blaufränk-

isch listed at Wine Enthusiast magazine under the "100 Best Buys"! And ever since the President of China discovered the "Goldberg Reserve" on his visit to Austria, exports flourish in the Far East. With new photovoltaic cells, the winery takes yet another step (along with its use of solar energy and wood chip heating) towards renewable energy and making an important contribution to environmental protection. Sustainable agricultural practices in the vineyard mean that this producer has abstained from the use of insecticides and pesticides for years and uses pheromones in plant protection methods. Sensitivity towards protecting natural resources and improving vine resilience are prime focusses. After all, one wants to pass on an intact environment to one's children.

(90–92) Blaufränkisch Goldberg Reserve 2014
93 Blaufränkisch Goldberg Reserve 2013
Dark ruby with purple highlights and a broad transparent rim. Wild cherry and herbal spice with a touch of orange, liquorice and sandalwood. Plenty of finesse is displayed with juicy, elegant acid and fine tannin texture framing pleasant red berry fruit notes. Lemon and minerals join in on the finale.
93 Blaufränkisch Goldberg Reserve 2012

94 Blaufränkisch Cupido 2012
Dark ruby with purple highlights and a thin transparent rim. The multifaceted bouquet displays blackberry jam and a touch of nougat over delicate nuances of liquorice and mandarin zest. Ripe wild cherry with clove and juniper spice are appetizingly highlighted by juicy acidity and chocolaty tannins. The finish is long and harmonious. Very dependable ageing potential.
94 Blaufränkisch Cupido 2011

92 Blaufränkisch Alte Reben 2012
92 Blaufränkisch Alte Reben 2011

(94–96) Mittelburgenland DAC Reserve
V-Max 2012
94 Mittelburgenland DAC Reserve V-Max 2011

(89–91) Mittelburgenland DAC Goldberg 2015
91 Mittelburgenland DAC Goldberg 2013
91 Mittelburgenland DAC Goldberg 2012

(88–90) Blaufränkisch Vitikult 2014

89 Blaufränkisch vom Weingebirge 2015

(92–94) elegy 2012 ME/CS
95 elegy 2011 ME/CS

92 terra o. 2013 BF/CS/SY/ME
93 terra o. 2012 SY/ME/CS/BF
93 terra o. 2011 BF/CS/SY/ME

(89–91) Maestro 2014 BF/ME/CS
91 Maestro 2013 CS/BF/ME
91 Maestro 2012 BF/CS/ME

(89–91) Siglos 2015 ZW/BF
90 Siglos 2013 ZW/BF

90 Pinot Noir Weisses Kreuz 2013
91 Pinot Noir Weißes Kreuz 2012
91 Pinot Noir Weißes Kreuz 2011

Weingut Hundsdorfer

7311 Neckenmarkt, Lange Zeile 10
T: +43 (2610) 42034, F: +43 (2610) 42034 40, M: +43 (664) 3815259
info@hundsdorfer.at, www.hundsdorfer.at

Winemaker: Anton Handsdorfer
Contact Person: Anton and Elisabeth Handsdorfer
Hectares: 18
Fairs: VieVinum, ProWein
Distribution partners: CH, B, DE, NL, USA, PL

Anton Hundsdorfer produces a broad assortment of red wines from 18 hectares of vineyards in parcels surrounding the wine village of Neckenmarkt. Special attention is given the processing of grapes from the individual plots to achieve the best results from each charge of grapes. Hundsdorfer strives for optimal terroir expression and wants to make it possible to taste the fine nuances of the various vineyard plots in the glass. The family's philosophy is to offer their customers high quality wines for fair prices. It is possible for wine enthusiasts to make their own impressions of the wines in a roomy, cosy tasting room.

Two lines of red wines are offered for sale. The first is the line of classic, traditional wines matured in large oak casks and vats while the premium series is matured in small oak barrels. Numerous successes at tastings have been achieved, for example at the Burgenland Wine Premier. There they won medals in 2002, 2009, and 2011. In 2012, they were the first winery from Burgenland to win three medals at the regional championship. The Anton Hundsdorfer winery was also champion at the SALON Österreich Wein in 2008 and 2013. These accolades highlight the quality consciousness that reigns at the Hundsdorfer wine estate.

92 Zweigelt Reserve 2013
94 Zweigelt Reserve 2012
Deep ruby with purple highlights and a transparent rim. The attractive bouquet features delicate nuances of sandalwood and spice under blackberry and nougat. Complex with juicy acidity and round supportive tannins providing structure to sweetly extracted fruit and spice. The finish is long and chocolaty. Good ageing potential.

92 Syrah Reserve 2012

90 St. Laurent Reserve 2012
91 St. Laurent Reserve 2011

89 St. Laurent Classic 2013

91 Mittelburgenland DAC Reserve 2012
92 Mittelburgenland DAC Reserve 2011

91 Mittelburgenland DAC Hochberg 2013
89 Mittelburgenland DAC Hochberg 2011

92 Merlot Reserve 2013
92 Merlot Reserve 2012
92 Merlot Reserve 2011

91 Cabernet Sauvignon Reserve 2012
92 Cabernet Sauvignon Reserve 2011

93 Canis 2012 ZW/BF/ME/CS
92 Canis Reserve 2011 ZW/BF/ME/CS

★★★
Rotweine Lang

7311 Neckenmarkt, Herrengasse 2
T: +43 (2610) 42384, F: +43 (2610) 42384 6
office@rotweinelang.at, www.rotweinelang.at

Winemaker: Ing. Stefan Lang
Contact Person: Andrea and Stefan Lang
Production: n. a. (100 % red)
Hectares: 30
Fairs: Dornbirner Frühjahrs- and Herbstmesse, VieVinum, ProWein, Vinobile Montfort
Distribution partners: CH, B, RC, DE, CZ, NL, GB, H

Just what is the secret behind this award-winning winery in Mittelburgenland – is a secret that Andrea and Stefan Lang are keeping to themselves. Their focus is in every case on the Blaufränkisch variety and they always give it the time it needs to mature in wood barrels – "good wine needs long!". It is not without reason that Stefan Lang is known as the "Blaufränkisch artist". Many great wines have stemmed from this 30-hectare red wine estate. The family remodelled the over 300-year-old farmhouse and united tradition with modernity. The passion of an entire family flows into this modern red wine estate. Old traditions remain while innovation takes the winery forward into the future. This is reflected in the Lang family's passion, lifestyle in and around the world of wine, in their responsibility towards the environment and their soils and – especially for wine lovers – in the quality of their wines.

90 Fusion One 2014 ME/BF
91 Fusion One 2013 ME/BF
Dark ruby with an opaque core, purple highlights and a discreet transparent rim. Dark berry jam and ripe plum with herbal spice on the nose and in the mouth. Medium complexity with ripe cherry and plenty of well integrated tannins. Fine extract sweetness and cassis on the finish.
92 Fusion One 2012 ME/BF

94 Excelsior 2011 BF/ME/CS/SY

92 Mittelburgenland DAC Reserve L1 2013
92 Mittelburgenland DAC Reserve L1 2012
94 Mittelburgenland DAC Reserve L1 2011

93 Blaufränkisch V-MAX Grandé Réserve 2012

90 Blaufränkisch Vitikult 2015
90 Blaufränkisch Vitikult 2013
Deep dark ruby with purple highlights and a thin transparent rim. Dark berries, sea buckthorn berries, and dried fruit. Powerful and refreshingly structured with juicy acidity. Dark berries and a touch of chocolate on the finish. Offers uncomplicated drinking pleasure.
90 Blaufränkisch Vitikult 2012

89 Blaufränkisch classic 2015
89 Mittelburgenland DAC Classic 2013
89 Blaufränkisch Classic 2012

Rotweingut Prickler

7361 Lutzmannsburg, Bachgasse 4
T: +43 (2615) 87742, F: +43 (2615) 87742 40, M: +43 (664) 3610540
rotweingut@prickler.at, www.prickler.at

Winemaker: Christian Prickler
Contact Person: Herbert and Christian Prickler
Production: n. a. (2 % white, 98 % red)
Hectares: 20
Fairs: VieVinum, ProWein, Weinmesse Innsbruck
Distribution partners: on request

"Wine is our great passion," is the motto of the Prickler family. At their estate, quality comes first. Every step of wine production is looked after with attention to the smallest of details. The mild Pannonian climate pampers the vineyards with the most sunshine hours in all of Austria. The vineyards are distributed over the elevated Lutzmannsburg plateau where a unique microclimate and ideal soils far from busy traffic prevail. Elfi tends the vines with attentive care and respect for nature to ensure top-quality grapes. Herbert's many years of experience combined with the energetic enthusiasm of his and Elfi's son, Christian, lend to the wines a unique family signature. Frequent accolades for the Prickler wines confirm the family's quality efforts. Healthy grapes and restricted yields result in mild red wines with high concentration and quality.

The roots of wine cultivation in the area of Lutzmannsburg date back to pre-Roman times more than 2000 years ago. The earliest recorded documentation is from 1218. Lutzmannsburg can thus lay claim to the earliest mention of wine cultivation in all of Burgenland. Throughout the centuries wine has been the primary economic source of the village and continues to be so today.

(90–92) **Mittelburgenland DAC Sonnberg 2015**
90 **Mittelburgenland DAC Sonnberg 2014**
Dark ruby with purple highlights and a transparent rim. Cherry and plum mingle with spicy tobacco notes and orange zest. Juicy and complex with delicate oak spice and blackberry flavours that continue over the palate and through the finish. A very versatile wine with food.
91 **Mittelburgenland DAC Sonnberg 2013**

(88–90) **Mittelburgenland DAC 2015**
89 **Mittelburgenland DAC Classic 2014**
88 **Mittelburgenland DAC Classic 2013**

(89–91) **Blaufränkisch Vitikult 2015**
89 **Blaufränkisch Vitikult 2013**
91 **Blaufränkisch Vitikult 2011**

(88–90) **Cabernet Sauvignon 2014**
90 **Cabernet Sauvignon 2013**
90 **Cabernet Sauvignon 2012**

(88–90) **Zweigelt Kirchner 2015**

(87–89) **Zweigelt Classic 2015**
88 **Zweigelt 2014**
87 **Zweigelt Classic 2013**

91 **Merlot 2012**
92 **Merlot 2011**

89 **Thermal 2012 BF/ZW/ME/CS**
90 **Thermal 2011 BF/ZW/ME/CS**

★★★★
Weingut Tesch

7311 Neckenmarkt, Herrengasse 26
T: +43 (2610) 43610, F: +43 (2610) 42230, M: +43 (664) 2623756
titan@tesch-wein.at, www.tesch-wein.at

Winemaker: Josef Christian Tesch
Contact Person: Josef, Carmen and Helene Tesch
Production: 90.000 bottles (3 % white, 97 % red)
Hectares: 21
Fairs: VieVinum, ProWein
Distribution partners: S, CH, B, RC, DE, H

The Tesch winery is a traditional family enterprise in which the entire family participates in its success. Between 1979 and 1982, Josef "Pepi" Tesch and his brother, Hans, vinified a small quantity of Blaufränkisch that insiders continue to consider a catalyst of the "Austrian red wine wonder". For many years, Pepi's main efforts were dedicated to his leading position with the Winzerkeller Neckenmarkt wine cooperative. He simultaneously managed the family winery, attentively looking after vinification and wine maturation. Meanwhile, the red wine visionary of Mittelburgenland (Central Burgenland) has entered his well-deserved retirement and has handed responsibility for the winery over to his son, Josef Christian Tesch. Although "Joe" Tesch took over management of the family winery in 2011, growing up with wine was always a central theme, and he identified with the winery quite early on. Joe Tesch loves the outdoors and is and enjoyer of life who adores working in the vineyards. In the wine cellar, he greatly values preciseness and organization. The young viticulturalist and winemaker has brought new energy to this traditional winery without ever ignoring its roots. The name Tesch and, especially, the family's wines, have been highly recognized for some time now. Authenticity and the regional identity of Mittelburgenland are the focus in vinification. The resulting wines are of highest quality and the dedication to the region is certainly tangible. "Every vintage and every vineyard parcel make different demands," says Joe Tesch. "The conscientious cultivation, sustainable vineyard management and manual harvesting are the foundation for our high quality wines. We concentrate on typical regional grape varieties and hand select them for vinification." says Joe Tesch.

(93–95) Blaufränkisch Patriot 2012
94 Blaufränkisch Patriot 2011
Dark ruby with an opaque core, purple highlights, and a thin transparent rim. The multifaceted bouquet features concentrated blackberry jam, velour leather, pleasant sandalwood touch, and fine balsamic spice notes. Full bodied and tightly woven with abundant well integrated tannin. Blackberry and sour cherry flavour the very long finish. Will benefit from further bottle maturation.

92 Blaufränkisch Selection 2013
92 Blaufränkisch Selection 2012
93 Blaufränkisch Selection 2011

(90–92) Mittelburgenland DAC Reserve 2013
92 Mittelburgenland DAC Reserve 2011

90 Mittelburgenland DAC Hochberg 2014
90 Mittelburgenland DAC Hochberg 2013
92 Mittelburgenland DAC Hochberg 2011

89 Mittelburgenland DAC Classic 2014
89 Mittelburgenland DAC Classic 2012
90 Mittelburgenland DAC Classic 2011

88 Zweigelt Classic 2014

93 Titan 2013 BF/ME/CS
Dark ruby with purple highlights and a thin transparent rim. The nose is still rather restrained, but reveals delicate dark berry fruit and a touch of cassis over a subtle background of spicy tobacco. Silky textured tannins are well integrated in juicy dark forest berry jam. Salty minerals and a touch of chocolate come in on the finish of this elegant accompaniment to food.
93 Titan 2012 BF/ME/CS
95 Titan 2011 BF/CS/ME

93 Jana Paulina 2012 ME/CS
93 Jana Paulina 2011 ME/CS

90 Kreos 2013 ZW/SY/ME/BF
90 Kreos 2012 BF/SY/ZW/ME
94 Kreos 2011 ME/SY/BF/CS

(87–89) Exclusive Cuvée 2015 BF/ZW/ME

89 Carpo 2013 ZW/BF/ME

(88–90) BZ Cuvée 2015 BF/ZW

Weingut Wellanschitz

7311 Neckenmarkt, Lange Zeile 28
T: +43 (2610) 42302, F: +43 (2610) 42302 4, M: +43 (664) 4567114
info@wellanschitz.at, www.wellanschitz.at

Winemaker: Stefan, Georg and Stefan David Wellanschitz
Contact Person: Wellanschitz family
Production: n. a. (3 % white, 97 % red)
Hectares: 39,8
Fairs: VieVinum, ProWein
Distribution partners: CH, SK, RC, DE, CZ, USA

When you stand at the highest peak of the vineyards in Neckenmarkt and let your eyes sweep over the Mittelburgenland landscape, you can see all of the Wellanschitz family vineyards. There, near Unterpersdorf, is the Alte Weingebirge; in Horitschon is the Gfanger, and on clear days you can see all the way to Raiding, where the Raga vineyard is located. To the east is the flat Great Hungarian Plain, and even the southern tip of Lake Neusiedl is visible. It is the Neckenmarkt vineyard hills and their steep south-facing slopes that make this expansive view possible. The Blaufränkisch vines here have been thriving in the soils of micha-schist and granite-gneiss with sandy loam for several decades. Customary in the region is to refer to the "Grosslage Hochberg" as a three-section vineyard area with the Hochberg itself as its own individual site. The first hill is the Spiegelberg, which is a small, steep plot at the foot of the Grosslage. Then comes the Bodigraben, in the middle and bordering the Hochberg. The Hochberg itself reaches 480 metres and is the "roof" of this three-fold complex. A little further to the east, but still facing south, is the Sonnensteig, a long-stretching slope that culminates in an elevated plateau. Between the Grosslage Hochberg and the Sonnensteig is the southwest-exposed Burgstall site, a somewhat cool, shaded vineyard that is part of the same geological foundation. These soils yield elegant, finesse-rich wines that can be often unapproachable in their youth, but promise enormous ageing potential.
The geology on the west side of Neckenmarkt is quite different. The vineyards Neuberg and Rüsselsgrund form a soft slope and at their foot is the high plateau where the Hussi site is located. The marine limestone over sandy loam is reminiscent of what is found in north Burgenland. The interplay of the cool influence of the neighbouring spruce forest and the heat-retaining limestone create a microclimate that exudes a Burgundy-like character.
The extensive assortment of Blaufränkisch wines, which play the leading roll at Wellanschitz, highlight the diversity of individual vineyard sites in Mittelburgenland and make a valuable contribution to the preservation of the Blaufränkisch tradition of the region.

92 Blaufränkisch Well 2014
93 Blaufränkisch Well 2013
Deep dark ruby with purple highlights and a broad, somewhat paler rim. Blackberry and a touch of orange zest with delicate sandalwood and balsamic nuances. Complex, with round sweet fruit laced with abundant fine-grained tannin. A pleasant touch of red berries join in on the long mineral finale. A very elegant and light-footed style.
93 Blaufränkisch Well 2012

92 Blaufränkisch Sonnensteig 2013
94 Blaufränkisch Sonnensteig 2011

90 Blaufränkisch Hussi 2014
92 Blaufränkisch Hussi 2013
92 Blaufränkisch Hussi 2012

90 Blaufränkisch Hochberg Alte Reben
     Neckenmarkter Fahnenschwinger 2013

91 Blaufränkisch Hochberg 2014
90 Blaufränkisch Hochberg 2012
90 Blaufränkisch Hochberg 2011
90 Blaufränkisch Altes Weingebirge 2014

91 Blaufränkisch Altes Weingebirge 2013
91 Blaufränkisch Altes Weingebirge 2012

93 Blaufränkisch Bodigraben 2012

(89–91) Blaufränkisch klassisch 2015

89 Cabernet Sauvignon Rüsselsgrund 2014
93 Cabernet Sauvignon Rüsselsgrund 2013
Deep dark ruby with purple highlights and a broad, somewhat paler rim. Blackberry and a touch of orange zest with
delicate sandalwood and balsamic nuances. Complex, with
round sweet fruit laced with abundant fine-grained tannin.
A pleasant touch of red berries join in on the long mineral
finale. A very elegant and light-footed style.
92 Cabernet Sauvignon Rüsselsgrund 2012

91 Syrah 2012

92 Fraternitas 2013 BF/CS
90 Fraternitas 2012 BF/CS
92 Fraternitas 2011

89 Hotter 2013 BF/ZW/ME/SY

92 Weißer Burgunder Muschelkalk
   Alte Reben 2013
93 Weißer Burgunder Muschelkalk
   Alte Reben 2011

92 Grüner Veltliner Neckenmarkt 2012

Idyllic landscape – expressive red wines

The unspoilt, rustic Südburgenland countryside offers a unique mosaic of parent rock material and cool Styrian climatic influences. This provides optimal conditions for a number of grapes, but above all, for an inimitable style of Blaufränkisch.

© ÖWM/ARGE Naturparke Ing. Franz Kovacs

There are many surprising aspects of Südburgenland. The most obvious is the structure of cultivation of the 498 hectares of vineyards. The majority of grape growers are hobby winemakers, or supplement their income with another job or profession. Only a small number of the larger producers are commercially known beyond the region's borders. Much of the wine is consumed locally in buschen-schanken (wine taverns). Despite this, it cannot be disputed that the region is idyllic for wine.

Südburgenland is the coolest part of Burgenland and it has quite a fascinating geology. In the northern and central parts of the wine region, on the southern slopes of the Güns Mountains and in the areas of Hannersdorf, Königsberg, Eisenberg and Csaterberg the vines are rooted upon calcareous phylite, greenschist and serpentinite. Freshwater opals are another remarkable feature that can be found in the vineyards at Csaterberg.

The unique Blaufränkisch of Südburgenland has been authorised to carry the Eisenberg DAC or Eisenberg DAC Reserve protected designations of origin. Other black and white grape varieties also yield pleasing wines and may appear either under the Südburgenland or Burgenland protected geographical indications.

In the most southerly point, around the villages of Heiligenbrunn and Moschendorf, a peculiar specialty called Uhudler is made from the fruit of ungrafted hybrid vines. Its pungent aroma of wild strawberries draws a surprising following. Südburgenland remains an insider's tip, far from the overcrowded traditional wine-growing towns. However, there is a spirit of optimism amongst the younger generation of winemakers, particularly as the thermal health spa resorts, along with the festivals held in the Burg Güssing castle bring a growing number of tourists to the region without jeopardising the peaceful, idyllic wine landscape.

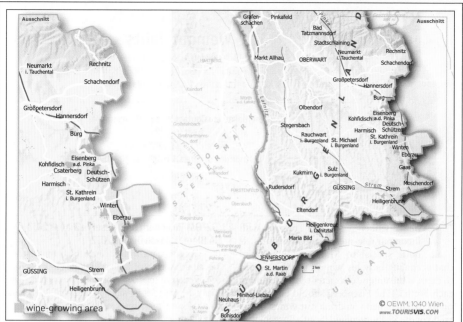

Ausschnitt

Neumarkt i. Tauchental
Rechnitz
Schachendorf
Großpetersdorf
Hannersdorf
Burg
Eisenberg
Kohfidisch a.d. Pinka
Csaterberg   Deutsch-Schützen
Harmisch
St. Kathrein i. Burgenland
Winten
Eberau
GÜSSING   Strem
Heiligenbrunn

wine-growing area

Grafen-schachen   Pinkafeld
Bad Tatzmannsdorf
Stadtschlaining
Markt Allhau   OBERWART   Neumarkt i. Tauchental   Rechnitz
Schachendorf
Großpetersdorf
Hannersdorf
Burg
Olbendorf
Eisenberg
Stegersbach   Kohfidisch a.d. Pinka   Deutsch-Schützen
Rauchwart i. Burgenland   Harmisch   St. Kathrein i. Burgenland
St. Michael i. Burgenland   Winten
Eberau
Kukmirn   Sulz i. Burgenland   Gaas
Rudersdorf   GÜSSING   Strem   Strem   Moschendorf
Eltendorf   Heiligenbrunn
Heiligenkreuz i. Lafnitztal
Maria Bild
JENNERSDORF
St. Martin a.d. Raab   0   2 km
Minihof-Liebau
Neuhaus
Bonisdorf

Ausschnitt

© OEWM, 1040 Wien
www.TOURISVIS.COM

◆ Weingut Jalits, Badersdorf

◆ Weingut Kopfensteiner, Deutsch Schützen

◆ Weingut Krutzler, Deutsch Schützen

◆ Weingut Schützenhof, Deutsch Schützen

Weingut Jalits

7512 Badersdorf, Untere Dorfstraße 18
T: +43 (664) 3303827, F: +43 (3366) 78311
office@jalits.at, www.jalits.at

Winemaker and Contact Person: Mathias Jalits
Hectares: 13
Fairs: ProWein, VieVinum
Distribution partners: CH, B, L, DE, NL, USA

The Eisenberg, a wine region with incomparable merits and attributes, is quite special to Mathias Jalits – and that is exactly how his wines taste. He strives to express the unique character of this region in each bottle. "The Eisenberg should be tangible on the palate when you drink our wines" is the credo of the Südburgenland (South Burgenland) vintner. Sand, clay and heavy loam soils in a convex-shaped site that opens towards the southeast and is protected from icy northern winds all provide optimal conditions for powerful, minerally Blaufränkisch vines to thrive. Blaufränkisch is the winery's main variety, but Cabernet Sauvignon, Pinot Noir, Merlot, Zweigelt and a tiny amount of Welschriesling also grow in the vineyards on the slops of the Eisenberg. Mathias Jalits is the fifth generation of the family to practice viticulture here. He took over management of the family enterprise in 2001 and has since steadily expanded the vineyard area while keeping a persistent focus on quality and regional identity. He is not one to brave risky experiments, neither in the vineyard, nor the cellar. "Traditional regional identity should be reflected in my wines. That is me, that is Südburgenland, and that is how our wines should be." That Mathias Jalits is spot-on with his philosophy is repeatedly confirmed by outstanding Falstaff wine ratings. We can really look forward to superb wines that we will be tasting from this producer in the coming years.

(92–94) **Eisenberg DAC Reserve Diabas 2013**
94 **Blaufränkisch Diabas 2012**
Dark ruby with purple highlights and a thin transparent rim. The attractive bouquet features delicate blackberry jam and pronounced spice over a background of liquorice and cherry. Juicy and elegant with well integrated, fine-grained tannins. Sweet fruit lingers in the aftertaste. Possesses great length and ageing potential.
93 **Blaufränkisch Diabas 2011**

(90–92) **Eisenberg DAC Reserve Szapary 2014**
93 **Eisenberg DAC Reserve Szapary 2011**

92 **Eisenberg DAC Reserve 2013**
Dark ruby with purple highlights and a thin, transparent rim. Blackberry and a hint of black currant with an undertone of juniper spice and orange zest. Abundant fine-grained tannins are bedded in juicy black fruit. Cassis appears in the mineral finale.
92 **Eisenberg DAC Reserve 2012**

(90–92) **Eisenberg DAC 2015**
89 **Eisenberg DAC 2014**
90 **Eisenberg DAC 2013**

(88–90) **Zweigelt 2015**
88 **Zweigelt 2014**
90 **Zweigelt 2013**

(91–93) **Steinberg 2014 BF/ME/CS**
92 **Steinberg 2013 BF/ZW/CS**
93 **Steinberg 2012 BF/ME**

91 **Cabernet Sauvignon 2011**

88 **Welschriesling 2013**

★★★
Weingut Kopfensteiner

7474 Deutsch Schützen, Untere Hauptstraße 31
T: +43 (3365) 2236, F: +43 (3365) 2236 5
weingut@kopfensteiner.at, www.kopfensteiner.at

Winemaker: Thomas Kopfensteiner
Contact Person: Astrid Kopfensteiner
Hectares: 15
Fairs: VieVinum, ProWein
Distribution partners: on request

The Kopfensteiner family winery is situated in the idyllic landscape of Südburgenland (South Burgenland) near the Hungarian border. It is managed by their son, Thomas, and was formerly only a part-time operation. The vineyard area was steadily expanded in the 1990s and now comprises 15 hectares in Deutsch Schützen and on the Eisenberg mountain. The assortment of grape varieties includes Welschriesling, Weissburgunder (Pinot Blanc), Zweigelt, and Blaufränkisch as well as Cabernet Sauvignon and Merlot. The main focus is on Blaufränkisch, which is the leading variety in Südburgenland, where it finds most advantageous conditions. The Kopfensteiners' philosophy of uncompromising quality and conscientious work in the vineyard and cellar ensure the production of quality products that are typical for the region. Along with the Blaufränkisch wines, the flagship is the blend called "Border" – a wine that although impressive in its youth, first shows its full potential with a few years bottle maturation. The vineyards are cultivated attentively and with much care. Meticulous cluster and leaf thinning pair with soil and climate to yield ripe, perfectly healthy fruit. "It is not over-motivated mechanization and certainly not the so-called 'new vinification technologies' that are our focus," says Manfred Kopfensteiner. "It is simply ensuring that physiologically ripe grapes free from green tannins are sourced for our quality wines."

(91–93) Eisenberg DAC Reserve Saybritz 2014
92 Eisenberg DAC Reserve Saybritz 2013
Dark ruby with purple highlights and a thin transparent rim. Fresh herbs and peppery spice with nuances of cassis, blackberry and tobacco. Juicy lingonberry jam is highlighted by refreshing acidity and well integrated tannins. Vibrant finish and a very appetizing style.
93 Eisenberg DAC Reserve Saybritz 2012

92 Eisenberg DAC Reserve Szapary 2012

(92–94) Eisenberg DAC Reserve Reihburg 2014
93 Eisenberg DAC Reserve Reihburg 2012

(89–91) Eisenberg DAC Reserve Weinberg 2014
91 Eisenberg DAC Reserve Weinberg 2013
92 Eisenberg DAC Reserve Weinberg 2012

89 Eisenberg DAC 2014
89 Eisenberg DAC 2013
90 Eisenberg DAC 2012

90 Merlot 2013
90 Merlot 2009

(88–90) Zweigelt 2015
88 Zweigelt 2014

(91–93) Border 2014 BF/ME
92 Border 2013 BF/CS/ME
Dark ruby with purple highlights and a thin transparent rim. Dark forest berries, a touch of wild cherry, and nuances of tobacco and herbal spice. Juicy, elegant and well balanced with fine-grained tannins and refreshing acidity. The long finish features minerals and a touch of nougat. Good ageing potential.
93 Border 2012 BF/ME/CS

Weingut Krutzler

7474 Deutsch Schützen, Untere Hauptstraße 6
T: +43 (3365) 2242, F: +43 (3365) 20013
weingut@krutzler.at, www.krutzler.at

Winemaker and Contact Person: Reinhold Krutzler
Production: n. a. (3 % white, 97 % red)
Hectares: 12
Fairs: VieVinum, ProWein
Distribution partners: J, CDN, CH, SK, DE, NL, N, GB, H, USA

The Krutzler winery is now in its fifth generation. The first quality wines were bottled in 1966, and ever since then, the family has committed itself to the best quality possible. The estate's 12 vineyard hectares are planted around the village of Deutsch Schützen and the Eisenberg mountain only with red grape varieties, primarily Blaufränkisch. In fact, the compact and clearly defined assortment of single vineyard wines is focused on the Blaufränkisch cultivar. However, not one of the Krutzler wines could really be called "everybody's darling". These are the wines with edges and corners; that express climatic ideosyncracies and speak of their terroir - wines that reflect the uncompromising philosophy of their vintner. All vineyard plots are situated in a south- to southeast-facing amphitheatre bordered by an oak and pine forest. This wind-protected aspect is influenced by the warm Pannonian steppe air. The soils are mineral-rich schist and iron-rich loam. This unique terroir with a long vegetation period and low yields brings inimitable wines of character. The very best sites of Deutsch Schützen, at the foot of the Eisenberg, are sources for the Blaufränkisch Reserve. Only Blaufränkisch vines that are at least 25 years old are utilized for this wine. Prolonged cask maturation is the foundation for powerful, spicy wines with profound mineral character. The best Blaufränkisch grapes are selected by hand for the flagship wine Perwolff. This meticulously vinified wine exhibits extraordinary longevity and has helped the small village of Deutsch Schützen achieve world fame. The historic name of this village was documented as "Perwolff" in 1221. The Perwolff 2007 was named as the best red wine of the year at the Falstaff Red Wine Premier in 2009. The Krutzler winery has received numerous national and international accolades and has been accepted into the prestigious "Renommierte Weingüter Burgenland" vintner association.

(92–94) Blaufränkisch Perwolff 2014
93 Blaufränkisch Perwolff 2013
Dark ruby with purple highlights and a thin transparent rim. Sandalwood spice, a touch of dark berries, nuances of velour leather and nougat, and a hint of liquorice. Juicy, red cherry flavours the abundant tannins. Red berries linger long on the refreshing finish.
94 Blaufränkisch Perwolff 2012

92 Eisenberg DAC Reserve 2014
91 Eisenberg DAC Reserve 2013
92 Eisenberg DAC Reserve 2012

(89–91) Eisenberg DAC 2015
89 Eisenberg DAC 2014
91 Eisenberg DAC 2013

89 Blaufränkisch 2015
88 Blaufränkisch 2014
90 Blaufränkisch 2013

(91–93) Blaufränkisch Alter Weingarten 2014
92 Alter Weingarten 2013 BF/ZW
93 Alter Weingarten 2012 BF/ZW

93 Merlot 2014
92 Merlot 2013
Deep dark ruby with an opaque core, purple highlights and a thin transparent rim. A multifaceted bouquet invites with notes of sandalwood, a touch of nougat and dark berry jam. Juicy black cherry, fine-grained tannins and sweet extract in the finish. Good ageing potential.
93 Merlot 2012

Weingut Schützenhof

7474 Deutsch Schützen, Winzerstraße 41
T: +43 (3365) 2203, F: +43 (3365) 2203 85, M: +43 (664) 1099333
weingut@schuetzenhof.cc, www.schuetzenhof.cc

Winemaker: Markus and Walter Faulhammer
Contact Person: Faulhammer family
Production: 40.000 bottles (7 % white, 93 % red)
Hectares: 11
Fairs: VieVinum, ProWein
Distribution partners: CH, DE, USA

The Schützenhof winery, located in Deutsch-Schützen at the foot of the Eisenberg, has existed since 1816, and is now in its sixth generation as a family winery. This producer has been bottling their quality wines since 1952. The diversity of the wine assortment is unusually broad for this area. The main focus is naturally on red wines and, in particular, on the varieties Blaufränkisch and Zweigelt. The varieties Merlot, Cabernet Sauvignon and Pinot Noir also yield excellent wines. A typical regional Welschriesling, a rather exotic blend of Chardonnay and Riesling, and a sparkling wine from Muscat Blanc à petits grains and Welschriesling called "briszante" round out the assortment of wines. The cornerstones of the excellent quality produced here are the age of the vines (some over 90 years old), sustainable vineyard management, experience and know-how, and exceptionally gentle vinification. The winery building itself was awarded the Burgenland Architecture Prize in 2005. Its transparency and functionality are not only aesthetic, but they also allow minimal mechanical intervention to preserve varietal character and prevent loss of aroma. The Eisenberg site brings intense mineral character, fruitiness and potential for ageing – wines which offer tremendous drinking pleasure with their full body and inimitable character. The winery respects wine as a cultural treasure. It writes its own rules and abstains from releasing the wines too early in favour of balance and longevity. Wines are not released before maturing at least 12 – and sometimes even 30 – months or more. This financial expense is justifiably explained once you taste the wines and realize that each bottle speaks for itself.

93 Eisenberg DAC Reserve Senior 2013
93 Eisenberg DAC Reserve Senior 2012
Dark ruby with purple highlights and a discreetly fading rim. Blackberry and cassis with notes of sandalwood and dark berries in the backgound. Juicy, sweet fruit, well integrated tannins and a tightly woven texture. Good length and ageing potential.
94 Eisenberg DAC Reserve Senior 2011

91 Eisenberg DAC Reserve 2013
92 Eisenberg DAC Reserve 2012

91 Eisenberg DAC Blaufränkisch Pur 2014
90 Eisenberg DAC Pur 2013
91 Eisenberg DAC Pur 2012

93 Merlot 2011
Dark ruby with purple highlights and a thin transparent rim. Caramel and nougat with undertones of delicate cherry fruit, clove and juniper. Complexity is underscored by silky tannins and juicy acidity. Red berries and discreet orange notes linger on the finish of this versatile food wine.
92 Merlot 2009

91 Pinot Noir 2014
91 Pinot Noir 2013
91 Pinot Noir Szapary 2012

93 Cabernet Sauvignon 2011

90 Rotburger Ratschen 2014
89 Zweigelt Ratschen 2013

91 Kastellan 2012 CS/ME/BF
93 Kastellan 2009 BF/ME/PN

91 Dunkelbunt 2013 ZW/BF/CS

89 Funkelbunt 2015 GM/WR

INTERNATIONAL

falstaff

AUSTRALIA (AUS)

Fox Beverages
1350 Woollahra, PO Box 588
T: +61 (0) 416115355
F: +61 (2) 94754456

Vinous + Vinous Imports
1450 Camperdown, PO Box 93
T: +61 (2) 95727285
F: +61 (2) 95727742
info@vinous.com.au
www.vinous.com.au

Vintage & Vine Pty Ltd
1515 West Chatswood, PO Box 5139
T: +61 (2) 94205088
F: +61 (2) 94205099
david@vintageandvine.com
www.vintageandvine.com

Luxury Beverage Group
2000 Sydney, Level 10
67 Castlereagh Street
T: +61 (2) 8011 1549
F: +61 (2) 9238 8003
info@luxurybeverages.com.au
www.luxurybeveragegroup.com

Ultimo Wine Centre
2007 Ultimo
C21/99 Jones Street
T: +61 (2) 92112380
F: +61 (2) 92112382
info@ultimowinecentre.com.au

World Wine Estates
2073 Pymble, 18 Kiparra St
T: +61 (2) 93808808
F: +61 (2) 93808840
james@worldwineestates.com.au
www.worldwineestates.com.au

Enoteca Sydney Comida Pty Ltd.
2016 Redfern
283 Chalmers Street
T: +61 (2) 96981660
F: +61 (2) 96981660
andreas@enotecasydney.com

Enoteca Sydney Wine Merchant
2015 Alexandria
17-27 Power Avenue
T: +61 (2) 96981660
F: +61 (2) 96981660
comida@bigpond.com.au
www.enotecasydney.com

Cogito Wines
2041 East Balmain
Level 1, Darling Street
nick@cogitowines.com.au
www.cogitowines.com.au

Young & Rashleigh Wine Merchants & Cuttings Wine
2065 Crows Nest, 2 Bruce Street
T: +61 (2) 99675900
F: +61 (2) 99675944
justin@youngandrashleigh.com
www.youngandrashleigh.com

Deja Vu Wine Company Ltd.
2073 Pymble, PO Box 783
T: +61 (412) 771992
F: +61 (2) 94996123
acameron@dejavuwines.com.au
www.dejavuwines.com.au

Heart & Soil Wine Imports
3066 Collingwood, 7–9 Keele Street
T: +61 (408) 432456
info@heartandsoil.com.au

CellarHand Wine Distribution
3121 Richmond
Suite 9 / 8 Bromham Place
T: +61 (3) 92748444
F: +61 (3) 94216419
sales@cellarhand.com.au
www.cellarhand.com.au

Archer & Co Pty Ltd
3000 Melbourne, 443 Little Collins St
T: +61 (4) 00518170
www.archerandco.com.au

Beach Avenue Wholesalers Pty Ltd.
3175 Dandenong, 38–42 Ordish Road
T: +61 (3) 87911400
F: +61 (3) 97069809
sales@baw.com.au, www.baw.com.au

Russell Gehling Wines
3206 Albert Park
Unit 1/76 Kerferd Road
T: +61 (488) 770160
F: +61 (3) 96969160
rg@russellgehlingwines.com.au

Smashing Bottles
4006 Fortitude Valley
Suite 2, 374 Brunswick Street
T: +61 (7) 32523946
sales@smashingbottles.com.au

Euro Pacific Liquor Pty Ltd.
4035 Albany Creek, 34 Maud Street
T: +61 (7) 32643648
F: +61 (7) 33253834
info@europacificliquor.com.au
www.europacificliquor.com.au

GBH Vineyards
4226 Robina, PO Box 495
T: +61 (408) 312266
F: +61 (7) 55930889
gbhvineyards@westnet.com.au
www.gbhvineyards.com.au

Mezzanine Wine
3067 Abbotsford
112 Trennery Crescent
T: +61 (1300) 5558821
customerservicesa@casama.com.au

Negociants Australia
5000 Adelaide, 195 Grote Street
T: +61 (8) 81124212
F: +61 (8) 81124280
negaus@negociants.com
www.negociantsaustralia.com

George Street Wines
5031 Thebarton, 58–62 George Street
T: +61 (8) 83517116
F: +61 (8) 83517226
admin@georgestreetwines.com.au

Muster Wine & Spirit Co.
5052 Belair, 27 Gault Road
T: +61 (430) 360650
david@musterwineco.com.au
www.musterwineco.com.au

Decantwines
5063 Fullarton, PO Box 23
T: +61 (8) 83383205
F: +61 (8) 83623411
hq@decantwines.com
www.decantwines.com

Garage wines
5171 Mclaren Vale, PO Box 2427
T: +61 (0) 412480486
F: +61 (0) 885582901
chrishill@garagewine.com.au
www.garagewine.com.au

the spanish acquisition
8006 Victoria
PO Box 12158 a'beckett Street
T: +61 (3) 93491804

BELGIUM (B)

Why Not Wein
1040 Brussels, Rue des Bataves 19
T: +32 (498) 317551
rene.clausen@whynotwein.eu
www.whynotwein.eu

Delhaize Group
1080 Brussels
Rue Osseghemstraat 53
T: +32 (2) 4122111
F: +32 (2) 4122222
www.delhaizegroup.com

**Le Vin Autrichien –
De Oostenrijkse Wijn**
1081 Brussels
Place Van Hoegaerde 22
T: +32 (2) 4118308
F: +32 (2) 4118391
kurt.ryslavy@skynet.be
www.ryslavy.com

Colruyt
1500 Halle
Edingensesteenweg 196
T: +32 (2) 3635545
F: +32 (2) 3600207
help@colruytgroup.com

Best Caviar
1700 Dilbeek-Brussels
Grote Sijpestraat 12
T: +32 (2) 5690034
F: +32 (2) 5670669
info@bestcaviar.be
www.bestcaviar.be

Mampaey Wines and Spirits
1702 Groot-Bijgaarden
A.Gossetlaan 23
T: +32 (24) 665858
F: +32 (24) 660063
info@mampaey-wines.be
www.mampaey-wines.be

Vinea W.C.T.
1755 Gooik, Stuivenbergstraat 20
T: +32 (2) 4608600
F: +32 (2) 5698500
info@vinea.be
www.vinea.be

Vinikus & Lazarus
1785 Merchtem, Spiegellaan 26
T: +32 (478) 346984
F: +32 (52) 408691
gerd@vinikusenlazarus.be
www.vinikusenlazarus.be

RoodWitRood
1820 Melsbroek, Hof van Boetsfort 8
T: +32 (475) 380627
koen@roodwitrood.be
www.roodwitrood.be

Despert & Co. N.V.
2018 Antwerp, Schulstraat 18–20
T: +32 (323) 80584
F: +32 (323) 75113
info@despert.be, www.despert.be

**Oostenrijks Wijnhuis
Guy Janssens**
2240 Viersel
Liersebaan 315
T: +32 (475) 714597
F: +32 (3) 4750071
contact@oostenrijkswijnhuis.be
www.oostenrijkswijnhuis.be

WeinWelt
2400 Mol, Jakob Smitslaan 57/201
T: +32 (495) 198906
or +32 (476) 051273
info@weinwelt.be, www.weinwelt.be

Wijnhandel de Kok
2500 Lier
Hagenbroeksesteenweg 180
T: +32 (3) 4808595
F: +32 (3) 4802971
info@wijnen-dekok.com
www.wijnen-dekok.com

Primovino, Ivo Legrand
2547 Lint, Kleinmijlveld 42
T: +32 (3) 2889352
info@primovino.be

Axybel
2560 Kessel-Station, Beemdweg 7
T: +32 (3) 4910191
F: +32 (3) 4892765
axybel@axybel.be, www.axybel.be

Global Wineries
2950 Kapellen, Starrenhoflaan 46
T: +32 (3) 3268170
F: +32 (3) 6331320
info@globalwineries.com
www.globalwineries.com

HoMa Vinum Maarten Horions
3520 Zonhoven
Zaakvoerder Demerstraat 9
T: +32 (471) 415144
Homavinum@gmail.com

Ad Bibendum Fine Wines
3800 Brustem, Alfajetlaan 2220
T: +32 (11) 262700
F: +32 (11) 262766
info@adbibendum.be
www.adbibendum.be

Predikaat
3806 Velm-St. Truiden
Halingenstraat 72
T: +32 (11) 593308
eric@predikaat.be
www.predikaat.be

VéRa Vinum OHG
4720 Kelmis, Moresneterstraat 15
T: +32 (87) 765913
F: +32 (87) 851325
info@veravinum.com

Nico Knott AG, Nico Knott
4750 Nidrum, Bermicht 8
T: +32 (80) 445604
F: +32 (80) 444930
knott@swing.be
www.hotel4jahreszeiten.com

Matthys Wijnimport
8200 Bruges, Gistelsesteenweg 228
T: +32 (50) 386380
F: +32 (50) 381677
frank@matthys-wines.be
www.matthys-wines.be

Crombé - The Belgian Winehouse
8500 Kortrijk, Doenaertstraat 20
T: +32 (5621) 1987
F: +32 (5620) 5198
info@crombewines.com
www.crombewines.com

Wine in a Bottle
8550 Zwevegem, Theofiel Toyeplein 1
T: +32 (473) 938019
yves.vandewal@wineinabottle.be
www.wineinabottle.be

Rabotvins, Roland Blancquaert
9000 Ghent, Vogelenzang 1-4
T: +32 (9) 2258986
F: +32 (9) 2240573
info@rabotvins.com
www.rabotvins.com

Wijnen Jan Rots BVBA
9000 Ghent,
Sophie van Akenstratt 11-101
T: +32 (47) 6358787
jan@wijnenjanrots.be
www.wijnenjanrots.be

Vitis Vin
9031 Ghent
Industriepark Drongen 15b
Tel: +32 (9) 2200817
info@vitisvin.be
www.vitisvin.be

Wijnhuis Tinto
9070 Heusden
Blauwesteenstraat 75
T: +32 (9) 2523360
info@wijnhuistinto.be
www.wijnhuistinto.be

Vano Vino Wine Selectors
9090 Melle, Tuinstraat 1E
T: +32 (9) 3297389
F: +32 (9) 3297392
info@vano-vino.be

Wijnhandel Bauwmans
9120 Haasdonk, Zandstraat 74
Tel: +32 (3) 7758660
info@justwine.be
www.justwine.be

VejaVino bvba
8301 Duinbergen
Zeegrasstraat 13
T: +32(499)673500
info@vejavino.be
www.vejavino.be

De Wijnkamer g.c.v.
9200 Dendermonde, Denstraat 72
T: +32 (478) 904840
info@dewijnkamer.be
www.dewijnkamer.be

Les Verres Bavards
9200 Schoonaarde
Jozef de Troetselstraat 23
T: +32 (52) 428442
F: +32 (52) 423268
info@lesverresbavards.be
www.topwijnen.net

Leirovins
9230 Wetteren, Oude Heerbaan 9
T: +32 (9) 3690795
F: +32 (9) 3660717
leirovins@telenet.be
www.leirovins.be

Istrian Chill Out Wines
9840 De Pinte, Bosstraat 5
T: +32 (495) 598016
patrick.dhondt88@outlook.com
www.istrianchilloutwines.be

Portovino N.V., Jan de Clerq
9991 Maldegem, Ringbaan 32
T: +32 (50) 718757
F: +32 (50) 718737
info@portovino.be, www.portovino.be

BULGARIA (BG)

Wineforum Bulgaria O.O.D
1124 Sofia, Reka Osam 1, app. 6
T: +359 (11) 84331000

Project-AW
1202 Sofia, Benkowski 55
T: +359 (2) 9836366
F: +359 (2) 9836366
info@project-aw.com
www.project-aw.com

Bibendum
1407 Sofia, 137 Philip Kutev Street
T: +359 (2) 9621742
F: +359 (2) 9624085
vip@bibendum.bg
www.bibendum.bg

wine.unlimited O.O.D
1421 Sofia, Lipa Street 2
T: +359 (2) 9634798
office@wine-unlimited.com

Avexim
1505 Sofia, Jundolastr. 13
T: +359 (2) 8162884
aveximbg@gmail.com
www.avexim.bg

Vinodistribucia Ltd.; Bibendum O.O.D
1517 Sofia, 247 Botevgradsko
shosse blvd., administrative bldg. 2
7th floor, office 2704
T: +359 (2) 8140810
bibendum@bibendum.bg
www.bibendum.bg

Zagreus AD
4270 Parvomay, Iglika Street 30
T: +359 (336) 98091
zagreus@zagreus.org

BRASIL (BRA)

The Special Wineries
CEP 0471-020 Sao Paulo
Rua Geraldo dos Campos Moreira 17
T: +55 (11) 37426648
www.thespecialwineries.com

CANADA (CDN)

Renaissance Wine Merchants Ltd.
AB T2G 3A4 Calgary
3303 - 8 Street SE
T: +1 (403) 2960170
F: +1 (403) 2960175
mferrier@renwine.com
www.renaissancewine.ca

Artisan Wines
AB T8N 3T3 St. Albert
410 Lakeside Green
T: +1 (780) 9083611
F: +1 (780) 4600386
dave@artisanwines.ca
www.artisanwines.ca

Farmstead Wines
BC V51Y1 Vancouver
2016 Ferndale Street
T: +1 (877) 8877813
info@farmsteadwines.com
www.farmsteadwines.com

Mark Anthony Group
BC V5T 4T5 Vancouver
887 Great Northern Way
T: +1 (888) 3941122
info@markanthony.com
www.markanthonywineandspirits.ca

Marquis Wine Cellars
BC V6E 1M3 Vancouver
1034 Davie Street
T: +1 (604) 6840445
info@marquis-wines.com
www.marquis-wines.com

Marram Wines
BC V7V 3P1 Vancouver
PO Box 91403
T: +1 (604) 7897569
F: +1 (778) 9454964
info@marramwines.com
http://www.marramwines.com

Banville & Jones
MB R2M 3W7 Winnipeg
1616 St. Mary's Road
T: +1 (204) 9489463
F: +1 (204) 9489466
wine@banvilleandjones.com
www.banvilleandjones.com

Heritage Spirits & Wines Ltd.
MB R2W 4Y5 Winnipeg
600 McGregor Street
T: +1 (204) 5896144
F: +1 (204) 5824509

MLCC Manitoba Liquor Control Board
MB R3C 2X1 Winnipeg
1555 Buffalo Place
P.O. Box 1023
T: +1 (800) 2653912
F: +1 (204)2843500
www.liquormarts.ca

Violet Hill Wine Imports Ltd.
ON L0N 1S8 Shelburne
427385 25th Side Road Mono
T: +1 (905) 5860449
phallett@xplornet.com

Family Wine Merchants
ON L2R 6P7 St. Catharines
1469 Pelham Road
T: +1 (905) 6849771
F: +1 (905) 6848444
info@familywinemerchants.com
www.familywinemerchants.com

PMA Peter Mielzynski Agencies Ltd.
ON L6H 7S8 Oakville
231 Oak Park Boulevard, Suite 400
T: +1 (905) 2572116
F: +1 (905) 2572286
info@pmacanada.com
www.pmacanada.com

Crimson Imports
ON L7N 3K5 Calgary
PO Box 81122
T: +1 (403) 4752475
F: +1 (403) 4511752
info@crimsonimports.ca
www.crimsonimports.ca

David C. Walker Wine Inc., Vins de Terroir
ON L7N 3K5 Canmore
819 Wilson Way, Suite 4
T: +1 (403) 6785690
F: +1 (866) 5432934
davidcwalker@shaw.ca

DeLancey Direct Inc.
AB T2E 5T1, Calgary
3112 11 Street, Suite 204
T: +1 (403) 2503390
F: +1 (587) 4004615
sales@delanceydirect.com
www.delanceydirect.com

Horizon Wines
ON L7N 3K5 Canmore, 5 Woodside Lane
T: +1 (403) 6098396
F: +1 (403) 6098558
horizonwines@telus.net

Klebesits Wine Imports Ltd.
ON L7N 3K5 Gormley
17 Cedar Ridge Road
T: +1 (905) 8880030
F: +1 (905) 8885031
h.klebesits@klebesitswine.com
www.klebesitswine.com

Thompson Vintage Trade Ltd.
ON L7N 3K5 Burlington
400 Swinburne Road
T: +1 (905) 6342325
F: +1 (905) 6345174
cheryl@vintagetrade.com
www.vintagetrade.com

Vinexx
ON L7N 3K5 Hamilton
14 Homewood Avenue
T: +1 (905) 5251113
F: +1 (905) 5253338
rlutz@vinexx.com, www.vinexx.com

Eurovintage International Inc.
ON M3A 3R3 Toronto, 1315 Lawrence Ave East, Suite 407
T: +1 (416) 4942881
info@eurovintage.com
www.eurovintage.com

Lamprecht International Ltd.
ON M4K 3N1 Toronto
169 Hopedale Avenue
T: +1 (416) 4213908
F: +1 (416) 4216963
lamprechtinternational@rogers.com
www.lamprechtinternational.com

The Small Winemakers Collection
ON M4M 3H3 Toronto, 100 Broadview Avenue, Suite 318
T: +1 (416) 4637178
info@smallwinemakers.ca
www.smallwinemakers.ca

Lifford Wine Agency
ON M4Y 2G8 Toronto, 471 Jarvis St.
T: +1 (416) 4404101
F: +1 (416) 4402726
enquiries@liffordwine.com
www.liffordwine.com

Liquor Control Board Ontario
ON M5E 1A4 Toronto
55 Lakeshore Boulevard East
T: +1 (416) 4639496
F: +1 (416) 4639496
www.lcbo.com

Abcon International Wine Merchants
ON M9N 3V2 Toronto, 2009 Lawrence Avenue West, Suite 10
T: +1 (416) 7668235
F: +1 (416) 7668245
francoise@abconwine.com
www.abconwine.com

H.H.D. Imports Inc.
ON N2V 1W2 Waterloo
79 Rankin Street, Unit 7
T: +1 (519) 8847600
F: +1 (519) 7468368
info@hhdimports.com
www.hhdimports.com

La Céleste Levure
QC H2T 1S1 Montréal
5344 Boulevard Saint-Laurent
T: +1 (514) 9485050
F: +1 (514) 9485030
info@lacelestelevure.ca
www.lacelestelevure.ca

DBV – Dépôt des Bières et Vins Inc.
QC H3H 1P6 Montréal
1967 rue Baile
T: +1 (514) 9331961
F: +1 (514) 9333340
dbvins@sympatico.ca
www.dbvins.bouchapier.ca

Clos des Vignes
QC H3K 1G6 Montréal
1751 rue Richardson, Suite 4119
T: +1 (514) 9850647
F: +1 (514) 9859441
info@lccvins.com, www.lccvins.com

Le Maître de Chai
QC H3K 3G9 Montréal
1643 rue Saint Patrick
T: +1 (514) 6589866
F: +1 (514) 2846165
contact@lemaitredechai.qc.ca
www.lemaitredechai.qc.ca

Opimian
QC H4A 1T6 Montréal
5165 Sherbrooke Street W. Suite 420
T: +1 (514) 4835551
opim@opim.ca, www.opim.ca

Mosaiq Inc.
QC H9P 2V9 Dorval
1405 Route Transcannadienne
4230 Boulevard St. Jean, No. 219
T: +1 (514) 6761433
F: +1 (514) 6967805
info@mosaiq.ca, www.mosaiq.ca

Les Vins Alain Bélanger
QC J0E 1M0 Dunham, 4500 Strobl
T: +1 (450) 5383782
F: +1 (450) 5384288
info@lvab.ca
www.lvab.ce

Divin Paradis
QC J4B 5S4 Boucherville
760 Jaques Porlier
T: +1 (450) 6451532
F: +1 (450) 6451555
divinparadis@sympatico.ca

CHINA (CN)

ASC Fine Wines
100027 Beijing
7th floor, Block D, The Place No. 9 Guanghua Road
T: +86 (10) 65873808101
F: +86 (10) 65873809
homedelivery@asc-wines.com
www.thewinerepublic.com

Ewald´s Restaurant
200042 Shanghai
Building 1, 999 Gaojing Road
T: +86 (21) 59887251
ewald@gusto-shanghai.com
www.gusto-shanghai.com

EMW Shanghai Trading Co. Ltd.
200042 Shanghai
Room 202, Man Po International Business
T: +86 (21) 62824966
F: +86 (21) 62824969
info@emw-wines.com
www.emw-wines.com

Montrose Fine Wines
200042 Shanghai
Room 101, No.11 Yu Jing Gang Road, Zhabei District
T: +86 (21) 33676507
F: +86 (21) 33676509
www.montrose.com.hk

Shanghai City Supermarket
200042 Shanghai
Room 1701, Haisen Int'Mansion, 1496 Kang Ding Road
T: +86 (21) 62327070
F: +86 (21) 62322177
customerservice@cityshop.com.cn
www.cityshop.com.cn

Liside Trading Co. Ltd.
200125 Shanghai, 1728 Cheng Shan
Road, Blk. 75, Room101
T: +86 (21) 50490792
F: +86 (21) 50490792
office@liside-shanghai.com
www.liside-shanghai.com

Djoser European Quality Wine
518054 Shenzhen, A32, Yue Liang Wan
Shanzhuang Villa Nanshan
T: +86 (755) 26392022
F: +86 (755) 26392022
eqwines@gmail.com

Wein N Plus Co. Ltd
610041 Chengdu
One Crystal Place, 360 Tianhui Road,
Hi-Tech Zone, Woom 1604
T: +86 (28) 84433999
F: +86 (28) 83379919
sales_wine@weinnplus.com

Cottage Vineyards (International) Ltd.
Hong Kong, 2/F., 5 Lan Fong Road
Causeway Bay
T: +86 (852) 23951293
F: +86 (852) 35424599
tastings@cottagevineyards.com
www.cottagevineyards.com

Schmidt Marketing (Consumer Products) Ltd
Hong Kong, 13/F Chinachem
Exchange Square, No. 1 Hoi Wan
Street, Quarry Bay
www.schmidtvinothek.com

Wine Culture Limited
Hong Kong, 16th floor Wyndham
Place, 40-44 Wyndham Street
T: +852 2810 1186
info@wineculture.com.hk

Sunnygrapes Food & Beverage
Shanghai, RM 1201, Nr. 915 Zhen
Bei Road
T: +86 (216) 180110509
F: +86 (216) 1294191
office@sunnygrapes.com
www.sunnygrapes.com

CROATIA (HR)

Heinemann d.o.o. Croatia
10000 Zagreb, Ulica Grada Mainza 18
T: +385 (1) 3702734
F: +385 (1) 3702700
info@heinemann.hr

Vino Alpe Adria C d.o.o. Zagreb
10000 Zagreb, Trpinjska 3
T: +385 (1) 4647004
F: +385 (1) 4647050
info@vino-alpe-adria.com

Vino-Trade d.o.o.
10000 Zagreb, Vlaska 40
T: +385 (1) 2337677
info@vinotrade.hr, www.vinotrade.hr

Vivat Fina Vina d.o.o.
10000 Zagreb, Frana Folnegovića 1b
T: +385 (1) 6195332
F: +385 (1) 6195966
info@vinotrade.hr
www.vivat-finavina.hr

Fahnenberg i Nier d.o.o.
10020 Zagreb, Karlovacka cesta 4c
T: +385 (1) 3691314
F: +385 (1) 3691315

CYPRUS (CYP)

M.M wines
2062 Nicosia
4B Demou Herodotou, Strovolos
T: +357 (99) 460291
m.mwines@cablenet.com.cy
www.mmaustrianwines.com

Vino Cultura
3010 Lemesos, 2B Spetson Str., 1082
Agioi, Omologite
T: +357 (22) 676707
info@vinocultura.net

La Maison du Vin
3605 Limassol
49 Ayiou Athanasiou Street
T: +357 (25) 736220
la.maison.du.vin@cytanet.com.cy
www.lamaisonduvin.com.cy

CWS – Collection of wine samples
4047 Limassol, Halmark Complex
Geogriou A Street
T: +357 (25) 311292
galeon1@mail.ru

CZECH REPUBLIC (CZ)

Malvino s.r.o.
10303 Praha 10, Okrasná 127
T: +420 (602) 216090
info@malvino.cz, www.malvino.cz

Flambée
11000 Praha 1, Husova 5
T: +420 (224) 401234
F: +420 (224) 248513
info@flambee.cz

Domaine R & W s.r.o.
11000 Praha 1, Jilská 22/452
T: +420 (224) 234336
F: +420 (272) 701742
domaine@domaine.cz
www.domaine.cz

Embocadura s.r.o., Marketa Gusti
11000 Praha 1, Soukenická 1192/17
T: +420 (222) 314980
info@embocadura.cz
www.embocadura.cz

Globus International, s.r.o. – Best Wines
12800 Praha 2, Jaromírova 127/61
T: +420 (222) 562021
info@bestwines.cz
www.bestwines.cz

Vino Handl
12800 Praha 2, Vratislavova 21/26
T: +420 (777) 098095
info@vinohandl.com
www.vinohandl.com

Banimpex
14000 Praha 4, Tymlova 14
T: +420 (777) 885533
banimpex@banimpex.cz
www.banimpex.cz

AustriaWein
14100 Praha 4, Hrusická 2514/10
T: +420 (775) 030203
info@austriawein.cz
www.austriawein.cz

ITH Wine Selection s.r.o.
15500 Praha 5, Holeckova 15
T: +420 (257) 312757
F: +420 (257) 312662
podroom@winegarden.cz
www.winegarden.cz

Bacchus s.r.o.
16000 Praha 6
Dejvická 32 Praha-Cakovice
T: +420 (283) 933231
F: +420 (283) 931583
info@bacchus.cz, www.bacchus.cz

Vino & spol.
16000 Praha 6, Lindleyova 2723/5
T: +420 (224) 322349
info@vinospol.cz, www.vinospol.cz

Premier Wines
16100 Praha 6
Ruzyně, U Silnice 949/11
T: +420 (774) 046081
info@1er.cz, www.1er.cz

M. Král & spol.
16200 Praha 6, Plánickova 445/13
T: +420 (234) 096511
F: +420 (234) 096510
info@mkral.cz, www.mkral.cz

Veltlin Wine Bar, Bioclub s.r.o.
18600 Praha 8, Křižíkova 488/115
T: +420 (777) 082316
info@veltlin.cz, www.veltlin.cz

Vinom Wine s.r.o.
18600 Praha 8, Pernerova 48
T: +420 (605) 437486
marek.foltyn@vinom.eu
www.vinom.eu

Alimpex Food a.s.
19800 Praha 9, Českobrodská 1174
alimpex@alimpex.cz
www.alimpex.cz

Vinařství Ludwig, s.r.o.
25263 Roztoky, Palackého 956
T: +420 (220) 910371
F: +420 (220) 911292
roztoky@vinnesklepy.cz
www.vinnesklepy.cz

Farka a Farka
37000 Ceské Budejovice, Ceská 66
T: +420 (387) 318359
v.farka@volny.cz

Milan Zila MBM Blatná
38801 Blatná, U Sladovny 315
www.vinozila.cz
mbm@vinozila.cz

Stabrix
53003 Pardubice, Štrossova 905
T: +420 (737) 705645
info@rakouskavina.eu
www.rakouskavina.eu

Moravská banka vín
60300 Brno, Hlinky 88
T: +420 (543) 248107
F: +420 (532) 296359
bankavin@bankavin.cz
www.bankavin.cz

Vinaria
61500 Brno, Jugoslávská 4
T: +420 (545) 211214
F: +420 (545) 211214
info@vinaria.cz, www.vinaria.cz

Vinifiti Wine Seller
69002 Breclav, Jana Palacha 121/8
T: +420 (519) 324800
F: +420 (519) 324900
info@vinifiti.cz, www.vinifiti.cz

Domaine Hugo
69102 Velké Bílovice
Velke Bilovice 606
T: +420 (775) 593698
hugo@domainehugo.cz
www.domainehugo.cz

Vinarte s.r.o.
75501 Vsetin, Josef Sousedika 1730
T: +420 (573) 034304
vino@vinarte.cz
www.vinarte.cz

DENMARK (DK)

Kjaer & Sommerfeldt A/S
1117 Copenhagen, Gammel Mønt 4
T: +45 (70) 156500
ksc@kogs.dk, www.kogs.dk

Ubbes Vinhandel
1471 Copenhagen, Ny Vestergade 16
T: +45 (33) 154450
ubbe@ubbevin.dk,www.ubbevin.dk

österreich vin
1263 Copenhagen, Esplanaden 3
T: +45 (33) 323911
F: +45 (21) 699839
sr@osterreich.dk, www.osterreich.dk

Ludv. Bjorns Vinhandel
1553 Copenhagen
H.C. Andersens Boulevard 42
T: +43 (33) 151613
lb-vin@lb-vin.dk
www.lb-vin.dk

Norma Vinimport
1970 Frederiksberg, Rosenørns Allé 36
T: +45 (35) 369240
F: +45 (35) 369270
vin@normavin.dk

Vinothek Marquart
2300 Copenhagen, Thorshavnsgade 24
T: +45 (32) 523202
vin@vinothek-marquart.dk
www.vinothek-marquart.dk

Gastro-Wine ApS
2650 Hvidovre, Kanalholmen 25-29
T: +45 (41) 426632
cs@gastro-wine.dk
www.gastro-wine.dk

Barrique Vin
2665 Vallensbæk Beach, Egeskovvej 9
T: +45 (33) 244111
F: +45 (33) 244101
mail@barrique.dk, www.barrique.dk

Vinslottet I Greve
2670 Greve, Håndværkerbyen 42
T: +45 (43) 691162
F: +45 (43) 691165
jonas@vinslottet.nu, www.vinslottet.nu

Laudrup Vin & Gastronomi
2740 Skovlunde, Mileparken 13
T: +45 (44) 848086
info@laudrupvin.dk
www.laudrupvin.dk

Gottlieb Vin
2765 Smørum, Rabrovej 25, Ledoje
T: +45 (31) 451584
agj@gottliebvin.dk
www.gottliebvin.dk

Bergman Vin Import
2980 Kokkedal, Avderødvej 4B
T: +45 (48) 280035
F: +45 (48) 280635
mail@bergmanvin.dk
www.bergmanvin.dk

Erik Sørensen Vin
2980 Kokkedal
Fredensborg Kongevej 57
T: +45 (43) 609900
F: +45 (43) 609910
vin@eriksorensenvin.dk
www.eriksorensenvin.dk

Philipson Wine
2980 Kokkedal
Kokkedal Industripark 10
T: +45 (70) 226888
F: +45 (70) 229936
pwmail@philipsonwine.com
www.philipsonwine.com

Bacchus Vinimport
3000 Helsingør
Mads Holms vej 63
T: +45 (40) 138044
F: +45 (49) 220405
bacchus-vinimport@mail.dk
www.bacchus-vin.dk

TWC Wine Aps
3050 Humlebaek, Kromosewej 7
T: +45 (45) 762121
twc@twc-wine.dk, www.twc-wine.dk

Michael Jepsen Vinimport
3400 Hillerød, Trollesmindevaenget 8
T: +45 (48) 264421
F: +45 (48) 264421
trolles@post.tele.dk
www.mjvinimport.dk

Arnholt Wine
4683 Rønnede, Industriskellet 4
T: +45 (40) 506236
vin@arnholt.dk, www.arnholt.dk

CH-Vin
5000 Odense, Odinsgade 15
T: +45 (40) 524814
F: +45 (66) 147672
Info@chvin.dk, www.chvin.dk

Hansen Vinhandel A/S
5100 Odense, Vestergade 97-101
T: +45 (63) 128200
F: +45 (63) 128249
vin@hjhansen.dk
www.hjhansen-vin.dk

Korsholm Vin
5462 Morud, Filipagrenen 4
Tel: +45 (29) 244623
jimmi@korsholm-vin.dk
www.korsholm-vin.dk

Haller Vine
5500 Middelfart, Mandal Allé 8c
T: +45 (64) 406451
F: +45 (64) 406451
info@hallervine.dk, www.hallervine.dk

Vino Theket
6340 Kruså, Fjordvejen 56, Kollund
T: +45 (74) 671220
F: +45 (74) 671219
info@vinotheket.dk, www.vinotheket.dk

Vinotheket A/S
6340 Krusaa, Fjordvejen 56
T: +40 (74) 1216
info@vinotheket.dk
www.vinotheket.dk

Atomwine
7100 Vejle, Storhaven 7
T: +45 (23) 311410
F: +45 (75) 821318
info@atomwine.dk
www.atomwine.dk

A Vinstouw Aps
7400 Herning, Krøjgaardvej 4
T: +45 (97) 121416
vin@a-vinstouw.dk
www.a-vinstouw.dk

Excellent Wine
7400 Herning, Industriparken 16
T: +45 (97) 125777
F: +45 (97) 225750
wine@excellentwine.dk
www.excellentwine.dk

Hagelquist Vine
8000 Aarhus, Balticagade 7
T: +45 (86) 138763
info@hagelquist.dk
www.hagelquist.dk

Cappa Vin
8240 Risskov, Silndalsvej 21
T: +45 (86) 336270
F: +45 (26) 258055
cappa@cappa.dk, www.cappa.dk

Strobel Vinimport
8330 Beder, Elmosevej 51
T: +45 (86) 209622
F: +45 (86) 209645
info@strobelvin.dk, www.strobelvin.dk

Bichel Vine
8530 Hjortshøj, Mejlbyvej 501
T: +45 (86) 229400
F: +45 (86) 229499
post@bichel.dk, www.bichel.dk

Oestrigsk Vinimport
8600 Silkeborg, Uglesøvej 1
T: +45 (86) 837492
info@oestrigsk-vinimport.dk
www.oestrigsk-vinimport.dk

Vinmonopolet
8600 Silkeborg, Mads Clausens Vej 5
T: +45 (87) 200888
mail@vinmonopolet.dk
www.vinmonopolet.dk

Amka
8930 Randers, Østre Boulevard 29
T: +45 (86) 419600
F: +45 (86) 411037
amka@amka.dk, www.amka.dk

Jysk Vin – det gode glas
8960 Randers, Haraldsvej 60
T: +45 (86) 404444
jyskvin@jyskvin.dk, www.jyskvin.dk

Sigurd Müller Vinhandel
9200 Aalborg, Otto Monsteds Vej 2
T: +45 (98) 185099
F: +45 (98) 188165
vin@smv.dk, www.smv.dk

ESTONIA (EST)

Veinipööning
10140 Tallinn, Viru St. 18, 4th floor
T: +372 (641) 8631
F: +372 (534) 20916
info@vinoteek.ee

AS Liviko
10144 Tallinn, Masina 11
T: +372 (6) 678052
F: +372 (6) 678050
liviko@liviko.ee, www.liviko.ee

Bestwine OÜ
10146 Tallinn, Harju1
T: +372 (6) 228976
info@bestwine.ee, www.bestwine.ee

Wine Store Tallinn
10151 Tallinn, Lootsi 7
T: +372 (669) 8850
info@winestore.ee, www.winestore.ee

Winehouse OÜ
10151 Tallinn, Narva mnt. 11D
T: +358 (207) 579663
F: +358 (207) 579666
sales@winehouse.ee

OÜ HS Kaubandus
10152 Tallinn, Narva mnt. 63
T: +372 (6) 101188
F: +372 (6) 101186
harry.saar@starman.ee

Avallone AS
11215 Tallinn, Kauge tee 3
T: +372 (6) 706868
F: +372 (6) 706869
myyk@avallone.ee
www.avallone.ee

Tridens AS
11415 Tallinn, Lõõtsa 2
T: +372 (6) 031800
F: +372 (6) 031801
info@tridens.ee, www.tridens.ee

Grape AS
74114 Maardu, Vana-Nara mnt. 1 B
T: +372 (6) 349100
grape@grape.ee
www.grape.ee

Balen OÜ – Connoisseur
75312 Harjumaa
Läike tee põik 1
Peetri küla, Rae vald
T: +372 (6000) 950
F: +372 (6000) 959
balen@balen.ee, www.balen.ee

Manipenny
76505 Saue, Lehtla 11
T: +372 (501) 4547
F: +372 (501) 6678050
rein@manipenny.ee
www.manipenny.ee

Lucca Wine Trade
76902 Harkujärve, Keskpäeva tee 1
T: +372 (553) 3335
lucca@restoranlucca.ee

FINLAND (FIN)

Bioviini Oy
00100 Helsinki, Eerikinkatu 12 LH 7
T: +358 (40) 9133398
F: +358 (9) 6988214
eva.backman@bioviini.fi, www.bioviini.fi

Fondberg Oy
00120 Helsinki
Yrjönkatu 11 D 20
T: +358 (9) 6120960
F: +358 (9) 61209610
www.fondberg.fi

Funky Wine Imports Oy
00120 Helsinki
Iso-Roobertinkatu 3-5
T: +358 (40) 5585959
funky@funkywineimports.fi
www.funkywineimports.fi

Fine Wine Finland
00130 Helsinki
Lilla Robertsgatan 4-6 N77
T: +358 (40) 8698381
niclas@finewinefinland.com

Moestue & Cask Ab Ltd.
00130 Helsinki, Kanavaranta 7 D
F: +358 (425) 963317
jonas@moestuecask.com
www.moestuecask.fi

Fine Brands Oy
00140 Helsinki, Pietarinkatu 22A
T: +358 (9) 6980167
F: +358 (9) 6980198

Interbrands Wines & Spirits Oy
00140 Helsinki, Pietarinkuja 3
T: +358 (9) 6829310
jaana.virkki@interbrands.fi
www.interbrands.fi

Wintage Imports Helsinki
00140 Helsinki, Kasarmikatu 6b
T: +358 (44) 5889109
info@wintage.fi
www.wintage.fi

Nordalco Oy
00150 Helsinki, Henry Fordinkatu 6B
T: +358 (40) 5441234
info@nordalco.fi, www.nordalco.fi

Viinitie Oy
00150 Helsinki, Laivurinkatu 37
T: +358 (40) 5887060
toni.immanen@viinitie.fi
www.viinitie.fi

Viinimaa
00180 Helsinki, Kaapeliaukio 1,
T: +358 (207) 013013
viinimaa@altia.fi
www.viinimaa.fi

Sky Cellar Oy
00180 Helsinki, Porkkalankatu 22
T: +358 (207) 013303
F: +358 (207) 013300
joachim.kurten@skycellar.fi
www.skycellar.fi

Winestate Oy
00180 Helsinki, Ruoholahdenkatu 21
T: +358 (9) 5658900
F: +358 (9) 56589010
pasi.ketolainen@winestate.fi
www.winestate.fi

Alko Oy
00181 Helsinki, Salmisaarenaukio 1T
+358 (20) 71111
F: +358 (20) 7115386
palaute@alko.fi, www.alko.fi

Carelia Wines
00260 Helsinki, Mannerheimintie 56
T: +358 (9) 27090976
F: +358 (9) 27090977
carelia@carelia.info, www.carelia.info

LCS Wines & Consulting
00330 Helsinki
Munkkiniemen puistotie 18 A 23
T: +358 (40) 5257520
leena.stromberg@lcswines.com
www.lcswines.com

Servaali Oy
00370 Helsinki, Atomitie 2c
T: +358 (9) 4542350
F: +358 (9) 45423510
sales@servaali.fi
www.servaali.fi

Hartwa Trade AB Oy
00380 Helsinki
Hiomotie 32, P.O. Box 250
T: +358 (20) 717111
F: +358 (20) 7172526
paivi.puustinen@hartwall.fi
www.hartwa-trade.fi

Arvid Nordquist
00380 Helsinki, Kutomotie 9 C
T: +358 (10) 8325600
F: +358 (9) 6820366
kuluttajakontakti@arvidnordquist.fi
www.arvidnordquist.fi

Beverage Partners Finland Oy
00500 Helsinki, Vilhonvuorenkatu 11 A
T: +358 (9) 6229190
F: +358 (9) 62291922
joakim.ignatius@bpf-finland.fi
www.bpf-finland.fi

Vindirekt Finland Oy
00540 Helsinki
Sörnäisten rantatie 22 E
T: +358 (9) 7745930
F: +358 (9) 77459370
vindirekt@vindirekt.fi
www.vindirektfinland.fi

Chris Wine & Spirits
00560 Helsinki, Arabiankatu 12
T: +358 (9) 6829660
F: +358 (9) 68296690
info@chris-wine.fi
www.chris-wine.com

Domaine Wines Oy
01530 Vantaa
WTC Airport
Lentäjäntie 3
T: +358 (40) 5569994
F: +358 (9) 2976060
dwf@domainewines.fi
www.domainewines.fi

Haugen-Gruppen OY
01720 Vantaa, Tiilitie 6
T: +358 (10) 3090700
laura.paija@haugen-gruppen.fi
www.haugen-gruppen.fi

Norex Spirits Oy Ab
02200 Espoo
Piispansilta 9 A, 3rd floor
T: +358 (9) 5259370
F: +358 (9) 52593715
myynti.spirits@norexint.fi
www.norexint.fi

PromoHouse Oy
02360 Espoo, Hannuntie 6
T: +358 (40) 5012525
F: +358 (207) 579666
info@promohouse.fi

Vinum Import Oy ltd.
20100 Turku
Yliopistonkatu 34, 2nd floor
T: +358 (50) 5706020
kimmo.syrjanen@vinum.fi
www.vinum.fi

Dovesta Oy
20380 Turku
Bergenheiminpolku 8 B
T: +358 (50) 5525099
F: +385 (2) 2359257
dovesta.oy@saunalahti.fi
www.dovesta.fi

Tampereen Viinitukku Oy
33960 Pirkkala, Vaittintie 8
T: +358 (10) 3090800
F: +358 (10) 3090810
tilaukset@tampereenviinitukku.fi
www.tampereenviinitukku.fi

FRANCE (F)

Le Nez de St. Pierre
Jacquey Martia
21000 Dijon, 26 rue Admiral Courbet
T: +33 (380) 530381
F: +33 (380) 450377
contact@nez-de-saint-pierre.com
www.nez-de-saint-pierre.com

Vivavin
21200 Beaune, 5 place Marey
T: +33 (380) 227704
info@vivavin.com, www.vivavin.com

Terres de Vins
26100 Romans-sur-Isère
10 rue Jean Perriolat
T: +33 (475) 713640
F: +33 (475) 713640
contact@terresdevins.com
www.terresdevins.com

Cousin & Cie
33000 Bordeaux, Place du Parlement
2 rue du Pas-St-Georges
T: +33 (556) 012023
F: +33 (556) 482320
shop@cousin.fr, www.cousin.fr

La Médocaine s.a.r.l.
33290 Ludon-Médoc
2 route du Grand Verger
T: +33 (5) 57884608
F: +33 (5) 57888630
lamedocaine@lamedocaine.com
www.lamedocaine.com

Rhônalia
73100 Aix-les-Bains, 46, Rue Vaugelas
T: +33 (0) 479612591
F: +33(0) 974443234
www.rhonalia.com

Vini Cultura Austriae
75007 Paris, 184 rue de L'Université
T: +33 (6) 72776566
office@vini-cultura-austriae.com
www.vini-cultura-austriae.com

Bistro du Sommelier
75008 Paris, 97 Boulevard Haussmann
T: +33 (1) 42652485
bistrot-du-sommelier@noos.fr
www.bistrotdusommelier.com

Vins du Monde
75008 Paris, 29 rue Marbeuf
T: +33 (1) 58563838
F: +33 (1) 53764840
info@vinsdumonde.com
www.vinsdumonde.com

Oenotropie
75010 Paris, 58 rue du Chateau d'Eau
T: +33 (9) 79293195
F: +33 (1) 42590986
info@oenotropie.com
www.oenotropie.com

D°Vin
75015 Paris, 17 rue Auguste Chabriére
T: +33 (6) 16024523
contact@dvin-paris.com
www.dvin-paris.com

G.V.A.H
83000 Toulon, 5 rue Picot
T: +33 (6) 12444138
F: +33 (4) 42629831

Les Chais St. Laurent
93380 Pierrefitte-sur-Seine
1–3 Avenue Laennec
T: +33 (1) 48266210
contact@chais-saint-laurent.com
www.chais-saint-laurent.com

GREAT BRITAIN (GB)

Connolly's Wine Merchants Ltd.
B3 1EU Birmingham
Arch 13, 220 Livery Street
T: +44 (121) 2363837
sales@connollyswine.co.uk
www.connollyswine.co.uk

Noel Young Wines
CB2 9LS Cambridge
56 High Street
T: +44 (1223) 566744
noel@nywines.co.uk
www.nywines.co.uk

Thirsty
CB4 1EN Cambridge
46 Chesterton Road
T: +44 (1223) 464436
sam@verregourmand.com

Astrum Wine Cellars
CR4 4FG Mitcham Surrey
Unit 7 – Falcon Business Centre,
Willow Lane Industrial Estate 14
Wandle Way
T: +44 (20) 33284620
F: +44 (20) 33284625
info@astrumwinecellars.com
www.astrumwinecellars.com

Newcomer Wines Ltd.
E1 6GY London
Unit 8 - 2-10 Bethnal Green Road
T: +44 (7447) 512061
office@newcomerwines.com
www.newcomerwines.com

Corney & Barrow
E1W 1YZ London
1 Thomas More Street
T: +44 (20) 72652400
F: +44 (20) 72652444
wine@corneyandbarrow.com

Raeburn Fine Wines
EH4 1DS Edinburgh
21/23 Comely Bank Road
T: +44 (118) 9225100
F: +44 (118) 9225115
info@vintageroots.co.uk
www.vintageroots.co.uk

Savage Selection Ltd.
GL54 3EG Northleach
The Ox House, Market Place
T: +44 (1451) 860896
F: +44 (1451) 860896
wine@savageselection.co.uk
www.savageselection.co.uk

Coe Vintners
IG4 5EY Ilford
53 Redbridge Lane East
T: +44 (20) 85514966
F: +44 (20) 85506312
www.coevintners.com

Alliance Wine Co Ltd.
KA15 1LN Beith
7 Beechfield Road, Willowyard Estate
T: +44 (1505) 506060
F: +44 (1505) 506066
agency@alliancewine.co.uk
www.alliancewine.co.uk

GK Wine House LTD
183 Brox Road, KT16 OLJ Ottershaw
T: +44 (20) 32864120
info@gkwinehouse.co.uk
www.gkwinehouse.co.uk

Bacchus Wine
MK46 4AJ Olney, 38 Market Place
T: +44 (1234) 711140
wine@bacchus.co.uk
www.bacchus.co.uk

Kipferl Ltd., Austrian Delicatessen
N1 8ED London, 20 Camden Passage
T: +44 (20) 77041555

Gauntleys of Nottingham Ltd.
NG1 2ET Nottingham, 4 High Street
T: +44 (115) 9110555
www.gauntleys.com

Enotria Winecellars Ltd.
NW10 6NF London, 4–8 Chandos
Park Estate, Chandos Road
T: +44 (20) 89615161
info@enotria.co.uk
www.enotria.co.uk

O.W. Loeb & Co. Ltd.
SE1 3JT London, 3 Archie Street
T: +44 (20) 72340385
finewine@owloeb.com
www.owloeb.com

The Wine Society
SG1 2BT Stevenage
Gunnels Wood Road
T: +44 (1438) 741177
www.thewinesociety.com

Lea & Sandeman Co Ltd.
SW10 9PR London
170 Fulham Road
T: +44 (20) 72440522
charles@leaandsandeman.co.uk
www.leaandsandeman.co.uk

Philglas & Swiggot Marylebone
SW11 1NG London
21 Northcote Road
T: +44 (20) 79244494
karen@philglas-swiggot.co.uk
www.philglas-swiggot.com

Oddbins
SW19 8UG London
31–33 Weir Road, Wimbledon
T: +44 (20) 71988473
customer.services@oddbins.com
www.oddbins.com

Berry Bros. & Rudd
SW1A 1EG London, 3 St. James's
Street
T: +44 (20) 70228973
orders@bbr.com, www.bbr.com

Liberty Wines
SW4 6LY London, 6 Timber Mill Way
T: +44 (20) 77205350
info@libertywine.co.uk
www.libertywines.co.uk

Fields, Morris & Verdin Ltd.
SW8 3NS London
24–34 Ingate Place, Battersea
T: +44 (20) 78190360
F: +44 (20) 33012888
order@fmvwines.com
www.fmvwines.com

Indigo Wine Ltd.
SW9 8BJ London
Bon Marche Centre
41-251 Ferndale Road
T: +44 (20) 77338391
F: +44 (20) 77338391
info@indigowine.com
www.indigowine.com

Tanners Wines Ltd.
SY1 1XD Shrewsbury
26 Wyle Cop
T: +44 (1743) 234500
www.tanners-wines.co.uk

Guy Anderson Wines
TA13 5BW Southern Petherton
Left Bank, 28 St. James Street
T: +44 (1460) 240009
info@guyandersonwines.co.uk
www.guyandersonwines.co.uk

New Generation Wines
TN24 8DH Ashford
Woodcote House
15 Highpoint Business Village
T: +44 (1233) 656787
F: +44 (1233) 624078
info@newgenerationwines.com
www.newgenerationwines.com

Fortnum & Mason plc.
W1A 1ER London
181 Piccadilly
T: +44 (845) 3001707
F: +44 (207) 4373278
www.fortnumandmason.com

Dynamic Vines
W1F 7PP London
26 Fouberts Place
T: +44 (207) 2872179
fredericgrappe@dynamicvines.com
www.dynamicvines.com

Bulles Blanc Rouges
W1J5AZ London
49 Berkeley Square
T: +44 (7779) 802287
nisrine@bullesblancrouge.com

Top Selection Ltd.
W1S 2XL London
16 Conduit Street
T: +44 (20) 74994440
F: +44 (20) 74994448
info@topselection.co.uk
www.topselection.co.uk

Clark Foyster Wines Ltd.
W5 4QT London
15 South Ealing Road
T: +44 (20) 88327470
sales@cfwines.co.uk
www.clarkfoysterwines.co.uk

Albion Wine Shippers Ltd.
WC1N 3LW London
56 Lambs Conduit Street
T: +44 (20) 72420873
sales@albionwineshippers.co.uk
www.albionwineshippers.co.uk

GHANA (GHA)

Say Cheers
233 Ghana, Plot #24 Spintex Road,
T: +233 (302) 811407
info@koonad.com
www.saycheersghana.com

GREECE (GR)

Aiolos Ltd.
17563 Athen
L. Katsoni 9-11, Paelo Faliro
T: +30 (1) 9887341
www.aioloswines.gr

HUNGARY (H)

Lamicoop Kft
1033 Budapest, Szölökert köz 9
T: +36 (1) 3881368

Zwack Unicum Ltd.
1095 Budapest, Soroksári út 26
T: +36 (1) 4762300
borvalogatas@zwackunicum.hu
www.zwackunicum.hu

Kisbécs
1126 Budapest, Németvölgyi út 36-38
T: +36 (30) 5770706
info@kisbecs.hu
www.kisbecs.hu

Heinemann Testvérek Kft.
2310 Szigetszentmiklós
Leshegy út 30
T: +36 (24) 525090
F: +36 (24) 525099
info@heinemann.hu
www.heinemann.hu

ICELAND (IS)

Rolf Johansen & Company
124 Reykjavik, Skútuvogur 10a
T: +354 (595) 6700
rjc@rjc.is, www.rjc.is

Vinheimar ehf.
230 Keflavík, Vikurbraut 13
T: +354 (421) 3800
F: +354 (421) 3802
vinheimar@vinheimar.is
www.vinheimar.is

INDIA (IN)

Sansula
400 021 Bombay
95 Mittal Chambers
T: +91 (22) 66669111
norma@sansula.com
www.sansula.com

INDONESIA (RI)

Megaguna Semesta Raya PT.
12730 Jakarta
JL. Kemang Raya 45B
T: +62 (21) 71792577
kemang@vinplus.biz

IRELAND (IRL)

Mitchell & Son, Wine Merchants Ltd.
Dublin
54 Glasthule Road, Sandycove
T: +353 (1) 2302301
F: +353 (1) 2302305
glasthule@mitchellandson.com
www.mitchellandson.com

**Searsons Wine Merchants
Wholesale Ltd.**
Dublin
Monkstown Crescent, Monkstown
T: +353 (1) 2800405
info@searsons.com
www.searsons.com

The Corkscrew Wine Company
Dublin 2, 4 Chatham Street
T: +353 (1) 6745731
info@thecorkscrew.ie
www.thecorkscrew.ie

Terroirs Ltd. Donnybrook
Dublin 4
103 Morehampton Road
Donnybrook
T: +353 (1) 6671311
F: +353 (1) 6671312
info@terroirs.ie
www.terroirs.ie

harrison wineSelect
Dublin 15
5 Bramley Heath, Castleknock
T: +353 (1) 8206407
office@wineselect.at
www.wineselect.at

Vinum-X-Tellus
Kerry, Cahir Lodge
Cahir East, Kenmare
T: +353 (21) 6011002
info@vinum-x-tellus.ie
www.vinum-x-tellus.ie

Wines Direct
Westmeath
49 Lough Sheever
Corporate Park, Mullingar
T: +353 (44) 9340634
online@winesdirect.ie
www.winesdirect.ie

The Wicklow Wine Co.
Wicklow, 7 Main Street
T: +353 (404) 66767
info@wicklowwineco.ie
www.wicklowwineco.ie

ISRAEL (IL)

Kippis Ltd.
40500 Even Yehuda
40 Hadekel Street
T: +972 (9) 8912449
info@kippis.co.il

Kelta Ltd.
76858 Aseret
5 Haoren Street, POB 66
T: +972 (8) 8596941
gidi@kelta.co.il
www.kelta.co.il

ITALY (I)

Roscioli
00186 Rome
Via di San Salvatore in Campo
T: +39 (06) 6875287
info@winetastingrome.com
www.winetastingrome.com

Enogourmet
03100 Frosinone
Via vado del tufo
T: +39 (0775) 880095
F: +39 (0775) 835681
info@enogourmet.it
www.enogourmet.it

Filari di Luna
10141 Turin, Via Viberti
T: +39 (011) 3825393
info@filaridiluna.it
www.filaridiluna.it

Gaja Distribuzione
12050 Barbaresco, Via Torino 36 B
T: +39 (0173) 635158
carla.forzano@gajawines.com
www.gajadistribuzione.it

Alser
20068 Peschiera Borromeo
Via Liberazione 63/18
T: +39 (02) 5475130
F: +39 (02) 55307538
info@alservini.com
www.alservini.com

Enoteca La Barrique
22063 Cantù
Via Marmolada 1
T: +39 (031) 730875
F: +39 (031) 730875
info@enotecalabarrique.it
www.enotecalabarrique.it

Pellegrini S.p.A.
24034 Cisano Bergamasco
Via Mazzini 43
T: +39 (035) 781010
F: +39 (035) 787278
info@pellegrinispa.net
www.pellegrinispa.net

CUZZIOL Grandivini S.R.L..
31025 Santa Lucia di Piave
Via Serenissima, 19
F: +39 0438456575
www.origamiconsulting.it

Il Tagliere S.r.l.
35127 Padua
Via Dei Ronchi, 1 - Z.I. Camin
T: +39 (049) 8961956
F: +39 (049) 8969448
info@iltagliere.it
www.iltagliere.it

Proposta Vini
38057 Pergine Valsugana
Via degli Artigiani 16
T: +39 (0461) 534795
F: +39 (0461) 539442
info@propostavini.com
www.propostavini.com

Meraner Weinhaus
39012 Merano
Via Roma 76
T: +39 (0473) 012130
info@meranerweinhaus.com
www.meranerweinhaus.com

Karadar Diether
39038 Innichen
Schranzhoferstr.2
T: +39 (0474) 913159
F: +39 (0474) 912454
info@karadarshop.com

Ossanna GmbH
39049 Sterzing
Wiesen-Pfitsch 11
T: +49 (0472) 060500
info@ossanna.it
www.ossanna.it

Weindiele/Winestore
39053 Tiers, St.Georgstr.9
T: +39 (0471) 642106
info@weindiele.com
www.weindiele.com

Vinum
39100 Bolzano
Brennerstraße 28
T: +39 (0471) 061620
info@vinum.it
www.vinum.it

Vino & Design srl.
42100 Reggio Emilia
Via del Chionso 14
T: +39 (0522) 506284
info@vinoedesign.it
www.vinoedesign.it

Teatro del Vino
50041 Calenzano
Via V. Emanuele 33/1
T: +39 (055) 8811394
info@teatrodelvino.it
www.teatrodelvino.it

Dallevigne s.p.a.
50059 Vinci
Via del Torrino 19
T: +39 (0571) 902444
F: +39 (0571) 509960
info@dallevigne.com
www.dallevigne.com

Heres s.p.a.
52028 Terranuova Bracciolini
frazione Penna 152
T: +39 (0555) 341093
F: +39 (0559) 738253
info@heres.it
www.heres.it

JAPAN (J)

Gomaibashi
020-0823 Iwate
1-18-52 Kado, Moriokashi
T: +81 (19) 6211014
yutaka@gomaibashi.com
www.gomaibashi.com

Edelwein & Co. Ltd.
028-3203 Iwate
10-18-3 Ohasama, Ohasama-machi
T: +81 (19) 8483037
F: +81 (19) 8482412
info@edelwein.co.jp
www.edelwein.co.jp

Azuma Co. Ltd.
102-0093 Tokyo
Hirakawacho, Chiyoda-ku
T: +81 (3) 34543033
F: +81 (3) 34543321
www.azumacorp.jp

Nomura Unison Co. Ltd.
104-0061 Tokyo
1-10-19-7F Ginza, Chuo-ku
T: +81 (3) 35387854
F: +81 (3) 35387855
www.nomura-g.co.jp

Mercian Corporation
104-8305 Tokyo
Ajinomoto Kyobashi Building
1-5-8 Kyobashi, Chuo-ku
T: +81 (3) 32313905
F: +81 (3) 32760152
chateau@mercian.co.jp
www.mercian.co.jp

Mavie Corporation
107-0052 Tokyo
Mavie Corporation
T: +81 (3) 68229066
F: +81 (3) 55738682
akasaka@mavie.co.jp
www.mavie.co.jp

Fwines Co. Ltd.
141-0031 Tokyo
7-20-9 Nishi-Gotanda Building. 2F
Shinagawa-ku
T: +81 (3) 57452192
F: +81 (3) 57452198
t_kiyozuka@fwines.sgn.ne.jp
www.fwines.co.jp

Alcotrade Trust Inc.
142-0043 Tokyo
4-13-12 Futaba, Shonagawa-ku
T: +81 (3) 57020620
F: +81 (3) 57020621
sales@alcotrade.com
www.alcotrade.com

Union Liquors Co. Ltd.
150-0012 Tokyo
3-17-7 Hiroo, Shibuya-ku
T: +81 (3) 34868381
F: +81 (3) 34869541
info@union-liquors.com
www.union-liquors.com

Racine Co. Ltd.
160-0008 Tokyo
Park Side Yotsuya 5F
San-ei-cho 18-20
Shinjuku-ku
T: +81 (3) 53663931
F: +81 (3) 53664870
yasukogoda@racines.co.jp
www.racines.co.jp

Nouvelles Selections
171-0022 Tokyo
102, 2-4-1, Minami-Ikebukuro
Toshima-ku
T: +81 (3) 59571955
F: +81 (3) 39899501
www.nouvellesselections.com

Senna
231-0032 Kanagawa
3-12-1-705 Furo-cho, Naka-ku,
Yokohama-shi
T: +81 (45) 6510881
shimada@senna.co.jp
www.senna.co.jp

Fushimi Wine Business
236-0052 Kanagawa
6-1-31 Tomioka-Nishi
Kanazawa-ku
Yokohama-shi
T: +81 (45) 7714587
F: +81 (45) 7714401
fwrkurokawa@bg.wakwak.com
www.wine.jp

Sanko Hasumi Shoten Co. Ltd.
332-0034 Saitama
4-4-2 Nakimi Kawaguchi-shi
T: +81 (48) 2417150
F: +81 (48) 2417151
info@hasumi-wine.co.jp
www.hasumi-wine.co.jp

Nihon Grande Champagne
461-0032 Aichi, 3-20-15 Dekimachi,
Higashi-Ku, Nagoya-shi
T: +81 (52) 7119761
F: +81 (52) 7211210
yoko@ngc-japan.co.jp

Herrenberger Hof Ltd.
567-0878 Osaka, Kuragauchi 2-10-15
Ibaraki-shi
T: +81 (72) 6247540
F: +81 (72) 6238703
h-hof@tia-net.com
www.tia-net.com/h-hof

Mottox Inc.
577-0802 Osaka
1-9-10 Kosakahonmachi
Higashi-Osaka-shi
T: +81 (6) 67254925
F: +81 (6) 67254923
k_kono@mottox.co.jp
www.mottox.co.jp

Iida Co. Ltd.
581-0085 Osaka
1-1-29 Yasunaka-cho, Yao-shi
T: +81 (72) 9236 ext. 244
F: ext. 892
sekine@iidagroup.co.jp
www.iidawine.com

Estate Wines Japan
651-0056 Kobe, 4-8-4
7F Kumochi-cho
Chuo-ku, Hyogo
T: +81 (90) 43026158
F: +81 (797) 233205
wsfwine@gol.com
www.estatewinesjapan.com

Bond & Co. Ltd
652-0833 Hyōgo, 1-1-4
Shimagami-Cho
Hyogo-ku, Kobe-shi
T: +81 (78) 6716004
www.bondco.co.jp

LATVIA (LV)

Eirovins SIA
1009 Riga
Rujienas 2a
T: +371 (6) 7290021
eirovins@eirovins.lv
www.eirovins.lv

TB Dizains SIA
2015 Jūrmala, Pilsonu 8
T: +371 (6) 7147094
F: +371 (6) 7147097
info@interbaltija.lv
www.tbpalace.com

Tabakas Nams Grupa SIA
2107 Riga
T: +371 (6) 7147400
F: +371 (6) 7147420
tng@tng.lv, www.tng.lv

A/S Interbaltija AG
2167 Mārupe Municipality
Dzirnieku 18 Mārupe
T: +371 (6) 7068930
F: +371 (6) 7068933
info@interbaltija.lv
www.interbaltija.lv

Interbaltija AF
2167 Marupe
Dzirnieku iela 18
T: +371 (6) 7068930
F: +371 (6) 7068933
info@interbaltija.lv
www.interbaltija.lv

LITHUANIA (LT)

Gero Vyno Parduotuvé
01135 Vilnius, Stiklių g. 10
T: +370 (6) 9816819
info@notrevie.lt
www.notrevie.lt

Eugesta
02189 Vilnius, Meistru 10
T: +370 (5) 2397739
F: +370 (5) 2397733
info@eugesta.lt
www.eugesta.com

VynoKlubas
08101 Vilnius, Stumbru st 15
T: +370 (5) 2159438
info@vynoklubas.lt
www.vynoklubas.lt

UAB Istvestas
09308 Vilnius, Konstitucijos pr. 20
T: +370 (686) 70943
info@istvest.com
www.istvest.com

LUXEMBOURG (L)

Vinoteca Sàrl
1714 Luxembourg
83, rue de Hollerich
T: +352 (266) 83843
info@vinoteca.lu
www.vinoteca.lu

Grands Crus Sélection S.A.
1842 Howald
18, Avenue Grand-Duc Jean
T: +352 (262) 96053

Vimowa SA
5695 Emerange
1, Dublinsbierg
T: +352 (621) 55360
F: +352 (266) 60078
veurope@pt.lu
www.vimowa.lu

**Elite Wines c/o
Contrails International**
6170 Godbrange
41, rue de village
info@elitewines.lu
www.trick.lu

Caves Wengler s.a., Gérard Wengler
6581 Rosport
2, rue Neuve
T: +352 (73) 0373
F: +352 (73) 0168
info@wengler.lu
www.wengler.lu

Celliers de Grand Crus
6601 Wasserbillig
Route de Vin 5, Mertert
T: +352 (74) 8481
F: +352 (74) 8504
info@cgc.lu, www.cgc.lu

Europe Vins SA
6773 Grevenmacher, 8, rue du Pont
T: +352 (750) 545205
www.europe-vins.lu

Arkomed SA – sissy.lu
6975 Rameldange, 33, Am Bounert
T: +352 (34) 0133
F: +352 (34) 7234
info@sissy.lu, www.sissy.lu

A.R.S. GROUPE S.A.
9647 Doncols, 7, Bohey
T: +352 (95) 8453
F: +352 (95) 8874

**Supermarché Massen
S.A. – Vinothek**
9999 Weiswampach, Op der Haart 24
T: +352 (26) 901
F: +352 (26) 901300
massen@massen.lu, www.massen.lu

MALAYSIA (MAL)

That Little Wine Bar
10050 George Town
54 Jalan Chow Thye
T: +60 (4) 2268182
info@thatlittlewinebar.com
www.thatlittlewinebar.com

Luen Heng F&B Sdn. Bhd.
56000 Kuala Lumpur, No. 8 Jalan
Kilang Midah, Taman Midah
T: +60 (3) 91730398
F: +60 (3) 91730498
lha@luenheng.com
www.luenheng.com

MEXICO (MX)

Vinos Vinedos y Bodegas
11000 Mexico
Cerrada de Sierra Candela
T: +55 (5202) 4722109
import@vvb.com.mx

NETHERLANDS (NL)

Chabrol
1013 EH Amsterdam
Haarlemmerstraat 7
T: +31 (20) 622 27 81
F: +31 (20) 6228332
info@chabrolwines.com

AW Wijn
1051 GA Amsterdam
Fannius Scholtensstraat 56
T: +31 (20) 6862707
info@awwijn.nl
www.awwijn.nl

La Branche Wijnimport
1054 XV Amsterdam
Nicolaas Beetstraat 152
T: +31 (20) 6125720
F: +31 (20) 6125755
info@labranche.nl
www.labranche.nl

De WijnEngel
1073 KZ Amsterdam
David Blessstraat 5-2
T: +31 (6) 12214117
F: +31 (6) 12214117
info@dewijnengel.nl
www.dewijnengel.nl

YanFlorijn Wijn
1095 Amsterdam
Makassarstraat 128-B
www.yanflorijn.nl

Grapedistrict
1096 AK Amsterdam
Wenckebachweg 43a
T: +31 (20) 6651115
info@grapedistrict.nl
www.grapedistrict.nl

De Wijnkelder Almere
1325 KH Almere,
Peggy Ashcroftstraat 34
T: +31 (36) 8445256
info@ dewijnkelderalmere.nl
www.dewijnkelderalmere.nl

Miranda Beems Wijnimport
1382 MN Weesp
Anna Horstinkstraat 33
T: +31 (0) 294267307
F: +31 (0) 294267308
info@mirandabeems.com
www.wijnadvies.com

Wijnimport J. Bart
1440 AE Purmerend
Postbus 231
T: +31 (299) 689111
F: +31 (299) 689110
info@wijnimportbart.nl
www.wijnimportbart.nl

Gall & Gall Headquarters
1506 MA Zaandam
Provincialeweg 11
T: +31 (0) 886599111
www.gall.nl

Vino Via
1812 RC Alkmaar, Diamantweg 22
T: +31 (72) 52750 ext. 10
info@vinovia.com

Wijnimport Jos Rijnaarts
1821 BN Alkmaar, Edisonweg 14
T: +31 (72) 5118537
F: +31 (72) 5113155
info@josrijnaarts.nl

Winterberg Wijnen
1943 GT Beverwijk
Acacialaan 66
T: +31 (251) 220005
info@winterbergwijnen.nl
www.winterbergwijnen.nl

Bourgondisch Lifestyle
1943 LR Beverwijk
Plantage 120A
T: +31 (251) 220332
F: +31 (251) 211213
info@bourgondischlifestyle.nl
www.bourgondischlifestyle.nl

Okhuysen
2003 RM Haarlem
Postbus 501
T: +31 (23) 5312240
F: +31 (23) 5324815
vineus@okhuysen.nl
www.okhuysen.nl

Vinites
2011 RT Haarlem
Jansstraat 1-5
T: +31 (23) 5539090
F: +31 (23) 5539070
info@vinites.com
www.vinites.com

Hans Moolenaar Wijnkoperij
2061 CX Bloemendaal
Zomerzorgerlaan 26
T: +31 (23) 5257739
F: +31 (23) 5258035
info@hansmoolenaar.nl
www.hansmoolenaar.nl

Turkenburg Tradition Wijnkoopers
2061 CX Bodegraven
Spoorstraat 19
T: +31 (172) 613703
info@turkenburgtradition.nl
www.turkenburgtradition.nl

Lekker Sapje
2312 LA Leiden, Lekker Sapje
T: +31 (6) 535484
lekker@lekkersapje.nl
www.lekkersapje.nl

Noordman Wijnimport
2318 BZ Leiden, Flevoweg 17
T: +31 (71) 5221405
info@noordmanwijn.nl
www.noordmanwijn.nl

Résidence Wijnimport, F. Kranenburg
2371 TT Roelofarendsveen
Veenderveld 55
T: +31 (71) 5683300
F: +31 (71) 5683301
binnendienst@residence-wijnen.nl

Wijnhaven Wijnimport
2600 AJ Delft
Postbus 360
T: +31 (15) 2131121
www.wijnhaven-wijnimport.nl
www.eurowines.nl

Wijnkoperij R.M. de Geus
2645 EK Delfgauw
Overslagweg 1
T: +31 (15) 3805034
F: +31 (15) 3640471
info@degeuswijn.nl
www.degeuswijn.nl

Poot Agenturen
2678 LH De Lier
Jan van de Laarweg 12
T: +31 (174) 512561
F: +31 (174) 514123
info@poot.nl
www.pootagenturen.nl

DGS Wijncopers
2742 RC Waddinxveen
Distripark – Doelwijk
Exportweg 2
T: +31 (180) 635135
F: +31 (180) 635140
info@dgswijn.nl
www.dgswijn.nl

Cees van Noord BV
2909 RE Capelle aan den IJssel
Priamsingel 211
T: +31 (30) 2315462
F: +31 (30) 2340367
wijnkoperij@ceesvannoord.nl
www.ceesvannoord.nl

Red Gum Fine Wines BV
2988 AT Ridderkerk, Waaldijk 37
T: +31 (6) 53995607
F: +31 (180) 437370
info@redgum.nl
www.redgum.nl

Good Grapes
2990 AB Barendrecht, Postbus 87
T: +31 (180) 744010
F: +31 (84) 7264025
contact@goodgrapes.nl
www.goodgrapes.nl

Terroirwijn
3024 AJ Rotterdam, Coolhaven 106
T: +31 (10) 4367636
info@terroirwijn.nl
www.terroirwijn.nl

Cartosio Wijnkoperij
3111 AW Schiedam
Tuinlaan 56A
T: +31 (10) 2735420
F: +31 (10) 4265255
info@cartosio.nl
www.cartosio.nl

Hosman Vins
3111 BW Schiedam, Westvest 44
T: +31 (10) 4264672
F: +31 (10) 4730008
sales@hosmanvins.nl
www.hosmanvins.nl

Hosman Fréres Wijnkoperij
3134 EP Vlaardingen, Nieuwstraat 1
T: +31 (10) 4347230
F: +31 (10) 4343539
info@hosmanfreres.nl
www.hosmanfreres.nl

Trouvaille BV – Rietveld Wines
3439 LD Nieuwegein
Fort Jutphaas 3
T: +31 (30) 6560696
F: +31 (30) 2817744
ischa@trouvaille.nl
www.rietveldwines.com

Werkhoven Wijnen
3439 MP Nieuwegein
Pascalbaan 3
T: +31 (30) 6020143
F: +31 (30) 6020144
info@werkhovenwijnen.nl
www.werkhovenwijnen.nl

D. R. Trading
3523 CL Utrecht, Rotsoord 13,
T: +31 (30) 2321123
info@drtrading.nl
www.drtradingshop.nl

Q-Vignes Wijnimport
3732 HJ De Bilt, Dorpsstraat 44
T: +31 (30) 2200477
info@qvignes.nl, www.qvignes.nl

Imperial Wijnkoperij, Regina Meij
3734 BD Den Dolder
Dolderseweg 79-F
T: +30 (22) 94658
F: +30 (22) 52977
info@imperialwijnkoperij.nl
www.imperialwijnkoperij.nl

Baas en Zoon Wijnkoperij
3735 MV Bosch en Duin, Spoorlaan 1
T: +31 (30) 6931468
info@baaswijn.com
www.baaswijn.nl

Groupe LFE – Wines Worldwide
3738 TP Maartensdijk
Dierenriem 3–5
T: +31 (346) 213044
F: +31 (346) 212702
info@groupelfe.com
www.groupelfe.nl

Dacor Wijnen
3742 CH Baarn, Cantonlaan 5
T: +31 (6) 51955298
info@dacorwijnen.nl
www.dacorwijnen.nl

Weldam Wines Bv
3812 RV Amersfoort, Textielwg 18a
T: +31 (33) 2584686
info@weldamwines.nl
www.weldamwines.nl

Camminga Wijnen
3888 LW Uddel, Uddelsekampweg 24
T: +31 (6) 55167750
info@cammingawijnen.nl
www.cammingawijnen.nl

Jan Snoeyenbos Wijnimport
3960 BA Wijk bij Duurstede
Postbus 27
T: +31 (6) 53700795
snoeyenbos@aon.at
www.members.aon.at

Smaragd Wijnen
3972 Driebergen-Rijsenburg
Gooijerdijk 16
T: +31 (6) 42080666
info@smaragdwijnen.nl
www.smaragdwijnen.nl

Wijn en verwonderen
4101 BB Culemborg
Achterstraat 38
T: +31 (345) 508575
info@wijnenverwonderen.nl
www.wijnenverwonderen.nl

Walraven Sax
4811 VB Breda
Prinsenkade 5
T: +31 (76) 5256480
F: +31 (78) 5256499
order@walravensax.nl
www.walravensax.nl

Wijnkoperij De Lange
4901 KB Oosterhout, Heuve 13
T: +31 (162) 447847
F: +31 (162) 423060
info@wijnkoperijdelange.nl
www.wijnkoperijdelange.nl

Jean Arnaud Wijncom
5015 BR Tilburg
Orionstraat 30
T: +31 (13) 5841200
F: +31 (13) 5841201
info@jeanarnaud.com
www.jeanarnaud.com

Verbunt Wijnkopers
5048 AP Tilburg
De Kroonstraat 1
T: +31 (13) 5498400
F: +31 (13) 5498401
info@verbunt.nl
www.verbunt.nl

Wijnboetiek le Robinet
5211 DL 's-Hertogenbosch
Sint Jansstraat 11
T: +31 (73) 6148368
info@lerobinet.com
www.lerobinet.com

Wijn Verlinden
5253 AG 's-Hertogenbosch
Postbus 296
T: +31 (73) 6488011
F: +31 (73) 6412134
info@wijnverlinden.nl
www.wijnverlinden.nl

Benier Global Wines
5263 GK Vught
Kemplenlandstraat 13A
T: +31 (73) 6568209
F: +31 (73) 6569582
benier@benierglobalwines.com
www.benierglobalwines.nl

Van Eyck Wijnkelders
5701 Helmond, Heistraat 4C-4D
T: +31 (492) 522595
F: +31 (492) 527054
info@vaneyck.nl
www.vaneyck.nl

Wijntransport BV
5871 CM Broekhuizenvorst
Beerendonkerweg
T: +31 (77) 4632147
info@wijntransport.nl
www.wijntransport.nl

Leon Colaris Wijnhandel
6003 DK Weert, Franklinstraat 1
T: +31 (495) 532462
F: +31 (495) 543470
info@colaris.nl
www.colaris.nl

Firma AOR
6041 Roermond, Roerzicht 45
k.adams@aorroermond.eu

Vojacek Wijnen
6211 LT Maastricht
Tongerseweg 15
T: +31 (43) 3253170
F: +31 (43) 3258644
info@vojacek.nl
www.vojacek.nl

Thiessen
6211 SW Maastricht, Grote Gracht 18
T: +31 (43) 3251355
F: +31 (43) 3214715
wijnhandel@thiessen.nl
www.thiessen.nl

Vojacek Wines
6211 Maastricht, Tongerseweg 15
T: +31 (0) 433219726
contact@winesupply.nl
www.jules-maastricht.com

Sauter Wijnen
6226 NV Maastricht, Withuisveld 16 A
T: +31 (43) 3637799
F: +31 (43) 3634748
info@sauterwijnen.nl

Chateau Gilbert
6363 BW Wijnandsrade
Opfergeltstraat 2C
T: +31 (6) 53458200
info@chateaugilbert.nl
www.chateaugilbert.nl

Rando Trading Company
6365 AC Schinnen, Thull 14
T: +31 (46) 4431768
rando@oostenrijksewijn.info
www.oostenrijksewijn.info

Women on Wine
6521 CT Nijmegen
Van Heutszstraat 29
T: +31 (6) 20011757
www.womenonwine.nl

Robbers & van den Hoogen
6824 BC Arnhem, Velperweg 23
T: +31 (26) 4455912
F: +31 (26) 4458884
wijnhandel@robbersenvandenhoogen.nl
www.robbersenvandenhoogen.nl

Les Généreux
7201 DR Zutphen
Pelikaanstraat 4a
T: +31 (575) 543667
info@lesgenereux.nl
www.lesgenereux.nl

Wijnkoperij Henri Bloem
7311 EN Apeldoorn, Asselsestraat 52
T: +31 (55) 5221470
F: +31 (55) 5221496
apeldoorn@henribloem.nl
www.henribloem.nl

Chateau Het Loo
7315 Apeldoorn, Korteweg 63
T: +31 (6) 21272266
info@chateauhetloo.nl
www.chateauhetloo.nl

Heisterkamp Wijnkopers
7631 AE Ootmarsum
Eerste Stegge 2
T: +31 (541) 292222
F: +31 (541) 292024
wijnkopers@heisterkamp.com
www.heisterkamp.com

Wijnhandel Still Sparkling
7371 GG Loenen, Hoofdweg 115
T: +31 (55) 5051333
info@stillsparkling.nl
www.stillsparkling.nl

Wijnhuis Twentsch
7661 RL Vasse, Denekamperweg 148
T: +31 (541) 680279
F: +31 (541) 514161
info@twentschwijnhuis.nl
www.twentschwijnhuis.nl

Obiovino
8016 CV Zwolle
Van Pallandtmarke 107
T: +31 (6) 26170144
info@obiovino.nl
www.obiovino.nl

Lovian BV
8401 BL Gorredijk, Badweg 48
T: +31 (513) 469490
F: +31 (513) 465164
www.lovian.nl

Wijnvoordeel BV
8401 BL Gorredijk, Badweg 48
www.wijnvoordeel.nl

Austrian Trade Consultancy
8607 AT Sneek
Louw Doniastraat 2 - 109
T: + 31 (515) 438885
austriantrade@hotmail.com
www.proefoostenrijk.com

Enoconsul
9712 TJ Groningen
Grote Rozenstraat 64
T: +31 (50) 3123700
F: +31 (50) 3111619
bestel@goedewijn.info
www.goedewijn.info

NEW ZEALAND (NZ)

Wine Direct Warehouse
1052 Auckland
69 St Georges Bay Road, Parnell
T: +64 (9) 3779553
askus@winedirect.co.nz
www.winedirect.co.nz

Caro's Wine Merchants
1052 Auckland
114 St Georges Bay Road, Parnell
T: +64 (9) 3779974
wine@caros.co.nz
www.caros.co.nz

Scenic Cellars
3330 Taupo
114 Spa Road
PO Box 1300
T: +64 (7) 3784626
info@sceniccellars.co.nz
www.sceniccellars.co.nz

Wine Matters Ltd.
8039 Riccarton
8 Poplar Street, PO Box
T: +64 (3) 339635473
F: +64 (3) 3512158

NORWAY (N)

Vinmonopolet AS
0130 Oslo
Pb. 6953 St. Olavsplass
T: +47 (22) 015000
F: +47 (22) 015190
kundesenter@vinmonopolet.no
www.vinmonopolet.no

Fondberg AS
0159 Oslo, Grensen 16
T: +47 (23) 106580
huset@fondberg.no
www.fondberg.no

Norwegian Wine Imports AS
0159 Oslo
Lille Grensen 7
T: +47 (22) 426100
F: +47 (22) 910015
mail@norwegianwineimports.no
www.norwegianwineimports.no

Eurowine AS
0278 Oslo, Karenlyst Allé 10
T: +47 (24) 111710
F: +47 (24) 111719
mail@eurowine.no
www.eurowine.no

Trans Nordic Selections AS
0278 Oslo, Karenslyst Allé 11
T: +47 (23) 086090
F: +47 (23) 086091
norway@transnordic.com
www.transnordic.com

Arvid Nordquist AS
0283 Oslo, Lilleakerveien 2 E
T: +47 (23) 896870
F: +47 (22) 503099
www.arvidnordquist.no

Better Wines
0284 Oslo
Ullernchausseen 119
T: +47 (22) 221515
post@betterwines.no
www.betterwines.no

Moestue Grape Selections AS
0352 Oslo, Hegdehaugsveien 31
T: +47 (23) 203200
F: +47 (23) 203201
christopher@moestue.com
www.moestue.com

Podium Wines AS
0352 Oslo, Hegdehaugsveien 31
T: +47 (23) 203226
F: +47 (23) 203201
info@podiumwines.no
www.podiumwines.no

Best Buys International AS
0377 Oslo, Hoffsveien 70 c
T: +47 (21) 501880
F: +47 (21) 501881
www.bestbuys.no

AMKA
0473 Oslo, Sandakerveien 24D
T: +47 (23) 114910
F: +47 (22) 832430
amka@amka.no, www.amka.no

Vectura AS
0503 Oslo
Haslevangen 16, 6764, Rodeløkka
T: +47 (22) 975500
www.vectura.no

House of Wine AS
0569 Oslo, Konghellegata 3
T: +47 (22) 556666
F: +47 (22) 556665
post@houseofwine.no
www.houseofwine.no

AR Wines
0963 Oslo, Bergensveien 47
arwines@arwines.no

SR Wine Imports
1344 Haslum, Sørhalla 22 D
T: +47 (916) 26249
info@srwine.no
www.srwine.no

Strag Gruppen
1364 Fornebu,Rolvsbuktveien 17
T: +47 (67) 103030
F: +47 (67) 103031
office@strag.no
www.strag.no

Vinarius AS
1366 Lysaker, Vollsveien 13H
T: +47 (66) 776010
F: +47 (66) 776009
www.vinum.no

Wine Tailor AS
1414 Trollåsen
Rosenholmveien 25, Postboks 654
T: +47 (66) 817150
winetailor@winetailor.no
www.winetailor.no

Vinlådan ApS
2605 Brøndby
Midtager 29 B
www.vinladan.nu

Sagawine AS
3217 Sandefjord
Uranienborgvn. 4
post@sagawine.no

Red & White AS
3408 Tranby, Dølasletta 7
T: +47 (32) 242290
F: +47 (32) 242291
office@redwhite.no
www.redwhite.no

Terroir Wines
4006 Stavanger, Skansegaten 13
T: +47 (97) 181818
F: +47 (51) 839501
knut@terroir.no
www.terroir.no

PHILIPPINES (RP)

Werdenberg Corp.
1272 Manila, WIC Building
7431 Yakal Street, Makati City
T: +63 (892) 0128
F: +63 (817) 1217
info@werdenberg.com
www.werdenberg.com

Vienna Coffee Shop
6014 Mandaue, April Building
T: +63 (32) 3462650
F: +63 (32) 3453928

POLAND (PL)

Enoteka Polska
00-238 Warsaw, Ul. Dluga 23/25
T: +48 (22) 8313443
enoteka@enotekapolska.pl
www.enotekapolska.pl

Klub Demeter
00-484 Warsaw, Ul. Górnoślaska 24
T: +48 (22) 601331055
info@klubdemeter.pl
www.klubdemeter.pl

Mielzynski Sp. z o.o.
01-066 Warsaw
Ul. Burakowska 5/7
T: +48 (22) 8873805
F: +48 (22) 8873805
wino@mielzynski.pl
www.mielzynski.pl

Ambra S. A.
02-819 Warsaw
Ul. Pulawska 336
T: +48 (22) 5663402
F: +48 (22) 5663303
warszawa@ambra.com.pl
www.ambra.com.pl

AMKA Sp. Z. o. o.
05-510 Konstancin-Jeziorna,
Wągrodzka 11
T: +48 (22) 7540093
amka@amka-wina.pl
www.amka-vin.com

Centrum Wina Sp. z o.o.
02-819 Warsaw
Ul. Pulawska 336
T: +48 (22) 5663400
poczta@centrumwina.com.pl
www.centrumwina.com.pl

Pojedli Popili sp. z o.o.
21-025 Niemce
Pryszczowa Gora 9a
T: +48 (500) 052513
winosklad@montedivino.pl
www.montedivino.pl

Austrovin
25-900 Kielce
Domaszowice 182A
T: +48 (60) 3999715
biuro@austrovin.pl
www.austrovin.pl

Wina.pl
31-158 Kraków
Ul. Krowoderska 46/1
T: +48 (12) 6329466
F: +48 (12) 6345021
info@wina.pl
www.wina.pl

Wine Passion
31-215 Kraków, Zabiniec 101F/6
T: +48 (5359) 424747
mail@winepassion.pl
www.winepassion.pl

Salus International Sp. z o.o.
40-273 Katowice, Ul. Pulaskiego 9
T: +48 (32) 7880089
biuro@salusint.com.pl
www.salusint.com.pl

Wienico
40-273 Katowice, Ul. Pulaskiego 9
T: +48 (5170) 45308
www.wienico.com

Winoikieliszki.pl
45-525 Opole, Strzelecka 53a
T: +48 (77) 4558516
w.wojtanowski@winoikieliszki.pl
www.winoikieliszki.pl

Vinationale Sp. z o.o.
63-400 Ostrów Wielkopolski
Ul. Spichrzowa 10
T: +48 (62) 7376665
F: +48 (62) 7376670
import@vinationale.pl
www.vinationale.pl

Vino Vintana Polska
71-417 Szczecin, Ul. Felczaka 8
T: +48 (91) 4223388
biuro@vinovintana.pl
www.vinovintana.pl

101 Win
72-600 Świnoujście
Popielscy i Syn s.c. ul. Wojska
Polskiego 93
T: +48 (91) 4627652
www.101win.pl

PORTUGAL (P)

Niepoort Vinhos
4400-071 Vila Nova de Gaia,
Rua Cnadido dos Reis 670
verena@niepoort-vinhos.pt

UVA Portugal
4450-287 Matosinhos
540-544, Rua de Sousa Aroso
T: +351 (22) 9364360
F: +351 (22) 9364361

REPUBLIC OF MALEDIVES (MV)

Alifu Alifu Atoll
009130 Alif Alif Atoll
Indian Ocean MV
sommelier@constancehotels.com

ROMANIA (RO)

Decebal Consulting
050084 Bucharest
49-51 Drumul Sabareni
T: +40 (21) 2212780
F: +40 (21) 2212780

Vini del Mondo s.r.l.
050084 Bucharest, Splaiu
Independenteii 42-44, Sector 5
T: +43 (699) 190315
office@vinidelmondo.net

Tepaso Impex
400541 Cluj-Napoca
Al. Peana, 19
T: +40 (745) 596227

S.C.Vital Activ s.r.l.
400541 Cluj-Napoca
Str. Busuiocului 37
T: +40 (749) 094254
office@vinuriaustriece.ro
www.vinuriaustriece.ro

RUSSIA (RUS)

DP-Trade
109052 Moscow
Nizhegorodskaya Str. 29
T: +7 (495) 9379460
F: +7 (495) 9379461
alexpinskiy@dp-trade.ru
www.wine-dp-trade.ru

Fort Ltd.
115230 Moscow
Varshavskoe sh. 36, Korpus 1
T: +7 (495) 7751414
F: +7 (495) 7751444
fort@fortltd.ru
www.fortltd.ru

MB Group Impex
121205 Moscow, 36/9, Novy Arbat
T: +7 (095) 2907645
mbgimpex@aha.ru
www.mbg-wine.ru

Vinoterra
123022 Moscow
2nd. Zvenigorodskaya Str. Bild 13/37
office
T: +7 (495) 6476444
F: +7 (495) 2590339

Veld-21 Ltd.
123022 Moscow
3 Zvenigorodskoye sh.
T: +7 (495) 7273929
F: +7 (495) 7273929
www.veld21.ru

Kazumian
125047 Moscow
1-y Tverskoy-Yamskoy Per. 18/3
T: +7 (495) 5003838
F: +7 (495) 5003839
www.kazumian.com

Bravo-D
125412 Moscow
Uliza Pyatnitskaya
D31/2 Korp 3
www.bravo-d.ru

VinoGrad
614000 Perm
Gorkova Straße 9
T: +7 (342) 2183865
www.vinograd-perm.ru

SERBIA (SRB)

Ars Vini d.o.o.
11000 Belgrade
Vojvode Stepe 18
T: +381 (11) 2469740

SINGAPORE (SGP)

Unique Food & Wine Pte. Ltd.
068911 Singapore
138 Robinson Road #10–01
T: +65 (8) 63967935
sales@uniquefoodandwine.com
www.uniquefoodandwine.com

Vinothek Leopold
088517 Singapore
96 Tanjong Pagar Road
T: +65 (6) 5347644
vinothek@leopold.sg
www.leopold.sg

ewineasia.com
089065 Singapore
39 Keppel Road,
Tanjong Pagar
Distripark #02–01E
T: +65 (6) 2223977
F: +65 (6) 2516636
www.ewineasia.com

Ampelia
118635 Singapore
294 Pasir Panjang Road #07–02
The Palisades
T: +65 (9) 6220716
ampelia@singnet.com.sg
www.ampeliasg.com

The Oaks Cellars Pte. Ltd.
169074 Singapore
315 Outram Road #12–09, Tan Boon
Liat Building
T: +65 (6) 2242611
customercare@oaks.com.sg
www.oaks.com.sg

Beautiful Wine
199554 Singapore
298 Beach Road #01–40
The Concourse
T: +65 (6) 3921236
F: +65 (6) 3921286
info@beautifulwine.com.sg
www.beautifulwine.com.sg

Taste Fine Wine Merchant
208833 Singapore
113B Jalan Besar
T: +65 (6) 7550330
F: +65 (6) 2996200
marketing@taste.com.sg
www.taste.com.sg

Indoguna Pte. Ltd.
758221 Singapore, 36 Senoko Drive
T: +65 (6) 7550330
F: +65 (6) 7559522
info@indoguna.com.sg
www.indoguna.com

SLOVAKIA (SK)

Vinimka
81101 Bratislava, Ventúrska 3
T: +421 (911) 111746
lucny@vinimka.sk
www.vinimka.sk

Class Food Bratislava s.r.o.
81108 Bratislava
Feriencikova 1
T: +421 (2) 52733403
F: +421 (2) 52733403
office@classfood.sk

Wineloversclub.sk s.r.o.
81108 Bratislava, Dunajská 46
obchod@wlc.sk
www.wineloversclub.sk

Slowin Bratislava s.r.o.
83106 Bratislava, Pri Šajbách 12
T: +421 (31) 5625378
slowin@slowin.sk
www.slowin.sk

HIC Slovakia s.r.o.
84106 Bratislava,
Bratislavská 51
T: +421 (2) 65440141
F: +421 (2) 65440143
office@finewines.sk
www.finewines.sk

Tomax s.r.o.
85104 Bratislava
Panónska cesta 16
T: +421 (2) 63537105
F: +421 (2) 63815646
kamenar@tomax-ba.sk
www.tomax-ba.sk

ELESKO Trading a.s.
90001 Modra,
Partizánska 2275
T: +421 (2) 20922640
info@invino.sk, www.invino.sk

Italmarket Slovakia a.s. IMS & IMS
90032 Borinka, Borinka 149
T: +421 (2) 60103010
F: +421 (2) 60103030
www.italmarket.sk

SLOVENIA (SI)

Kozelj d.o.o.
1218 Komenda, Moste 54
T: +386 (1) 8343560
F: +386 (1) 8343561
info@kozelj.si, www.kozelj.si

Roko d.o.o.
2311 Hoče–Slivnica
Miklavska Cesta 73
T: +386 (2) 3303812
F: +386 (2) 3303812
www.roko.si

SOUTH KOREA (KR)

Curious Wine Corporation
134818 Seoul
204 Jinhwangdo-ro (Dunchondong Jiha)
cho_jungyong@hotmail.com

Nature Wine
463829 Seongnam-Si
B1, 61-3 Imae-Dong, Bundang-gu
Tel: +82 (70) 77162381
mail@naturewine.com
www.naturewine.com

SPAIN (E)

Vinum Ibiza
07840 Ibiza, Calle Los Rosales 40
T: +34 (609) 867079
goran@vinumibiza.com
www.vinumibiza.com

Vila Vini Teca
08003 Barcelona, Agullers 7
T: +34 (902) 327777
www.vilaviniteca.es

Cuvée 3000
08013 Barcelona
Lepant 149
T: +34 (932) 651096
F: +34 (932) 319997
cuvee3000@cuvee3000.com
www.cuvee3000.com

Vinos Dulces
08017 Barcelona
Calle Alcalde Miralles 9
T: +34 (93) 4067477
F: +34 (93) 4067477
info@vinosdulces.com
www.vinosdulces.com

Nico James S.L.
08770 Barcelona
Apartado de Correos 191
T: +34 (902) 747985
F: +34 (902) 747986
info@nicojames.es,
www.nicojames.es

Lavinia Selección SA
28006 Madrid
José Ortega y Gasset 16
T: +34 (91) 6503392
clientes@lavinia.es
www.lavinia.es

Restaurante & Vinothek Riff
46005 Valencia
Calle Conde Altea 18 E
T: +34 (96) 3335353
www.restaurante-riff.com

Eurocestas S.L.
48940 Leioa
Calle Maiatzaren Bata 9
T: +34 (944) 630044
F: +34 (944) 630933
www.eurocestas.com

SWEDEN (S)

Divine AB
10123 Stockholm
Östra Järnvägsgatan 16
Box 151
T: +46 (8) 4121630
info@divine.se
www.divine.se

Bibendum AB
10251 Stockholm, Box 27084
T: +46 (8) 59811100
F: +46 (8) 59811110
info@bibendum.se
www.bibendum.se

VinUnic AB
10392 Stockholm
PO Box 7471
T: +46 (8) 6608415
info@vinunic.se
www.vingruppen.se

Carovin
10450 Stockholm
PO Box 24005
T: +46 (8) 6510995
F: +46 (8) 6510996
info@carovin.se
www.carovin.se

Giertz Vinimport AB
11148 Stockholm
Blasieholmsgatan 4A
T: +46 (8) 218388
F: +46 (8) 213382
info@giertz.se, www.giertz.se

Domaine Wines AB
11160 Stockholm
Holländargatan 20
T: +46 (8) 54610700
F: +46 (8) 54610799
info@domaine.se
www.domaine.se

Johan Lidby Vinhandel AB
11236 Stockholm
Polhemsgatan 20 A
T: +46 (8) 7920350
F: +46 (8) 7920355
info@johanlidbyvinhandel.se
www.johanlidbyvinhandel.se

AMKA
11344 Stockholm
Upplandsgatan 91A
T: +46 (8) 51484980
www.amka.se

Handlavin
11543 Stockholm
Älvkarleövägen 26
T: +46(0)70/5957713
peder@handlavin.se
www.handlavin.se

Primewine Sweden AB
11556 Stockholm
Frihamnsgatan 30, Magasin 3
T: +46 (8) 6795200
F: +46 (8) 6795213
info@primewine.se
www.primewinegroup.com

Klunk AB
11633 Stockholm
Bondegatan 21
T: +46 (8) 51069100
F: +46 (8) 50853100
hello@handpicked.se
www.handpicked.se

Wine Trade Sweden AB
11639 Stockholm
Katarina Bangata 29
T: +46 (8) 6638030
F: +46 (70) 5572624
post@winetrade.se
www.winetrade.se

Gullberg „by Stockwine"
11826 Stockholm, Götgatan 58 C
T: +46 (8) 7125330
F: +46 (8) 7125339
info@gullbergbystockwine.se
www.gullbergbystockwine.se

Örjan & Feuer HB
12065 Stockholm
Korphoppsgatan 42
T: +46 (8) 6427959
F: +46 (8) 6427959
vinhus@orjanofeuer.se
www.orjanofeuer.se

Janake Wine Group AB
12162 Johanneshov
Slakthusgatan 9
T: +46 (8) 58644050
F: +46 (8) 58644051
info@janake.se
www.janake.se

LB Vinimport AB
14130 Huddinge
Fridhemsvägen 9
T: +46 (0) 708811763
info@lbvinimport.se
www.lbvinimport.se

Miguel Torres Sverige AB
16440 Kista, Torshamnsgatan 39A
T: +46 (8) 54583390
F: +46 (8) 54583399
info@torres.se
www.torres.se

Vinovativa, Jörgen Lindström
16865 Bromma
Mariehällsvägen 37A
T: +46 (8) 4446170
info@vinovativa.se
www.vinovativa.se

Arvid Nordquist
Vin & Spirithandel AB
17125 Solna
Ekensbergsvägen 117
T: +46 (8) 7991800
F: +46 (8) 294162
info@arvidnordquist.se
www.arvidnordquist.se

ITM - Inter Trade Marketing AB
18142 Lidingö, Sagavägen 14
T: +46 (8) 7655290
F: +46 (8) 4460118
itm-wine@itmab.nu, www.itmab.nu

Viniberum
18146 Lidingö, Rönnvägen 9
T: +46 (8) 7678675
info@viniberum.se
www.viniberum.se

Jakobsson & Söderström
21120 Malmö, Skeppsbron 5
T: +46 (40) 6614600
contact@js-vin.com
www.js-vin.com

Vinicom
23930 Skanör, Mellangatan 64
T: +46 (733) 423241
F: +46 (40) 597264
mathias@vinicom.se

Helsingborgs Vinhus
25656 Helsingborg, Skaftgatan 45
T: +46 (42) 281190
F: +46 (42) 281091
info@vinhus.se, www.vinhus.se

C & E Gastro-Import AB
25657 Ramlösa, Dannfeltsgatan 12A
T: +46 (42) 296000
sverige@gastro-import.com
www.gastro-import.se

Heba Trading AB
37252 Kallinge, Kyrkvägen 5
T: +46 (457) 24085
F: +46 (457) 20620
info@heba.se, www.heba.se

Vinobele Wine Agency
41271 Gothenburg
Prästgårdsängen 14
T: +46 (31) 227922
info@vinobele.se
www.vinobele.se

WINE SELECTION AB
45191 Uddevalla, Stångevägen 29
T: +46 (522) 83191
wine@amongre.se
www.wineselection.se

Stenbacken Vinimport
45793 Tanumshede, Tegneby 16
T: +46 (524) 81481
v.larsson@telia.com

BonumVinum
50331 Borås, Yxhammarsgatan 25
T: +46 (705) 953585
robert@bonumvinum.se
www.bonumvinum.se

Granqvist Beverage House AB
52230 Tidaholm
Vulcanön, Vulcans väg 1
T: +46 (502) 14888
info@granqvistbev.com
www.granqvistbev.com

Cavarosa Wine
58226 Linköping, Hamngatan 15b
T: +46 (70) 5660180
F: +46 (70) 5137079
info@cavarosawine.se
www.cavarosawine.se

TAIWAN (RC)

High Tip International Co. Ltd.
00104 Taipei
1F, 18-1, Lane 14, Chilin Road
T: +886 (2) 25234577
F: +886 (2) 25423650
amadeusjason@gmail.com
www.kaffeeamadeus.com

GEM HI Trading Co. Ltd.
00105 Taipei, 2 Alley 69, Lane 161
Tun Hwa S. Road, Section 1
T: +886 (2) 27781667
F: +886 (2) 27720715

Trade & Development F&B
00110 Taipei
2Fl-4, 149 Keelung Road, Section 1
T: +886 (2) 27691728
gerryglesinger@yahoo.co.uk

Elfland International Co. Ltd.
00114 Taipei
4F-2, No. 168 Ruiguang Road
T: +886 (2) 26598323
F: +886 (2) 26598606
info.elfland@gmail.com
www.dasbier.com.tw

JF Gourmet Co., Ltd.
23444 Taipei
2F., No.16, Lane 299, Ren-Ai Road
T: +886 (2) 22327900
F: +886 (2) 22327900
johannes@jfgourmet.com.tw

Shin Wan Intern. Trade Co. Ltd.
10465 Taipei, 1F, 11, Lane 164
Sung-Chiang Road
T: +886 (2) 25234577
swsuntop@ms17.hinet.net

Gi Jane House Co., Ltd., Amanda Lui
Taichung, 48 Mufang Street
T: +886 (4) 3058775
gijane@ms22.hinet.net
www.gijane.com.tw

THAILAND (TH)

fin – fabulous is needed
10110 Bangkok, 8/22 Soi Sammitre
Ratchadapisek Road
T: +66 (2) 6530154
F: +66 (2) 6530155
info@fin-wine.com, www.fin-wine.com

Black Forest Distribution Co. Ltd.
83150 Phuket
123/30-33 Moo. 7
Wichitsongkram Road
drink@phuketwine.com
www.phuketwine.com

TURKEY (TR)

ADCO Gida
34400 Kağıthane, Gursel Mahallesi
Imrahor Caddesi No. 27
T: +90 (212) 2109310
F: +90 (212) 2109300
vinum@kemergida.com
www.adcogida.com.tr

UKRAINE (UA)

Fozzy Group Corporation
02090 Kiev
13 Kalachevskaya Street
T: +380 (44) 4963201
F: +380 (44) 4963201
www.fozzy.ua

Vitis Group LLC
03056 Kiev
143a Borschagivska Street
T: +380 (44) 4576865
F: +380 (44) 4576866
office@vitis.com.ua, www.vitis.ua

SV Plus Ltd.
04073 Kiev, 160 Frunze Street
T: +380 (44) 4923540
office@sv-plus.com.ua
www.sv-plus.com.ua

Wine Bureau LLC
04080 Kiev
64 Kostantynivska, Office 315
T: +380 (44) 3907500
F: +380 (44) 3907960
www.goodwine.ua

UNITED ARAB EMIRATES (UAE)

Emirates Fine Wine, Maritime & Mercantile Intl. LLC
PO Box 70 Dubai, MMI Dubai
T: +971 (4) 3040400
F: +971 (4) 3881575
contactus@mmi.ae
www.mmidubai.com

Truebell Marketing & Trading LLC
PO Box 4146 Sharjah
T: +971 (6) 5342111
F: +971 (6) 5342112
spirits@truebell.org
www.truebell.org

African & Eastern (NE) Ltd.
PO Box 32321 Al Barsha
Grosvenor Business Tower, 16th Floor
T: +971 (4) 4344500
reception@ane.ae
www.africaneastern.com

UNITED STATES
OF AMERICA (USA)

Circovino
AZ 85701 Tucson
222 North Court Avenue
T: +1 (719) 4183493
sariya@circovino.com
www.circovino.com

Vinum Noricum – The Satin Ballroom Wine
CA 90025 Los Angeles
1545 Sawtelle Boulevard, Suite 10
T: +1 (310) 9097239
info@vinumnoricum.com
www.vinumnoricum.com

Winemonger
CA 94960 San Anselmo
164 Sleepy Hollow Drive
T: +1 (866) 9666437
www.winemonger.com

Morandell Imports
CA 90248 Los Angeles
17107 S. Figueroa Street
T: +1 (310) 3285010
info@morandell.us
www.morandell.us

Blue Danube Wine Company
CA 94023 Los Altos, PO Box 1011
T: +1 (650) 9414699
F: +1 (650) 9414699
info@bluedanubewine.com
www.bluedanubewine.com

Regal Wine Co.
CA 94558 Napa, 80 Technology Center
T: +1 (856) 9856388
F: +1 (865) 9855848
info@regalwine.com
www.regalwine.com

The Age of Riesling
CA 94702 Berkeley, 1813 Short Street
T: +1 (510) 5492444
F: +1 (510) 5492525
ageofriesling@comcast.net
www.theageofriesling.com

Global Wine Company
CA 94903 San Rafael
1401 Los Gamos Drive, Suite 230
T: +1 (415) 3393050
info@globalwineco.com
www.globalwineco.com

Martine's Wines, Inc.
CA 94949 Novato
285 Bel Marin Keys Boulevard
Suite Q
T: +1 (800) 3441801
info@mwines.com
www.martineswines.com

Magellan Wine Imports Inc., Erik Quam
CO 80130 Highlands Ranch
6246 Red Canyon Drive, Unit F
T: +1 (720) 2726544
F: +1 (303) 9974915
erikquam@magellanwineimports.com
www.magellanwineimports.com

Slocum & Sons Inc.
CT 06473 North Haven
30 Corporate Drive
T: +1 (203) 2398000
info@slocumandsons.com
www.slocumandsons.com

Metrowine Distribution Inc.
CT 06902 Stamford
20 Acosta Street, Suite 300
T: +1 (888) 5389501
F: +1 (914) 6824615
contact@metrowine.com
www.metrowine.com

Lionstone International
IL 60045 Lake Forest
28188 Ballard Drive
T: +1 (847) 2478755
info@lionstone.com
www.lionstone.com

Vin Divino Ltd.
IL 60613 Chicago
3921 North Lincoln Avenue
T: +1 (773) 3346700
F: +1 (773) 3344488
info@vindivino.com
www.vindivino.com

Winesellers Ltd.
IL 60714 Niles
7520 N. Caldwell Avenue
T: +1 (847) 6471100
info@winesellersltd.com
www.winesellersltd.com

Potomac Selections Inc.
MD 20785 Landover
3601 West Street, Unit D
T: +1 (301) 5838844
F: +1 (301) 5838802
www.potomacselections.com

Total Wine & More
MD 20817 Bethesda
6600 Rockledge Drive
T: +1 (855) 3289463
www.totalwine.com

Haus Alpenz LLC
MI 55436 Edina, 5127 Skyline Drive
T: +1 (612) 4140022
info@alpenz.com
www.alpenz.com

Bordeaux Fine & Rare
NC 27615 Raleigh
3216 Wellington Ct, Suite 105
T: +1 (919) 8509463
john@bfrwine.com
www.bfrwine.com

Legendary Wine Company, Eric J. Costa
NH 03841 Hampstead
PO Box 57370 Cambridge Road
T: +1 (603) 4371100
info@legendarywine.com
www.legendarywine.com

Winebow, Inc.
VA 23060 Glen Allen
4800 Cox Road, Suite 300
T: +1 (800) 3659463
F: +1 (800) 4828369
info@winebow.com
www.winebow.com

Niche Import Co.
NJ 07927 Cedar Knolls
45 Horsehill Road, Suite 105A
T: +1 (973) 9938450
niche@ourniche.com
www.ourniche.com

Vignaioli Selection
NY 10001 New York
18 West 27th Street, 11th Floor
T: +1 (212) 6863095
F: +1 (212) 6863097
dino@vignaioliamerica.com
www.vignaioliamerica.com

Willette Wines
NY 10011 New York
33 West 19th Street, Suite 401
T: +1 (646) 6191350
F: +1 (212) 8980106
liz@willettewines.com
www.willettewines.com

USA Wine Imports Sandi Barte
NY 10013 New York
285 West Broadway, Suite 340
T: +1 (212) 9417133
F: +1 (212) 9417174
sandi@usawineimports.com
www.usawineimports.com

Domaine Select Wine Estates
NY 10016 New York
105 Madison Avenue, 13th Floor
T: +1 (212) 2790799
info@domaineselect.com
www.domaineselect.com

V.O.S. Selections, Inc.
NY 10018 New York
555 Eighth Avenue, Suite 1209
T: +1 (212) 9676948
F: +1 (212) 9676986
wine@vosselections.com
www.vosselections.com

Frederick Wildman & Sons Ltd.
NY 10022 New York
307 East 53rd Street
T: +1 (212) 3550700
F: +1 (212) 3554719
info@frederickwildman.com
www.frederickwildman.com

Duggans Distillers Products Corp.
NY 10913 Blauvelt
560 Bradley Parkway West, Unit 1
T: +1 (845) 3587230
duggansdist@optonline.net
www.duggansdist.com

Martin Scott Wines Martin Gold
NY 11042 Lake Success
1981 Marcus Avenue, Suite E117
T: +1 (516) 3270808
www.martinscottwines.com

Palm Bay Imports
NY 11050 Port Washington
48 Harbor Park Drive
T: +1 (516) 4024700
F: +1 (516) 9218405
dfriedman@palmbay.com
www.palmbayimports.com

Vintage Epicure
NY 11050 Port Washington,
1 Pleasant Avenue, Suite E
T: +1 (917) 2449463
info@vintageepicure.com
www.vintageepicure.com

Acid Inc. Selections
NY 11101 New York, 45–48 Vernon
Boulevard, 2nd floor
T: +1 (718) 7772243
info@aiselections.com
www.aiselections.com

Bayfield Importing Ltd.
NY 11101 Long Island City
51–02 21st Street, 6th floor
T: +1 (718) 4820200
F: +1 (718) 4820255
info@bayfieldimporting.com
www.bayfieldimporting.com

Savio Soares Selections
NY 11201 Brooklyn
10 Jay Street, Suite 722
T: +1 (718) 7974114
F: +1 (718) 7974116
savio@savioselections.com
www.savinho.com

The Artisan Collection
NY 11201 Brooklyn, 365 Bridge Street
T: +1 (718) 5960722
info@theartisancollection.us
www.theartisancollection.us

Apollo Fine Spirits
NY 11520 Freeport
191 Hanse Avenue, Freeport
T: +1 (516) 5645600
info@apollowinespirits.com
www.apollowinespirits.com

Michael Skurnik Wines Inc.
NY 11791 Syosset
575 Underhill Boulevard, Suite 216
T: +1 (516) 6779300
F: +1 (516) 6779301
info@skurnikwines.com
www.skurnikwines.com

Indie Wineries
NY 11937 East Hampton
16 Three Mile Harbor HCRD
T: +1 (646) 9511384
F: +1 (646) 3045670
info@indiewineries.com
www.indiewineries.com

Ewald Moseler Selections
OR 97214 Portland
1221 SE 3rd Avenue
T: +1 (503) 7160997
F: +1 (503) 6219201
ewald@moseler.com
www.moseler.com

Boutique Wine Collection
PA 19139 Philadelphia
4501 Spruce Street
T: +1 (914) 9546583
office@boutiquewines.info
www.boutiquewines.info

Weygandt-Metzler Importing Ltd.
PA 19375 Unionville,
PO Box 56
T: +1 (610) 4860700
F: +1 (610) 4866452
info@weygandtmetzler.com
www.weygandtmetzler.com

BevCo Int., LLC
TX 77055 Houston
11339 Todd Street
T: +1 (281) 5004055
F: +1 (877) 3498876
bevcoadmin@BevCoInternational.com
www.bevcointernational.com

Select Wines, Klaus Wittauer
VA 20151 Chantilly
14000 Willard Road, Suite 3
T: +1 (703) 6318100
coakley@selectwinesinc.com
www.selectwinesinc.com

Hop & Wine Beverage
VA 20164 Sterling
45490 Ruritan Circle
F: +1 (703) 4219463
www.hopandwine.com

Broadbent Selections Inc.
VA 23221 Richmond
15 South Sheppard Street
T: +1 (804) 3531818
F: +1 (804) 353.1844
info@broadbent.com
www.broadbent-wines.com

The Robins Cellars
VA 23233 Richmond
9878 Maryland Drive
T: +1 (804) 3465060
F: +1 (804) 3463060
info@therobinscellars.com
www.therobinscellars.com

Noble Wines Ltd
WA 98118 Seattle, 9860 40th Ave
Street
T: +1 (206) 3265274
noble@noblewinesltd.com
www.noblewinesltd.com

AUSTRIA

falstaff

VINEYARD ESTATES A–Z

www.falstaff.at

NEW: THE WEB PAGE FOR CULINARY ENJOYMENT

UP TO DATE: news and background reports from the wine-, gourmet- and bar-scene

MODERN: elegant design, optimized for desktop AND smartphones

FAST: short loading time an optimized search function

EXTENSIVE: More than 5500 restaurants & 54,000 wines – ratings included

falstaff
GENIESSEN WEIN ESSEN REISEN

Follow us on
facebook.com/falstaff.magazin

falstaff

Falstaff Publications Ltd.
Führichgasse 8/2
A-1010 Vienna, Austria